The Earth System

Third Edition

Lee R. Kump
James F. Kasting
Robert G. Crane

ISBN: 978-93-325-7573-8

First Impression, 2016

This edition is manufactured in India and is authorized for sale only in India, Bangladesh, Bhutan, Pakistan, Nepal, Sri Lanka and the Maldives. Circulation of this edition outside of these territories is UNAUTHORIZED.

Published by Pearson India Education Services Pvt. Ltd, CIN: U72200TN2005PTC057128.

Head Office: 15th Floor, Tower-B, World Trade Tower, Plot No. 1, Block-C, Sector 16, Noida 201 301, Uttar Pradesh, India.

Registered Office: The HIVE, 3rd Floor, Metro zone, No 44, Pillaiyar Koil Street, Jawaharlal Nehru Road, Anna Nagar, Chennai, Tamil Nadu 600040. Phone: 044-66540100, Website: in.pearson.com Email: companysecretary.india@pearson.com

Digitally printed in India by Saurabh Printers Pvt. Ltd. in the year of 2021.

Table of Contents

GLOSSARY

15-μm CO$_2$ band   An absorption band that is a result of a vibration frequency of the CO$_2$ molecule that allows the molecule to absorb infrared radiation at a wavelength of about 15 μm, near the peak of Earth's outgoing radiation. Very little of this radiation is allowed to escape directly to space, and so CO$_2$ is an important contributor to the *greenhouse effect*.

Ablation zone   The lower part of a glacier where more snow melts during the summer than accumulates during winter.

Absolute vorticity   The sum of the planetary and relative *vorticities* experienced by a moving fluid.

Absorption coefficient   The efficiency with which a molecule absorbs *electromagnetic radiation* of a given wavelength.

Accumulation Zone   The upper (colder) part of a glacier where more snow accumulates in winter than melts in summer.

Accretion   A process by which small bodies orbiting the Sun (or a planet) collide to form larger ones.

Acid   A solution with a high concentration of hydrogen ions, that is, with a pH less than 7.

Acid rain   Acidic rainwater produced when various acids, including sulfuric acid produced from SO$_2$ oxidation, combine with natural rainwater.

Action spectrum   The relative efficiency with which UV photons at different wavelengths contribute to a specific biological response in a specific *organism*.

Active layer   The top layer of permafrost (at the surface) that alternately freezes in winter and thaws in summer.

Adaptation   A characteristic that enhances an *organism's* survival or reproductive success.

Albedo   The reflectivity of a surface, usually expressed as a decimal fraction of the total incident sunlight reflected from the surface.

Amino acids   Organic compounds containing an amino (NH$_2$) group and a carboxyl (COOH) group. They are the basic building blocks for proteins.

Anion   A negatively charged ion.

Anoxic   Totally devoid of oxygen.

Anoxic basin   A region of the ocean in which deep water is completely devoid of oxygen; rare in today's ocean.

Anoxygenic photosynthesis   A type of *photosynthesis*, carried out by certain types of *bacteria*, in which no O$_2$ is released.

Antarctic Bottom Water (AABW)   Bottom water that forms in the Weddell Sea off Antarctica. The AABW circles Antarctica and flows northward as the deepest layer in the Atlantic, Pacific, and Indian ocean basins.

Anthropogenic   Induced by humans.

Anti-greenhouse effect   Absorption of sunlight (and radiation of infrared energy) by particles or gases high up in the stratosphere. This prevents sunlight from reaching a planet's surface and, hence, causes surface cooling.

Aphelion   The position in a planet's orbit that is farthest from the Sun.

Archaea   One of the three primary domains of life, as determined by sequencing of ribosomal RNA. The Archaea (like the *Bacteria*) are all single-celled, prokaryotic *organisms*. Includes the *methanogens*.

Asteroid belt   A region between Mars and Jupiter that has a high concentration of asteroids. The asteroid belt represents the remains of a tenth, inner planet that failed to form or was destroyed by a large *meteorite* impact early in the history of the solar system.

Asteroids   Pieces of rocky material composed of minerals and metallic elements; they range in size from dust size to 1000 km in diameter and most reside in the *asteroid belt*, but some are diverted to planet-crossing orbits by gravitational disturbance.

Asthenosphere   The zone of most ductile upper *mantle* just below the lithosphere; may contain small amounts of molten rock.

Atmosphere   The thin envelope of gases that surrounds most planets; one of the four major components of the Earth system.

Atomic number   The number of protons in the nucleus of an atom. All atoms of a given element have the same atomic number.

Autotroph   An *organism* (*producer*) that can derive its energy for growth and reproduction from either solar or chemical energy.

Bacteria   One of the three primary domains of life, as determined by sequencing of ribosomal RNA. The Bacteria (like the *Archaea*) are all single-celled, prokaryotic *organisms*.

Banded iron-formations (BIFs)   Laminated rocks consisting of alternating layers of iron minerals and chert that were formed almost exclusively during the first half of Earth's history.

Barometric law   A relationship stating that atmospheric pressure decreases by about a factor of 10 for each 16-km increase in altitude. More technically, atmospheric pressure decreases exponentially with altitude.

Basal shear stress   The stress applied parallel to the slope at the bed of a glacier.

Basalt   An *igneous rock* that reaches Earth's surface as lava and cools rapidly; the major rock type in the oceanic crust.

Base   A solution with a low concentration of hydrogen ions, that is, with a pH greater than 7.

Biodiesel   A type of *biomass* fuel that is produced from fats or oils, particularly soybean oil. It is widely available in Europe.

Biodiversity   The variety of life-forms, for example, the number of species in an area.

Biological pump   A transfer of CO$_2$ and nutrients from the surface waters to the deep ocean as a result of *photosynthesis* in shallow waters, of the settling of organic matter, and of decomposition in deep waters. This process operates on a much faster time scale (days to months) than the *thermohaline circulation* of the oceans.

Biological sulfate reduction   A metabolic pathway in which sulfate is combined with organic matter to produce energy. The sulfate is reduced and the organic matter is oxidized during the reaction.

Biomass   The total combined weight of organic material in each trophic level. In terrestrial ecosystems the biomass is reduced by 90 to 99% at each higher trophic level.

Biomass-based fuels   Liquid fuels, such as methanol and *ethanol*, that are produced from fast-growing plants. Unlike *fossil fuels*, burning these substances does not contribute to atmospheric CO$_2$ buildup.

Biome   A region with a characteristic plant community.

Biosphere   The part of the Earth system that directly supports life, including the oceans, atmosphere, land surface, and soils.

Biota   All living *organisms*.

Bioturbation   The stirring of sediments by worms and other burrowing *organisms* that live at the seafloor.

Black smoker   A mid-ocean ridge hydrothermal vent from which clouds of black particles of iron sulfide (FeS) are precipitating.

Blackbody   A body that emits electromagnetic radiation e? well at all wavelengths.

Blackbody radiation   Radiation given off by a black? radiation is characterized by the body's absolute te?

Body waves   Seismic waves that travel throug? as they spread outward from the *earthquake's* as either *P waves* or *S waves*.

Bottom water   Very dense, cold water that forms along the edges of *sea ice* in certain areas near the poles and subsides, making up the bottom layer of ocean water as it circulates throughout the world's oceans.

Boyle's law   A relationship stating that, with temperature held constant, the pressure and volume of a gas are inversely proportional. In other words, the product of pressure and volume is a constant.

Buffer   A dissolved substance that helps maintain a stable pH. Carbonate ion is an important pH buffer in seawater.

Buoyancy   A tendency of an object to float, rise, or sink when submerged in a fluid.

C_3 plants   Plants that fix carbon into a three-carbon chain during *photosynthesis*. These plants (which include about 95% of all terrestrial plants) should be positively affected by CO_2 fertilization.

C_4 plants   Plants that fix carbon into a four-carbon chain during the initial step of *photosynthesis*. These plants (which include about 5% of all terrestrial plants, such as corn and sugar cane) experience little CO_2 fertilization at CO_2 levels near 350 ppm.

CAFE standard   Corporate Automobile Fleet Efficiency standards. These U.S. regulations ensure that the average fuel efficiency of vehicles sold in the United States must be equal to a certain value, currently 27.5 mpg for passenger cars.

Calvin cycle   The biochemical pathway by which green plants convert CO_2 into organic carbon during *photosynthesis*, a method of *carbon fixation*.

Cap carbonates   Thick layers of carbonate rocks overlying glacial deposits. They are thought by some geologists to be formed from rapid weathering in the aftermath of Snowball Earth episodes.

Captured rotation   A rotation in which a planet (or moon) always shows the same side to a star (or planet). Earth's Moon is a good example.

Carbon capture and storage (CCS)   The technique of capturing CO_2 from coal- or oil-fired power plants and burying it deep underground, so as to keep it out of the *atmosphere*.

Carbon fixation   The biochemical process that occurs during *photosynthesis* by which atmospheric CO_2 is converted to organic carbon.

Carbon sequestration   This term is equivalent to *carbon capture and storage*. It refers to the process of capturing and burying CO_2 released from *fossil fuel* burning.

Carbon tax   A tax that might be levied on CO_2 produced from *fossil fuels*. No such tax exists in the United States at the moment; however, economists have suggested that this would be an effective way to reduce CO_2 emissions.

Carbonate metamorphism   A chemical reaction occurring at high temperatures and pressures between sedimentary carbonate minerals and silica-rich sediments that forms calcium silicate minerals and releases CO_2.

Catalyst   A compound that increases the rate of a chemical reaction and is itself unchanged by the reaction.

Catalytic cycle   A set of chemical reactions facilitated by the presence of a *catalyst*. *Ozone* can be destroyed by catalytic cycles involving nitrogen oxides and chlorine.

Cation   A positively charged ion.

Cellulosic ethanol   *Ethanol* (C_2H_6) produced from the woody parts of plants, i.e., from cellulose. Most ethanol in the United States is currently produced from corn.

Chaotic orbit   An orbit that is particularly sensitive to slight perturbations that lead to large, unpredictable changes in an orbiting object's position at a later time.

Chapman mechanism   A set of four chemical reactions that describe the production and loss of *ozone* in a simplified (pure N_2–O_2) *atmosphere*.

Characteristic response time   How long a reservoir takes to respond measurably to large imbalances in inflow or outflow, calculated in the same way as *residence* time.

Charles's law   A relationship stating that, with pressure held constant, the volume and temperature of a gas are directly proportional. In other words, the quotient of volume and temperature is a constant.

Chemical evolution   The sequence of chemical reactions leading up to the origin of life.

Chemosynthesis   The biological production of organic matter by *bacteria* that utilize energy stored in chemical compounds (inorganic matter) rather than solar energy.

Chlorofluorocarbons (CFCs)   Synthetic compounds containing chlorine, fluorine, and carbon. These gases, also called freons, contribute to the *greenhouse effect* and are harmful to the *ozone layer*.

Chloroplasts   Inclusions (organelles) within cells that are responsible for *photosynthesis*. They contain DNA that is remarkably similar to cyanobacterial DNA.

Cholesterol   An organic compound found in *eukaryotes*, which is a precursor to steranes found in the fossil record.

Chondrites   "Primitive" *meteorites* that have never been melted. They are thought to be remnants of the original material from which the planets formed.

Cloud condensation nuclei (CCN)   Small particles, often consisting of sulfate aerosols, that catalyze the condensation of water vapor into cloud droplets.

CO_2 compensation point   The critical CO_2 concentration below which plants are unable to photosynthesize and hence, grow. Technically, it is the CO_2 level below which the rate of *photorespiration* exceeds that of *photosynthesis*.

CO_2 fertilization   An increase in the growth rate of plants by the addition of CO_2 to the atmosphere.

Coal   A hydrogen- and carbon-bearing compound produced under high-pressure and high-temperature conditions of burial deep within the solid Earth; a *fossil fuel* formed from high concentrations of organic matter in terrestrial sediments.

Column depth   The total amount of *ozone* per unit area above Earth's surface. Usually reported in *Dobson units*.

Comets   Balls of frozen gases (water, ammonia, methane, and carbon dioxide) containing rocky and metallic debris that are mostly in distant orbits around the Sun, beyond Pluto (see *Oort cloud*).

Community   A characteristic assemblage of two or more groups of interacting species.

Component   An individual part of a system. A component may be a reservoir of matter or energy, a system attribute, or a subsystem.

Condensation   The process by which a gas becomes a liquid.

Conduction   Transfer of heat energy by direct contact between individual molecules.

Consumers   *Organisms*, such as animals, that are incapable of utilizing solar energy directly but must instead consume plants or other photosynthesizers to utilize the chemical energy stored in plant tissues.

Continental drift   Theory stating that the supercontinent *Pangea* began to break apart at the beginning of the Mesozoic era (200 million years ago) and that the continents then slowly drifted into their current positions; a concept proposed by Alfred Wegener in the early 20th century that has been supplanted by the (related) theory of *plate tectonics*.

Continental ice sheet   An ice sheet covering a large area (50,000 km or more) that spreads outward in all directions under its own weight. Most of today's ice cover is found in the two continental ice sheets of Greenland and Antarctica.

Continental shelves   The shallow, submerged part of continental margins, bounded on the landward side by the coastline and on the seaward side by steep slopes falling to great depths.

Continuously habitable zone (CHZ)   The region around a star where a planet can remain habitable for some finite time interval.

Convection　Transfer of heat energy by the circulating motions of a fluid that is heated from below; one of the three primary mechanisms of heat transfer.

Convergence　The inward movement of air or water to a region in the *atmosphere* or ocean.

Core　The central part of a planet or of the Sun. Earth's core—one of the three components of the solid Earth—is dense, is composed mostly of metallic iron and nickel, and has a solid inner and a liquid outer part.

Coronagraph　An instrument added to a telescope in order to block out the light from a star and allow faint objects (including planets) to be seen around it. The coronagraph takes its name from instruments used to block out the light from the Sun in order to observe its corona.

Coriolis effect　The apparent tendency for a fluid (air or water) moving across Earth's surface to be deflected from its straight-line path. Fluids are deflected to the right of their initial path in the Northern Hemisphere and to the left in the Southern Hemisphere.

Corona　The extremely hot (1–2 million K) outer layer of the Sun from which the solar wind arises. The corona becomes visible during a total solar eclipse.

Cost–benefit analysis　An economic analysis in which the costs of a certain action are weighed against its benefits.

Coupling　The links between any two components of a system. Couplings can be positive or negative.

Craton　The old, tectonically dormant regions of the continents that have served as the nuclei for continental accretion over the past 3 to 4 billion years.

Critical point　The temperature and pressure at which a phase boundary ceases to exist. It is the highest temperature and pressure combination at which a separate liquid and gaseous phase of a compound can exist.

Crust　The thin, outer layer of the solid Earth; consists of light, rocky matter that is in contact with the *atmosphere*, *hydrosphere*, and *biota*.

Cryosphere　The portion of the Earth's surface that is mostly frozen, including both the polar caps and mountain glaciers.

Cyanobacteria　*Bacteria* capable of both oxygenic and anoxygenic *photosynthesis*; formerly known as blue-green algae.

Deforestation　The clearing of all the trees off an area of land.

Dendrochronology　A method of dating trees by counting their annual growth rings. The ring widths can be used to infer environmental conditions during the growing season.

Denitrification　The conversion of *fixed nitrogen* into N_2 or N_2O by bacteria.

Deserts　Areas of low rainfall, generally less than 250 mm per year. Deserts may be warm (such as those located in the subtropics) or cold (as in the central plateau of Antarctica).

Detrital mineral　A mineral grain found in a sediment that was never completely dissolved during the weathering process.

Deuterium　A stable *isotope* of hydrogen that has one neutron in its nucleus; denoted as ^2H or D.

Discount rate　A factor by which future costs or benefits are reduced in each succeeding year to account for economic growth and/or the preference of people for having money sooner rather than later.

Dissociate　To come apart. Acids dissociate in solution, forming anions plus hydrogen ions (protons).

Divergence　The outward movement of air or water from a region in the *atmosphere* or ocean.

Dobson unit (DU)　A unit for measuring the column depth of *ozone*. One DU is equivalent to a layer of pure ozone 0.001 cm thick at 1 atmosphere pressure.

Domains　The three primary divisions of life, as determined from sequencing of ribosomal RNA. Includes the *Archaea*, the *Bacteria*, and the *Eukarya*.

Dose rate　The number of UV photons per unit time that lead to a specific biological response, such as sunburn or skin cancer.

Downwelling　The sinking of surface water caused by convergence and water accumulation at the surface.

Drake equation　A formula used to estimate the number of other intelligent civilizations in our galaxy with which we might one day establish radio communication.

Dropstones　"Misplaced" chunks of rock dropped into marine sediments by melting icebergs.

Earth system　The group of interacting components (*atmosphere*, *hydrosphere*, solid Earth, and *biota*) that influence conditions at the Earth's surface.

Earthshine　Light reflected from the dark side of the Moon. It carries the spectrum of Earth because it comes from sunlight reflected from Earth's surface (and then from the Moon).

Earthquake　The sudden release of stored energy as the result of rapid movement between two lithospheric blocks.

Eccentricity　The degree to which a rotating object's orbit is elliptical. Eccentricity is defined for Earth's orbit as the distance from the center of the orbit to its foci (one of which is occupied by the Sun), divided by the average distance between Earth and the Sun.

Economic discounting　In cost-benefit economic models, the practice of devaluing costs and damages that occur in the future compared to those incurred today.

Ecosphere　Synonym for *habitable zone*.

Ecosystem　A subset of the *biota*, consisting of assemblages of plant, animal, and microbial species that interact with each other and with their surrounding environment.

Ecotone　The diffuse boundary between two *ecosystems*.

Effective radiating temperature　The temperature a planet such as Earth would have if the planet radiated as a *blackbody* (or if it had no *atmosphere*).

Ejecta　The debris thrown away from an impact event.

Ekman spiral　Describes the tendency for surface ocean water to be deflected to the right (left) of the layer above it in the northern (southern) hemisphere due to the *Coriolis effect*. Each layer is moved by the layer above so that the deeper below the surface the further each layer is deflected to the right or left, producing a spiraling effect with depth.

Ekman transport　The net direction of transport in the water column as a result of the Ekman spiral. The movement is at 90° to the wind direction (to the right in the Northern Hemisphere and to the left in the Southern Hemisphere).

El Niño　Originally, a warm ocean current that appears off the coast of Peru and Ecuador shortly after Christmas and flows for only a few weeks; the name now describes a major shift in the oceanic circulation that occurs in this region every 2 to 10 years.

El Niño–Southern Oscillation (ENSO)　A climatic event in the tropical Pacific Ocean in which the main area of surface convection moves from the western to the central Pacific. This event is associated with large-scale changes in the ocean circulation, the atmospheric circulation, and tropical precipitation patterns. The effects of an ENSO event may also spread beyond the tropics, causing anomalous weather conditions in many midlatitude locations.

Electromagnetic radiation　A self-propagating electric and magnetic wave such as visible light, ultraviolet, or infrared radiation.

Electromagnetic spectrum　The full range of different forms of electromagnetic radiation, which differ by *wavelength* (or, conversely, by *frequency*).

Endemic species　Species that are indigenous, or native, to a particular location.

Endosymbiosis　A biological system in which one *organism* lives inside another in a mutually interdependent relationship.

Enzymes　Proteins that catalyze various biochemical reactions.

Eon　One of the four major subdivisions of geologic time.

Ethane C_2H_6 A compound composed of 2 single-bonded carbon atoms and 6 hydrogen atoms that can be formed photochemically from methane, CH_4. Ethane is also a *greenhouse gas* that may have helped warm the Archean Earth.

Ethanol (C_2H_6)   A *biomass* fuel currently in widespread use in the United States. Most U.S. ethanol is produced from corn. Brazil produces ethanol from sugar cane.

Equilibrium state   A state in which the system is in equilibrium, that is, the state in which the system will remain unless something disturbs it. An equilibrium state can be stable or unstable.

Erosion   The transport of the products of weathering to basins where sediment accumulates; the process whereby crustal materials, decomposed and loosened by weathering, are transported by winds, landslides, and streams.

Erythemal action spectrum   The action spectrum for sunburn in humans.

Eukaryotes (Eukarya)   One of the three primary domains of life, as determined by sequencing of ribosomal RNA. The Eukarya (also known as eukaryotes) are *organisms* that have cell nuclei. They include all higher plants and animals.

Evaporation   The process by which a liquid is converted to a gas.

Evaporite deposit   Mineral deposit formed by the evaporation of seawater from shallow seas. The remaining salts are concentrated and precipitate from solution.

Evolution   The descent, with modification, of preexisting life forms. The *natural selection* of favorable genetic mutations is the dominant mechanism of evolution.

Exploitation efficiency   The proportion of the available *biomass* that is transferred from one trophic level to the next.

Extinction   The loss of all individuals within a species.

Extrasolar planets   Planets orbiting stars other than the Sun.

Feedback factor   The ratio of the equilibrium response to forcing (the response with feedback) to the response without feedback. Feedback factors less than 1 are indicative of negative feedback: The equilibrium response (with feedback) is smaller than the response to forcing without feedback. Feedback factors greater than 1 indicate positive feedback: The equilibrium response is larger than the response to the forcing itself.

Feedback loop   A linkage of two or more system components that forms a round-trip flow of information. Feedback loops can be positive or negative.

Ferric iron   Iron in its highest (3+) oxidation state; insoluble in water.

Ferrous iron   Iron in its intermediate (2+) oxidation state; soluble in anoxic seawater.

Firn   An intermediate step in the transformation of snow to glacier ice.

Fixed nitrogen   Compounds containing a nitrogen atom bonded to something other than another nitrogen atom.

Flux   The amount of energy (or number of photons) in an electromagnetic wave that passes perpendicularly through a unit surface area per unit time.

Food chain   A progression of *organisms* each dependent on the one before for food.

Food web   An intricate interlacing of *food chains*, more typical of natural communities.

Forcing   A persistent disturbance of a system; a longer-term disturbance than a perturbation.

Fossil fuels   Fuels such as coal, oil, and natural gas that are formed from the partially decomposed organic remains of *organisms*, concentrated in sedimentary rocks.

Fractionated   Separated according to some parameter. When applied to different *isotopes*, the term implies separation by mass.

Freezing nuclei   Mineral or organic particles in the *atmosphere* around which ice crystals will form.

Frequency   The number of wave crests that pass a fixed point in 1 second.

Gaia hypothesis   A theory suggesting that Earth is a self-regulating system in which the *biota* play an integral role.

General circulation model (GCM)   A three-dimensional computer model of the global *atmosphere* (or ocean) that simulates winds (currents), moisture transport, and energy balance; also called a global climate model.

General gas law   The relationship that combines *Boyle's law* and *Charles's law* and states that the product of the pressure and volume of a gas is directly proportional to temperature. In other words, the quotient of the product (pressure) × (volume) and temperature is a constant.

Geoengineering   The process of directly modifying Earth's climate in such a way as to counteract the warming effects of *anthropogenic* CO_2. Injecting sulfate aerosols into the *stratosphere* to increase Earth's *albedo* is one suggested geoengineering technique.

Geostrophic current   A current that flows around oceanic *gyres*; produced where the *Coriolis effect* that deflects the flow into the center of a gyre is balanced by the downslope flow from the higher sea-surface elevations in the gyre center. The resulting flow is clockwise in the Northern Hemisphere (counterclockwise in the Southern Hemisphere), approximately parallel to the ocean slope, and in the same direction as the wind-driven flow.

Geothermal heat   Heat flowing from Earth's interior up to its surface.

Geothermal power   The production of electricity by using temperature gradients within the solid Earth as the energy source.

Giant impact hypothesis   A theory of lunar formation in which the Moon forms as the result of a glancing collision between Earth and a Mars-sized body.

Glacial interval   An interval of time during the Pleistocene when ice sheets covered much of northern North America and Scandinavia and other parts of northern Europe and Asia (as well as Greenland and Antarctica). Globally averaged surface temperatures during glacial intervals were about 10°C, and atmospheric CO_2 concentrations were about 200 ppm.

Glacial striations   Grooves carved into bedrock by rocks frozen to the base of a moving glacier.

Glacial surge   The sudden, rapid movement of a glacier.

Global warming   A warming of Earth's atmosphere due to an anthropogenic enhancement of the *greenhouse effect*.

Granite   A common *igneous* silicate rock that solidifies below Earth's surface and forms the cores of many mountain ranges. Granite is less dense than basalt, so when a continental plate of granitic composition collides with an oceanic plate, the oceanic plate is subducted beneath the continental plate.

Greenhouse effect   The natural mechanism by which a planet's surface is warmed by infrared-absorbing gases in its *atmosphere*.

Greenhouse gases   Gases such as carbon dioxide, methane, nitrous oxide, and water vapor that warm a planet's surface by absorbing infrared radiation and reradiating some of it back toward the surface. Greenhouse gases, whether natural or *anthropogenic*, contribute to the atmospheric *greenhouse effect*.

Gross domestic product (GDP)   The total value of goods and services produced by the entire population of a country.

Groundwater   Water that penetrates through soil and rock and collects below the surface.

Gyre   A large, circular circulation pattern in the ocean. Gyres in the Northern Hemisphere circulate clockwise, whereas those in the Southern Hemisphere circulate counterclockwise.

H_2O rotation band   A strong absorption band that is a result of rotational *frequencies* of the water molecule in vapor form. The H_2O molecule absorbs infrared radiation of *wavelengths* about 12 μm and longer.

Habitable zone (HZ)   The region around a star in which a life-supporting planet might be found; generally, the region where liquid water could exist on a planet's surface.

Hadley circulation The process by which an air mass undergoes convergence at the tropics and divergence at about 30° N or 30° S latitude in one large convection cell.

Half-life The time it takes for half the initial quantity of radioactive *isotope* to decay.

Halocline A steep salinity gradient in the *pycnocline* zone that marks the transition between the surface zone and the deep ocean. Salinity rises rapidly with increasing depth in the halocline.

Halons Artificial chemicals containing the elements bromine, chlorine, fluorine, and carbon, used mostly in fire extinguishers.

Heavy bombardment period The time interval between 4.6 and 3.8 billion years ago when Earth and the other terrestrial planets were being regularly bombarded by large *planetesimals*.

Hematite A mineral composed of fully oxidized iron. It has a reddish color when present as small, dispersed grains.

Hertzsprung–Russell (H–R) diagram A type of graph in which stars are displayed in terms of their absolute luminosities (vertical scale) and surface temperatures (horizontal scale).

Heterocysts Specialized cells within some filamentous *bacteria* that are responsible for *nitrogen fixation*.

Heterogeneous reaction A chemical reaction that occurs on a solid surface.

Heterotroph An *organism* (*consumer*) that depends on other organisms (*autotrophs* or *producers*) to produce its food.

Holocene epoch The geological epoch extending from 10,000 years ago to the present; an interglacial interval.

Holocene Climatic Optimum A warm period that occurred during the Mid-Holocene.

Homogeneous reaction A chemical reaction between molecules that are in the gas phase.

Hotspots Biogeographic regions containing at least 0.5% of the world's 300,000 known vascular plants and which have lost at least 70% of their primary vegetation.

Hydrologic cycle The major reservoirs of water in the Earth system and the pattern of water storage and movement throughout that system.

Hydrosphere The component of Earth system that includes the various reservoirs of water and ice on Earth's surface.

Hydrothermal vents Cracks in the seafloor, especially around mid-ocean spreading ridges, through which heated and chemically modified seawater circulates.

Hydroxyl radical A highly reactive molecule that plays a variety of important roles in atmospheric chemistry; chemical formula OH.

Hyperthermophilic bacteria *Organisms* that have optimal growth temperatures above 80°C (176°F).

Ice shelves Floating sea ice formed at the margins of continents.

Ice-rafting A process by which chunks of rock are carried to sea by icebergs. The icebergs eventually melt, and the rocks may be preserved as *dropstones* in sediments.

Igneous rock Rock formed by the cooling and solidification of magma. If the magma solidifies beneath Earth's surface, the rocks are intrusive; if the magma erupts as lava at a volcano, the magma cools rapidly into extrusive rocks.

Impact degassing The venting of water and other volatile compounds directly into a planet's atmosphere during impacts of comets or asteroids onto its surface.

Infrared (IR) radiation *Electromagnetic radiation* of fairly low energy and *wavelengths* longer than those of visible light from 0.7 to 1000 μm.

Inorganic carbon Carbon not associated with compounds that are typically formed by living *organisms* and that do not contain carbon–carbon or carbon–hydrogen bonds.

International equity The concept that people living in one country should be considerate of the welfare of people living elsewhere. With regard to *global warming*, this concept implies that people living in developed, high-CO_2-emitting countries like the United States should be aware of the effects of global warming in poorer (or lower-lying) countries.

Intergovernmental Panel on Climate Change (IPCC) An international group of scientists who periodically review the status of climate change science and issue consensus reports about both the climate science and the possible effects of climate change on humans.

Instrumental value The degree to which a species' existence benefits another species (normally, humans) in some way.

Interferometer An instrument consisting of two or more telescopes connected electronically so that their images can be combined.

Intergenerational equity Treating different generations of people equally (in economic terms). Multigenerational problems such as *global warming* bring up considerations of intergenerational equity.

Interglacial period An interval during the *Pleistocene*, such as the *Holocene*, when continental ice sheets were restricted to Greenland and Antarctica. Globally averaged surface temperatures during interglacial intervals were about 15°C, and atmospheric CO_2 concentrations were about 280 ppm.

Interplanetary dust particles (IDPs) Small particles collected in Earth's *stratosphere* that originated in space.

Interstellar clouds Clouds of dust and gas from which stars occasionally form.

Intertropical convergence zone (ITCZ) A region of the tropics where surface heating causes uplift in the *atmosphere*, allowing subtropical air to flow inward to produce a *convergence* zone. This zone moves north and south of the equator as the seasons change.

Intrinsic value A species' value for its own sake, regardless of whether it benefits humans.

Inverse-square law A relationship describing the rate at which the solar *flux* decreases with increasing distance.

Iridium An element that is rare at Earth's surface but is concentrated in Earth's core and in extraterrestrial materials.

Isochron diagram A diagram in which one plots the abundance of two different radiogenic *isotopes* (e.g., ^{206}Pb and ^{207}Pb) measured in a number of different rock samples against each other. If the rocks all have the same age, then the data should fall on a straight line. The slope of the line gives the age of the rocks.

Isotopes Atoms of a given element that have different numbers of neutrons in their nuclei.

K–T boundary The boundary between the Cretaceous (K) and Tertiary (T) periods, about 65 million years ago, when the dinosaurs and many other species went extinct.

Kelvin (absolute) temperature scale A metric temperature scale in which the degree has the same size as a Celsius degree, but in which the zero point is moved downward by 273.15°, to absolute zero.

Kerogen Dispersed organic matter (hydrocarbons) in rocks.

Keystone species A species that plays a vital function in the operation of an *ecosystem*.

Kyoto Protocol An international treaty proposed in 1997 that limited CO_2 emissions for those countries that signed it. (The United States never did.) The emissions limitations applied only to developed countries.

Lagrange points Five points of neutral gravitational stability in the Earth-Sun system. Similar Lagrange points can also be identified for other planets and for the Earth-Moon system.

La Niña The opposite phase of the Southern Oscillation from *El Niño* conditions. It represents a stronger or more extreme version of the "normal" circulation in the tropical Pacific.

Latent heat The heat energy released or absorbed during the transition from one phase to another, such as when water evaporates.

Latent heat of fusion   The energy required to effect a change of phase between a solid and a liquid. Converting a solid to a liquid requires an addition of energy; converting a liquid to a solid releases energy to the environment.

Latent heat of vaporization   The energy required to effect a change of phase between a liquid and a gas. Converting a liquid to a gas requires an addition of energy; converting a gas to a liquid releases energy to the environment.

Lead–lead dating   A radiometric age dating technique that relies on measurements of two different *isotopes* of lead produced from two uranium isotopes that have different half-lives.

Limestone   A *sedimentary* rock composed largely of calcium carbonate minerals, mainly calcite.

Lithification   The transformation of sediments into *sedimentary* rocks; typically involves compaction and the precipitation of mineral cements between sediment grains.

Lithosphere   The uppermost *mantle* and rigid *crust*, above the *asthenosphere*. The lithosphere is divided into plates that move relative to one another in the process of *plate tectonics*.

Little Ice Age   An interval of colder temperatures from the 15th to 19th centuries, interrupted by a warmer interval in the 17th century.

Loess   Wind-blown glacial silt.

Luminosity   The brightness of a star such as our Sun.

Macrofossils   Fossils of multicellular *organisms* that are large enough to see easily with the naked eye.

Magma   Molten, or liquid, rock that forms *igneous rock* when cooled.

Magma ocean   A layer of molten rock covering the entire surface of a planet. The Moon is thought to have had one early in its history. Earth may have had one as well.

Magnetic dynamo   The mechanism whereby *convection* of the liquid-iron outer core generates Earth's magnetic field.

Main-sequence star   A middle-aged star that lies on a band of stars running from the upper left to the lower right of a plot of luminosity versus effective radiating temperature (*H–R diagram*).

Mantle   One of the three layers of the solid Earth; a thick, rocky layer between the core and *crust*. Composed primarily of silicate minerals.

Mass extinction   An extraordinary extinction event in which more than 25% of all extant families are lost.

Mass number   The combined number of protons and neutrons in the nucleus of an atom.

Maunder Minimum   The interval from A.D. 1645 to 1715, when very few *sunspots* were recorded.

Medieval warm period   A period of mild conditions in northern Europe and the North Atlantic that reached a maximum at about A.D. 1100.

Mesosphere   An atmospheric layer that extends from about 50 to 90 km above the surface; temperature decreases with altitude there.

Metamorphic rocks   Rocks formed from exposure to high temperatures, high pressures, chemically active fluids, or any combination of these agents. The rocks must remain in the solid phase to be classified as metamorphic; if melting occurs, they are called *igneous*.

Meteorite   A comet or asteroid that strikes Earth. Strictly speaking, the material that remains after such an impact.

Methane clathrate hydrate   An icelike combination of methane (CH_4) and water (H_2O) in which one methane molecule is trapped in a "cage" of 5 or 6 water molecules.

Methane sulfonic acid (MSA)   An acid that is produced from biogenic dimethyl sulfide and forms cloud condensation nuclei in the atmosphere.

Methanogenesis   Methane production carried out by certain *bacteria*.

Methanogenic bacteria   Anaerobic *bacteria* that convert carbon dioxide and hydrogen (or other substances) into methane.

Methanogens   Methanogenic *bacteria*.

Methanotropic bacteria   Aerobic *bacteria* that consume methane and incorporate the carbon from that methane into their body tissues.

Microfossils   The fossilized remains of single-celled *organisms*.

Mid-ocean ridge   A linear chain of subsea volcanic mountains on the seafloor that is the site of formation of new oceanic *lithosphere*.

Mie scattering   Scattering of radiation by particles that are of approximately the same size as the *wavelength* of radiation being scattered. Reduces to *Rayleigh scattering* (or geometric optics, i.e., ray tracing) in the small (large) particle limit.

Mineral   A naturally occurring inorganic solid of definite crystal structure and chemical composition.

Migration   When applied to growing planets, this term describes their ability to move inwards or outwards from their parent star as a consequence of gravitational interactions with gas, dust, and smaller *planetesimals*.

Mixed layer   The surface layer of the ocean that is mixed by wind action.

Moho   The *crust–mantle* boundary, marked by a sharp increase in *seismic wave* speeds.

Monsoon   A seasonal reversal in the surface winds caused by large-scale differential heating of land and ocean surfaces. Monsoon circulation is defined by the windfields but usually also has a direct impact on rainfall.

Montreal Protocol   An international treaty signed in 1987 that limited freon and *halon* emissions.

Moraine   A ridge of sediment deposited by a glacier.

Mountain glaciers   Ice fields formed on the cold, upper reaches of mountains.

Mutation   A random change in the DNA of an *organism*. This can lead to evolution if the mutation is advantageous to the survival of the organism.

Natural selection   The unequal survival and reproduction of *organisms*, owing to environmental pressures that result in the preservation of favorable adaptations. The relatively nonselective nature of *mass extinctions* suggests that natural selection may not play an important role in these large events.

Negative coupling   A link indicating that a change (increase or decrease) in one component leads to a change of the opposite direction (decrease or increase, respectively) in the linked component.

Negative feedback loop   A *feedback loop* with an odd number of negative couplings. Negative feedback loops tend to diminish the effects of disturbances.

Neutrinos   Massless particles given off in nuclear reactions.

Nice model   A model of solar system formation in which the giant planets migrate during the first few humdred million years, ultimately leading to a period of heavy bombardment of the inner solar system around 3.8–3.9 billion years ago.

Niche   The role a particular *organism* plays in the ecosystem: decomposer, surface grazer, etc.

Nitrogen fertilization   The stimulation of plant growth caused by the addition of anthropogenic *fixed nitrogen*, commonly from automobile exhaust.

Nitrogen fixation   A process by which some *organisms* (primarily prokaryotes) convert N_2 into *fixed nitrogen*.

Nitrogenase   An enzyme used by nitrogen-fixing *organisms* to convert N_2 into *fixed nitrogen*.

Normal stress   Stress exerted orthogonal to a surface.

North Atlantic Deep Water (NADW)   Cold, dense water that forms in the northernmost Atlantic Ocean, sinks, and flows southward at depth into the rest of the Atlantic Ocean.

Nuclear fission   The splitting of a heavy atomic nucleus into two fragments, accompanied by the release of energy.

Nuclear fusion   The combining of lightweight atomic nuclei into a heavier nucleus accompanied by the release of energy.

Nucleotides   Organic compounds consisting of a sugar, a base, and a phosphate group. Nucleotides are the basic building blocks of DNA and RNA.

Number density   A measure of the concentration of a gas. The units of number density are molecules per cubic centimeter.

Nutrient   Substances normally obtained in the diet that are essential to *organisms*.

Obliquity   The angle of a planet's spin axis relative to a line drawn perpendicular to the plane of the planet's orbit around the Sun; also called *tilt*.

Odd nitrogen   Any pure nitrogen-containing compound that has an odd number of nitrogen atoms; NO and NO_2. Odd nitrogen is similar to *fixed nitrogen* in that the nitrogen atom is coupled to atoms other than another N atom.

Odd oxygen   Any pure oxygen-containing atom or molecule that has an odd number of oxygen atoms; O and O_3.

Oort cloud   A distant region of the solar system, beyond Pluto, from which long-period comets originate.

Origination   The appearance of a new species.

Organic carbon   Carbon associated with compounds that are typically formed by living *organisms* and that contain carbon–carbon or carbon–hydrogen bonds.

Organism   A living system.

Oxidation state   The degree of oxidation of an atom, molecule, or compound. Substances with a low oxidation state have a large number of available electrons; substances with a high oxidation state do not.

Oxidized carbon   Carbon that, in compounds, is combined with oxygen. The carbon atoms in skeletons composed of $CaCO_3$ and in atmospheric CO_2 are oxidized carbon.

Oxygen minimum zone   A zone at intermediate depths in the ocean—about 1 km from the surface—where dissolved oxygen concentrations reach a minimum (and nutrient concentrations reach a maximum), as a result of high oxygen demand by aerobic decomposers and low oxygen supply from the surface ocean or from below.

Oxygenic photosynthesis   The normal, O_2-generating type of *photosynthesis* carried out by plants.

Ozone   A form of oxygen that is much less abundant than, and chemically unlike, the oxygen that we breathe. The ozone that is dispersed in the stratosphere blocks the Sun's harmful ultraviolet radiation.

Ozone hole   A patch of extremely low ozone concentration in the ozone layer. This hole has appeared near the South Pole each October since about 1976.

Ozone layer   A chemically distinct region of the atmosphere (specifically, the stratosphere) that protects Earth's surface from the Sun's harmful ultraviolet radiation.

Ozonesondes   A balloon-borne instrument that measures the concentration of stratospheric *ozone*.

P wave   Primary wave; a seismic *body wave* transmitted as a series of compressions and expansions in the overall direction of wave movement through Earth's interior. P waves can travel through fluids or solids.

Paleoclimate   Past climate.

Paleoclimatology   The study of past climates.

Paleontologist   A scientist who studies the history of life using the fossil record.

Paleosols   Ancient soils that have been preserved can be used as an indicator of past atmospheric oxygen levels.

Palynology   The study of pollen and organic microfossils.

Pangea   A supercontinent consisting of all the land masses of Earth that formed about 300 million years ago and broke apart about 200 million years ago.

Partial pressure   In a mixture of gases, the pressure a gas would exert if it were the only gas present (i.e., the contribution of each individual gas to the total pressure exerted by the mixture).

Per capita   Per person.

Perihelion   The position in a planet's orbit that is nearest to the Sun.

Period   A unit of geologic time, shorter than an era and longer than an epoch. Also, the time required for a planet to go around the sun.

Periodicity   A time interval of regular recurrence of a phenomenon.

Permafrost   Permanently frozen ground.

Perturbation   A temporary disturbance of a system; a shorter-term disturbance than a *forcing*.

Petroleum   A hydrogen- and carbon-bearing compound produced under high-temperature conditions of burial deep (3–4 km) within the *crust*; a *fossil fuel* formed from high concentrations of organic matter in marine sediments.

pH   A measure of acidity, defined as the negative logarithm (to the base 10) of the hydrogen ion concentration (in moles per liter). Acids have pH values less than 7, and bases have pH values greater than 7. A pH of 7 is defined as neutral.

Phase diagram   A graph that shows the conditions (usually temperature and pressure) under which thermodynamically distinct phases of a compound (e.g., ice, liquid water, and water vapor) can exist in equilibrium.

Photic zone   The portion of the oceans where there is sufficient sunlight for *photosynthesis*; about the upper 100 m of the water column.

Photochemical models   Computer models used to simulate atmospheric chemistry.

Photochemical reactions   Chemical reactions initiated by the absorption of a *photon*.

Photodissociation   The splitting of a molecule by the absorption of light or by UV radiation; also called *photolysis*.

Photolysis   The splitting of a molecule by the absorption of light or by UV radiation; also called *photodissociation*.

Photolyze   To split a molecule apart with visible or ultraviolet radiation.

Photon   A single, discrete particle, or pulse, of *electromagnetic radiation*.

Photorespiration   Respiration induced by the absorption of sunlight. (The combining of organic matter with oxygen to yield CO_2, H_2O, and energy.)

Photosphere   The surface layer of the Sun from which most of its energy, including *visible radiation*, is emitted.

Photosynthesis   The process by which an organism such as a green plant uses sunlight, carbon dioxide, and water to produce organic matter and oxygen.

Phototrophic   Attracted to light. Most phototrophic organisms use sunlight for some metabolic purpose, such as (but not necessarily limited to) *photosynthesis*.

Photovoltaic cells   Specially designed panels that directly convert sunlight into electricity.

Plages   Bright (higher temperature) areas that surround *sunspots* on the surface of the Sun.

Planetary vorticity   The angular rotation about a vertical axis at Earth's surface brought about because of Earth's rotation.

Planetesimals   Small protoplanets formed during planetary accretion.

Plate tectonics   Theory by which Earth's surface is divided into rigid plates of seafloor and continent that move relative to one another through time.

Pleistocene epoch   The geological epoch, extending from 1.8 million years ago to 10,000 years ago, that is characterized by oscillations in and out of the glacial state.

Polar front zone   A zone of steep temperature gradients formed at approximately 60° N and 60° S latitude, where cold, polar air meets the warm air moving poleward from the subtropics.

Polar stratospheric clouds (PSCs) Collections of droplets, consisting of a mixture of water and nitric acid, that are involved in the formation of the Antarctic ozone hole.

Polar vortex The circular, downward-sinking whirlpool of stratospheric air over the poles in winter. The polar vortex is more pronounced in the Southern Hemisphere than in the Northern Hemisphere.

Polarity The direction of orientation of a magnetic field. Earth's polarity (the geographic location of the North and South poles) flips irregularly on geological time scales.

Polymerase chain reaction (PCR) A method of amplifying small strands of DNA. This allows organisms (including humans) to be unambiguously identified from extremely small tissue samples.

Polymerize To join together in a long, repeating chain. *Photolysis* of methane leads to the formation of long hydrocarbon polymers.

Polynyii Irregularly shaped open water areas within the sea-ice cover (singular, polynya).

Population All of the members of a single species that live in a given area.

Positive coupling A link indicating that a change (increase or decrease) in one component leads to a change of the same direction (increase or decrease, respectively) in the linked component.

Positive feedback loop A *feedback loop* with an even number of, or zero, *negative couplings*. Positive feedback loops tend to amplify the effects of disturbances.

Precession The rotation of a planet's spin axis around a line drawn perpendicular to its orbital plane.

Primary producer A plant (or other type of photosynthesizer or chemosynthesizer) that provides energy used by *consumers*.

Primary productivity The amount of organic matter produced by *photosynthesis* in a unit time over a unit area of Earth's surface; also called productivity.

Prokaryotes Single-celled *organisms* that lack a cell nucleus.

Proteins Biochemical compounds, composed of amino acids, that perform a wide variety of functions within cells, including assisting with DNA replication.

Proto-Sun The central bulge in the solar nebula that later formed the Sun.

Proxy data Data that cannot be obtained by direct measurement but can be inferred from other evidence.

Pycnocline A steep density gradient (caused by changing temperature, salinity, or both) that marks the transition between the surface zone and the deep ocean. On the order of a kilometer in thickness, it is characterized by a rapid downward increase in density. The steep density gradient in the pycnocline zone makes this layer very stable.

Pyrite An iron-bearing mineral that becomes oxidized during weathering in today's oxygen-rich atmosphere.

Radial velocity method The method of looking for extrasolar planets by observing the back-and-forth wobble that they induce in the star's motion, using the Doppler effect.

Radiation (of heat energy) The outward transfer of heat energy in the form of electromagnetic rays emitted by a body; one of the three primary mechanisms of heat transfer.

Radiative-convective model (RCM) A one-dimensional computer model of the *atmosphere* that can be used to simulate the greenhouse effect. In an RCM, the climate system is greatly simplified by averaging the incoming solar and outgoing infrared radiation over Earth's entire surface.

Radiative forcing A term used by climatologists to describe the change in the net downward infrared flux at the *tropopause* caused by a given concentration of *greenhouse gases*, clouds, or aerosols.

Radioactive decay Radioactivity; the spontaneous disintegration of an unstable nucleus of one element, creating a different nucleus of a different element and releasing particles and radiation.

Radiocarbon dating A particular type of radiometric age dating that uses the half-life of ^{14}C to date materials that contained living organisms. It has been used to date materials back to about 50,000 years ago.

Radiometric age dating A method of calculating the age of a sample of material by knowing the half-life of a radioisotope within it. This method has provided absolute dates for the geologic time scale and for other specific events in Earth's history.

Rare earth elements Elements with atomic numbers 57 to 71. The pattern of rare earth elements in banded iron formations resembles that in modern mid-ocean ridge hydrothermal fluids.

Rayleigh scattering Scattering of radiation by particles that are small compared to the *wavelength* of radiation being scattered. Applies to scattering of sunlight by air molecules.

Reactive chlorine Chlorine compounds that either destroy *ozone* directly, such as Cl and ClO, or are readily converted into these compounds by *photolysis*.

Red giant A large, reddish star that is in the immediate post-main-sequence phase of its evolution.

Redbeds Sedimentary deposits in which the individual grains are coated with the mineral hematite (Fe_2O_3); thought to have formed under conditions of relatively high atmospheric O_2.

Redfield ratio The ratios of the nutrient elements that marine organisms incorporate into their tissues; these ratios appear to be nearly identical in all species of photoplankton. For these *organisms*, the atomic ratio of carbon:nitrogen:phosphorus is very nearly 106:16:1.

Reduced carbon Carbon that, in compounds, is combined mainly with other carbon atoms, hydrogen, or nitrogen; *organic carbon* is a form of reduced carbon. Reduced carbon tends to be reactive in the presence of oxygen gas.

Reduced gases Gases, such as H_2 or CH_4, that can react with oxygen. Such gases typically contain the element hydrogen.

Relative humidity The amount of water vapor contained by a unit volume of air divided by the amount of water vapor that volume would contain if the air were saturated.

Relative vorticity *Vorticity* produced by processes (other than Earth's rotation) that induce a rotary motion in a fluid (such as clockwise or counterclockwise surface wind patterns acting on the ocean surface, or current shear in the oceans).

Replication The process by which an *organism* produces a new version of itself, generally modified by *mutation*. One of the three critical steps of Darwinian evolution.

Residence time The average length of time a substance spends in a given reservoir that is at a steady state with respect to the processes that add and remove the substance to and from the reservoir. Residence time is calculated as the ratio of the reservoir size to the rate of inflow or outflow (which are equal at steady state).

Ribosomes Small inclusions (organelles) within cells that are responsible for protein synthesis.

RNA world A hypothetical period of evolutionary history in which organisms were based entirely on RNA, unlike the modern world, in which *organisms* depend on RNA, DNA, and proteins.

Rock cycle The cyclical process of creation and destruction of rocks through tectonic, weathering, metamorphic, and igneous processes.

Rocks Consolidated mixtures of crystalline materials called *minerals*.

Runaway glaciation An out-of-control climate in which a planet's surface becomes entirely covered by snow and ice.

Runaway greenhouse An out-of-control climate in which all water on a planet's surface is present as vapor. The oceans are completely evaporated.

S wave Secondary or shear wave; a seismic *body wave* transmitted as displacements perpendicular to the overall direction of wave travel through Earth's interior. S waves can travel only through solids.

Salinity   The salt content of a water mass; often expressed in parts per thousand (modern usage requires that salinity be expressed without units).

Scattering   Redirection of the path of an incident electromagnetic wave by particles (including air molecules) in its path.

Sea ice   Ice that forms on the surface of the ocean.

Seafloor spreading   The formation of hot, new oceanic *crust* from *magma* extruded at *mid-ocean ridges*. Once it forms, the new seafloor spreads to the sides of the ridges and is replaced at the ridge axis by an even younger new seafloor.

Seasonal temperature contrast   The difference in average temperatures between summer and winter.

Sedimentary rock   Rock formed by the compaction and lithification of sediments or by the chemical or biochemical precipitation of *minerals*.

Sediments   Layers of unconsolidated material that is transported by water or by air.

Seismic wave   An *earthquake*-produced wave that ripples through Earth's interior, away from the earthquake's focus, as a result of the elastic deformation of the solid Earth. Two types of seismic waves are generated: *body waves* and *surface waves*.

Serpentinization   Production of serpentine minerals via reaction of water with ultramafic (iron- and magnesium-rich) rocks. Produces either hydrogen or methane.

Shear stress   The stress (force) exerted parallel to a surface.

Shelly fossils   The fossilized remains of shelled organisms. The first such fossils occur just before the Cambrian period at the beginning of the Phanerozoic eon.

Siberian Traps   Volcanic deposits of Late Permian age that today cover 2 million square kilometers of the Siberian region of Russia; at the time of their eruption, they may have covered 3–4 times as much area. The Siberian Trap eruptions have been implicated in the end-Permian *mass extinction*.

Siderophile   Literally "iron-loving," refers to elements that tend to dissolve readily into molten iron, and thus are concentrated in Earth's *core*.

Silicate mineral   A mineral rich in silicon and oxygen. A major class of rock-forming minerals, the silicates make up most of Earth's *crust*.

Slab   Downgoing plate; the portion of oceanic lithosphere that is subducted into the mantle at a subduction zone.

Solar maximum   A time of high sunspot activity and corresponding high solar UV *flux*.

Solar minimum   A time of low sunspot activity and corresponding low solar UV *flux*.

Solar nebula   The cloud of gas and dust surrounding the Sun shortly after it formed.

Solar-power satellites   Hypothetical satellites that would collect solar energy up in space and beam it back to Earth using microwaves or lasers.

Solar thermal power   A method of conversion of sunlight into electricity in which the sunlight is first used to heat a fluid that, in turn, drives a turbine.

Solar wind   A stream of charged particles, mostly hydrogen and helium ions, emanating from the Sun's corona.

Solar zenith angle   The angle between the Sun and a line drawn perpendicular to the ground. The solar zenith angle is $0°$ when the Sun is directly overhead and $90°$ when it is setting.

Solid Earth   The component of the Earth system that includes all rocks and all unconsolidated rock fragments. The *core*, *mantle*, and *crust* make up the solid Earth.

Southern Oscillation (SO)   An oscillation in sea-level pressure between the western and central/eastern portions of the tropical Pacific Ocean.

Southern Oscillation Index (SOI)   A measure of the pressure difference between the western and central eastern parts of the tropical Pacific Ocean. Strong negative values indicate *ENSO*

conditions, whereas strong positive values indicate *La Niña* (non-ENSO) conditions.

Speciation   The origination of new species.

Spectroscopy   A technique in which the composition of a material, such as a gas, is analyzed according to the details of its *electromagnetic spectrum*.

Spörer Minimum   An interval of low *sunspot* activity between A.D. 1450 and 1534.

Stable equilibrium   A state in which the system will remain if left undisturbed and to which the system will return when disturbed.

Stable isotope   An *isotope* that does not spontaneously change into another isotope or into an atom of another element by *radioactive decay*.

State   The set of important attributes of a system that characterize the system at a particular time.

Steady state   A condition in which the state of a system component is unchanging in time. A reservoir is in steady state when the rates of inflow and outflow are equal.

Stefan–Boltzmann law   A relationship stating that the *flux* of radiation emitted by a *blackbody* is related to the fourth power of the body's absolute temperature; derived from the Planck function.

Steranes   Organic compounds found in rocks that are produced from degradation of sterols (such as cholesterol) in *eukaryotic organisms*.

Stochastic resonance   A system subject to random (stochastic) perturbations and periodic forcings may be forced across a threshold when the forcings and perturbations act in concert (resonate) to change the state of the system.

Stratosphere   The stable atmospheric layer between 10 and 15 km and 50 km above the surface; temperature increases with altitude there. The stratosphere contains most of Earth's ozone.

Stress   A measure of force exerted per unit area.

Stromatolites   Laminated or domed structures in rocks produced by layers of single-celled *organisms*.

Strongly reduced atmosphere   An *atmosphere* composed mostly of compounds rich in hydrogen (e.g., CH_4 and NH_3) and containing no molecular oxygen (O_2).

Subduction   The process whereby one plate of oceanic *lithosphere*, and at times its sediment cover, is carried underneath another plate (either oceanic or continental) in a convergent margin.

Subsidence   The sinking of air from higher levels in the *atmosphere* down toward the surface. Also the vertical movement of Earth's *crust* toward the *mantle*.

Succession   A progressive change in species composition of a community, often in response to a disturbance, but sometimes resulting from the colonization of previously uninhabited areas (e.g., bare rock). Fast growing, rapidly reproducing species usually colonize first, but then are replaced by slower-growing but competitively advantaged species.

Sulfate-reducing bacteria   *Bacteria* that make a metabolic living by combining sulfate with organic matter.

Sunspot   Dark areas of lower-than-normal temperatures on the surface of the sun.

Super-Earth   An extrasolar planet between about 1 and 10 Earth masses. Such planets are thought to consist of a mixture of rocks and water, like Earth.

Supercooled water   Liquid water that exists at temperatures below 273 K.

Surface waves   *Seismic waves* that travel only across Earth's surface as they spread outward from the *earthquake's* surface.

Symbiosis   A relationship between two species in which the two are dependent on each other to the degree that neither can live alone.

Syngas   A flammable mixture consisting of various amounts of carbon monoxide (CO) and hydrogen (H_2). Syngas can be produced by running hot steam through coal.

System   An entity composed of diverse but interrelated parts (components) that function as a complex whole.

Taxon   An individual taxonomic group (species, genus, and so on).

Taxonomy   The systematic organization of living or fossil *organisms* into a hierarchy.

Terrestrial planets   The four rocky, inner planets of the solar system: Mercury, Venus, Earth, and Mars.

Thermal drag   The ocean's ability to delay climate warming (or cooling) as a result of its large heat capacity.

Thermal expansion   The tendency of a substance (such as water above 4°C) to expand when heated.

Thermal inertia   The ability of a body to conduct and store heat.

Thermohaline circulation   The circulation of the deep oceans; driven by density differences that result from variations in temperature and salinity.

Thermokast   Topographic features that form in the landscape due to the melting and subsidence of previously frozen ground.

Thermophiles   Shorthand for *thermophilic bacteria*.

Thermophilic bacteria   *Bacteria* that have optimal growth temperatures between 40 and 80°C.

Thermosphere   The atmospheric layer higher than about 90 km above the surface; temperature increases with altitude there.

Tidal locking radius   The distance from a star within which a planet is likely to develop a captured rotation, that is, the same side of the planet always faces the star.

Tidal power   The production of electricity by using long, floating booms to harness the energy of ocean tides.

Till   Sediment transported by glaciers and ice sheets, comprising materials of a large range of grain sizes and compositions.

Tillite   Rock composed of lithified till. One of several pieces of evidence used to identify past glaciations.

Trace gases   Gases such as methane, nitrous oxide, and freons that are present in Earth's atmosphere in very low concentrations.

Transform fault   A fracture in the *lithosphere* between two lithospheric plates that, relative to each other, are sliding past one another (parallel to the boundary) in opposite directions.

Transient response   The time-dependent (nonequilibrium) change in a quantity, such as temperature, in response to a *perturbation*.

Transit   The passage of a planet in front of a star, temporarily blocking some of the star's light.

Triple point   The point in a phase diagram at which all of the phase boundaries meet. In the case of water it is the temperature and pressure at which water can exist in a stable state in all three phases (solid, liquid and gas).

Troposphere   The lowermost, convective layer of Earth's *atmosphere* between the surface and 10 to 15 km above it; temperature decreases rapidly with altitude there. Weather is confined to the troposphere.

Ultramafic rocks   *Igneous rocks* that are rich in iron and magnesium and low in quartz. Peridotite is a common example.

Ultraviolet (UV) radiation   *Electromagnetic radiation* of fairly high energy and *wavelengths* from 400 to about 10 nm, shorter than those of *visible radiation*.

Unstable equilibrium   A state in which the system will remain if left undisturbed, but even slight disturbances will carry the system to some other (stable) *equilibrium state*.

Unstable isotope   An *isotope* that spontaneously changes into another isotope or into an atom of another element by radioactive decay.

Uplift   Any process by which air is forced to rise upward in the atmosphere. Also an upward vertical tectonic movement of Earth's crust.

Upwelling   The rising of cooler, nutrient-rich ocean water to the surface to replace warm, divergent surface water.

Uraninite   A uranium-containing mineral that is normally destroyed during weathering in an O_2-rich atmosphere.

Vascular plants   Plants that have a well-developed stem or trunk for transporting water and nutrients from the ground up to their leaves. They also tend to have well-developed root systems, which take up water and nutrients and help support the plant.

Visible radiation   Visible light; *electromagnetic radiation* of moderate energy and a relatively narrow range of *wavelengths*, from about 400 to 700 nm. Within this range, the color of the light depends on its wavelength.

Visible spectrum   The range of component *wavelengths* of visible light; the colors of the rainbow.

Volatile compounds   Chemical compounds that vaporize (turn into gases) at relatively low temperatures.

Vorticity   The tendency of a fluid to undergo rotary motion. A tendency for counterclockwise motion is referred to as positive vorticity; a tendency for clockwise motion is negative vorticity.

Water–gas shift reaction   The chemical reaction: $CO + H_2O$ $CO_2 + H_2$. This reaction could be used to convert syngas to clean-burning (non-CO_2-emitting) H_2.

Wavelength   The distance between two adjacent wave crests.

Weakly reduced atmosphere   An *atmosphere* composed mainly of N_2 and CO_2, plus small amounts of reduced (H-rich) gases and virtually no free O_2.

White dwarf   A small, compact star that represents the final stage in the evolution of a star such as our Sun.

Wien's law   A relationship stating that the *flux* of radiation emitted by a *blackbody* reaches its peak value at a *wavelength* that depends inversely on the body's absolute temperature; derived from the Planck function.

Wilson cycle   A plate tectonic cycle of supercontinent assembly and destruction; each cycle lasts about 500 million years.

Wind power   The production of electricity from windmills, utilizing Earth's solar-energy-driven winds.

Wolf Minimum   An interval of low *sunspot* activity between A.D. 1282 and 1342.

Younger Dryas   A 1,300-year climatic reversal to glacial conditions that began 12,900 years ago after the end of the last glaciation. Evidence of climate change at this time is seen in various parts of the world, but the main effects of the Younger Dryas event appear to be centered on the North Atlantic region.

Zircon   A mineral composed of zirconium silicate that has been used to date some of the oldest rocks on Earth.

Zooplankton   Free-floating, marine consumers, including small invertebrates and microorganisms that cannot photosynthesize and therefore feed on phytoplankton.

Global Change

Key Questions

- What is meant by a "systems approach" to Earth science?
- How does global warming differ from the greenhouse effect, and is global warming actually occurring today?

- What is the Antarctic ozone hole, and what is its significance?
- Should we be concerned about tropical deforestation?
- What can understanding Earth's past tell us about Earth's future?

Chapter Overview

Earth is currently being altered at an unprecedented rate by human activity. The buildup of greenhouse gases in the atmosphere has already warmed Earth's climate by a small amount, and may warm it significantly in the future unless steps are taken to reduce greenhouse gas emissions globally. The accumulation of chlorine-containing compounds in the atmosphere has damaged the ozone layer over part of the globe. Deforestation of the tropics may be causing large decreases in biodiversity. How serious are these problems, and how do they compare with past changes in the Earth system? This chapter lays out the evidence of these changes and explains why an integrated, systems approach is useful in analyzing them.

INTRODUCTION

Our world is changing. In fact, Earth has always been changing and will continue to do so for ages to come. Yet, there is a difference between the changes occurring now and those that occurred previously. Earth is changing faster today than it has throughout most of its 4.6-billion-year history. Indeed, it may be changing faster than it ever has, except perhaps in the aftermath of giant meteorite

impacts. The cause of this accelerated pace of change is simple: human activity. Human populations have expanded in numbers and in their technological abilities to the point at which we are now exerting a significant influence on our planet. The effects of our actions are seen most clearly in the thin envelope of gases that supports our existence, the *atmosphere,* but they are observable elsewhere as well. Forests, mountains, lakes, rivers, and even the oceans exhibit the telltale signs of human activity.

To what extent are these **anthropogenic** (human-induced) changes a cause for concern? All of us can think of situations in which human influence has clearly been detrimental to the environment—for example, cities plagued with polluted air and water. But these are local problems, and they are hardly new. Humans have generated local pollution ever since they first developed agricultural societies around 10,000 years ago. Human inhabitants of Easter Island (which lies off the southwest coast of South America) may have set the stage for the demise of their culture about 700 years ago through **deforestation**—that is, by the clearing of all the trees—of the island. Advanced technology is not needed to damage one's immediate surroundings.

Today, however, because technological advances abound and because there are simply more people on

Earth than ever before, human influence extends to the global environment. For example, *global climate,* the prevailing weather patterns of a planet or region over time, is being altered by the addition of greenhouse gases to the atmosphere. **Greenhouse gases** are gases that warm a planet's surface by absorbing outgoing *infrared radiation*—radiant heat—and reradiating some of it back toward the surface. This process is called the **greenhouse effect.** (The analogy is not perfect, however, because the glass walls of a greenhouse keep the air warm by inhibiting heat loss by upward air motions rather than by absorbing infrared radiation.) The greenhouse effect is a natural physical process that operates in all planetary atmospheres. For example, the greenhouse effect, and not solely proximity to the Sun, is thought to account for the high surface temperature of Venus—460°C (860°F), compared with about 15°C (59°F) at Earth's surface. On Earth, some greenhouse gases (such as water vapor) are entirely natural, but others are partly or wholly anthropogenic. The most abundant anthropogenic greenhouse gas on Earth is carbon dioxide, CO_2, which is produced by the burning of **fossil fuels** (fuels such as coal, oil, and natural gas that are composed of the fossilized remains of organisms) and by deforestation. When trees are cut down, they decay, and the carbon in their trunks, branches, and leaves is released as CO_2. Carbon dioxide is also a component of volcanic emissions, and it is cycled rapidly back and forth by living plants and animals. Thus, its abundance is controlled by a combination of natural and human-controlled processes.

Humankind is also capable of damaging Earth's fragile ozone layer. The **ozone layer** is a chemically distinct region within the *stratosphere,* part of the atmosphere. The ozone layer protects Earth's surface from the Sun's harmful *ultraviolet radiation.* Ultraviolet radiation is what gives us suntans but also sunburns. **Ozone (O_3)** is a form of oxygen that is much less abundant than, and chemically unlike, the oxygen that we breathe (O_2). As we shall see, the **ozone hole** over Antarctica, a patch of extremely low ozone concentration in the ozone layer, is almost certainly anthropogenic in origin.

We are also now deforesting parts of the planet—mainly the tropics—at a rate that was not possible until the 19th century. As we cut down the forests, we kill off many species of plants and animals that live there. Hence, we are now causing substantial decreases in **biodiversity,** or the number of species present in a given area.

The effects of these global environmental problems on humans are more difficult to assess than are the effects of local air and water pollution. Depletion of the ozone layer is a worrisome prospect, but serious losses of ozone have so far been confined to the region near the South Pole, where few people live. Small decreases in ozone have been observed at midlatitudes, but these are not yet thought to pose a serious hazard to health. Loss of biodiversity in the tropics has thus far only indirectly affected people who live at temperate latitudes. Tropical deforestation and fossil

fuel burning could affect everyone by causing **global warming,** a warming of Earth's atmosphere due to an anthropogenic enhancement of the greenhouse effect. Once hotly debated in scientific as well as political circles, because it was difficult to detect, global warming has by now become quite recognizable. Some of the evidence for it is described in this chapter. There is less agreement, though, as to just how urgent the problem is and what steps might be taken to address it.

Three Major Themes

One major theme of ours will be global environmental issues such as these. All of us should be able to make our own decisions as to which modern environmental problems are worth worrying about and which, if any, are not. Making such decisions intelligently requires at least some knowledge of the scientific questions involved. Some of the issues, global warming in particular, are also politically contentious because the actions needed to address them are potentially very costly. In such cases, it is important that both policymakers and citizens understand the problem at a reasonably detailed level.

To understand how humankind is changing the environment today, we need also to understand how the environment was changing before humans came on the scene. Otherwise, it is difficult to distinguish short-term, anthropogenic trends from longer-term, natural trends. So, a second major theme of ours is global change in the past. Climate is a good example of the overlap of short and long time scales of global change, and one to which we will return frequently. Earth's climate is predicted to warm over the next few decades to centuries as a consequence of the buildup of CO_2 and other greenhouse gases in its atmosphere. Evidence of past climates has come from cores drilled into sediments on the ocean floor. (**Sediments** are layers of unconsolidated material that is transported by water or air.) This evidence indicates that we are in the midst of a relatively short *interglacial period* (a warm interval marked by the retreat of Northern Hemisphere ice sheets) in between *glacial periods* (cold intervals marked by the buildup of these ice sheets). Hence, in the absence of anthropogenic influence, the planet would be destined over the next few thousand years to slip slowly into the next Ice Age. Which of these tendencies—global warming or the transition to a glacial period—will win out? We will argue that warming is likely to win out in the short term, because the rate of increase of atmospheric CO_2 and other greenhouse gases is faster than the historical rate of interglacial-to-glacial climate change. Thus, the question of time scales is important. Understanding how and why climate has changed in the past can help us understand how it may change in the future.

We are introduced to these two major themes in this chapter. A third major theme of ours is *systems*—in particular, the *Earth system.*

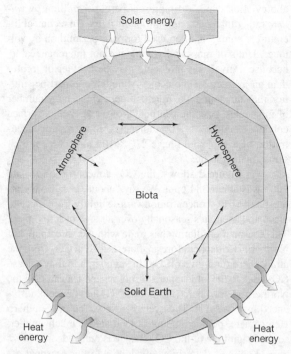

FIGURE 1 Schematic diagram of the Earth system, showing interactions among its four components. (*Source:* From R. W. Christopherson, *Geosystems: An Introduction to Physical Geography,* 3/e, 1997. Reprinted by permission of Prentice Hall, Upper Saddle River, N.J.)

For now, let us say just that a **system** is a group of components that interact. The **Earth system** is composed of four parts: the atmosphere, the hydrosphere, the biota, and the solid Earth (Figure 1). As we have seen, the **atmosphere** is a thin envelope of gases that surrounds Earth. The **hydrosphere** is composed of the various reservoirs of water, including ice. Sometimes the ice component is separated into its own subcategory, termed the **cryosphere**. The **biota** include all living organisms. (Some ecologists define the *biosphere* as the entire region in which life exists, but we will avoid that term here, because it overlaps our other system components). The **solid Earth** includes all **rocks,** or consolidated mixtures of crystalline materials called *minerals,* and all unconsolidated rock fragments. It is divided into three parts: the core, mantle, and crust. The **core** of any planet or of the Sun is the central part. Earth's core is a dense mixture of metallic iron and nickel and is part solid, part liquid. The **mantle** is a thick, rocky layer between the core and crust that represents the largest fraction of Earth's mass. The **crust** is the thin, outer layer, which consists of light, rocky matter in contact with the atmosphere and hydrosphere.

One of our goals is to show how the different components of the Earth system interact in response to various internal and external influences, or *forcings*. A well-known example of a forcing is the variation in the amount of sunlight received in each hemisphere during the course of a year. The response to this forcing, which is governed by the interaction between the atmosphere and the hydrosphere, is the seasonal cycle of summer and winter. But there are other, more subtle forcings at work as well that may engage all four components of the Earth system. Some examples are given later in this chapter.

This chapter is devoted to problems, such as global climate history and modern global change, that cut across traditional disciplinary boundaries and that involve interactions among different parts of the Earth system. The systems approach adopted in this text can lead to a more in-depth understanding of such problems by providing a convenient way of analyzing complex interactions and predicting their overall effect.

GLOBAL CHANGE ON SHORT TIME SCALES

We start our discussion of the Earth system by introducing three major, global environmental changes that are occurring today: global warming, ozone depletion, and tropical deforestation. Afterward, we will backtrack to discuss how the Earth system operated in the past and how that may help us predict what will happen to it in the future.

Evidence of Global Warming

The most pervasive, and at the same time controversial, environmental change that is occurring today is global warming. This issue is extremely complex because it involves many different parts of the Earth system. It is controversial because it is difficult to separate anthropogenic influences from natural ones and because its causes are deeply rooted in our global industrial infrastructure; hence, these causes would be difficult to eliminate. A major goal of this text, therefore, is to help the reader understand global warming and to put it in the context of past climatic change.

Although the terms "greenhouse effect" and "global warming" are sometimes used interchangeably, the two phenomena are very different. The greenhouse effect is an indisputably real, natural process that keeps the surfaces of Earth and the other terrestrial planets warmer than they would be in the absence of an atmosphere. Global warming is an increase in Earth's surface temperature brought about by a combination of industrial and agricultural activities. These activities release gases that bolster the greenhouse effect. To be fair, not all scientists are convinced that global warming has begun. Almost all researchers agree that the climate has warmed over the past century, but not all of them are convinced that this warming is a result of human activities. However, the number of global warming skeptics has dwindled over the past several years. An important milestone was reached in 2007 when the influential

Intergovernmental Panel on Climate Change (IPCC) released a new report—its fourth since 1990. Using language much stronger than in previous versions, the new report says: "Warming of the climate system is unequivocal, as is now evident from observations of increases in global average air and ocean temperatures, widespread melting of snow and ice, and rising global average sea level." The importance attached to this conclusion was underscored when the Nobel Foundation awarded its 2007 Peace Prize jointly to the IPCC and to former U.S. vice president Al Gore, who has vigorously promoted understanding of this issue around the globe. We concur with the IPCC findings, and we base much of our discussion of global warming on its report.

MEASUREMENTS OF ATMOSPHERIC CO_2: THE KEELING CURVE The data that have aroused much of the current concern about global warming are shown in Figure 2. The graph shows the atmospheric CO_2 concentrations measured at the top of Mauna Loa, a 4300-m-high volcano in Hawaii, over the last 50 years. Mauna Loa was chosen as the measurement site because the air blowing over its summit—clean air from the western Pacific Ocean—is far removed from local sources of pollution. The measurements were begun in 1958 by Charles David Keeling of the Scripps Institute of Oceanography. For this reason, the data are often referred to as the "Keeling curve." Dr. Keeling passed away in 2005, just 3 years prior to the time of this writing. His name is honored by environmentalists everywhere because his straightforward, but precise, measurements begun half a century ago are still the most powerful evidence that our atmosphere and climate are changing.

In Figure 2 the concentration of atmospheric gas is measured in *parts per million,* or *ppm.* A value of 1 ppm of a particular gas means that one molecule of that gas is present in every million air molecules. We shall use the abbreviation "ppm" to represent parts per million *by volume* rather than parts per million *by mass.* (In technical literature, "ppmv" is often used for parts per million by volume.) Units of mass and volume are not interchangeable, because a given gas molecule may be heavier or lighter than an average air molecule. Although one part per million may not sound like much, it represents a large number of molecules. A cubic centimeter of air at Earth's surface contains about 2.7×10^{19} molecules, so a 1-ppm concentration of a gas would have 2.7×10^{13} molecules in that same small volume.

As Figure 2 shows, the CO_2 concentration in late 2007 was about 384 ppm. We say "about" because the atmospheric CO_2 concentration varies slightly from place to place and oscillates seasonally over a range of 5 to 6 ppm. This seasonal oscillation has to do with the "breathing" of Northern Hemisphere forests. Forests take in CO_2 from the atmosphere (and give off O_2) in summer, and they release CO_2 back to the atmosphere during winter. Hawaii is in the Northern Hemisphere (latitude 19° N) and hence is influenced by this cycle. The cycle is reversed in the Southern Hemisphere, but the amount of land area is much smaller, so the magnitude of the CO_2 change is reduced.

Keeling's data show, in addition to this seasonal oscillation, that atmospheric CO_2 levels have increased significantly since 1958. The mean CO_2 concentration that year was about 315 ppm, or 71 ppm lower than the average 2008 value. The average rate of increase in CO_2 concentration since then has been 71 ppm/50 yr, or about 1.4 ppm/yr. More-detailed inspection of the curve reveals that the rate of CO_2 increase rose from 0.7 ppm/yr in the early 1960s to 1.9 ppm/yr over the last decade. Most of the increase in atmospheric CO_2 has been caused by the combustion of coal, oil, and natural gas, but tropical deforestation is also partly to blame.

The evidence that atmospheric CO_2 is increasing is indisputable. Similar measurements have been conducted at many different stations around the globe. The long-term increase in CO_2 is visible in every set of measurements and is essentially the same as that seen at Mauna Loa. (The range of the seasonal fluctuations, however, varies with the location.) For this reason, both scientists and policymakers agree that the long-term trend in atmospheric CO_2 is real rather than an artifact.

CO_2 Data from ICE Cores When did this increase in atmospheric CO_2 begin, and what was the CO_2 level before that time? If we had to rely entirely on measurements made in the modern era, we would not be able to answer these questions. This is where analysis of the record of climate in the past can help. The composition of the atmosphere in the past can be determined by analyzing the composition of air bubbles trapped in polar ice. The bubbles are formed as snow at the top of an ice sheet is compacted, and their composition is preserved as they are buried under more

FIGURE 2 Measurements of atmospheric CO_2 concentrations at the top of Mauna Loa in Hawaii. These data are known as the "Keeling curve." (*Source:* C. D. Keeling and T. P. Wharf, Scripps Institute of Oceanography, La Jolla, California, http://scrippsCO2.ucsd.edu.)

snow. The age of the ice can be determined by drilling deep into the ice, removing a section of it, and counting the annual layers of snow accumulation. Figure 3 shows results from ice cores—cylindrical sections drilled into the ice—taken at several locations on Antarctica. Figure 3a compares the CO_2 composition of

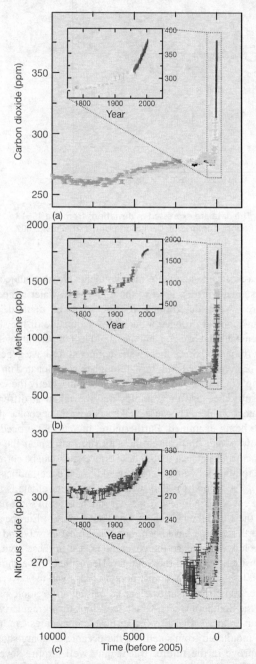

FIGURE 3 Atmospheric CO_2 concentrations over the past 1000 years, as determined from ice cores and from direct atmospheric measurements (The dashed line is the Keeling curve.) (*Source: After Climate Change, 1994,* Intergovernmental Panel on Climate Change, Cambridge: Cambridge University Press.)

the air bubbles in the ice with a "smoothed" version of the Keeling curve (the dashed curve, from which the seasonal oscillation has been removed). The fact that the ice-core measurements match up well with the direct atmospheric measurements in 1958 is convincing evidence that the ice-core technique for determining atmospheric CO_2 concentrations yields reliable results.

According to these measurements, the buildup of atmospheric CO_2 began early in the 19th century—well before the dawn of the Industrial Age, which started in earnest around 1850. The rise in CO_2 levels between 1800 and 1850 has been attributed to the deforestation of North America by westward-expanding settlers and is thus known as the *pioneer effect*. The ice-core measurements show that the *preindustrial CO_2 concentration* (the value circa 1800) was about 280 ppm. Evidently, humans have been responsible for almost a 40% increase in atmospheric CO_2 concentration over the past two centuries.

OTHER GREENHOUSE GASES Carbon dioxide is not the only greenhouse gas whose concentration is currently on the rise. Methane (CH_4) and nitrous oxide (N_2O) have also been increasing as a result of human activities, primarily agriculture. Their concentrations have also been measured in ice cores (Figures 3b and 3c), along with CO_2. The methane concentration has more than doubled from a preindustrial concentration of about 700 ppb (parts per billion) to approximately 1800 ppb (or 1.8 ppm) today. Nitrous oxide has been less strongly influenced by human activities because it has large natural sources. Certain **chlorofluorocarbon** compounds (**CFCs**) are also produced by human activities. Also called *freons,* CFCs are synthetic compounds containing chlorine, fluorine, and carbon. Collectively, such gases that are present in the atmosphere in very low concentrations, called **trace gases,** are thought to have contributed almost as much additional greenhouse effect over the past few decades as has CO_2. (Because CO_2 is much less abundant than N_2 or O_2 it is also classified as a trace gas, but it is more than 200 times as plentiful as any of the other gases mentioned here and hence deserves to be in a class by itself.) The CFCs have also been implicated in the destruction of stratospheric ozone, as we discuss later in this chapter. For now, we simply note that the evidence for an increase in anthropogenic greenhouse gases is unequivocal: Humans are indeed modifying the composition of Earth's atmosphere. This has been recognized for at least 40 years.

OBSERVED CHANGES IN SURFACE TEMPERATURE The observed rise in greenhouse gases is quite well documented, but what about the effects of this rise? Is there any direct evidence that climate is changing as a result?

The answer to this question is yes, according to the IPCC, but agreement on this answer has been reached only within the last few years, and as noted previously, a few scientists still remain skeptical. Historical data indicate

FIGURE 4   Change in global average surface temperature since 1861. The data are expressed as deviations from the 1961 to 1990 mean value.   (*Source:* IPCC, *Climate Change 2007,* Fourth Assessment Report, Cambridge: Cambridge University Press, 2007, Chapter 3, p. 241, http://www.ipcc.ch/ipccreports/ar4-wg1.htm.)

that Earth's surface temperature is on the increase. The data are not as easy to interpret as are the greenhouse gas data discussed earlier, but they are considered to be reliable. At a number of stations around the world, scientists have made accurate atmospheric temperature measurements that date back more than a century. Ocean-crossing ships have also routinely measured sea-surface temperatures during most of this time. Figure 4 illustrates the combined data from both types of historical measurements for the entire globe. The mean surface temperature from 1961 to 1990 has been subtracted from the data. The global mean surface temperature has increased from about 0.3°C below this mean value prior to 1900 to about 0.5°C above this mean value today. The overall temperature increase during the 20th century was thus approximately 0.8°C (1.4°F). This increase is broadly consistent with the warming expected from a 40% rise in atmospheric CO_2. However, comparing Figure 4 with Figure 3, one can see that the surface temperature does *not* increase as uniformly or at the same rate as does atmospheric CO_2. Evidently, the climate is influenced by other factors as well. Problems do exist with these historical temperature data. For example, weather stations located near cities are subject to a well-documented "heat island" effect: As a city grows and as more area becomes covered with dark surfaces such as asphalt, more sunlight is absorbed and the local air temperature can increase by as much as 3°C. This systematic error has been removed from the data shown in Figure 4, but it is still a source of uncertainty, because it is difficult to remove accurately. (*Systematic* errors exhibit a regular pattern. *Random* errors do not follow any pattern.)

Sea-surface temperature measurements are also subject to systematic errors. Prior to the mid-1900s, water temperatures were determined by the "bucket method." A crewmember dropped a bucket over the side of the ship, then hauled it back up and measured its temperature with a thermometer. Since then, water temperatures have generally been measured with flow-through devices located on the ship's hull. The two methods do not yield exactly the same results, because the samples may be taken at different water depths and because buckets can warm or cool as they are being examined. Furthermore, the current procedure draws water up through the ship (normally near the engines) and can heat it up. These effects, too, can be corrected for, but not without creating additional uncertainties.

A second problem with the temperature data is that the coverage in time and space is much better in some parts of the world than in others. Populated areas of Europe and North America have been monitored most closely and for the longest time, so the coverage is best in these regions. Most land areas in the Southern Hemisphere have shorter and less-consistent temperature records. And the coverage over some regions of the ocean, particularly remote parts of the Southern Ocean where few ships travel regularly, is sparse indeed. Because sea-surface temperatures can now be monitored from satellites, the oceanic database should improve in the future. But it may well require several decades of such measurements to establish reliable trends.

Despite such difficulties, climatologists who collect and analyze these surface temperature data are confident that the observed 0.8-degree warming trend over the past century is real. This does not mean, though, that it has been caused by human activities. Evidence shows that the climate was unusually cool between about 1500 and 1850. This period has been termed the "Little Ice Age." At least part of the warming since that time may represent a recovery from that naturally cool period rather than warming produced by anthropogenic greenhouse gases. This is another illustration of why it is necessary to understand the past if we want to predict the future.

An additional puzzle in the data shown in Figure 4 is that the warming trend seemed to slow, or stop entirely, between about 1940 and 1970. In the Northern Hemisphere, temperatures actually declined by a few tenths of a degree during this period. The decrease over Northern Hemisphere land areas is so pronounced that, by 1970, some climatologists were concerned that Earth might be entering a new glacial period. This worry was heightened by the historical data mentioned earlier that indicated that the present interglacial period might be nearing its end.

One possible explanation for the 1940 to 1970 cooling trend is that it was caused by increased reflection (and thus decreased absorption) of sunlight by *sulfate aerosol particles*. These tiny airborne particles are formed from sulfur dioxide (SO_2) emitted by the burning of coal. Most of the coal burning has taken place in the Northern Hemisphere, so this hypothesis could also explain why that hemisphere cooled more than did the Southern Hemisphere. Recent climate model simulations show that the magnitude of the aerosol effect is sufficient to account for the observed trend. But coal burning also releases CO_2 and hence should contribute to global warming—just the opposite of the observed effect during this 30-year period. This situation is a good example of why it is necessary to understand the whole Earth system in some detail if we are to interpret properly the changes that are occurring.

We cannot assume, however, that even though coal burning may have cooled Earth from 1940 to 1970, it will continue to do so in the future. In the United States, SO_2 is now being removed, or "scrubbed," from smokestack emissions in order to reduce its contribution to acid rain. **Acid rain** is produced when various acids, including sulfuric acid formed from the oxidation of SO_2, dissolve in rainwater. Acid rain can kill fish and damage plants in regions downwind from strong sources of pollution. It has been a problem in parts of the northeastern United States and in eastern Canada because there are many coal-fired power plants along and northward of the Ohio River valley. Other parts of the world, notably Europe, have problems with acid rain as well. Paradoxically, cleaning up smokestack emissions to cut down on acid rain may exacerbate the problem of global warming by reducing sulfate aerosol concentrations in the atmosphere.

Even if we were to quit scrubbing SO_2 out of smokestack gases, the ultimate effect of coal burning would be to warm Earth's atmosphere. Sulfate aerosols are removed from the lower atmosphere by precipitation in a matter of weeks, whereas CO_2 lingers in the atmosphere for decades to centuries. Thus, the CO_2 effect on climate is cumulative, whereas the aerosol effect is not. This example points out the importance of being aware of the time scale on which a global change occurs.

CHANGES IN THE CRYOSPHERE   So far, we have focused on global average temperatures, and we have seen that they have been gradually increasing. In some parts of the globe, however, especially regions near the North Pole, the temperature appears to have been increasing much more rapidly. In central Alaska, for example, the warming over the past century has been close to 3°C, or almost four times the global average value. And this warming near the North Pole appears to be having dramatic effects on the amount of sea ice in the Arctic Ocean. Figure 5 shows a comparison between the minimum sea ice extent in 2005 and 2007 and that back in 1979. The images, which are actually a composite of microwave images from orbiting satellites, were taken in late September when the ice pack typically reaches its minimum size. As one can see, the ice pack in 2005 was appreciably smaller—roughly 5.3 million km², as compared to 7.8 million km² in the earlier image. So, the sea ice minimum decreased by an astounding 30% in just 26 years! And the 2007 sea ice minimum was even smaller: 4.2 million km², or 20% less than the 2005 value!

Based on this observed rapid decrease in sea ice, some researchers have speculated that the Arctic Ocean could be entirely ice-free in late summer by the year 2012. Already, the fabled Northwest Passage—the long-sought-after sea route between the Atlantic and Pacific oceans—is open for a few weeks each year. That in itself is a mixed blessing. It could facilitate oceangoing trade between Europe and the Far East (and the American West Coast). But it is bad news for polar bears and perhaps also for the Inuit Indians of northern Alaska and Canada who earn their subsistence from the existing polar ecosystem.

More disturbingly, large increases in north polar temperatures could potentially lead to increased melting of the Greenland ice sheet, and this, in turn, could raise sea level. The disappearance of Arctic sea ice does not affect sea level because the amount of seawater tied up as ice is precisely compensated by the downward pressure that the floating ice exerts on the ocean. (This is an application of Archimedes' principle, which states that a body immersed in a fluid is buoyed up by a force equal to the weight of the displaced fluid.) One can test this principle by placing several ice cubes in a glass and then filling it to the rim with water. As the ice cubes melt, the glass does not overflow, even though parts of the floating cubes were initially above the rim. Similarly, as Arctic sea ice melts, sea level remains the same. But the Greenland ice cap is supported by land, not by water, and so any meltwater from Greenland (or Antarctica) contributes directly to sea level rise. If the entire Greenland ice cap were to disappear, sea level would increase by approximately 6 meters, or 20 feet, and the effects

FIGURE 5 Arctic sea ice minimum extent in 1979, 2005, and 2007 as measured from orbit by the Special Sensor Microwave Imager (SSMI). The pictures are electronically processed composites of images obtained in late September when the Arctic ice pack is at its smallest extent.   (*Source:* NASA/Goddard Space Center.)

on continental coastlines would be catastrophic. Fortunately, land ice is much thicker than sea ice, and so the rate at which the Greenland ice sheet might vanish should be much slower than that of Arctic sea ice—probably hundreds to thousands of years, as opposed to decades. But the physics of ice sheets is complex, and there are some indications that melting of the Greenland ice sheet is happening faster than expected and it is a major cause for concern among glaciologists who study this problem.

POSSIBLE CONSEQUENCES OF GLOBAL WARMING. Although there is still some debate about whether humans have already altered the global climate, most climatologists agree that we will do so in the future if we continue to consume large amounts of fossil fuel. Should this be a cause for concern? In terms of the change in mean global temperature, we might expect people living in hot places such as India to be worried whereas those living in Siberia would look forward to the change. But the problem is not quite so simple: A change in temperature might cause other changes as well. A rise in sea level is one frequently mentioned concern. Sea level has already risen by at least

10 cm over the past century. The likely cause is *thermal expansion* of a gradually warming ocean; like most forms of matter, water expands when it is heated (except between 0 and 4°C when, paradoxically, it contracts). But warmer temperatures could also induce melting of mountain glaciers and ice caps. Increases in sea level on the order of several meters are possible within the next few centuries, and even larger changes are possible in the very long term. Such changes could have serious consequences for people in coastal areas and would be catastrophic for those in small island states. Other, associated climatic changes may also have a broad-scale impact on agriculture, including decreases in soil moisture in certain areas and the spread of tropical insect pests. There is also some, admittedly controversial, evidence that the intensity of tropical hurricanes may be increasing as the climate warms. (See the box titled "Are Hurricanes Getting Stronger with Time?") We will return to these possible side effects of global warming later; for now, note simply that the issues are complex and that there are very few simple answers. We also note that this is another reason to study past climate: Earth has

been significantly warmer at various times in its past, and we may learn something about what it could be like in the future by examining those past time periods.

Evidence of Ozone Depletion

Global warming is not the only global environmental problem that has caught the attention of the public. Since at least 1985, the potential depletion of stratospheric ozone has also been in the news. (Stratospheric ozone should not be confused with *tropospheric* ozone—ozone near ground level—which is also often in the news because it is a component of *smog*.) The **stratosphere,** where most of Earth's ozone is located, is a layer of the atmosphere that extends from about 10 to 50 km in altitude. Stratospheric ozone is important to living organisms because it absorbs many of the Sun's harmful

A CLOSER LOOK
Are Hurricanes Getting Stronger with Time?

Hurricane Katrina (Box Figure 1) formed over the Bahamas on August 23, 2005. It crossed over Florida as a weak, Category 1 storm, then grew rapidly in strength as it drew energy from the unusually warm surface waters of the Gulf of Mexico. Within a few days, it had turned into a powerful Category 5 hurricane—the highest rating given to such storms—meaning that it had sustained winds over 155 mph, or 249 km/hr. On August 29, it slammed into the U.S. Gulf Coast as a Category 3 storm (111–130 mph). But it was still enormous in extent, with hurricane-force winds extending out more than 120 miles from its center. The low pressure at its center, combined with the onshore winds on the eastern side of the hurricane, caused a powerful storm surge of as much as 14 feet that overwhelmed the levees holding back Lake Pontchartrain and the southernmost outlets of the Mississippi River. The consequences for New Orleans were devastating. Large parts of the city were flooded, over 700 people were killed in New Orleans alone, and the nearby Mississippi Gulf Coast was similarly ravaged.

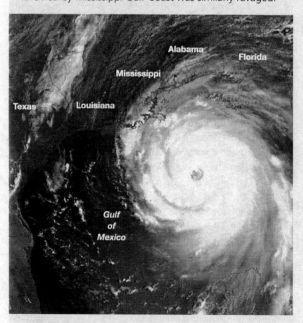

BOX FIGURE 1   Hurricane Katrina near peak strength, August 28, 2005.   (*Source:* Jeff Schmaltz, MODIS Rapid Response Team, NASA/GSFC.)

In that same year, 2005, two important papers were published in the prestigious journals *Nature* and *Science*. The first, by Kerry Emanuel of the Massachusetts Institute of Technology, suggested that warmer sea-surface temperatures induced by anthropogenic greenhouse gases might result in stronger hurricanes in the future. Hurricanes derive their tremendous power by tapping the energy present in surface water. Sunlight, combined with the strong winds generated by the hurricane, causes seawater to evaporate. When it recondenses as rain, its energy (or **latent heat**) is released, and this adds still more energy to the hurricane. Emanuel used existing meteorological datasets dating back to 1930 to show that these changes have actually been occurring, especially over the last 30 years.

The second paper, by Peter Webster of the Georgia Institute of Technology and his colleagues, provided additional evidence to support this hypothesis. Their key findings are shown in Box Figure 2. Many of the data for their analysis come from satellites, and so the record dates back only to 1972. Box Figure 2a shows sea-surface temperatures in various ocean basins. As one can see, they have all warmed by several tenths of a degree over this time period, consistent with the global average surface temperature data shown in Figure 4. Box Figure 2b shows the percentage of hurricanes of different categories over the entire globe per pentad. (A pentad is a period of 5 years.) The total number of hurricanes per pentad has remained roughly constant over this time period, so the *frequency* of hurricanes has not changed. But the percentage of the stronger Category 4 and 5 hurricanes has nearly doubled, suggesting that the *intensity* of hurricanes is increasing with time. This result is therefore consistent with Emanuel's independent analysis.

Whether or not this trend will continue into the future is unclear. The datasets used in both papers are too short to rule out the possibility that some decadal-scale natural cycle could account for the observed trend in hurricane strength. And Hurricane Katrina itself was not all that exceptional and cannot necessarily be attributed to global warming. Nevertheless, the combination of the two papers and the natural disaster really set the meteorological research community rocking. Large numbers of people live along tropical or subtropical coastlines that are affected by such storms. If stronger hurricanes are indeed to be expected in the future, many people will be concerned.

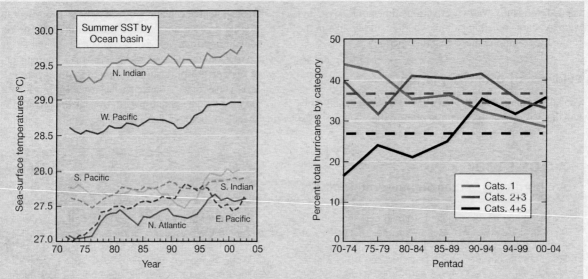

BOX FIGURE 2 (a) Observed change in summer sea-surface temperature (SST) of different ocean basins, 1972–2003. (b) Number of hurricanes of different categories during this same time period. The dashed lines indicate the average number of hurricanes in Categories 1, 2 and 3, and 4 and 5. The uppermost curve is the maximum recorded wind speed for all hurricanes, which has remained more or less constant with time. Legend: NIO—Northern Indian Ocean, WPAC—Western Pacific, SPAC—Southern Pacific, SIO—Southern Indian Ocean, EPAC—Eastern Pacific, NATL—North Atlantic. (*Source:* P. J. Webster et al., *Science* 309, 2005, p. 1844.)

ultraviolet rays. Ultraviolet radiation causes skin cancer and other health problems in humans. It adversely affects other organisms as well—notably, microscopic algae that are the base of the food chain in aquatic environments.

The year 1985 was a key one in stratospheric ozone research, because it marked the discovery of the ozone hole above Antarctica. Each year since about 1976, stratospheric ozone levels near the South Pole have fallen by large amounts during October, which is springtime in the Southern Hemisphere. Figure 6b shows year-to-year variations of the mean ozone *column depth* above Halley Bay in Antarctica for Octobers between 1957 and 2001. (The location of Halley Bay and other sites in Antarctica is shown in Figure 6a.) The ozone column depth is the total amount of ozone per unit area above a certain location. The decrease in ozone near the South Pole during October is striking: Ozone levels during October dropped by about half during a short period between 1975 and 1990. Since then, they have remained relatively constant. During the rest of the year, ozone levels in this region have remained close to normal throughout this time period. What has been destroying half the ozone over Antarctica during one particular month?

As soon as the ozone hole was discovered, atmospheric scientists guessed that chlorine compounds were to blame. By 1974, scientists had confirmed that chlorine is capable of destroying stratospheric ozone, and stratospheric chlorine levels have been increasing for the past few decades. Scientists are now fairly certain that the ozone hole is caused by chlorine compounds released from the breakdown of

anthropogenic CFCs. The definitive evidence was provided in 1987, when a NASA research plane flew directly into the hole. One of the plane's instruments measured chlorine monoxide, ClO, which was thought to be a main culprit in ozone destruction; another instrument measured ozone (Figure 7). Outside the hole, ozone concentrations were at their normal stratospheric level, and ClO concentrations were very low. Inside the hole, ozone values were more than a factor of two lower, and ClO values were about 15 times higher, than the respective values outside the hole. Faced with such a strong inverse relationship, even scientists who had been skeptical about the connection between stratospheric chlorine and ozone depletion were driven to conclude that the chlorine was directly responsible for destroying the ozone.

The real concern about ozone depletion is not whether it is occurring over Antarctica in October but whether it might occur at hazardous levels over populated regions of the globe. (The few people living down in the far southern portions of Chile and New Zealand are already concerned, because they are so close to Antarctica.) So far, nothing as dramatic as the Antarctic ozone hole has been seen elsewhere. However, during the 1990s ozone did decrease gradually at midlatitudes in both hemispheres, perhaps because CFC concentrations in the upper stratosphere were still going up at that time. The good news is that the midlatitude ozone decrease appears to have slowed or stopped in recent years, and the ground-level concentrations of most CFCs are now decreasing because production of these gases has been reduced or eliminated. Hopefully, the world has acted in time to prevent ozone depletion from becoming a catastrophic problem.

(a)

(b)

FIGURE 6 (a) Map of Antarctica showing the location of Halley Bay and other research sites. (b) Mean total ozone over Antarctica during the month of October. The units, called Dobson units, measure the gas per unit area between Earth's surface and the top of the atmosphere (a measurement known as the column depth). One Dobson unit (DU) is equivalent to a 0.001-cm-thick layer of pure ozone at the surface. (*Source:* http://www.antarctica.ac.uk/met/jds/ozone/images/zmeanoct.jpg.)

Deforestation and Loss of Biodiversity

Ever since a substantial portion of the human population switched from being hunters and gatherers to being farmers some 10,000 years ago, humans have been altering the land surface. More and more of Earth's land is being "managed" in one way or another—to the extent that it is now fairly difficult to find land areas that are pristine.

Most of these changes have tended to reduce the complexity of the landscape, such as when forested areas (or grasslands) have been cleared and replaced with a single crop species. When the natural vegetation cover is removed, it is not simply the plant species that are lost. With the plants go all the animals (mammals, birds, insects, and so on) and microorganisms that depended on that vegetation in order to live. New species may replace them, but normally the number of species decreases; that is, biodiversity is reduced. When a species is unable to move away or adapt, the change in land use can result in extinction of the species.

A CLOSER LOOK
The Discovery of the Antarctic Ozone Hole

The story of the discovery of the ozone hole above Antarctica is one of the classic misadventures of modern science. Measurements of Antarctic ozone made from Earth's surface date back to 1956 and represent by far the longest continuous record of atmospheric ozone levels. But these measurements were made at only one site, Halley Bay, where a research station happened to be located. Continuous measurement of ozone levels above the entire Antarctic continent (and the rest of Earth) began in 1979 with the launching of the Total Ozone Mapping Spectrometer (TOMS) instrument on the Nimbus 7 satellite.

TOMS was a sophisticated and expensive instrument that should have been fully capable of detecting significant Antarctic ozone depletion within the first few years of going into orbit. It did not do so, however. The ozone hole was first reported at Halley Bay in 1985 by the British scientist Joseph Farman and his colleagues, who had relied on their "old-fashioned" ground-based instruments. TOMS failed to detect the hole, it was later discovered, because the computer that processed the raw satellite data had been programmed to reject as "noise" any ozone measurements below a particular cutoff value. Values as low as those observed over Antarctica in October were considered too low to be real!

On learning about the Halley Bay measurement, the TOMS scientific investigators reanalyzed their original data using a technique that retained the anomalously low values. The ozone hole was there, all right! Had it not been for the ground-based measurements, however, the hole might have gone undetected for years. Besides providing a wonderful illustration of the perils of having rigid preconceptions, the story of the discovery of the ozone hole shows that dedicated individuals working with relatively simple equipment can still make important contributions to modern science.

The genetic information that is shared by—and only by—all the members of that species is thus lost permanently.

Some of the best-known examples of animal species that have gone extinct are the woolly mammoth, the saber-toothed tiger, the dodo bird, and the dinosaurs. Many species that exist today, such as the mountain gorilla and the giant panda, are faced with the threat of extinction. The potential loss of these large mammals represents only the most visible of many similar threats.

The largest, and potentially the most significant, species loss occurring today is taking place in tropical rainforests. These warm, moist forests are centered around the equator. Marked by lush vegetation, they are the most biodiverse habitat on Earth. But they are rapidly disappearing due to deforestation: The trees have been cleared for grazing, farming, timber, and fuel. By 1990, the total area of tropical rainforests had been reduced to less than half the estimated prehistoric cover. The rapidity of deforestation of the Amazon rainforest is illustrated in Figure 8. Exactly how fast the tropical forests are disappearing is difficult to determine, but the loss rate is thought to approach 1.8% per year. If deforestation continues at such a rate, by the first quarter of the 21st century almost half the remaining rainforests will be lost, along with 5 to 10% of all the species on Earth.

Which Changes Should Concern Us the Most?

The concerns about the loss of tropical species are, in some ways, less immediate than the concerns about ozone depletion or global warming. One worry is that the tropical plants are a potential source of medicines for fighting cancer and other diseases. This concern is valid, but it does not have the urgency of the prospect of instantaneous sunburn on exposure to the Sun or of entire states or even entire nations being submerged by a rising sea level.

This does not mean, however, that species loss is not a serious problem. Indeed, in some ways it may be the most serious problem of all. One way of judging the severity of a problem is to estimate how long it would take Earth to recover. If we take this approach, ozone depletion is the least serious problem. The lifetime of chlorofluorocarbons in the atmosphere is on the order of 50 to 150 years, when they are eventually destroyed by solar ultraviolet radiation. This range is long enough to raise serious concerns, but the ozone level should be restored within a few human generations if the preventive measures now in place are continued or strengthened.

By this measure, global warming is a more serious problem, because the time scale for recovery could be much longer than 150 years. If we actually do consume an appreciable amount of the fossil fuels that are still available to us, atmospheric CO_2 levels could remain elevated for many thousands of years. Most of the excess CO_2 would be absorbed by the oceans during this time, but even then it would not be completely gone. As we will see in later chapters, it would likely take more than a million years for the excess CO_2 to be removed from the oceans and for atmospheric CO_2 to return to its preindustrial level.

Although this time scale sounds long, it is short in comparison with the time required to restore global biodiversity. Analysis of the fossil record shows that the time scale for recovery of biodiversity after a **mass extinction** (the dying out of many species within a geologically short time interval) is on the order of tens of millions of years. In fact, the system never does recover completely: Although many new species appear and flourish after a mass extinction, they are *different* from the ones that went extinct. That is why humans, instead of dinosaurs, now rule Earth! So, if we do induce a mass extinction of tropical species by deforestation, things will never again be the same.

FIGURE 8   Satellite photos of Amazonia in 1975 and 2001. (*Source:* USGS.)

FIGURE 7   [See color section] (a) Simultaneous measurements of ozone (O_3) and chlorine monoxide (ClO) made from a NASA aircraft as it flew into the Antarctic ozone hole in September 1987. The hole was entered at a latitude of about 68° S. The units ppt and ppb stand for "parts per trillion" and "parts per billion," respectively. (b) Contour plots of ClO and O_3 concentrations obtained from spacecraft measurements. These data also show that ozone is low where ClO is high.   (*Source:* From R.W. Christopherson, *Geosystems: An Introduction to Physical Geography,* 3/e, 1997. Reprinted by permission of Prentice Hall, Upper Saddle River, N.J.)

GLOBAL CHANGE ON LONG TIME SCALES

We have touched on three major global environmental changes that are occurring in the Earth system today: global warming, ozone depletion, and tropical deforestation. To understand fully the significance of these changes, however, we must understand how the Earth system operated prior to human intervention. Here, we preview three examples of past global change—glacial–interglacial cycles, mass extinction, and changes in solar luminosity—and show how the geologic record provides evidence that allows us to study such changes.

Before we look at these examples of past global change, let us see where they occur on the *geologic time scale* (Figure 9). Geologic time is divided into various intervals at several different levels. *Eons,* at the broadest level, are subdivided into *eras;* in turn, eras are broken

FIGURE 9 The geologic time scale. (*Source:* From W. K. Hamblin and E. H. Christiansen, *Earth's Dynamic Systems,* 8/e, 1998. Reprinted by permission of Prentice Hall, Upper Saddle River, N.J.)

down into *periods,* which may be further split into *epochs.* The glacial–interglacial cycles that we will discuss, which lasted from about 2.5 million years ago until approximately 10,000 years ago, occurred during the Pliocene and Pleistocene epochs. The mass extinction that we shall talk about occurred at the boundary between the Cretaceous and Tertiary periods, approximately 65 million years ago. A *period,* typically lasting tens of millions of years, is generally a longer unit of geologic time than an *epoch.* Finally, the solar luminosity changes that we will discuss have occurred throughout the entire 4.5 billion years of Earth history.

Glacial–Interglacial Cycles: The Ice-Core Temperature Record from Vostok and Dome C

A set of ice cores drilled between the mid-1980s and the early 1990s at Vostok, Antarctica, near 80° S latitude, has provided a wealth of information about the Pleistocene glaciations. More recently, a new core drilled in 2003 at Dome C, about 560 km from Vostok (see Figure 6a), has provided an even longer and more detailed record. The most important results from the Dome C ice core are shown in Figure 10. The bottom curve shows the measured range of CO_2 concentrations; the top curve shows the

estimated change in local temperature, as determined from the deuterium content of the ice. **Deuterium,** D, is an **isotope** of hydrogen that has both a proton and a neutron in its nucleus. (Normal hydrogen, H, has only a proton.) It is used as a proxy for temperature: higher (less negative) δD values indicate warmer temperatures over the Antarctic continent and the surrounding polar oceans.

The section of the Dome C ice core that has been fully analyzed is about 3.3 km deep and it extends back for an extraordinarily long time, some 800,000 years. The reason that both the Vostok and Dome C records extend so far back in time is that snow accumulates very slowly at these sites—the equivalent of only about 2.5 cm of water per year. This value is comparable to the mean annual precipitation over the Sahara Desert. Other parts of the polar ice sheets are approximately as thick, just under 4 km, but have faster accumulation rates. The short-term CO_2 record shown in Figure 3 comes from Siple Station, near the coast of Antarctica; there the snow accumulation rate is equivalent to about 50 cm of water per year. Cores from such locales cover much shorter periods of time than does the Dome C core, even if they are just as deep.

The time interval spanned by the Dome C core extends well beyond the last Ice Age. For the past 2.5 million

FIGURE 10 Measurements of atmospheric CO_2 and temperature for the Dome C ice core. The temperature is determined from the deuterium content of the ice. (*Source:* IPCC, *Climate Change 2007,* Technical Summary, Fourth Assessment Report, Cambridge: Cambridge University Press, 2007, p. 24, http://www.ipcc.ch/ipccreports/ar4-wg1.htm.)

years, Earth's climate has fluctuated between intensely cold **glacial periods,** in which ice sheets advanced across North America and Europe, and relatively warm **interglacial periods** such as the present, in which the ice sheets retreated. The present interglacial period began— and thus the last Ice Age ended—about 11,000 years ago, as an upward surge in temperature in Figure 10 indicates. At 21,000 years ago, Earth was in full-glacial conditions. Around 130,000 years ago, the planet was in the midst of another warm, interglacial period.

Much of the story about the advance and retreat of the glaciers was already known from other sources of data prior to the drilling of the Vostok ice core. (We shall henceforth use the terms "Vostok" and "Dome C" interchangeably, as the ice cores from both locations tell us essentially the same thing. Most of the original groundbreaking discoveries actually came from Vostok.) What was new and surprising about the Vostok results was that they showed that atmospheric CO_2 and CH_4 concentrations had varied in concert with surface temperature. The Vostok data show that between 21,000 and 11,000 years ago, atmospheric CO_2 levels rose from about 200 ppm to close to its preindustrial value of 280 ppm, whereas CH_4 increased from about 350 to 650 ppb. The current CH_4 concentration is about 1700 ppb, or 1.7 ppm. The same abrupt increase in CO_2 and CH_4 concentrations occurred after the previous interglacial period ended, between 140,000 and 130,000 years ago. Indeed, at a finer level, many of the smaller peaks and valleys in the temperature-change curve correspond to specific peaks and valleys in the concentration records of the two gases.

Why would atmospheric CO_2, CH_4, and temperature co-vary in this way? One part of the answer involves the greenhouse effect: As levels of the greenhouse gases CO_2 and CH_4 increased, the magnitude of the greenhouse effect also increased, and the climate became warmer. But what caused atmospheric concentrations of CO_2 and CH_4 to vary in the first place? In particular, why did those concentrations increase so abruptly just after 140,000 years ago and again just after 21,000 years ago?

These are tough questions, and we shall return to them later. Humans could not have caused these changes. Our ancestors were still making tools out of stone and tending small wood fires—and not burning fossil fuels— when these changes took place. One possible mechanism for driving changes in atmospheric CO_2 levels is a change in the circulation pattern of the deep ocean. The deep ocean circulates because cold, salty (and hence, dense) surface water sinks and is replaced by warmer, less dense water from lower latitudes. The deep ocean contains large amounts of dissolved CO_2, some of which is released to the atmosphere when deep water flows upward to the surface. So, the rate at which the deep ocean overturns can affect the concentration of atmospheric CO_2. But the circulation pattern of the deep ocean depends on climate, which is driven by changes in temperature and in evaporation rates

at the sea surface. Thus, it would appear that atmospheric CO_2 levels affect climate and that climate, in turn, affects atmospheric CO_2 levels. What we have is a system in which the various components are tightly and intricately coupled. That is why a systems approach is the best way to understand global change.

MASS EXTINCTION: IRIDIUM AND THE K-T BOUNDARY AT GUBBIO Ever since dinosaur bones were first discovered, people have wondered why the dinosaurs disappeared. Dinosaurs flourished for more than 150 million years during an interval called the Mesozoic era, which ended 65 million years ago. At about the same time the dinosaurs disappeared, many other species went extinct as well. Some 60 to 80% of marine species died, as did numerous species of terrestrial plants and animals. Many possible reasons have been offered for their demise, including changes in climate, changes in vegetation, disease, destruction of the ozone layer by a nearby supernova (an exploding star), volcanic activity, and impact of an extraterrestrial body. No single hypothesis had attracted widespread support, however, until 1980.

That year, Luis and Walter Alvarez, of the University of California at Berkeley, and their colleagues published a paper about a clay layer they had studied in rocks from the mountains near Gubbio, Italy. The clay dated back 65 million years to the K-T boundary. **"K-T boundary"** stands for the transition between two time intervals: the Cretaceous period, abbreviated as "K" (to distinguish it from the Cambrian period, abbreviated as "C"), and the Tertiary period, abbreviated as "T." The Cretaceous period marked the end of the Mesozoic era and was followed by the Tertiary period, part of the Cenozoic era. The dinosaurs and other species disappeared at or just below the boundary between these two periods.

The layer of clay, only a few centimeters thick, was found between thick layers of *carbonate rock* (rock formed from the shells of certain marine organisms). The existence of this clay layer at the K-T boundary (Figure 11) had puzzled geologists for decades. This clay layer had been seen at Gubbio and at numerous other spots around the world, always at the boundary between rocks of the Cretaceous and Tertiary periods. Walter Alvarez, a geologist, had journeyed to Gubbio in an effort to determine how long it had taken for the clay layer to be deposited.

Luis Alvarez, a physicist (and Walter's father), had a clever idea about how to make that determination. He reasoned that he could calculate the time required to form the clay layer by measuring the abundance of the element *iridium* (Ir). Iridium is a metal in the platinum group of elements, which are very scarce in rocks of Earth's crust, because they are mostly dissolved in its molten iron core. These elements are always raining down on Earth as small particles of debris from asteroids or comets. The rate at which such debris hits Earth is known fairly accurately

FIGURE 11 The clay layer at the K-T boundary in sediments at Gubbio, Italy. (*Source:* Prof. W. Alvarez/ SPL/Photo researchers.)

FIGURE 12 Iridium concentration versus depth at Gubbio. The middle portion of the depth axis is a linear scale; the upper and lower portions are logarithmic. (*Source:* L. Alvarez, *Physics Today,* July 1987.)

from measurements of its abundance in cores drilled into the ocean floor. Hence, Luis Alvarez reasoned that he could use the measured iridium abundance in the Gubbio clay layer as a kind of "cosmic clock" to determine the time needed for the clay to have been deposited.

The experiment failed, but it did so for a reason that turned out to be very informative. When the Alvarez team measured the iridium levels at Gubbio, they found the results shown in Figure 12. The iridium abundance in the clay layer was up to 10 ppb by mass—more than 100 times higher than what the group expected to find. The amount of iridium in the clay layer was much too large to have been supplied by debris from asteroids or comets. The time required to accumulate that much iridium would have been so long that the signal would have been swamped by the normal deposition of Earth-bound sediments. (Clay accumulates on the ocean floor at a rate of about 1 cm per thousand years as a result of wind-blown dust that falls on the ocean surface. If the clay layer at the K-T boundary had taken more than a few thousand years to form, it should have contained a large proportion of terrestrial dust and, hence, a relatively small concentration of iridium.) The Alvarez team reasoned that the iridium must have come instead from the impact of some large, extraterrestrial object, such as an asteroid or a comet. Indeed, by calculating the amount of iridium deposited worldwide, the team estimated the mass of such an incoming body—on the order of 10^{15} kg, which corresponds to a diameter of about 10 km for a rocky asteroid. If the impacting object was a comet, it would have to have been even larger because comets are thought to contain less iridium than do asteroids.

The energy released by an impacting object of this size is enormous—equivalent to about 70 million, 1-megaton hydrogen bombs. Thus, it is plausible that such an event could have triggered extinctions on a mass scale. Since the Alvarez's did their work, additional evidence

corroborating a large impact 65 million years ago has been identified, including a deeply buried crater 200 km in diameter underlying the region around Chicxulub, Mexico, on the Yucatan Peninsula. Even this "smoking gun" does not prove that this impact was the cause of the mass extinction. It does demonstrate convincingly, though, that in the past the Earth system has experienced large shocks from which it has recovered, albeit slowly and in a modified form.

The changes that humans are causing in the Earth system today are less abrupt than those that occurred at the K-T boundary (assuming that the impact theory is correct), but they are still fast compared to most natural changes, and the results could still be catastrophic for certain elements of the biota. We have already noted that large land mammals such as gorillas and pandas are at risk. And with the vast majority of terrestrial species concentrated in the imperiled tropical rainforests, the potential for more-widespread mass extinctions is very high. A lesson learned from the K-T boundary crisis, that biodiversity can decrease dramatically over a relatively short time interval, may therefore hold value today.

Changes in Solar Luminosity

All the examples of global change discussed thus far have been based on observational data. Observations, after all, are the cornerstone of science. Not everything of importance is observable, however. For example, we cannot see inside the Sun. Yet we are confident that the Sun produces its energy through **nuclear fusion,** the joining of two or more light atomic nuclei to form one heavier nucleus. Specifically, four hydrogen nuclei (^{1}H) fuse to form one helium nucleus (^{4}He). This process, which is thought to occur continuously within the Sun, releases large amounts of energy. Even though we cannot observe this phenomenon directly, we are reasonably sure that the fundamental concept is correct.

The fact that the Sun produces energy in this way has important consequences for its long-term evolution. Four hydrogen nuclei take up more space, and therefore exert more pressure, than does one helium nucleus. The pressure in the Sun's core (where nuclear fusion occurs) would therefore be decreasing with time if the fusion of hydrogen into helium were the only process taking place. But what actually happens, models predict, is that the core contracts and heats up slightly as its helium content increases. The temperature rise increases the core's pressure and keeps the core from contracting further, so the Sun remains stable. As the core's temperature increases, so does the rate of nuclear fusion, just as the rates of most chemical reactions increase with increasing temperature. As a result, energy production within the Sun's core rises, and this rise is balanced by an increase in the amount of energy emitted at the surface. The more energy is emitted, the brighter the Sun appears. So, contrary to what we might intuitively expect, the Sun's **luminosity** (brightness) should gradually increase as it depletes its hydrogen fuel.

By how much has solar luminosity changed over the Sun's history? Model calculations performed by a number of different astronomers have reached essentially the same conclusion. Figure 13 shows a typical result, in which the unit of age on the horizontal axis is *byr B.P.,* or billions of years before the present. When the Sun first formed 4.6 billion years ago, it should have been about 30% less luminous than it is today. The Sun's luminosity increased slowly at first and then more rapidly as the buildup of helium in its core continued. At present, the Sun is thought to be brightening by about 1% every hundred million years. By the time the Sun ends its lifetime as a normal star, about 5 billion years from now, it is expected to have brightened by a factor of 2 to 3 as compared with today.

THE EFFECTS OF SOLAR LUMINOSITY CHANGES How would reduced solar luminosity have affected the early Earth? If all other factors had remained constant, the early Earth should have been colder than it is today. Indeed, calculations show that the entire ocean should have been ice-covered prior to 2 billion years ago. We know, however, that liquid water has existed on Earth's surface for at least the last 3.8 billion years, because sedimentary rocks (which form from sediments in liquid water) have been forming since that time. And organisms, which require liquid water to survive, have probably been around for at least 3.5 billion years. The early Earth could not have been a global iceball, at least not during the time for which a geologic record is available.

This apparent discrepancy is called the *"faint young Sun paradox."* We mention this paradox here because, like the Vostok CO_2 story, it is a problem that can be solved only by considering the Earth system as a whole. The most likely solution is that the level of greenhouse gases in Earth's primitive atmosphere was significantly higher than today. But why should this have been true, and why would greenhouse gas concentrations have declined as the Sun grew brighter? Does Earth's climate system have some built-in stability mechanism that has kept the mean surface temperature within survivable limits?

THE GAIA HYPOTHESIS James Lovelock, a British biochemist, and Lynn Margulis, an American biologist, have argued that life itself has been responsible for maintaining the stability of Earth's climate. In the process of **photosynthesis,** organisms such as green plants use sunlight, CO_2, and H_2O to produce organic matter and O_2. (*Organic matter* is the carbon-rich material of which organisms are composed.) Through photosynthesis, followed by carbon burial in sediments, Earth's biota may have lowered atmospheric CO_2 levels at just the right rate to counteract the gradual increase in solar luminosity. Alternatively, the biota may have affected the rate at which atmospheric CO_2 is sequestered in carbonate rocks. Carbonate rocks form from reactions of CO_2 with elements (primarily calcium and magnesium) derived from other types of rocks. This process is part of the *carbonate-silicate geochemical cycle.* In either case, Lovelock and Margulis suggest that Earth has remained habitable precisely because it is in some sense "alive."

FIGURE 13 Estimated change in solar luminosity with time. The unit of age on the horizontal axis, byr B.P., stands for "billions of years before the present." (*Source:* D. O. Gough, *Solar Physics* 74, 1981, p. 21.)

This theory of long-term climate stabilization is part of what Lovelock and Margulis called the Gaia hypothesis. In ancient Greek mythology, Gaia (pronounced guy-ah) was the goddess of mother Earth. In its most basic form, the **Gaia hypothesis** states that Earth is a self-regulating system in which the biota play an integral role. Some proponents of this hypothesis further suggest that the biota manipulate their environment for their own benefit or even, by optimizing the conditions for life, for the benefit of all living things. Such assertions are difficult to justify. Lovelock himself is quick to point out that the biota cannot be expected to cope with all possible disturbances. As an example, we cannot assume that we can safely emit CFCs into the atmosphere because Gaia will somehow protect the stratospheric ozone layer. But it is clear that the Gaia hypothesis is correct at some level: Organisms do play an important role in the overall functioning of the Earth system.

Some form of self-regulation must exist in order for Earth's climate to remain stable over long time scales. Higher greenhouse gas concentrations in the past are the most likely solution to the faint young Sun paradox. But whether the biota are essential to the control mechanism remains controversial. *Abiotic* (nonbiological) *feedbacks* in the carbonate–silicate cycle could have stabilized Earth's climate even if life were not present.

Chapter Summary

1. We deal with three main themes: modern global environmental issues, past global change, and the behavior of Earth's systems. To understand present environmental problems, we must know something about Earth's past and something about the way different components of the Earth system interact.
2. Humans are modifying the global environment in several ways:
   a. Global warming may be the most pervasive environmental change that faces us today. The increase in concentrations of greenhouse gases, including carbon dioxide (CO_2), methane (CH_4), nitrous oxide (N_2O), and chlorofluorocarbons (CFC_s), in the atmosphere is attributable to human activity. These gases are expected to warm Earth's climate over the next few decades to centuries by enhancing the natural greenhouse effect. They may have already begun to do so: Earth appears to have warmed by about 0.8°C over the past century, on the basis of surface temperature measurements made around the globe. It is still debated, however, whether this temperature rise is a consequence of increased greenhouse gas concentrations or simply a natural fluctuation in the climate system.
   b. The stratospheric ozone layer has already been severely affected by chlorine released from anthropogenic CFCs. The most dramatic impact has been confined to the Antarctic region during October. Strong regulatory steps have already been undertaken to ensure that the ozone layer will be protected in the future. Without such restrictions, the ozone layer's ability to absorb harmful ultraviolet rays from the Sun would be severely diminished.
   c. Massive deforestation is occurring in the tropics today, as it did in North America a century or more ago, when it contributed to the early rise in atmospheric CO_2. Deforestation both increases the buildup of atmospheric CO_2 and significantly decreases biodiversity. The effects of deforestation on biodiversity are permanent and irreversible.
3. Past changes in the Earth system may provide clues to how it will respond to global change in the future:
   a. Variations in surface temperature and atmospheric CO_2 concentrations recorded in ice cores illustrate the coupling between atmospheric CO_2 and climate and show how global warming today fits into the general pattern of glacial–interglacial cycles over the past 2.5 million years.
   b. Studies of the mass extinction at the end of the Cretaceous period 65 million years ago, when the dinosaurs and numerous other species forever vanished from Earth, may shed light on the loss of biodiversity that humans are causing today.
   c. Modeling studies of Earth's response to gradual increases in solar luminosity can help us understand how the climate system remains stable despite large changes in external forcing factors.

Key Terms

acid rain
anthropogenic
atmosphere
biodiversity
biota
chlorofluorocarbons (CFCs)
core
crust
cryosphere
deforestation
deuterium
Earth system
fossil fuels

Gaia hypothesis
glacial period
global warming
greenhouse effect
greenhouse gases
hydrosphere
interglacial period
Intergovernmental Panel on Climate
    Change (IPCC)
isotopes
K-T boundary
latent heat
luminosity

mantle
mass extinction
nuclear fusion
ozone (O_3)
ozone hole
ozone layer
photosynthesis
rocks
sediments
solid Earth
stratosphere
system
trace gases

Review Questions

1. a. What is meant by "anthropogenic greenhouse gases"?
   b. Name three such gases that are currently increasing in concentration in Earth's atmosphere.
2. What are the four fundamental components of the Earth system?
3. Explain the difference between global warming and the greenhouse effect.
4. a. By how much has Earth's atmospheric CO_2 concentration increased since the year 1800?
   b. How do we know this?
   c. What are thought to be the primary causes of this increase?
5. Cite two ways in which chlorofluorocarbons can affect the environment.
6. a. How far back in time do direct measurements of Earth's surface temperature extend?
   b. Why is it difficult to determine accurately the long-term temperature trend?

7. How might the burning of coal have had opposing effects on climate during the 20th century?
8. Why is stratospheric ozone important to humans?
9. To what two global environmental problems does tropical deforestation contribute?
10. How are hydrogen isotopes used to infer polar temperature records?
11. How is past surface temperature
    a. determined from the Vostok ice core?
    b. related to atmospheric CO_2 content?
12. Why is iridium a good indicator of impacts by extraterrestrial bodies?
13. a. How has solar luminosity changed during the past 4.6 billion years?
    b. What is the fundamental cause of this change?
14. What is the Gaia hypothesis, and what does it say about the importance of life on this planet?

Critical-Thinking Problems

Write a 1- to 2-page typewritten essay on the following questions:

1. Which of the three modern global change problems discussed in this chapter—global warming, ozone depletion, or loss of biodiversity—do you consider to be the most serious? Give reasons for your answer. If you wish, include information drawn from other sources.

2. How do global warming, ozone depletion, and loss of biodiversity compare with other environmental and social problems that the world faces today? You may wish to list the major problems, as you see them, in decreasing order of importance. Justify your answer with an explanation.

Further Reading

General

Intergovernmental Panel on Climate Change. 2007. *Climate change 2007,* Fourth Assessment Report (http://www.ipcc.ch).
Lovelock, James. 1995. *Gaia, a new look at life on Earth.* Oxford: Oxford University Press.
Schneider, S. H. 1997. *Laboratory Earth: The planetary gamble we can't afford to lose.* New York: Basic Books.

FIGURE 7 (a) Simultaneous measurements of ozone (O_3) and chlorine monoxide (ClO) made from a NASA aircraft as it flew into the Antarctic ozone hole in September 1987. The hole was entered at a latitude of about 68° S. The units ppt and ppb stand for "parts per trillion" and "parts per billion," respectively. (b) Contour plots of ClO and O_3 concentrations obtained from spacecraft measurements. These data also show that ozone is low where ClO is high. (*Source:* From R.W. Christopherson, *Geosystems: An Introduction to Physical Geography,* 3/e, 1997. Reprinted by permission of Prentice Hall, Upper Saddle River, N.J.)

Daisyworld
An Introduction to Systems

Key Questions

- What are systems?
- What are feedback loops?
- What are equilibrium states?

- Does viewing Earth as a system allow for deeper insight into the interrelationships among the physical and biological worlds?
- Can Earth's climate be self-regulating?

Chapter Overview

In this chapter, we develop the fundamentals of systems theory needed for the study of Earth as a system. First, examples from everyday life are used to introduce the important concepts of systems theory. Then we introduce the simplified climate system of the imaginary planet Daisyworld. Daisyworld is subjected to an increase in solar luminosity even more rapid than that which Earth has experienced over its history. Yet the hypothetical planet is able to counter the tendency for warming by increasing the reflectivity of its surface (by allowing for the spread of white daisies). We will see that this seemingly intelligent response arises without foresight or planning but rather as a natural consequence of interactions within the system. Through such feedbacks, natural systems can remain stable despite disturbances. Although the climate system of Daisyworld is oversimplified, we suspect that feedbacks like those it exhibits have played an important role in stabilizing Earth's climate over geological time.

THE SYSTEMS APPROACH

The systems approach has been used in virtually every area of inquiry, including branches of both the natural and social sciences. Human physiology is a good example of

where the systems approach is particularly illuminating. The human body is made up of a number of systems that perform the vital functions of life: a respiratory system that takes in oxygen and eliminates carbon dioxide; a cardiovascular system that circulates the blood, carrying oxygen and carbon dioxide around the body; a digestive system that processes food to fuel all body processes; a nervous system that senses changes in the internal and external environments and controls the activities of the other systems; an endocrine system that regulates ongoing processes such as growth and development; and so on. These systems are interrelated, functioning together to maintain the human body in a healthy state.

The Essentials of Systems

Each **system** is an entity composed of diverse but interrelated parts that function as a complex whole. The individual parts of a system are called **components.** A component can be a reservoir of matter (described by its mass or volume), a reservoir of energy (described by temperature, for example), an attribute of the system (such as body temperature or pressure), or a subsystem (such as the cardiovascular system, one of the interlinked subsystems of the human body). The components of the cardiovascular system itself include blood cells, blood vessels, and the heart.

The **state** of a system is the set of important attributes that characterize the system at a particular time. Body temperature, level of nutrition, and blood pressure are among the attributes that determine the state of the human body. The components of a system interact in such a way that a change in the state of the system is "sensed" throughout the system. In many systems, this linkage allows for the control of important attributes. For example, the endocrine system of the human body is capable of maintaining a nearly constant internal temperature despite large changes in the temperature of the surrounding environment. Suppose that your body temperature starts to rise as the air temperature around you rises. Your hypothalamus, a component of the endocrine system, then directs your sweat glands to increase their production of sweat, which helps cool you. If the ambient temperature then drops, your hypothalamus stops sending the signals to your sweat glands.

Couplings

It is clear from these examples from human physiology that the components of the human body "system" do not exist in isolation. They are linked, allowing for the flow of information from one component to the next. These links are called **couplings.** To understand how couplings allow for system regulation, consider an electric blanket. You set the temperature of the blanket (one system component) by adjusting a temperature controller. You adjust this controller to achieve a body temperature that is comfortable.

A *systems diagram* (Figure 1) allows us to keep track of the various couplings within a system. In a systems diagram, couplings are conventionally represented by arrows. There are two types of couplings. In the example of an electric blanket, an increase in blanket temperature causes an increase in body temperature; such a link is called a **positive coupling** (Figure 1a). In a positive coupling, a change (increase or decrease) in one component is a stimulus that leads to a change of the same direction in the linked component. When one component increases, a positively coupled component responds by increasing. When the first component decreases, the second component responds by decreasing. A positive coupling is represented by a solid arrow with a normal arrowhead, →.

In contrast, an increase in body temperature above the comfort level would lead you to *decrease* the amount of heat by turning down the controller. This coupling, from body temperature to blanket temperature, is a **negative coupling** (Figure 1b). In a negative coupling, a change in one component stimulates a change of the opposite direction in the linked component. When one component increases, a negatively coupled component responds by decreasing. And when the first component decreases, the second component increases. A negative coupling is represented by an arrow with a circular arrowhead, ──○.

Feedback Loops

The two couplings we described for the electric blanket create a "round trip," or **feedback loop,** between components (Figure 1c). *Feedback* is a self-perpetuating mechanism of change and response to that change. When you receive feedback from your friends, you are receiving their *re*action to an action of yours. Their reaction now becomes an action, and you *re*act to that action. You may modify your actions by either accentuating or suppressing them, and this modification will affect the nature of the subsequent feedback you receive. Consider Deb, who is Ed's employer. If Deb complains that Ed is dressing inappropriately at work, Ed may respond by dressing more conservatively, or he may instead dress the same or even more inappropriately. Either reaction (which is now an action) will undoubtedly cause a subsequent reaction—praise or criticism—from Deb. In terms of change and response, natural systems with feedback loops behave in a similar manner.

The feedback loop in the electric blanket example is referred to as a **negative feedback loop.** Negative feedback loops tend to diminish the effects of disturbances. An increase in body temperature, however caused, stimulates you to turn down the controller on the blanket. The blanket subsequently radiates less heat, and your body temperature then decreases.

In contrast to negative feedback loops, **positive feedback loops** amplify the effects of disturbances. To understand positive feedback loops, consider another electric-blanket example based on a real-life episode in the life of former U.S. president Jimmy Carter (Figure 2). Jimmy and his wife, Rosalynn, had an electric blanket with dual controls—one for his side of the blanket and another for

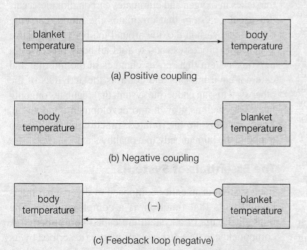

(a) Positive coupling

(b) Negative coupling

(−)

(c) Feedback loop (negative)

FIGURE 1 Systems diagrams; a negative feedback loop. (a) An increase (or decrease) in blanket temperature causes an increase (decrease) in body temperature—a positive coupling. (b) An increase (decrease) in body temperature causes you to decrease (increase) the blanket temperature—a negative coupling. (c) A negative feedback loop is created by the two couplings.

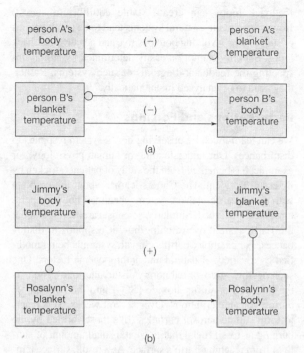

FIGURE 2 The consequences of combining feedback loops for a dual-control electric blanket. (a) Proper usage: Two independent, negative feedback loops. (b) Improper usage: A single positive feedback loop formed when the Carters inadvertently exchanged temperature controllers.

hers. In his autobiography, President Carter describes the irritation they were suffering:

> During each of the increasingly cold winter nights, we argued about the temperature of our electric blanket. Whenever I said it was too warm, Rosalynn said it was too cold, and vice versa.
>
> One morning I returned from an overnight trip to New York, and she met me at the front door with a warm hug and a smile. "I think our marriage is saved," she said. "I just discovered that our dual blanket controls have been on the wrong sides of the bed, and each of us was changing the temperature on the other's side." (Jimmy Carter, *Living Faith*, New York: Random House, 1996, p. 74.)

If the Carters had been thinking like systems scientists, the reason for their troubles would have immediately been obvious. A systems diagram for the proper use of the blanket is shown in Figure 2a. With their own controllers in hand, both persons would adjust their own blanket setting. If either person becomes chilly, he or she turns up the blanket controller and soon returns to a comfortable body temperature.

By inadvertently switching their temperature controllers, the Carters created a single, but more complicated, four-component feedback loop involving both controllers

(Figure 2b). The new loop is positive, consisting of two positive and two negative couplings. If Jimmy gets a bit warm, he unwittingly turns down Rosalynn's controller. She begins to feel a chill and so turns up what she thinks is her controller (but is actually Jimmy's). Jimmy gets even warmer, and then turns down Rosalynn's controller even further! This runaway response is characteristic of positive feedback loops.

A simple way to identify the "sign" of a feedback loop is to count the number of negative couplings. Negative feedback loops have an odd number of negative couplings; the rules of multiplication apply here. Recall that when two positive numbers are multiplied, the result is a positive number. When two negative numbers are multiplied, the result is also a positive number. But when a positive number and a negative number are multiplied, the result is always a negative number. Thus, if there is an odd number of negative couplings in a feedback loop, the loop is negative. If there are no negative couplings or an even number of them, the loop is positive.

Equilibrium States

The normal electric-blanket feedback loop (Figure 1c) acts to maintain body temperature (defining the state of the system) within a comfortable range. If your body temperature is just right, you do nothing to the blanket controller. We refer to this condition as an **equilibrium state** of the system; it will not change unless the system is disturbed. Because this state is created by a negative feedback loop, the equilibrium state is said to be **stable**: Modest disturbances from this state will be followed by system responses that tend to return the system to its equilibrium state. The equilibrium state of comfort for the Carter's feedback loop (Figure 2b) was **unstable**: The slightest disturbance from a comfortable state led to system adjustments that carried the system further and further from that state.

To visualize equilibrium states better, we can represent all the possible states of a system as a hilly surface and the present state as a ball that is free to move on that surface (Figure 3). The valleys represent stable equilibrium states, and the peaks represent unstable equilibrium states. After a small disturbance, a ball in a stable equilibrium state will roll back down the hill and return to its original state (Figure 3a). Valleys, or regions of stability, are defined by the peaks that surround them. A large disturbance—large enough to roll the ball out of its valley and over an adjacent peak—can carry the system to a different equilibrium state (Figure 3b). Thus, there are limits to the stability of stable equilibrium states.

In contrast, an unstable equilibrium has no region of stability. A ball disturbed ever so gently from its "resting" point at the top of a peak will roll down the hill and will land in a valley (Figure 3c). On its own, the ball will not return to its original state. The slightest disturbance pushes the state of the system toward a new *stable* equilibrium (if one exists).

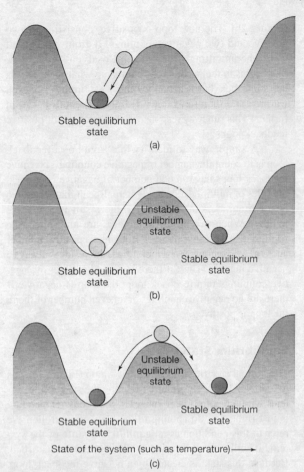

FIGURE 3 The equilibrium states of a system, represented as peaks (unstables) and valleys (stables). On disturbance, the system returns to stable equilibrium states but moves away from unstable equilibrium states.

It is unlikely that a given system would remain poised for any length of time at an unstable equilibrium state.

It appears that a system with a single feedback loop has a stable equilibrium state if the feedback loop is negative and an unstable equilibrium state if the feedback loop is positive. This conclusion is usually true, at least for the natural systems we will be discussing in this book. (See the Box "Thinking Quantitatively: Stability of Positive Feedback Loops" for a discussion of conditions under which positive

feedback loops can create stable equilibrium states.) However, in reality, natural systems tend to be combinations of subsystems involving both positive and negative feedback loops. Stability cannot be easily determined by simply inspecting the feedback diagrams of such systems. Rather, they need to be analyzed mathematically.

Perturbations and Forcings

We can learn much by observing how a system responds to disturbances. Our understanding of human physiology, for example, has benefited from the study of patients stricken by illness or accident. The Carters learned about the problem with their electric-blanket system when their body temperatures were disturbed. Similarly, scientists are learning about the Earth system by watching how it responds to disturbances. For example, Earth's climate system is being modified by a variety of natural and anthropogenic factors. One such **perturbation,** or temporary disturbance of a system, is the injection of sulfur dioxide (SO_2) into the atmosphere during volcanic eruptions. Over several weeks, SO_2 reacts to form sulfate aerosol particles (like those formed by the burning of fossil fuels) that prevent a small amount of sunlight from reaching Earth's surface. As a result, surface temperatures drop by a bit less than 0.5°C (1°F) globally (Figure 4). The climate system recovers from this perturbation several years later as the sulfur is naturally removed from the atmosphere. Because of natural climate variability it is difficult to conclusively ascribe a cool interval following a particular volcanic event to the eruption itself, so Figure 4 presents the average climatic response to the five largest eruptions of the last century or so.

A more persistent disturbance of a system is called a **forcing.** One forcing of Earth's climate is the gradual increase in the amount of sunlight Earth has been receiving over billions of years. How has the climate responded to this forcing? Many scientists argue that the tendency toward surface temperature rise that has accompanied the increased sunlight has been countered by a decrease in atmospheric CO_2 concentrations, reducing the greenhouse effect and thereby cooling the surface.

Understanding the response of the Earth system to forcings such as this is a major focus of this text. Rather than begin with the complex Earth system, however, we will consider the much simpler climate system of the hypothetical

FIGURE 4 The average climatic response to the five largest volcanic eruptions of the last 120 years: Krakatau (1883), Santa Maria (1902), Agung (1963), El Chichon (1982), and Pinatubo (1991). (*Source:* Courtesy NASA.)

THINKING QUANTITATIVELY:
Stability of Positive Feedback Loops

Although most isolated, positive feedback loops are unstable, stable equilibrium states can exist for positive feedback loops if the state of one component depends only on the current state of the other component (that is, the adjustment of the state of the system is instantaneous rather than incremental). Suppose a child's noisiness increases as the parent gets angrier, and the parent's anger increases as the child's noisiness increases, creating a positive feedback loop. This loop may be stable if the adjustments in anger level and noisiness are instantaneous, modest, and depend only on the current state of one another. For example, the child starts whining when a toy is taken away. The parent will become angry, but the child, having forgotten about the toy and now responding solely to the anger of the parent, may actually become quieter if the anger is moderate. As the child quiets, the parent's anger diminishes, and peace is restored (Box Figure 1).

Most natural systems do not behave in this way, however. The components of natural systems are generally *accumulators* or *reservoirs* of energy or mass, and their response depends not just on the immediate stimulus, but on the accumulation of past stimuli as well. Their response is also time-dependent: Their states do not respond immediately to a stimulus; instead, they do so over some interval of time. Equilibrium states characterized by positive feedback in such systems are always unstable. In the previous example, if the child's anger had been cumulative, the anger of the parent would simply have made the child noisier, and the situation would have escalated out of control.

As mentioned in the text, a true test of system stability must be performed mathematically. Because most natural systems are time-dependent, their behavior must be described by differential equations. Differential equations are beyond the level of most readers of this text; however, readers who have the required mathematical background are invited to follow the discussion below.

Suppose we have a system of two reservoirs whose states (e.g., amounts of material in the reservoirs) are represented by the variables $A(t)$ and $B(t)$, which are coupled in a feedback loop. Furthermore, suppose that an equilibrium state exists in this system, in which the reservoir sizes are denoted by A_{eq} and B_{eq}. We are interested in how these reservoirs will respond to a disturbance from their equilibrium state. This system can be described by the following two differential equations:

$$dA/dt = a\,(B - B_{eq})$$
$$dB/dt = b\,(A - A_{eq}).$$

Here, a and b are constants. The feedback loop is positive if both a and b are positive or if both constants are negative. If a and b have opposite signs, the feedback loop is negative. This follows from our definition of positive and negative couplings. A coupling is positive if component A responds in the same direction as the perturbation to component B; it is negative if the response is in the opposite direction.

The solution to these two coupled differential equations can be shown to be

$$A(t) - A_{eq} = \left\{ \frac{(A_0 - \beta B_0)}{2} \right\} \exp(\alpha t)$$

$$+ \left\{ \frac{(A_0 - \beta B_0)}{2} \right\} \exp(-\alpha t).$$

Here, A_0 and B_0 are the amounts that A and B are disturbed from their equilibrium values at the initiation of the disturbance, and $\alpha = \sqrt{ab}$ and $\beta = \sqrt{\dfrac{a}{b}}$. The second term on the right-hand side has a negative exponent and thus decays with time, but the first term has a positive exponent and thus will increase without limit as time progresses if α is a real number. Thus, if the product ab is positive, as it must be for a positive feedback loop, the system is clearly unstable. When a and b have opposite signs, though, as they do in a negative feedback loop, then the product ab is negative. The square root of a negative number is imaginary, so α is no longer a real number. In such a case, the system becomes a sinusoidal oscillator. The solution is always bounded, however, thus demonstrating that negative feedback loops are stable.

BOX FIGURE 1 In this system, the parent and child respond to each other's state instantaneously. The system is disturbed from its equilibrium state when the parent takes a toy away from the child. The child's noisiness increases, which causes an increase in the parent's anger level. In response, the child's noisiness actually diminishes because the parent's response elicits a noise level in the child that is less than its original perturbed level. As the child's noisiness diminishes, the parent's anger level diminishes until equilibrium is restored. The equilibrium state is stable despite being characterized by positive feedback in this special case where the parent and the child respond solely to the instantaneous state of the other. This is not true of most natural systems, and we cannot use this type of diagram to conclusively demonstrate the stability or instability of natural systems.

planet Daisyworld. This planet, whose only life-forms are daisies, derives from the creative imaginations of James Lovelock (who, with Lynn Margulis, originated the Gaia hypothesis) and his colleague Andrew Watson, an oceanographer. When the Gaia hypothesis was first proposed, a common criticism was that the biota would need to possess the capacity for foresight or planning if the Earth system were to be self-regulating (for example, able to prevent large fluctuations in the surface environment). Lovelock and Watson used Daisyworld to demonstrate that natural systems can be self-regulating on a global scale without the need for intelligent intervention. Let us see how.

THE DAISYWORLD CLIMATE SYSTEM

Imagine that the year is A.D. 2150. We have just determined that there is life on a nearby planet and have sent a manned mission there. On their arrival, the mission scientists observe that the planet is indeed supporting life, but only what appear to be daisies. Hence the scientists name the planet Daisyworld. These daisies are unusual, however: They are pure white in color. They appear to be getting their nutrients and water from the soil; the atmosphere has no clouds and no greenhouse gases. The daisies cover vast regions of the planet's surface; the rest of the surface is mantled in gray soil (Figure 5). This means that the amount of sunlight absorbed by the planet depends on the area of darker, bare soil relative to the area of lighter daisy cover. The more sunlight absorbed, the higher the surface temperature. Experiments carried out by the mission scientists show that the growth and spread of daisies across the planet's surface depends only on the temperature around them.

The mission scientists are alarmed because the planet's sun seems to be increasing in luminosity at a much faster rate than is our own Sun. They calculate that the planet will quickly become too hot to support daisy growth. However, they make this calculation without considering that the daisies are part of a global climate system in which the reflectivity of the planet is affected by any change in the daisy population. Might a systems approach yield a different prediction for the survival of daisies on Daisyworld in the face of an increasingly luminous sun?

We can represent the Daisyworld climate system on the global scale as a two-component system. One component is the area of white-daisy coverage, and the other is the average surface temperature of the planet. These two components form a system because they are interdependent: The extent of daisy coverage affects the surface temperature, and the surface temperature affects the growth rate of daisies, which in turn affects the daisy coverage of the planet. Let's explore these interrelationships more fully.

Couplings in the Daisyworld Climate System

RESPONSE OF SURFACE TEMPERATURE TO CHANGES IN DAISY COVERAGE From experience, we know that on a sunny day, dark surfaces, such as asphalt roadways, tend to feel warmer than light-colored surfaces, such as concrete sidewalks. Dark surfaces absorb more (that is, they reflect less) of the incoming solar energy than do light surfaces. The reflectivity of a surface is called the surface's **albedo** (Figure 6). Albedo is usually expressed as a decimal fraction of the total incoming (*incident*) energy reflected from the surface. Dark soil has a low albedo (0.05–0.15), whereas fresh snow has a high albedo (0.8–0.9). Table 1 lists the albedos of some common surfaces.

From the limited amount of information we have about Daisyworld, together with our intuition about albedo, we can graph the relationship between daisy coverage and surface temperature—in other words, the effect that

Gray soil

White daisy-covered regions

FIGURE 5 A view of Daisyworld from outer space.

TABLE 1 Albedos of Some Common Surfaces

Type of Surface	Albedo
Sand	0.20–0.30
Grass	0.20–0.25
Forest	0.05–0.10
Water (overhead Sun)	0.03–0.05
Water (Sun near horizon)	0.50–0.80
Fresh snow	0.80–0.85
Thick cloud	0.70–0.80

FIGURE 6 A visual comparison of high-albedo and low-albedo surfaces. Light-colored surfaces are more reflective (that is, have a higher albedo) than dark surfaces, which absorb more sunlight.

changes in daisy coverage has on temperature. Refer to the box "Graphs and Graph Making." We know that the surface temperature on Daisyworld is determined by the amount of daisies that cover the surface: The more daisies, the more sunlight reflects off their white petals, the less sunlight absorbed, and finally the cooler the surface temperature. The graph should have a *negative slope* (that is, "runs downward" from left to right), reflecting the fact that as daisy coverage increases, temperature decreases (Figure 7a). We *cannot* interpret the graph in Figure 7a to mean, however, that as surface tem-

perature drops, daisy coverage rises linearly. The way changes in surface temperature affect daisy coverage on Daisyworld is *not* the same as the way changes in daisy coverage affect surface temperature.

This graph can also be expressed as a coupling that links white-daisy coverage to temperature (Figure 7b). The coupling is negative: An increase in daisy coverage causes a decrease in surface temperature, and a decrease in daisy coverage causes an increase in temperature. Note that the "sign" of this coupling—negative—matches the sign of the slope in the graph.

Thus far in our discussion, the albedo of the planet has been a component of the Daisyworld climate system that we have treated only implicitly. However, we could treat albedo *explicitly* by adding it as a third component. The coupling that describes the effect of changes in white-daisy coverage on temperature is now seen as the combination of a positive and a negative coupling that links daisy coverage, albedo, and temperature (Figure 8). Decreased white-daisy coverage leads to a reduction in the average albedo (a positive coupling), and reduced albedo causes an increase in temperature (a negative coupling).

FIGURE 7 (a) Graph and (b) systems diagram of the effect of changes in white-daisy coverage on Daisyworld surface temperature.

FIGURE 8 The same overall coupling as that in Figure 7b, but with albedo shown explicitly. A positive and a negative coupling combine to form a negative coupling overall.

USEFUL CONCEPTS:
Graphs and Graph Making

Graphs are a powerful way to convey scientific information in an economical way. If a picture is worth a thousand words, a graph can be worth a thousand data points. There are a number of ways in which graphs are used in science, and we present many of them in this text. All graphs convey information about the relationship between two (or more) variables. (*Variables* represent any number value.) In a conventional *x − y* graph, data are plotted with the *independent variable* on the *x*-axis and the *dependent variable* on the *y*-axis. The value of the dependent variable depends on the value of the independent variable, but the converse is not true. For example, a graph showing hourly measurements of temperature over the course of several days at a particular place would plot temperature, the dependent variable, as a function of time, the independent variable (Box Figure 2a).

Graphs can be used to convey the sense of relationships even when data are not available. We may, for example, convey the notion that temperature varies more or less regularly from day to night with a sketch such as Box Figure 2b. We make it clear that no data are being plotted by plotting only a smooth curve; in labeling the axes for such a graph, we do not even show the scale of the graph. In other cases we may wish to put some bounds on the axes, but it would be misleading to place numbers on the axes in a graph for which actual values are not available.

BOX FIGURE 2 Examples of various uses of graphs. (a) Display of data: temperature measurements made at State College, Pennsylvania, during a three-day period. (b) Conveying a concept with no data: sinusoidal daily temperature variation.

When combined, the two couplings in Figure 8 form a negative coupling overall, like that shown in Figure 7. The rule for combining couplings is the same as the rule for determining the sign of feedback loops. The explicit treatment of albedo, therefore, does not change our conclusion regarding the overall sign of the coupling. For convenience and simplicity, then, we will often treat such couplings implicitly.

RESPONSE OF DAISY COVERAGE TO CHANGES IN TEMPERATURE In comparison with real daisies, we expect that Daisyworld daisies have an upper and lower temperature limit for survival. They must also have an *optimum*, or most favorable, temperature somewhere in between (let's specify that it is halfway between, for simplicity). A smooth curve drawn through these points is a *parabola* (Figure 9). The parabola is a characteristic shape for the temperature dependence of many plants on Earth. It intuitively makes sense that the abundance of an organism would be highest near the organism's optimum temperature and would drop to zero at the upper and lower limits of that organism's temperature range.

The sign of the coupling that reflects the response of daisy coverage to temperature changes depends on temperature, because the relationship is parabolic, as Figure 9 shows. If the temperature is below the optimum value for daisy growth, the coupling is positive. If the temperature is above the optimum value, the coupling is negative. This pattern is consistent with the slope of the parabola in Figure 9, which has opposite signs on either side of the optimum growth temperature for white daisies.

Equilibrium States in Daisyworld

We can determine the equilibrium states of Daisyworld by combining Figures 7 and 9. But note that temperature and daisy coverage are on opposite axes, so we cannot

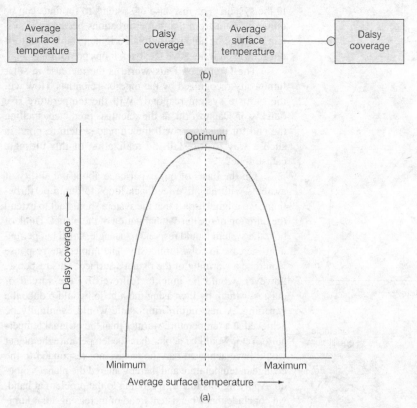

Optimum

Minimum   Maximum

Average surface temperature ——▶

(a)

FIGURE 9 (a) Graph and (b) systems diagram of the effect of changes in Daisyworld surface temperature on white-daisy coverage.

simply overlay the plots. Instead, we must invert the axes of Figure 7. This inversion does not change the nature of the coupling, it simply interchanges the positions of the two variables so that the axes will match up when we overlay the two graphs.

We can now overlay the two graphs (representing the two couplings); the resulting graph is shown in Figure 10a. The curves intersect at two points, labeled P_1 and P_2. These points of intersection are special because they represent the only states of the system that simultaneously fall on the curves showing both the effect that white-daisy coverage has on surface temperature *and* the effect that surface temperature has on white-daisy coverage. For example, at any point other than P_1 or P_2 on the parabola, the effect of temperature on daisy coverage is properly characterized, but the effect of daisy coverage on temperature is not. Conversely, at any point other than P_1 or P_2 on the straight line, the effect of daisy coverage on temperature is right, but the effect of temperature changes on daisy coverage is not.

Points P_1 and P_2 are the equilibrium states of this system, because they represent the states at which the system is said to be in *equilibrium*. If the system is already in one of these states, it will remain there unless something disturbs it. Note that neither equilibrium state corresponds to the optimum temperature.

But how will these equilibrium states respond to perturbation? We can evaluate the stability of these states

by constructing the systems diagrams for Daisyworld (Figure 11). Two feedback loops characterize the Daisyworld climate system—one that applies *below* the optimum temperature, to equilibrium state P_1, and another that applies *above* the optimum temperature, to equilibrium state P_2. The diagram applicable below the optimum has a positive and a negative coupling and is thus a negative feedback loop. The feedback loop applicable above the optimum has two negative couplings and is thus a positive feedback loop. Of the two equilibrium states, then, the one that is below the optimum temperature for daisy growth is stable, and the one that is above the optimum temperature for daisy growth is unstable.

Thus, the response of Daisyworld to perturbation depends on the temperature of the planet. At temperatures below the optimum for daisy growth, the system is characterized by negative feedback, which will tend to maintain the temperature and daisy coverage near a stable equilibrium state. (Note that the temperature is below the optimum for daisy growth.) If temperatures are perturbed above the optimum, the system will enter a region of positive feedback without a stable equilibrium state. If the perturbation is small, the temperature will return to the cool, stable equilibrium state below the optimum. Larger perturbations will carry the system over the edge of the stable equilibrium state's "valley" (Figure 10b), and temperatures will rise above the limits for daisy growth; the daisies die.

FIGURE 10   (a) The mutual influences of average surface temperature on white-daisy coverage (the parabola) and white-daisy coverage on surface temperature (the straight line). The intersection points (P_1 and P_2) are the equilibrium states of the system. (b) The stability of P_1 and instability of P_2.

EXTERNAL FORCING: THE RESPONSE OF DAISYWORLD TO INCREASING SOLAR LUMINOSITY

We have been investigating the behavior of the Daisyworld climate system by perturbing it from its equilibrium states and analyzing its response. Many of the disturbances, however, are persistent forcings that can be considered *external*

FIGURE 11   Feedback loops appropriate for small perturbations from equilibrium states P_1 and P_2, respectively.

to the system. The response of systems to forcings can be quite different from that to perturbations because the system may not be able return to an original, stable equilibrium state even if negative feedback loops predominate.

The forcing on Daisyworld is the increase in solar luminosity recognized by the mission scientists. How will the climate system respond? Will the temperature rise quickly on Daisyworld, as the scientists predicted, spelling the end for daisies, or will the climate system respond in such a way to forestall the realization of this ultimate catastrophe?

On the basis of our experience about the ability of systems with negative feedback loops to damp perturbations, we might suspect that the system should act to extend the duration of the daisy inhabitation of the planet. Think of how the system would respond to a single, small but permanent increase in solar luminosity. The immediate response would be a warming of the planet's surface. This response, however, would be quickly followed by the spread of daisies, which, by increasing the albedo, would reduce the warming. A new equilibrium state would eventually be achieved at a temperature warmer than the original temperature. Yet it would be cooler than the temperature the planet would have achieved had the daisies not responded to the change in temperature and thereby altered the planet's albedo. Applying this line of reasoning to the problem at hand, we conclude that a persistent trend of increasing solar luminosity should lead to a gradual evolution of the equilibrium temperature of the planet to higher and higher temperatures, but at a rate that is slower than the warming that would otherwise occur in the absence of the feedback between the daisies and their environment.

Response of Daisyworld Couplings to Forcing

To predict the future climate of Daisyworld more accurately, we need to understand how the increasing intensity of Daisyworld's sun will affect the couplings in the system. Because we are assuming that the daisies respond only to temperature changes and thus not to changes in the solar luminosity itself, we would *not* expect modification of the coupling that links surface temperature changes to white-daisy coverage (the parabola in Figure 9). As the sun becomes more intense, surface temperature will rise, and the percentage of daisy coverage will respond according the parabolic curve, as before. However, we *would* expect a change in the coupling that relates surface temperature to the extent of daisy coverage (the straight line in Figure 10a). For any amount of daisy coverage, the surface temperature will increase as the intensity of the sun increases. This is not to say that the temperature will rise indefinitely. Rather, for any particular value of daisy coverage, the temperature will be higher than expected from Figure 7. The graphical result is that the line in Figure 7 shifts upward as solar luminosity increases (Figure 12).

(a)

FIGURE 12 The effect of an increase in solar luminosity on the dependence of average surface temperature on white-daisy coverage. If the daisy coverage were fixed at a certain percentage, temperature would simply increase as shown by the arrows.

Response of Equilibrium States to Forcing

Let us again consider the response to an incremental increase in solar luminosity. If we combine Figures 9 and 12, we find, as before, that two equilibrium states exist (labeled P_1' and P_2' in Figure 13a). We can guess that, as before, only one of them will be stable, because the diagram has not changed fundamentally. Which one is it? The temperature at point P_1' is below the optimum growth temperature for daisies, so this situation is similar to that for point P_1. The temperature at point P_2' is above the optimum temperature for daisies, so this situation is similar to that for point P_2. Thus, we determine that P_1' is stable and P_2' is unstable.

However, we see that both the temperature and the daisy coverage at the new stable equilibrium are higher. Daisyworld has apparently reacted to increased solar luminosity by increasing the daisy coverage. The accompanying increase in albedo explains why the temperature at the stable equilibrium did not rise as much as it would have without feedback. Note that the "ridge" that defines the stability limit for P_1' is lower than it was before. This new equilibrium state is apparently less resistant to perturbations; further increases in solar luminosity should eliminate the stable equilibrium state entirely.

We can determine the effectiveness of this feedback mechanism by comparing the equilibrium temperature changes with and without feedback. Without feedback—that is, without any change in the daisy coverage—the temperature change that results from the increase in solar luminosity is large. The temperature change without feedback is represented in Figure 13a as ΔT_0. (Recall that ΔT means

(b)

FIGURE 13 (a) Response of Daisyworld to an increase in solar luminosity. (b) The stability of P_1 and P_1' and the instability of P_2 and P_2'.

the *change in temperature.*) With feedback, however, the temperature increase is smaller—but not zero. The temperature change of the new equilibrium state (with feedback) is represented as ΔT_{eq}, and the temperature change of the *feedback effect* itself is ΔT_f.

We can express the behavior of the Daisyworld system mathematically:

$$\Delta T_{eq} = \Delta T_0 + \Delta T_f.$$

In other words, the overall temperature change that results from increased solar luminosity is the sum of the temperature change with no feedback and the temperature change due to feedback. In our case, ΔT_{eq} is smaller than ΔT_0; the temperature effect of the feedback ΔT_f is negative. We can see this in Figure 13a: The arrow that represents ΔT_f points to the left—the negative direction—instead of to the right. Although we derived this equation for Daisyworld, it is a general relationship that can be applied to any stable equilibrium in a system involving feedback loops: The change in state of a system as it moves from one equilibrium to the next is the sum of the state change that would result without feedback and the effect of the feedback itself.

To quantify the strength of the feedback effect, we can define a value f, called the feedback factor. The **feedback factor** is the ratio of the equilibrium response to forcing (the response with feedback) to the response without feedback. In our example, this ratio is as follows:

$$f = \frac{\text{temperature change with feedback}}{\text{temperature change without feedback}} = \frac{\Delta T_{eq}}{\Delta T_0}.$$

Here f is less than 1, because the equilibrium response is smaller with feedback than it would have been without feedback. The value of f is between 0 and 1 whenever the feedback loop is negative but greater than 1 if the feedback loop is positive. As we mentioned previously, systems with positive feedback loops are stable only if they contain negative feedback loops as well. The feedback factor, f, can be defined only for stable systems, such as Daisyworld at point P_1. At point P_2, there is no stable equilibrium, and hence ΔT_{eq} is not defined there.

Climate History of Daisyworld

So far in our presentation of Daisyworld, we have avoided the use of actual values of temperature, daisy coverage, and albedo. However, we can assign reasonable values to the graphs to calculate the climatic response of Daisyworld to increasing amounts of sunlight. To present the details of the calculation would be premature. Suffice it to say that the calculations were based on typical growth curves for real daisies (see Figure 9), reasonable surface albedos for white daisies (0.9) and for gray soil (0.2), and a solar input similar to Earth's that also increases with time.

Figure 14a shows the history of white-daisy coverage, and Figure 14b shows the temperature history of Daisyworld from the time of its formation until the end of daisy inhabitation of the planet. (In these graphs, solar luminosity is plotted on the x-axis instead of time itself; solar luminosity increases more or less linearly with time. Scientists often make such substitutions so that their plots can be generalized; in this case, the plot is correct no matter how fast the change in luminosity occurs.) The solid curve in Figure 14b represents the "actual" surface temperature change on the daisy-inhabited planet. The dashed curve in Figure 14b shows how that surface temperature would differ if there were no daisies (in other words, no life-forms and no feedback). In the early years, temperature increases relatively rapidly. However, once the surface temperature rises above the minimum temperature for daisy survival, the white daisies begin to spread across the planet's surface. Their growth tends to cool the planet by increasing its albedo, and so the rate of warming slows dramatically. The daisy coverage expands rapidly at first, and then more slowly, in response to these increases in temperature, which are much smaller than we would predict for a lifeless (daisy-free) planet or for a planet with daisies but no feedback (and thus constant albedo).

(a)

(b)

FIGURE 14 The response of Daisyworld to increasing solar luminosity. (a) The change in daisy coverage of the planet in response to changes in solar luminosity (relative to the presumed present value). (b) The change in average surface temperature of Daisyworld in response to increasing solar luminosity (solid line) and the response on a lifeless planet with fixed albedo (dashed line).

Eventually, as the temperature approaches the optimal temperature for daisy growth, daisy coverage too reaches its optimum (maximum). Once the optimum is reached, any further increase in solar luminosity cannot be countered by an increase in white-daisy coverage; in fact, daisy coverage decreases, so the planet's temperature begins to increase rapidly. The feedback loop becomes positive. Once this happens, the system becomes unstable: The surface temperature rises rapidly, and the daisies go extinct. Thereafter, because it is dictated by the lower albedo of the gray soil on the lifeless planet, the temperature overlays the dashed curve in Figure 14b. This is a good demonstration of *threshold behavior*; an observer charting the spread of daisies would not likely have anticipated that the asymptotic spread would be followed by a crash in daisy coverage, nor would he necessarily have anticipated the sudden jump in temperature based on the past history of temperature change.

The Lessons of Daisyworld

By studying the hypothetical planet Daisyworld from a systems perspective, we have learned some interesting things about climate systems in general. First, a planetary climate system is not passive in the face of internal or external influences. There are feedback loops that respond to perturbations and forcings (in this case, solar luminosity). Negative feedback loops in the system counter the external forcings. On Daisyworld, the consequence of this feedback is a longer life span for the daisies than one would predict if there were no feedback in the system. We will see that Earth's climate system has negative feedback loops as well that keep its climate relatively stable on both short and long time scales.

Second, the climate regulation system of Daisyworld, and, by analogy, other nonhuman systems that self-regulate, is seemingly intelligent: The response of the daisies is exactly what is needed to counter the solar warming of the planet. Yet no foresight or planning is involved. The daisies simply respond to the increase in temperature, and the planet's temperature responds to the spread of daisies. Such behavior is not restricted to contrived systems like Daisyworld. Indeed, self-regulation is a property common to many natural systems with feedback loops. Lovelock conceived of Daisyworld as a means of demonstrating to his critics that the Gaia hypothesis (which he applied to Earth) did *not* require an intelligent biota. Organisms can be components of self-regulating, natural systems simply because they influence, and are influenced by, the physical environment in which they live.

It is unlikely that the biota would be capable of optimizing their environment for their own good, as seemed to be required by the Gaia hypothesis when it was first proposed. The Daisyworld experiment indicates that it is not necessary for the biota to be capable of optimizing their environment. The Daisyworld system does not *optimize* the temperature for daisies. The stable equilibrium temperature is below the optimum for daisy growth on white-daisy Daisyworld.

Note that the self-regulation is not perfect. As the sun became more luminous, Daisyworld's climate system responded with a temperature increase, but the increase was much more gradual than would have occurred on a lifeless planet (or one with fixed daisy coverage). Systems like the Daisyworld climate system typically adjust to forcings by a slow but continual modification of their equilibrium states. This response is different from that directed by a thermostat, for instance, which is designed to maintain a constant state (temperature). In a natural self-regulating system, there is no preset state (no optimum value) that the system is programmed to "seek out."

An important lesson from Daisyworld is that thresholds often exist in systems, including the climate system, that when surpassed can lead to rapid changes in system state. These abrupt transitions may have no forewarning: The system may evolve slowly and modestly to a persistent forcing up to the point that the threshold is reached and dramatic change occurs. Or, more commonly in natural systems, a random perturbation of a system approaching a threshold can nudge it across the threshold, carrying the system into its new state "before its time."

The real Earth is not unlike Daisyworld: Its surface temperature has been maintained within the tolerance limits of living organisms for more than 3 billion years, despite substantial changes in solar luminosity. As on Daisyworld, the reason for the long-term stability of Earth's climate is the existence of strong negative feedback. The feedback loops that operate on Earth are, not surprisingly, more complicated than the one that operates on Daisyworld. As we will see, climate scientists have observed such threshold behavior in the climate system during particular intervals of Earth history. They are furthermore concerned that the modern climate system, forced by human activity, might be approaching a climate threshold that separates the relatively cool global climate from a much warmer, "greenhouse" state.

Chapter Summary

1. Components of systems interact in ways that can either enhance or diminish the stability of the system.
   a. The components are linked by couplings, which can be either positive or negative.
   b. When couplings are arranged such that there is a round-trip flow of information, a feedback loop is formed. These feedback loops can be either positive or negative.
   c. Positive feedback loops amplify perturbations or forcings; negative feedback loops diminish them.
2. The presence of feedback loops leads to the establishment of equilibrium states.
   a. Negative feedback loops establish stable equilibrium states that are resistant to a range of perturbations; the system responds to modest perturbations by returning to the stable equilibrium state.
   b. Positive feedback loops establish unstable equilibrium states. A system that is poised in such a state will remain there indefinitely. However, the slightest disturbance carries the system to a new state.
3. The Daisyworld climate system is capable of resisting a warming trend induced by a sun that is becoming brighter with time.
   a. This capacity is the result of a negative feedback loop that involves the feedback between white-daisy coverage and temperature; it does not require foresight or planning.
   b. The key is the difference in albedo between the white daisies and the gray soil, together with the effect that temperature changes have on daisy growth and coverage.

c. Daisyworld has two equilibrium states, but only one is stable. This equilibrium state, in general, does not coincide with the optimum temperature for daisy growth.

d. The temperature response to an increase in solar luminosity can be thought of as a progression from one stable equilibrium state to the next. These equilibrium responses are the sum of the response that would occur without feedback plus the feedback

effect itself. In the case of Daisyworld, the temperature change without feedback is larger than that from one equilibrium state to the next: The feedback effect is negative. Thus, the rate at which the planet warms is slower than it would be if there were no feedback between daisy coverage and surface temperature. The interval over which the planet is inhabited by daisies is extended because of the presence of feedback.

Key Terms

albedo
component
coupling
equilibrium state
feedback factor
feedback loop

forcing
negative coupling
negative feedback loop
perturbation
positive coupling
positive feedback loop

stable equilibrium
state
system
unstable equilibrium

Review Questions

1. A perturbation that causes a decrease in component *A* leads to a decrease in component *B*. Is the coupling between these two components positive or negative?
2. What is a feedback loop?
3. Why do negative feedback loops tend to diminish the effect of disturbances?
4. What distinguishes a forcing from a perturbation?
5. Are all equilibrium states stable? Why or why not?
6. What is albedo? How does it influence climate?
7. How are daisies on Daisyworld able to regulate the hypothetical planet's temperature?

Critical-Thinking Problems

1. In the Dysfunctia family, when the children get noisy, the parents get mad. When the parents get mad, the children get noisy. Draw a systems diagram for the Dysfunctia family.
   a. Is the feedback loop negative or positive?
   b. Is the family stable or unstable?
2. Earth's average temperature is determined in part by the amount of CO_2 in the atmosphere, by way of the greenhouse effect. The atmospheric CO_2 content may in turn be affected by the photosynthetic activity of plants, which convert CO_2 into plant tissue. However, the rate of photosynthesis depends on the amount of CO_2 in the atmosphere and on global air temperature. The components of this system—atmospheric CO_2 content, global temperature, and photosynthesis rate—are intimately interconnected. By increasing global photosynthesis rates, plants would tend to lower the atmospheric CO_2 level. In doing so, however, the plants would tend to cool Earth. This cooling, together with the reduced CO_2 level, might tend to reduce the photosynthetic activity of plants.
   a. On the basis of this discussion, draw a systems diagram of the photosynthetic rate–CO_2–temperature system.
   b. How many feedback loops are there?
   c. Are the feedback loops positive or negative?
   d. Describe the response of the system to the following perturbations:
      (i) an increase in atmospheric CO_2;
      (ii) a decrease in temperature.
   e. Extra credit: How might the system respond to a continuous forcing—an increase in solar luminosity through time?
3. White-daisy Daisyworld has a companion planet that is similar in all ways except that the daisies are black.
   a. What is the effect of an increase in black-daisy coverage on planetary temperature? Express your answer graphically.
   b. Assuming that the effect of temperature on daisy coverage is the same on black-daisy Daisyworld as on white-daisy Daisyworld, draw a *stability diagram*—a diagram analogous to Figure 10—for black-daisy Daisyworld. Include two equilibrium states.
   c. Which of the two equilibrium states in part (b) is stable?
   d. Is the stable equilibrium state of part (c) cooler or warmer than that of white-daisy Daisyworld?
   e. How would this system respond to a *decrease* in solar luminosity? Express your answer graphically and in terms of the feedback factor *f*.
   f. Is *f* of part (e) greater than or less than 1?

4. The lines and curves shown in the graphs of this chapter can be converted to mathematical expressions that relate the values on the *y*-axis to those on the *x*-axis. The equation that relates the average planetary temperature (*T*) to percentage of daisy coverage (*C*) in Figure 10 is

$$T = 56 - \frac{C}{2},$$

while the curve that characterizes the dependence of daisy coverage on temperature is

$$C = 90 - \frac{(22.5 - T)^2}{4}.$$

a. The equilibrium states are defined as the values of *T* and *C* where the two equations are equal. Find these equilibrium states.

b. Find the equilibrium states for the case of higher solar luminosity on Daisyworld (Figure 10). You will have to define a new equation for the line. (*Hint:* The slope is the same; only the *y*-intercept has changed.)

Further Reading

General

Lovelock, James. 1991. *Healing Gaia: Practical medicine for the planet.* New York: Harmony Books.

Advanced

Levins, Richard. 1974. The qualitative analysis of partially specified systems. *Annals of the New York Academy of Sciences* 231:123–38.

Milsum, J. H. 1968. *Positive feedback: A general systems approach to positive/negative feedback and mutual causality.* New York: Pergamon Press.

Saunders, Peter T. 1994. Evolution without natural selection: Further implications of the Daisyworld parable. *Journal of Theoretical Biology* 166:365–73.

Global Energy Balance
The Greenhouse Effect

Global Energy Balance
The Greenhouse Effect

Key Questions

- What are the basic characteristics of electromagnetic radiation?
- What causes the greenhouse effect, and how is the magnitude of this effect determined?
- How do clouds affect the atmospheric radiation budget?
- What are the most fundamental feedbacks in the climate system?

Chapter Overview

Earth is heated by visible radiation from the Sun and cools by radiating infrared energy back to space. Earth's surface temperature depends on the amount of incident sunlight, the planet's reflectivity, and the greenhouse effect of its atmosphere. Certain gases in the atmosphere absorb outgoing infrared radiation and reradiate part of that energy back down to the surface. If this process did not occur, Earth's average surface temperature would be well below the freezing point of water, and life could not survive. Both the greenhouse effect and the amount of absorbed sunlight are strongly influenced by the presence of clouds. Clouds can either warm or cool the surface, depending on their altitude and thickness. Built-in feedback loops involving atmospheric water vapor and the extent of snow and ice cover are also fundamental aspects of the climate system. All these factors need to be considered in order to predict the response of Earth's climate to future increases in greenhouse gas concentrations.

INTRODUCTION

That Earth is suitable for life is largely a consequence of its temperate climate. A fundamental requirement for life as we know it is liquid water, and Earth is the only planet in our solar system that has liquid water at its surface. Venus, our nearest neighbor toward the Sun, has an average surface temperature of 460°C (860°F), hot enough to melt lead. Mars, the closest planet away from the Sun, has an average surface temperature of −55°C (−67°F), the coldest temperatures experienced at the South Pole. Earth's average surface temperature is 15°C (59°F), the same as the mean annual temperature of San Francisco. Earth is not only habitable, it is a relatively pleasant place to live.

Why is Venus too hot, Mars too cold, and Earth just right? This question is sometimes called the "Goldilocks problem" of comparative planetology. Intuition suggests that the answer is that Earth happens to lie at the right distance from the Sun (and hence would receive exactly the right amount of sunlight), whereas Venus and Mars do not (Figure 1). A closer look, however, reveals that it is not just the amount of sunlight that a planet receives that determines its surface temperature. A planet's surface is also warmed by the greenhouse effect of its atmosphere. A planet's atmosphere allows sunlight to come in but slows down the rate at which heat is lost. Without this greenhouse effect, Earth's average surface temperature would be about 33°C (59°F) colder than the observed value. Earth would be an icy, desolate world.

FIGURE 1   Venus, Earth, and Mars, shown roughly to scale.   (*Source:* NASA (left and center) and Photodisc/Getty Images (right).)

In this chapter, we discuss how the greenhouse effect works. We begin by considering the nature of electromagnetic radiation and why the Sun emits primarily one form of radiation (visible light), whereas Earth emits another (infrared radiation). We show that the incoming solar energy and outgoing infrared energy must be approximately in balance, and we demonstrate how this balance allows us to calculate the magnitude of the atmospheric greenhouse effect. Next, we discuss how both forms of energy are affected by atmospheric gases and by clouds, and we explain why some gases are greenhouse gases but others are not. Finally, we use the systems notation to introduce real climate feedback mechanisms, and we show why it is necessary to understand these feedbacks in order to estimate the climate changes that are occurring now as well as those that may occur in the future.

ELECTROMAGNETIC RADIATION

What exactly does it mean to say that Earth is heated by radiation from the Sun? From our sense of sight, we know that the Sun emits about 50% of its energy in the form of *visible light*. Let us start by considering what makes up light and other forms of *electromagnetic radiation*.

PROPERTIES OF ELECTROMAGNETIC RADIATION   A physicist would describe an electromagnetic wave as a propagating disturbance consisting of oscillating (regularly fluctuating) electric and magnetic fields that are perpendicular to each other. For our purposes, we can think of **electromagnetic radiation** as a self-propagating electric and magnetic wave that is similar to a wave that moves on the surface of a pond. A wave of any form of electromagnetic radiation—such as light, ultraviolet, or infrared radiation—moves at a fixed speed c (the "speed of light"). The numerical value of c for a light wave in a vacuum is 3.00×10^8 m/s. The wave consists of a series of crests and troughs (Figure 2). The distance between two adjacent crests is called the **wavelength.** It is typically denoted by

FIGURE 2   Simplified representation of an electromagnetic wave, illustrating the concept of wavelength. The solid curve shows the position of the wave at some time t. The dashed curve shows the wave at time $t + \Delta t$.

the Greek letter λ (lambda). An observer standing at a fixed point in the path of the wave would be passed by a given number of crests in one second. This number is called the **frequency** of the wave. It is represented by the Greek letter ν (nu).

If we neglect complexities like polarization, an electromagnetic wave can be described by these three characteristics: speed, wavelength, and frequency. Not all of these characteristics are independent. The speed of the wave must equal the product of the number of wave crests that pass a given point each second (the frequency) and the distance between the crests (the wavelength). We can express this relationship mathematically as

$$\lambda\nu = c,$$

or equivalently as

$$\nu = \frac{c}{\lambda}.$$

Distance between the wavelengths

The longer the wavelength of an electromagnetic wave, the lower must be its frequency, and vice versa. Conversely, the shorter the wavelength, the higher the frequency.

Photons and Photon Energy

Although we can think of electromagnetic radiation as a wave, at times it behaves more like a stream of particles. A single "particle," or pulse, of electromagnetic radiation is referred to as a **photon.** A photon is the smallest discrete (independent) amount of energy that can be transported by an electromagnetic wave of a given frequency. The energy *E* of a photon is proportional to its frequency:

energy of a photon $\Rightarrow$
$$E = h\nu = \frac{hc}{\lambda},$$

where *h* is a constant called *Planck's constant*, after the famous German physicist Max Planck. Its numerical value is 6.63×10^{-34} J-s (joule-seconds). Thus, high-frequency (short-wavelength) photons have high energy, and low-frequency (long-wavelength) photons have low energy. This difference in photon energy becomes important when electromagnetic radiation interacts with matter, because high-energy and low-energy photons have very different effects. High-energy photons can break molecules apart and hence cause chemical reactions to occur, whereas low-energy photons merely cause molecules to rotate faster or vibrate more strongly.

The fact that electromagnetic radiation behaves both as a particle and as a wave was one of the great discoveries of physics of the early part of the 20th century. This *wave–particle duality* is not restricted to electromagnetic waves. Rather, it is a general characteristic of matter and energy.

The Electromagnetic Spectrum

The full range of forms of electromagnetic radiation, which differ by their wavelengths (or by their frequencies), makes up the **electromagnetic spectrum** (Figure 3). Wavelengths in the visible range are typically measured in nanometers (nm). One *nanometer* is one-billionth of 1 meter. **Visible radiation,** or visible light, consists of a relatively narrow range of wavelengths, from about 400 to 700 nm. Within this range, the color of the light depends on its wavelength. Anyone who has observed a rainbow has witnessed this phenomenon. The longest visible wavelengths appear to our eyes as the color red, whereas the shortest wavelengths register as blue to violet. The colors of the rainbow—in other words, the range of component wavelengths of visible light—are referred to as the **visible spectrum.** The term "spectrum" indicates that the light has been separated into its component wavelengths.

About 40% of the Sun's energy is emitted at wavelengths longer than the visible limit of 700 nm in a region referred to as the *infrared* region of the electromagnetic spectrum. Wavelengths of **infrared (IR) radiation** are significantly longer than those of visible light. Hence, it is convenient to keep track of them in units called *micrometers* (μm) rather than in nanometers. One micrometer (formerly called *micron*) equals one-millionth (10^{-6}) of 1 meter. So, 1 μm equals 1000 nm. Infrared wavelengths range from 0.7 to 1000 μm. At even longer wavelengths within the electromagnetic spectrum, radiation is transmitted in the form of *microwaves* and *radio waves*. Radio waves can have wavelengths of many meters.

About 10% of the Sun's energy is emitted at wavelengths shorter than those of visible light as **ultraviolet (UV) radiation.** Wavelengths of the ultraviolet region extend from 400 nm down to about 10 nm. At shorter wavelengths are *X-rays* and *gamma rays*. These high-energy forms of electromagnetic radiation have little effect on our story here, but they do affect the chemistry of the uppermost atmosphere. X-rays, of course, are also used in medicine because they can penetrate skin and muscle tissue and allow us to see the underlying bones.

FIGURE 3 [See color section]
The electromagnetic spectrum.

The regions of the electromagnetic spectrum that are most important to climate are the visible and the infrared. The Sun emits energy in both of these spectral regions. Earth, as we shall see, emits primarily in the infrared. Solar ultraviolet radiation also affects the Earth system significantly by driving atmospheric chemistry. In addition, UV radiation would be lethal to most forms of life were it not almost totally blocked out by oxygen and ozone in Earth's atmosphere.

Flux

We will need one other basic concept from electromagnetic theory in order to proceed: the notion of flux. In general terms, *flux (F)* is the amount of energy or material that passes through a given area (perpendicular to that area) per unit time. In terms of fluid flow, for example, the flux is the volume of fluid that flows perpendicularly into or out of a unit area per unit time. Applied to electromagnetic radiation, **flux** is the amount of energy (or number of photons) in an electromagnetic wave that passes perpendicularly through a unit surface area per unit time.

To demonstrate the concept of flux, let us consider the light given off by an electric lightbulb. A typical, small lightbulb is labeled "60 watts." A *watt* (W) is a unit of *power*—formally, the rate at which work is done; informally, the intensity of the bulb in the SI system. One watt equals one joule (J) per second. Suppose that a person is standing some distance from such a lightbulb and holds up a sheet of paper directly facing the light (Figure 4a). The paper is illuminated by radiant energy from the bulb. The radiation crosses the paper perpendicularly from the lightbulb at a certain flux, or intensity per unit area. That flux is measured in watts per square meter (W/m^2). The magnitude of the flux depends on how far from the lightbulb the person is standing, but it does *not* depend on how big the paper is because flux is defined as the intensity per *unit* area.

The fact that flux is measured perpendicular to the direction the wave is traveling is important. Suppose that the person is holding the paper at an angle, rather than perpendicularly, to the light (Figure 4b). Although the total area of the paper remains the same, the flux of radiant energy reaching its surface is less because less radiation strikes a given unit area. This simple concept has direct, familiar consequences for Earth's climate. The polar regions are cooler than the tropics because the Sun's rays strike the ground at a higher angle at the poles. Summer temperatures are warmer than winter temperatures

Unit area

Incoming light

Paper is perpendicular to incoming light.

(a)

FIGURE 4 Schematic diagram of the concept of flux. The flux of radiation into the paper is reduced when the paper is tilted at an angle to the incoming light.

Paper is at an angle to incoming light.

(b)

because the Sun is higher in the sky during summer. For now, we simply need to understand the concept of flux.

The Inverse-Square Law

Figure 4 demonstrates that the flux of radiant energy from a lightbulb depends on how far away the observer (the person holding the paper) is standing. Likewise, the flux of solar energy decreases as distance from the Sun increases; that is why Venus is illuminated more strongly than Earth. The rate at which this *solar flux* decreases with increasing distance is described by a simple relationship. This relationship, called an **inverse-square law,** is expressed mathematically as

$$S = S_0 \left(\frac{r_0}{r}\right)^2,$$

The rate at which solar flux decreases w/ increasing distance

where S represents the solar flux at some distance r from the source, and S_0 represents the flux at some reference distance r_0 (Figure 5).

The inverse-square law has a straightforward physical interpretation: If we double the distance from the source to the observer, the intensity of the radiation decreases by a factor of $(1/2)^2$, or 1/4. Similarly, if we reduce the distance from the source to the observer by a factor of 3, the radiation intensity increases by a factor of 3^2, or 9.

As an example, consider a hypothetical planet, Planet X, located twice as far from the Sun as is Earth. What would be the solar flux hitting Planet X? Refer to Figure 5, and let the Sun be at the center of the two circles. Also, let the inner circle represent Earth's orbit and the outer circle represent the orbit of Planet X. Then r_0 is the average distance from Earth to the Sun, which is 149,600,000 km, defined as one *astronomical unit* (AU), and S_0 is the solar flux at Earth's orbit, 1366 W/m². (The value of S_0 is determined by satellite measurements.) So

according to the inverse-square law, for this example $r = 2$ AU, the solar flux incident at Planet X is

$$S = 1366 \text{ W/m}^2 \left(\frac{1 \text{ AU}}{2 \text{ AU}}\right)^2$$

$$= 341.5 \text{ W/m}^2.$$

We would have gotten precisely the same answer if we had expressed the distances in kilometers, but the arithmetic would have been harder.

The inverse-square law is of fundamental importance to the study of planetary climates. It allows us to determine quantitatively why Earth's climate differs from that of Venus and Mars. It also plays a crucial role in our understanding of the causes of the glacial–interglacial cycles of the last 3 million years of Earth's history. Small variations in the shape of Earth's orbit, combined with the inverse-square relationship between the distance from Earth to the Sun and solar flux, cause large changes in the climate of the polar regions and in the size and extent of the polar ice sheets.

TEMPERATURE SCALES

To understand climate, which is the prevailing weather patterns of a planet or region over time, we must first understand the concept of temperature. *Temperature* is a measure of the internal heat energy of a substance. Heat energy, in turn, is determined by the average rate of motion of individual molecules in that substance. For a solid, these motions consist of regular vibrations, whereas for a gas or liquid they are just random movements of molecules. The faster the molecules in a substance move, the higher its temperature.

Most areas of the world measure temperature (T) by the *Celsius* (formerly, *centigrade*) scale, which is measured in degrees Celsius (°C) and is part of the SI system of units. In the United States, temperature is typically measured in degrees *Fahrenheit* (°F). Scientists, particularly those studying climate, often use the **Kelvin (absolute) temperature scale,** measured in units called *kelvins* (K). (Note that temperatures in the Kelvin scale are given simply as kelvins, not as degrees Kelvin.)

The Celsius temperature scale is defined in terms of the freezing and boiling points of water at sea level (Table 1). At sea-level pressure, the freezing point is 0°C, and the boiling point is 100°C. Atmospheric pressure decreases with altitude, as we will see later in the chapter, so it makes a difference where the boiling point is determined. Water boils when its vapor pressure exceeds the overlying atmospheric pressure. Thus, the boiling point decreases with altitude. (This is why it takes longer to hard-boil an egg when you are camping in the mountains.

FIGURE 5   Diagram illustrating the inverse-square law.

TABLE 1 Freezing and Boiling Points of Water by Temperature Scale

Temperature Scale	Freezing Point	Boiling Point (at sea level)
Fahrenheit	32°	212°
Celsius	0°	100°
Kelvin (absolute)	273.15	373.15

The boiling water is not as hot, so it takes longer to cook the egg.)

The Fahrenheit temperature scale was originally defined on the basis of the temperature of a mixture of snow and table salt (0°F) and the temperature of the human body (about 100°F). Like the Celsius scale, it is defined today in terms of the physical properties of water: The freezing point is 32°F, and the boiling point is 212°F. The following relations allow us to convert temperatures between the Celsius and Fahrenheit scales:

$$T(°C) = \frac{T(°F) - 32}{1.8}$$

$$T(°F) = [T(°C) \times 1.8] + 32.$$

Note that converting a temperature *change* from one system of units to the other is easier, because the effect of the different zero points is removed. Thus, a temperature change of 1°C is equal to a change of 1.8°F. Conversely, a change of 1°F is equal to a change of 0.5556 (=1/1.8)°C.

Absolute temperature—that is, temperature on the Kelvin scale—is defined in terms of the heat energy of a substance relative to the energy it would have at a temperature of absolute zero. At *absolute zero*, the molecules of a substance are at rest (or, more precisely, are in their lowest possible energy state). A temperature change of 1 K is equal to a temperature change of 1°C. The zero point of the Kelvin scale is, however, lower than that of the Celsius scale by 273.15°. To convert temperature in degrees Celsius to kelvins, we use the following equation:

$$T(K) = T(°C) + 273.15.$$

Thus, a temperature of absolute zero corresponds to a Celsius reading of −273.15°C.

BLACKBODY RADIATION

To fully understand the greenhouse effect, we need one final concept from the world of physics: the concept of blackbody radiation. A **blackbody** is something that emits (or absorbs) electromagnetic radiation with 100% efficiency at all wavelengths. Consider a cast-iron ball (Figure 6). At room temperature, the ball looks black because it absorbs most of the light incident on it and gives off little visible radiation of its own. If we heat the ball, however, it begins to glow a dull red. If we heat the ball further, it eventually glows white hot because it radiates at all visible wavelengths. Recall that white light is a mixture of all the colors of the spectrum.

The radiation emitted by a blackbody is called **blackbody radiation.** It has a characteristic wavelength distribution that depends on the body's absolute temperature. This distribution can be described mathematically by a relation called the Planck function. The *Planck function* relates the intensity of radiation from a blackbody to its wavelength, or frequency. When shown graphically, this relation is also known as the *blackbody radiation curve*

FIGURE 6 Change in emitted radiation by a blackbody as it is warmed.

Room temperature   Hot   Hotter

FIGURE 7   (a) The Planck function, or blackbody radiation curve; (b) Wien's law; (c) the Stefan–Boltzmann law.

(Figure 7a). The Planck function itself is mathematically complicated and is beyond the scope of our discussion here. We can, however, use this relation to derive two simpler rules that are fundamental to an understanding of climate.

Wien's Law

The first rule derived from the Planck function that will assist us in studying climate is called Wien's law. **Wien's law** states that the flux of radiation emitted by a blackbody reaches its peak value at a wavelength λ_{max}, which depends inversely on the body's absolute temperature. According to this rule, hotter bodies emit radiation at shorter wavelengths than do colder bodies. Wien's law may be written as

$$\lambda_{max} \approx \frac{2898}{T},$$

where T is the temperature in kelvins and λ_{max} is the wavelength of maximum radiation flux in micrometers (Figure 7b).

Wien's law allows us to understand why the Sun's radiation peaks in the visible part of the electromagnetic spectrum and why Earth radiates at infrared wavelengths. The Sun emits most of its energy, including visible radiation, from its surface layer, called the **photosphere.** The temperature of the photosphere is about 5780 K. Thus, according to Wien's law, the Sun's radiation flux should maximize at 2898 μm/5780 $\approx$ 0.5 μm, or 500 nm (Figure 8). This is right in the middle of the visible spectrum. (The fact that the solar radiation flux peaks in the visible is no coincidence; our sense of vision presumably evolved as it did to take advantage of the solar spectrum.) Earth, meanwhile, has a surface temperature of about 288 K, so its radiation peaks at 2898 μm/288 $\approx$ 10μm—well into the infrared range. In reality, neither Earth nor the Sun is a perfect blackbody, so their emitted radiation flux is not exactly described by the Planck function. Nevertheless, Wien's

law is still useful in predicting the wavelength at which most of their radiant energy is emitted.

The Stefan–Boltzmann Law

A second rule derived from the Planck function that will prove useful in climate studies is called the Stefan–Boltzmann law. The **Stefan–Boltzmann law** states that the energy flux emitted by a blackbody is related to the fourth power of the body's absolute temperature:

$$F = \sigma T^4,$$

where T is the temperature in kelvins and σ (the lowercase Greek letter sigma) is a constant with a numerical value of 5.67×10^{-8} W/m^2/K^4. The total energy flux per unit area is proportional to the area under the blackbody radiation curve (Figure 7c).

As an example of how the Stefan–Boltzmann law can be applied, consider a hypothetical star that has a surface temperature twice that of the Sun. (We shall use stars

FIGURE 8   Blackbody emission curves for the Sun and Earth. The Sun emits more energy per unit area at all wavelengths.

rather than planets in this example because the radiation emitted from stars is more nearly approximated as blackbody radiation.) Our Sun has a surface temperature of about 5780 K, so the energy flux per unit area is

$$F_{Sun} = \sigma(5780 \text{ K})^4 \approx 6.3 \times 10^7 \text{ W/m}^2.$$

The other star releases energy at a rate of

$$\begin{aligned} F_{star} &= \sigma(2 \times 5780 \text{ K})^4 \\ &= 2^4 \times \sigma(5780 \text{ K})^4 \\ &= 16 \, F_{Sun}. \end{aligned}$$

Thus, the amount of energy released per unit area per unit time by the hot star is 2^4, or 16, times greater than that released by the Sun. Evidently, the amount of radiation emitted by a blackbody is a very sensitive function of its temperature.

PLANETARY ENERGY BALANCE

We now have all the tools necessary to analyze Earth's average climate in a quantitative manner. What we need to do next is put them together. The principle that we will apply is that of *energy balance*. To a first approximation, the amount of energy emitted by Earth must equal the amount of energy absorbed. In reality, this cannot be exactly true; if it were, Earth's average surface temperature would never change. The average surface temperature is changing—specifically, it is getting warmer. But it is getting warmer precisely because Earth's energy budget is slightly out of balance: The flux of incoming solar energy exceeds the outgoing IR flux by an almost imperceptible amount (a few hundredths of a percent). The imbalance may be caused by the increase in CO_2 and other greenhouse gases in the atmosphere, or it may be caused by natural fluctuations within the climate system. The latest evidence indicates strongly that the increase in greenhouse gases is dominating this change. When the climate system eventually reaches *steady state*, that is, when the surface temperature stops changing, the amount of energy going out will exactly equal the amount of energy coming in. But this will not happen until greenhouse gas levels are stabilized and the climate system is allowed sufficient time (at least 20 additional years) to come to equilibrium.

Physically, Earth's surface temperature depends on three factors: (1) the solar flux available at the distance of Earth's orbit, (2) Earth's reflectivity, and (3) the amount of warming provided by the atmosphere (i.e., the greenhouse effect). The solar flux, S, as mentioned earlier, is the amount of solar energy reaching the top of Earth's atmosphere. Not all this energy is absorbed, however. About 30% of the incident energy is reflected back to space, mostly by clouds. The reflectivity of a planet is called its *albedo*. It is usually expressed as the fraction of the total incident sunlight that is reflected from the planet as a whole. We shall designate albedo by the letter A.

To calculate the magnitude of the third factor, the greenhouse effect, it is convenient to treat Earth as a blackbody even though this is not exactly true. (The atmosphere radiates and absorbs energy better at some wavelengths than at others because of the presence of gases such as CO_2 and H_2O.) We do this by defining a quantity T_e that represents the **effective radiating temperature** of the planet. This temperature is the temperature that a true blackbody would need to radiate the same amount of energy that Earth radiates. With this definition in place, we can use the Stefan–Boltzmann law to calculate the energy emitted by Earth. By balancing the energy emitted with the energy absorbed, we obtain the following formula (see the Box "A Closer Look: Planetary Energy Balance"):

$$\sigma T_e^4 = \frac{S}{4}(1 - A).$$

This formula expresses the planetary energy balance between outgoing infrared energy and incoming solar energy.

Magnitude of the Greenhouse Effect

What is the significance of the effective radiating temperature? We can think of this quantity as the temperature at the height in the atmosphere from which most of the outgoing infrared radiation derives (see "Critical-Thinking," Problem 4). We can also think of it as the average temperature that Earth's surface would reach if the planet had no atmosphere (assuming that the albedo remained constant). To get a better understanding, let us calculate its value for the present Earth. We can solve the planetary energy balance equation for T_e by dividing both sides of the equation by σ and then taking the fourth root of each side:

$$T_e = \sqrt[4]{\frac{S}{4\sigma}(1 - A)}.$$

If we insert the known values of S (1366 W/m^2), A (30%, or 0.3), and σ (5.67 $\times$ 10^{-8} W/m^2/K^4), we get $T_e \approx$ 255 K. Thus, Earth's effective radiating temperature is a relatively chilly $-18°$C, or $0°$F.

We saw earlier, however, that the actual mean surface temperature of Earth, T_S, is 288 K, or about 15°C. The difference between the actual surface temperature and the effective radiating temperature is caused by the greenhouse effect of Earth's atmosphere. We can represent this mathematically by letting

$$\Delta T_g = T_s - T_e,$$

A CLOSER LOOK

Planetary Energy Balance

The derivation of the planetary energy balance equation is not difficult, but it does require that we consider the geometry of the Earth–Sun system. The starting point for the derivation is the relation

energy emitted by Earth = energy absorbed by Earth.

Let us first calculate the energy emitted by Earth. If we treat Earth as a blackbody with an effective radiating temperature T_e, the Stefan–Boltzmann law tells us that the energy emitted per unit area must be equal to σT_e^4. Earth radiates over its entire surface area, $4\pi R_{Earth}^2$, where R_{Earth} represents Earth's radius (Box Figure 1). Thus, the total energy emitted by Earth is

$$\text{energy emitted} = 4\pi R_{Earth}^2 \times \sigma T_e^4.$$

Now, let us calculate the energy absorbed by Earth. From the Sun, Earth would look like a circle with radius R_{Earth} and area πR_{Earth}^2. Note that it is the area of Earth projected against the Sun's rays that enters here, not half of the surface area of Earth. (Half of Earth's surface area would be $2\pi R_{Earth}^2$, but the Sun's rays do not strike all of this area perpendicularly.) The total energy intercepted must be equal to the product of Earth's projected area and the solar flux (S), or $\pi R_{Earth}^2 S$. The reflected energy is equal to this incident energy times the albedo (A). The difference between these two quantities is the energy absorbed by Earth:

energy absorbed = energy intercepted − energy reflected

$$= \pi R_{Earth}^2 S - \pi R_{Earth}^2 SA$$
$$= \pi R_{Earth}^2 S(1 - A).$$

BOX FIGURE 1 The amount of sunlight received by and reflected by Earth.

All that remains is for us to equate the outgoing and incoming energy. Using the expressions just calculated, we get

$$4\pi R_{Earth}^2 \times \sigma T_e^4 = \pi R_{Earth}^2 S(1 - A).$$

Canceling out πR_{Earth}^2 on both sides of this equation and dividing both sides by 4, we obtain the desired equation,

$$\sigma T_e^4 = \frac{S}{4}(1 - A).$$

where ΔT_g is the magnitude of the greenhouse effect. Thus, $\Delta T_g = 15°C - (-18°C) = 33°C$. A heuristic (i.e., somewhat simplified) explanation for what causes this greenhouse warming is given in the box titled "Thinking Quantitatively: How the Greenhouse Effects Works: The One-Layer Atmosphere."

To place this value in context, we can carry out similar calculations for Venus and Mars from known data of the albedos, surface temperatures, and orbital distances of these planets. (See "Critical-Thinking," Problem 2.) The results show that the solution to the Goldilocks problem posed at the beginning of this chapter is more complicated than we might have guessed. Evidently, a planet's greenhouse effect is at least as important in determining that planet's surface temperature as is its distance from the Sun.

We can also apply the planetary energy balance equation to the faint young Sun paradox. Recall that solar luminosity, and thus S, is estimated to have been

30% lower early in the solar system's history. It is easy to demonstrate that Earth's average surface temperature would have been below the freezing point of water under such circumstances, if the planetary albedo and the atmospheric greenhouse effect had remained unchanged (see "Critical-Thinking," Problem 5). We have already seen, though, that the early Earth had both liquid water and life on its surface. In later chapters, we discuss ways to resolve this apparent paradox.

ATMOSPHERIC COMPOSITION AND STRUCTURE

Atmospheric Composition

To understand the greenhouse effect in more detail, along with other aspects of climate and Earth's radiation budget, we must learn a few fundamental facts about the composition and structure of Earth's atmosphere. Table 2

THINKING QUANTITATIVELY

How the Greenhouse Effect Works: The One-Layer Atmosphere

Although we calculated that Earth's greenhouse effect provides 33°C of surface warming, our method of obtaining this result (by subtracting the calculated effective radiating temperature from the observed mean surface temperature) provides little insight into the physical mechanism that causes the warming. We can remedy this by doing a simple calculation that demonstrates how the greenhouse effect actually works.

Suppose we treat the atmosphere as a single layer of gas and that this gas absorbs (and reemits) all of the infrared radiation incident on it (Box Figure 2). Let us assume that it absorbs and emits infrared radiation equally well at all wavelengths, so that we can treat it as a blackbody, and that it has an albedo A in the visible spectrum, just like that of the real Earth. What are the temperatures of the gas layer and of the surface beneath it? We will call the layer temperature T_e and the surface temperature T_s, because these quantities are exactly analogous to those discussed in the text.

We can determine the values of T_e and T_s by balancing the energy absorbed and emitted by both the surface and the one-layer atmosphere. Let the amount of sunlight striking the planet be equal to $S/4$ (the globally averaged solar flux). The surface absorbs an amount of sunlight equal to $S/4 \times (1 - A)$, along with a flux of downward infrared radiation from the atmosphere equal to σT_e^4. The atmosphere absorbs an amount of upward infrared radiation from the ground equal to σT_s^4, and it emits infrared radiation in both the upward and downward directions at a rate of σT_e^4. (The real atmosphere also absorbs some of the incoming solar radiation, but we ignore that complication here.) Thus, we can write the overall energy balance in the form of two equations:

For the surface,

$$\sigma T_s^4 = \frac{S}{4}(1 - A) + \sigma T_e^4;$$

for the atmosphere,

$$\sigma T_s^4 = 2\sigma T_e^4.$$

(The factor 2 in the second equation arises because the atmosphere radiates in both the upward and downward directions.) If we now substitute the second equation into the left-hand side of the first equation and substract σT_e^4 from both sides, we obtain

$$\sigma T_e^4 = \frac{S}{4}(1 - A),$$

which is just the familiar energy-balance formula. But dividing the atmospheric energy-balance equation by σ and then taking the fourth root of both sides yields an additional result:

$$T_s = 2^{1/4}\, T_e.$$

Thus, the surface temperature is higher than the one-layer-atmosphere temperature by a factor of the fourth root of 2, or about 1.19. For $T_e = 255$ K, as on Earth at present, we get $T_s = 303$ K, and we calculate a greenhouse effect of

$$\Delta T_g = T_s - T_e = 48 \text{ K}.$$

This is higher than the actual greenhouse effect on Earth by about 15 K.

This example is not meant to be realistic. The real atmosphere is not perfectly absorbing at all infrared wavelengths, so some of the outgoing IR radiation from the surface leaks through to space. This effect tends to make ΔT_g smaller. Conversely, a more accurate calculation would subdivide the atmosphere into a number of different layers. Including more layers tends to make ΔT_g bigger and is the reason why a thick atmosphere, like that of Venus, can produce a really huge amount of surface warming. The calculation does, however, illustrate the basic nature of the greenhouse effect: By absorbing part of the infrared radiation radiated upward from the surface and reemitting it in both the upward and downward directions, the atmosphere allows the surface to be warmer than it would be if the atmosphere were not present.

BOX FIGURE 2 The greenhouse effect of a one-layer atmosphere.

Table 2 Major Constituents of Earth's Atmosphere Today

Name and Chemical Symbol	Concentration (% by volume)
Nitrogen, N_2	78
Oxygen, O_2	21
Argon, Ar	0.9
Water vapor, H_2O	0.00001 (South Pole)–4 (tropics)
Carbon dioxide, CO_2	0.039*

*In 2008.

lists the main constituents of Earth's present atmosphere and their relative abundances.

As Table 2 indicates, the three most abundant constituents of our atmosphere are nitrogen, oxygen, and argon. Nitrogen is a relatively *inert* (chemically unreactive) gas, but when split into its constituent atoms, it plays an important role in biological cycles. Oxygen, which is highly reactive, is the essential gas that all animals must breathe; it is required by many other life-forms as well. Argon is almost completely inert; it is the product of the radioactive decay of potassium, K, in Earth's interior. These three constituents—nitrogen, oxygen, and argon— are not greenhouse gases. In other words, they do not contribute to Earth's greenhouse effect.

Although they appear at the bottom of Table 2, water vapor and carbon dioxide are two of the most important atmospheric constituents. Besides being directly used by organisms, they are also strong greenhouse gases. We will soon see what makes a particular gas a greenhouse gas.

In addition to the major constituents listed in Table 2, Earth's atmosphere also contains a number of minor (or "trace") constituents that affect climate. The most important of these are methane, nitrous oxide, ozone, and freons. Their concentrations are generally much lower than those of the major constituents. Despite their low concentrations, these trace gases are important greenhouse gases. Table 3 lists the major greenhouse gases. (Note that water vapor and carbon dioxide are

Table 3 Important Atmospheric Greenhouse Gases

Name and Chemical Symbol	Concentration (ppm by volume)
Water vapor, H_2O	0.1 (South Pole)–40,000 (tropics)
Carbon dioxide, CO_2	390
Methane, CH_4	1.7
Nitrous oxide, N_2O	0.3
Ozone, O_3	0.01 (at the surface)
Freon-11, CCl_3F	0.00026
Freon-12, CCl_2F_2	0.00048

repeated here.) It is convenient to keep track of these gases in units of parts per million (ppm). Take a moment to convince yourself that the 0.00001–4% value of water vapor and the 0.039% value of CO_2 given in Table 2 are equivalent to the 0.1–40,000 ppm and 390 ppm values of water vapor and of CO_2 given in Table 3.

Table 3 is by no means a complete list of greenhouse gases. Several other gases affect climate to some extent or are otherwise important in atmospheric chemistry. The gases listed in Table 3, however, are the ones that are most important to the modern problem of global warming, and hence they are the ones on which we focus.

Atmospheric Structure

HOW ATMOSPHERIC PRESSURE VARIES WITH ALTITUDE Other characteristics of Earth's atmosphere that influence climate and the radiation budget are its pressure and temperature structure. *Pressure* may be defined as the force per unit area exerted by a gas or liquid on some surface with which it is in contact. The pressure exerted by the atmosphere at sea level is defined as one *atmosphere* (atm). A pressure of 1 atm is equivalent to about $15 \, lb/in^2$ in the English system and to 1.013 *bar,* or 1013 *millibars* (mbar), in the metric system. (The pressure unit in the SI system is the *pascal* /Pa, but this unit is cumbersome in atmospheric work: $1 \, Pa = 1 \times 10^{-5} \, bar \approx 9.9 \times 10^{-6} \, atm$.) An instrument used to measure atmospheric pressure is called a *barometer,* the name of which derives from the metric unit of measure "bar."

At higher levels in the atmosphere, the pressure decreases markedly (Figure 9a). This change in pressure is what makes your ears pop in an airplane. (The cabin is pressurized, or the popping would be much worse.) The decrease by altitude follows the **barometric law,** which states that atmospheric pressure decreases by about a factor of 10 for every 16-km increase in altitude. Thus, the pressure is about 0.1 bar at 16 km above the surface, 0.01 bar at 32 km, and so on. In more precise terms, the barometric law says that pressure decreases *exponentially* with altitude. Note from Figure 9a that the exponential decrease in pressure appears almost like a straight line when pressure is plotted on a logarithmic scale. The slight deviation from linearity is caused by the variation in temperature with altitude (discussed next). Pressure decreases faster with height in regions where the air is colder.

HOW ATMOSPHERIC TEMPERATURE VARIES WITH ALTITUDE The vertical temperature structure of the atmosphere is more complicated than the vertical pressure structure (Figure 9b). This temperature profile is the basis for distinguishing four regions within Earth's

FIGURE 9 (a) How pressure varies with altitude in Earth's atmosphere. (b) How temperature varies with altitude in Earth's atmosphere. The different regions of the atmosphere, determined by temperature regimes, are labeled.

atmosphere: the troposphere, the stratosphere, the mesosphere, and the thermosphere. Temperature decreases rapidly with altitude in the lowermost layer of the atmosphere, the **troposphere,** which extends from the surface up to 10–15 km (higher in the tropics, lower near the poles). Immediately above the troposphere is the **stratosphere,** which is located from about 10–15 to 50 km above the surface and in which temperature increases with altitude. Above the stratosphere, temperature decreases with altitude in the **mesosphere** (from about 50–90 km) and then increases once again in the uppermost layer, the **thermosphere** (above about 90 km). These temperature-based "spheres" overlap with atmospheric layers based on other characteristics. For example, the *ionosphere* (a layer that reflects radio waves) includes parts of both the thermosphere and the mesosphere. The very outermost fringe of the atmosphere, where the gas is so tenuous that collisions between molecules become infrequent, is often termed the *exosphere.*

The Troposphere   The atmospheric layers that are most important to climate studies are the two lowermost ones: the troposphere and the stratosphere. The troposphere is where most of the phenomena that we call weather—such as clouds, rain, snow, and storm activity—occur. It differs from the other atmospheric layers in that it is well mixed by convection. **Convection** is a process in which heat energy is transported by the motions of a *fluid* (a liquid or a gas). Such motions are generated when a fluid in a gravitational field, like that of Earth, is heated from below. A familiar example is the convective motion that occurs when a pot of water is heated on the burner of a stove (Figure 10). The warm water at the bottom of the pot is less dense than the cooler water at the top. As a result of this imbalance, the fluid overturns (it circulates, or convects) and will continue to do so as long as the pot is being

heated. If the water were heated uniformly or from above, convection would not occur.

We note for completeness that a third mode of heat transfer (in addition to radiation and convection) is **conduction**. Conduction is the transfer of heat energy by direct contact between molecules. The coils of the electric burner shown in Figure 10 heat the bottom of the pot by conduction. Conduction plays little role in atmospheric (or oceanic) heat transfer, however, so we will make no further mention of it.

The troposphere is convective because roughly half the incoming sunlight is absorbed by the ground and by the ocean surface. The energy from this light is eventually reradiated to space as IR radiation, but it cannot make its way directly from the surface in this form because IR

FIGURE 10   A pot of water on a stove, illustrating convection. The fluid circulates because it is heated from below.   (*Source:* From R. W. Christopherson, *Geosystems: An Introduction to Physical Geography,* 3/e, 1997. Reprinted by permission of Prentice Hall, Upper Saddle River, N.J.)

radiation is absorbed by atmospheric greenhouse gases and by clouds. So, the energy is instead transported by fluid motions until it reaches an altitude where the atmosphere is more transparent to IR radiation. Only then can the heat energy radiate away from Earth.

The upward convection of warm, moist air plays a major role in the global energy balance. Convection of heat in a moist atmosphere is more complicated than that in a dry atmosphere, because water can condense or evaporate. When water is evaporated from the ocean surface or from rivers and lakes, energy is taken up by the resulting vapor. This energy is referred to as the latent heat of vaporization. When the water vapor condenses to form clouds, the same amount of latent heat is released to the atmosphere. In more general terms, **latent heat** is the heat energy released or absorbed during the transition from one phase—gaseous, liquid, or solid—to another.

The Stratosphere   The stratosphere differs from the troposphere in several respects. The pressure is substantially lower in the stratosphere, in accordance with the barometric law. The two layers differ in composition as well. The stratosphere contains most of Earth's ozone. Stratospheric air is also very dry, containing less than 5 ppm of water vapor on average. Thus, condensation of water vapor does not occur, and so clouds and precipitation are absent. (An exception occurs in the polar regions during winter, where tenuous *polar stratospheric clouds* can form. These clouds play a key role in the development of the Antarctic ozone hole.) Stratospheric air is not convective and is therefore less well mixed than tropospheric air. Indeed, the name "stratosphere" derives from the word "stratified," which means layered.

The Vertical Temperature Profile   Why does the vertical temperature profile in Figure 9b exhibit all those curves? The reason has to do primarily with where the atmosphere is heated—that is, where solar energy is absorbed. The high temperatures near the ground are caused by the absorption of sunlight at Earth's surface, which then heats the atmosphere above it. The high temperatures near 50 km are caused by the absorption of solar UV radiation by ozone. The ozone concentration actually peaks some 20 km lower, in the middle stratosphere (Figure 11), but the heating rate is highest in the upper stratosphere because more UV radiation is available at those altitudes. The vertical heating distribution also explains why the stratosphere is not convective: The maximum heating occurs at the top of the layer, so there is no tendency for the air to rise. Above 50 km, both the ozone concentration and the heating rate decline, so the temperature decreases with altitude in the mesosphere. Finally, the temperature rise above 90 km in the thermosphere is

FIGURE 11   An approximate profile of the vertical variation of ozone concentration in Earth's atmosphere.

caused by the absorption of short-wavelength UV radiation by molecular oxygen, O_2.

PHYSICAL CAUSES OF THE GREENHOUSE EFFECT

We determined earlier that Earth's greenhouse effect warms the surface by some 33°C compared with the temperature we would expect if there were no atmosphere. This warming has been attributed to the presence of greenhouse gases, especially H_2O and CO_2. Why do some gases contribute to the greenhouse effect whereas others, such as O_2 and N_2, do not?

Molecular Motions and the Greenhouse Gases H_2O and CO_2

The defining property of a greenhouse gas is its ability to absorb or emit infrared radiation. Gas molecules can absorb or emit radiation in the IR range in two different ways. One way is by changing the rate at which the molecules rotate. The theory of *quantum mechanics* describes the behavior of matter on a microscopic scale—that is, the size of molecules and smaller. According to this theory, molecules can rotate only at certain discrete frequencies, just as most house fans can operate only at certain speeds. The rotation frequency is the number of revolutions that a molecule completes per second. Consider one photon of an electromagnetic wave that is incident on an individual molecule (Figure 12). If the incident wave has just the right frequency (corresponding to the difference between two allowed rotation frequencies), the molecule can absorb the photon. In the process, the molecule's rotation rate increases. Conversely, the rotation rate slows down when the molecule emits a photon.

FIGURE 12 The rotation rate of an individual H_2O molecule increases when the molecule absorbs a photon of infrared radiation.

The frequency (or wavelength) of the radiation that can be absorbed or emitted depends on the molecule's structure. The H_2O molecule is constructed in such a manner that it absorbs IR radiation of wavelengths of about $12 \, \mu m$ and longer. This interaction gives rise to a very strong absorption feature in Earth's atmosphere called the H_2O **rotation band.** It can clearly be seen in Figure 13, which shows the percentage of radiation at different wavelengths that is absorbed during vertical passage through the atmosphere. Virtually 100% of infrared radiation longer than $12 \, \mu m$ is absorbed, although some of this absorption is caused by CO_2 (see below). The H_2O rotation band extends all the way into the microwave region of the electromagnetic spectrum (above a wavelength of $1000 \, \mu m$), which is why a microwave oven is able to heat up anything that contains water.

A second way in which molecules can absorb or emit IR radiation is by changing the amplitude with which they vibrate. Molecules not only rotate, they also vibrate—their constituent atoms move toward and away from each other. Again consider an electromagnetic wave that is incident on a molecule. If the frequency at which the molecule vibrates matches the frequency of the wave, the molecule can absorb a photon and begin to vibrate more vigorously. (Similarly, a vibrating tuning fork will induce vibrations in a second tuning fork if the pitches of the two instruments

are the same. The pitch is proportional to the frequency of the sound wave.)

The *triatomic* (three-atom) CO_2 molecule can vibrate in three ways. We need to concern ourselves only with the *bending mode* of vibration (Figure 14). This vibration has a frequency that allows the molecule to absorb IR radiation at a wavelength of about $15 \, \mu m$. It gives rise to a strong absorption feature in Earth's atmosphere called the 15-μm CO_2 **band.** The 15-μm CO_2 band overlaps the H_2O rotation band and, hence, is hard to distinguish in Figure 13. It is, however, easily seen by satellites that look down at Earth's atmosphere from above. Because it occurs fairly near the peak of Earth's outgoing radiation, this absorption band is particularly important to climate. Earth's surface emits strongly in this wavelength region, but very little of this radiation is able to escape directly to space because it is absorbed by CO_2 molecules in the atmosphere. This is why CO_2 is such an important contributor to the greenhouse effect.

Other Greenhouse Gases

Water vapor and CO_2 are the most important greenhouse gases in Earth's atmosphere, but several other trace gases—notably CH_4, N_2O, O_3, and freons—also contribute to greenhouse warming (Table 3). These gases have more of an effect on outgoing radiation than their small concentrations would suggest because they absorb at different wavelengths than do H_2O and CO_2. Freons, for example, have absorption bands within the 8- to 12-μm *window region,* where both H_2O and CO_2 are poor absorbers (see Figure 13). Thus, one molecule of Freon-11 contributes much more to the greenhouse effect than does one CO_2 molecule. Ozone also has an absorption band in this region centered at $9.6 \, \mu m$. Thus, O_3 is a good greenhouse gas as well.

Now, recall that we asked the question, Why are O_2 and N_2 poor absorbers of IR radiation and, thus, do not

FIGURE 13 Percentage of radiation absorbed during vertical passage through the atmosphere. Absorption of 100% means that no radiation penetrates the atmosphere. The nearly complete absorption of radiation longer than $13 \, \mu m$ is caused by absorption by CO_2 and H_2O. Both of these gases also absorb solar radiation in the near infrared (wavelengths between about 0.7 and $5 \, \mu m$). The absorption feature at $9.6 \, \mu m$ is caused by ozone. (*Source:* Data originally from R. M. Goody and Y. L. Yung, *Atmospheric Radiation,* 2nd ed., New York: Oxford University Press, 1989, Figure 1.1.)

Bending mode
(15-μm band)

FIGURE 14   The bending mode of vibration of the CO_2 molecule.

Rotation   Vibration

FIGURE 15   Rotation and vibration for a diatomic molecule, such as N_2 or O_2.

FIGURE 16   Photo of Earth from space, showing clouds. (*Source:* NASA Headquarters.)

contribute significantly to the greenhouse effect? We are now ready to answer that question. *Diatomic* (two-atom) molecules can rotate and vibrate just like the more complicated molecules, H_2O and CO_2, discussed earlier (Figure 15). The O_2 and N_2 molecules, however, are perfectly symmetric: Both of their constituent atoms are identical. Hence, there is no separation of positive and negative electric charges within the molecule. As noted earlier, an electromagnetic wave actually consists of oscillating electric and magnetic fields. To a first approximation, these fields cannot interact with a totally symmetric molecule; the electromagnetic wave passes by such a molecule without being absorbed. (Note that CO_2 is a symmetric molecule because the three atoms are, on average, arranged in a line. However, the symmetry is broken when the molecule bends, allowing 15-μm radiation to be absorbed or emitted.)

EFFECT OF CLOUDS ON THE ATMOSPHERIC RADIATION BUDGET

Gases are not the only constituents of the atmosphere that affect its radiation balance; that balance is also influenced by the presence of clouds and aerosols. We will postpone the discussion of aerosols, because their climatic effects are usually rather small and short term. (Sulfate aerosols, for example, cooled Earth by about 0.5°C [1°F] for a year or two after the Mt. Pinatubo eruption.) The effects of clouds, though, are large and cannot be ignored (Figure 16). Unfortunately, these effects cannot always be calculated reliably either, and this leads to significant problems in climate prediction.

Types of Clouds

The effect of clouds on Earth's radiation budget is difficult to calculate quantitatively, partly because there are many different types of clouds (Figure 17). *Cumulus clouds* are the familiar puffy, white clouds that look like balls of cotton. They are composed of droplets of liquid water and are formed in convective updrafts. *Cumulonimbus clouds* are big, tall cumulus clouds that give rise to thunderstorms. *Stratus clouds* are gray, low-level water clouds that are more or less continuous. They cover much of the eastern United States during winter (especially central Pennsylvania, where the three authors of this book reside!). *Cirrus clouds* are high, wispy clouds composed of ice crystals rather than liquid water, because the temperature of the upper troposphere is well below the freezing point.

Opposing Climatic Effects of Clouds

Have you ever noticed that cloudy days are relatively cool, yet cloudy nights are relatively warm? That is because clouds affect planetary energy balance in two opposing ways. Clouds cool Earth during the daytime by reflecting incident sunlight back to space. We noted earlier that at present the planetary albedo is about 0.3. A large fraction of this is caused by clouds. In fact, without clouds, Earth's albedo would probably be closer to 0.1. According to the planetary energy balance equation, reducing the albedo from 0.3 to 0.1 would raise the effective radiating temperature of Earth by about 17°C (30°F). The increase in surface temperature on a cloud-free Earth would be smaller than this, however, because clouds also absorb and reemit outgoing infrared radiation and, thus, contribute significantly to the greenhouse effect. This effect dominates at night and helps keep cloudy nights warm.

To complicate matters further, the effect of any particular cloud depends on its height and thickness. Low, thick clouds, such as stratus clouds, generally cool the surface because their primary influence is to reflect incoming solar radiation. High, thin clouds, such as cirrus clouds, tend to warm the surface because they contribute

(a)	(b)

FIGURE 17 Photos of (a) stratus and (b) cirrus clouds. (*Source:* (a) Ralph F. Kresge/NOAA and (b) Dean Bergmann/ iStockphoto.)

more to the greenhouse effect than to the planetary albedo. The reason for the difference is twofold: First, the elongated ice crystals of which cirrus clouds are composed allow much of the incident solar radiation to pass through but absorb most of the outgoing IR radiation. In contrast, stratus clouds reflect much of the incoming visible radiation, in addition to absorbing radiation at IR wavelengths. Second, cirrus clouds occur higher in the troposphere than do stratus clouds and are therefore colder (Figure 18). According to the Stefan–Boltzmann law, cirrus clouds therefore radiate less IR energy to space. Because they absorb the upward-directed IR radiation from the warm surface and reradiate it at a lower temperature, cirrus clouds make a large contribution to the atmospheric greenhouse effect. Lower-lying stratus clouds

do this as well, but their radiating temperature is higher and so their contribution to the greenhouse effect is not as large.

Earth's Global Energy Budget

The various factors that we have just discussed can be combined to calculate a global energy budget for Earth, as in Figure 19. The incident solar flux in this diagram is normalized to 100 arbitrary "units" of radiation. These 100 units of incoming energy are balanced by 30 units of reflected solar energy (25 reflected by the atmosphere and 5 reflected by the surface) and 70 units of outgoing infrared radiation. About half the incident solar radiation makes it down to the surface; the other half is either

FIGURE 18 The different effects of high and low clouds on the atmospheric radiation budget. High, thin clouds are more transparent to incoming sunlight and radiate at a lower temperature than do low, thick clouds. The expressions σT_{high}^4, σT_{low}^4, and σT_s^4 represent the radiation flux at the temperature of high, thin clouds, at the temperature of low, thick clouds, and at the surface temperature, respectively.

FIGURE 19 Earth's globally averaged atmospheric energy budget. All fluxes are normalized relative to 100 arbitrary units of incident radiation. (*Source:* S. Schneider, "Climate Modeling," *Scientific American* 256, no. 5, 1987, pp. 72–80.)

reflected or absorbed by the atmosphere. Within the atmosphere, energy is transported by a combination of radiation, convection, and the latent heat associated with the evaporation and condensation of water vapor. This latter process is a very important one: Roughly half of the solar energy absorbed by the surface (24 out of 45 units) goes directly into evaporating water.

The greenhouse effect is shown here as an additional 88 units of downward-directed infrared radiation. Thus, the total energy flux absorbed by the surface is 133 units (= 45 units of solar radiation + 88 units of IR radiation). This value is almost twice the net amount of energy absorbed by Earth (70 units). The reason is that infrared radiation is absorbed and reemitted multiple times within the atmosphere, so the internal fluxes can actually be higher than the net input of energy. *At the top of the atmosphere, however, the net downward solar radiation flux (incoming minus reflected) must equal the outgoing infrared flux.* This statement is the principle of *planetary energy balance.*

INTRODUCTION TO CLIMATE MODELING

How can we utilize our knowledge of Earth's current energy budget to predict what Earth's surface temperature might have been in the past or how it might vary in the future? Because the climate system is complex, we need some sort of computer model to keep track of all the intricacies.

Instead of estimating the magnitude of the greenhouse effect by subtraction, as we did earlier in this chapter, we need to be able to calculate it directly from the measured or predicted concentrations of greenhouse gases.

Such a calculation must take into account the rotational and vibrational absorption bands of all the different greenhouse gases. Doing so quantitatively requires that we combine the predictions of quantum mechanics with laboratory measurements of the strengths of different absorption bands. Fortunately for climate modelers, a great deal of effort has gone into obtaining the required parameters. As a result, a voluminous database of information on the absorption characteristics of various molecules of atmospheric interest is now available.

Armed with these data, the climate modeler must next decide how to incorporate them into a computer model of the atmosphere. The most complete type of model is called an atmospheric **general circulation model (GCM),** also sometimes referred to as a *global climate model.* These elaborate computer models include a three-dimensional representation of the atmosphere (or oceans) that simulates winds (or currents), moisture transport, and energy balance. Atmospheric GCMs are replete with clouds, winds, snow, rain, and most of the other phenomena that we call weather. Thus, they are capable of predicting how climate varies on a regional basis. But GCMs have a number of drawbacks, the most serious of which is that they require large amounts of runtime on the world's fastest computers to simulate even a few years of global climate. GCMs play a central role in climate policymaking today. We begin here, however, with models that are somewhat less complicated and, hence, easier to understand.

One-Dimensional Climate Models—RCMs

For many purposes it is sufficient to construct simpler climate models that require less effort to program and less computer time to run. We have already seen one such model—the one-layer atmosphere model described in the box earlier in this chapter. But that model did not produce a good, quantitative estimate of the greenhouse effect, nor did it account for the contributions of different greenhouse gases. The simplest model that is capable of doing both of these things reliably is called a **radiative-convective model (RCM).** In an RCM, the climate system is approximated by averaging the incoming solar and outgoing IR radiation over Earth's entire surface. The vertical structure of the atmosphere (Figure 9) is taken into account (unlike in the one-layer model), but horizontal variations are ignored. Thus, such models are sometimes called one-dimensional climate models, in contrast with the three-dimensional GCMs. The vertical dimension (altitude) is then divided into a number of layers. The RCM calculates the temperature of each layer by taking into account the amount of energy received or emitted in the form of radiation, along with the effects of convection and latent heat release in the lowermost layers.

RADIATIVE EFFECT OF DOUBLING ATMOSPHERIC CO_2
Although RCMs are quite simple compared with the real climate system, they allow us to estimate the magnitude of the greenhouse effect as a function of the concentrations of various greenhouse gases in Earth's atmosphere. These models correctly predict that the greenhouse-induced temperature difference ΔT_g for the present atmosphere is 33°C, in agreement with the estimate derived earlier by the subtraction $\Delta T_g = T_s + T_e$. (This is *not* a trivial result. We would have to work through a lot of the relevant physics to come up with this answer.) More importantly, RCMs allow us to predict the average surface temperature increase that should result from an increase in the concentration of greenhouse gases. A commonly cited benchmark is the temperature change that would result from a doubling of the atmospheric CO_2 concentration from 300 ppm (its value near the turn of the 20th century) to 600 ppm. RCM calculations show that, all other factors being equal, such a change in CO_2 would produce an increase of about 1.2°C (2.2°F) in the global average surface temperature. This value is the temperature change ΔT_0 that would result in the absence of any feedbacks in the climate system.

In reality, we would expect other factors in the climate system to change as atmospheric CO_2 increases, and so a temperature change of +1.2°C is not the best estimate we could make of the effect of CO_2 doubling. To obtain a better estimate, we must consider what those climate feedbacks might be and how strongly they affect our answer.

CLIMATE FEEDBACKS

Climate feedbacks are extremely important because they can either amplify or moderate the radiative effect of changes in greenhouse gas concentrations. Here, we discuss several feedback processes that affect climate on Earth.

The Water Vapor Feedback

One of the most important feedbacks in the climate system involves the concentration of atmospheric water vapor. As noted earlier, water vapor is an excellent absorber of IR radiation and, hence, a good greenhouse gas. Unlike CO_2, however, water vapor is typically close to its *condensation point*—the temperature at which a vapor condenses to form a liquid. If Earth's surface temperature were to decrease for some reason, water vapor would condense out in the form of rain or snow, leaving less water vapor behind in the atmosphere. This reduction in atmospheric water vapor would cause a corresponding decrease in the greenhouse effect, which, in turn, would lower the surface temperature still further. Conversely, an increase in surface temperature would cause an increase in the rate at which water vapor evaporates from the oceans. This would increase the concentration of water vapor in the atmosphere, thereby increasing the greenhouse effect and further warming Earth's surface.

The net result of this interaction between water vapor abundance and Earth's surface temperature is a positive feedback loop that tends to amplify small temperature perturbations (Figure 20). This feedback loop can be incorporated in RCMs by assuming a fixed *relative humidity*

FIGURE 20 Systems diagram showing the positive feedback loop that includes atmospheric water vapor.

profile in the troposphere. **Relative humidity** is the concentration of water vapor in an air parcel divided by the concentration that would be present if the air parcel were *saturated* with water vapor (i.e., on the verge of condensation). When such a calculation is performed, the RCM predicts that the equilibrium change in surface temperature for CO_2 doubling, ΔT_{eq}, is about twice that which would have occurred otherwise. We can write

$$\Delta T_{eq} = \Delta T_0 + \Delta T_f,$$

where ΔT_0 is the temperature change with no feedbacks and ΔT_f is the change caused by the feedback. For the problem of CO_2 doubling, $\Delta T_0 = 1.2°C$ (2.2°F), $\Delta T_{eq} \approx 2.4°C$ (4.4°F), so the temperature change caused by the water vapor feedback is approximately 1.2°C. Furthermore, the feedback factor f is given by

$$f = \frac{\Delta T_{eq}}{\Delta T_0} = \frac{2.4°C}{1.2°C} = 2.$$

A feedback factor of 2 indicates that this is a strong, positive feedback on the climate system.

Snow and Ice Albedo Feedback

A second feedback loop that is expected to have some impact on modern global warming, but is especially important for glacial–interglacial variations, involves albedo changes caused by snow and ice. As Earth's climate cools, the extent of wintertime snow and ice cover increases in temperate regions. On longer time scales, the permanent ice cap in the northern polar regions expands toward the equator, resulting in the periods of glaciation known as the Ice Ages. Snow and ice have a much higher albedo than does land or water. Therefore, increases in snow and ice cover should cause further decreases in surface temperature. The result is a positive feedback loop that tends to amplify induced changes in Earth's surface temperature (Figure 21). As snow and ice cover are restricted to middle and high latitudes, modeling this feedback loop quantitatively requires the use of two-dimensional or three-dimensional computer models.

FIGURE 21 Systems diagram showing the positive feedback loop that includes snow and ice cover.

FIGURE 22 Systems diagram illustrating the negative feedback loop between surface temperature and the outgoing flux of infrared radiation. This feedback is the fundamental reason that Earth's climate is stable.

The IR Flux/Temperature Feedback

Both of the feedbacks discussed so far are positive. But systems that contain only positive feedback loops are unstable. Does this mean that Earth's climate is unstable? No! You would not be sitting there reading this text if that were true. Earth's climate system contains a very strong negative feedback that is so basic that it is often overlooked. The feedback loop that stabilizes Earth's climate on short time scales is the relationship between surface temperature and the flux of outgoing IR radiation (Figure 22). If Earth's surface temperature were to increase for some reason, the outgoing IR flux from the top of the atmosphere would also increase. But if the outgoing IR flux were to increase, the surface temperature would tend to decrease, because more energy would be lost from the Earth system. This feedback loop might appear to be trivial, but it is not; there are situations in which it can fail. In particular, the positive correlation between surface temperature and the outgoing IR flux can break down if the atmosphere contains a very large amount of water vapor. This, we think, is what happened to our sister planet, Venus, and it led to what is sometimes called a *runaway greenhouse*.

The Uncertain Feedback Caused by Clouds

Another important feedback process in the climate system is that provided by changes in clouds. Unfortunately, this feedback process is not as easy to quantify as the ones just discussed. You already know that clouds can either warm the surface, or cool it, depending on their height. This alone should provide a hint that estimating their feedback effect might be difficult. In addition to this problem, clouds are inherently three-dimensional: they form at some locations and not at others because of the way the winds blow. Most current 3-D climate models suggest that the net feedback effect of clouds is positive for the doubled CO_2 problem because the increase in high-altitude cirrus clouds (which cause warming) outweighs any increase in low-altitude stratus clouds (which cause cooling). But climate modelers agree that this ranks as one of their least secure predictions, and hence adds significant uncertainty to projections of future global warming.

In summary, we have now examined Earth's climate system in enough detail to understand how the atmospheric greenhouse effect warms the planet and how the planet's average surface temperature may respond to a human-induced increase in greenhouse gases. But Earth's climate cannot be described by just its average surface temperature.

The term "climate" includes many other related factors, such as latitudinal and seasonal temperature gradients, winds, and precipitation. To study these phenomena, we need to broaden our spatial perspective and consider the Earth system from a three-dimensional perspective.

Chapter Summary

1. Earth is warmed by the absorption of visible radiation from the Sun and is cooled by the emission of infrared radiation to space.
   a. Much of the infrared radiation emitted by Earth's surface is absorbed and reemitted by atmospheric gases.
   b. The result is a greenhouse effect that warms the surface by about 33°C. Without this natural greenhouse effect, Earth would be too cold to support life.
2. Only certain atmospheric gases, most importantly H_2O and CO_2, contribute to the greenhouse effect. These gases absorb infrared radiation by changing the rate at which individual molecules rotate or vibrate. Other trace gases, such as freons, can contribute substantially to the greenhouse effect by absorbing radiation at different wavelengths than do H_2O and CO_2.
3. Clouds affect the atmospheric radiation budget both by reflecting incident sunlight and by contributing to the greenhouse effect. Low, thick clouds tend to cool the surface; high, thin clouds tend to warm it.
4. Earth's climate system contains several well-understood feedbacks that play important roles in regulating climate change.
   a. The climate system is stabilized by a strong negative feedback loop between surface temperature and the outgoing infrared flux.
   b. The system is destabilized by a positive feedback loop involving atmospheric water vapor. Because it acts on short time scales, this feedback is likely to play an important role in contemporary global warming. Climate models predict a surface temperature response to CO_2 doubling that is twice that of models in which this feedback is neglected.
   c. The system is also destabilized by a positive feedback loop involving the extent of snow and ice cover due to the effect of albedo.
   d. Clouds may also contribute to climate feedback, but their effect is not well understood.

Key Terms

barometric law
blackbody
blackbody radiation
conduction
convection
effective radiating temperature
electromagnetic radiation
electromagnetic spectrum
15-μm CO_2 band
flux
frequency
general circulation model (GCM)
H_2O rotation band
infrared (IR) radiation
inverse-square law
Kelvin (absolute) temperature scale
latent heat
mesosphere
photon
photosphere
radiative-convective model (RCM)
relative humidity
Stefan–Boltzmann law
stratosphere
thermosphere
troposphere
ultraviolet (UV) radiation
visible radiation
visible spectrum
wavelength
Wien's law

Review Questions

1. How are the wavelength and frequency of an electromagnetic wave related?
2. What is a photon?
3. What physical law describes the manner in which the intensity of sunlight changes as the observer moves away from the Sun?
4. Name two physical laws that apply to blackbody radiation. What do these laws tell us about the nature of the emitted radiation?
5. What is the major contributor to Earth's albedo?
6. What are the three most abundant gases in Earth's atmosphere?

7. List the four layers of Earth's atmosphere. How are they defined?
8. Name three mechanisms by which heat energy can be transferred. Which two are important in Earth's global energy budget?
9. Identify two physical processes by which gases can absorb infrared radiation. Give examples of each process.
10. Why are O_2 and N_2 not greenhouse gases?
11. Describe the different ways in which climate is affected by high and low clouds.
12. Identify two positive feedback loops in Earth's climate system. Why is Earth's climate stable despite these destabilizing, positive feedbacks?

Critical-Thinking Problems

1. a. Given that a 300-K blackbody radiates its peak energy at a wavelength of about 10 μm, at what wavelength would a 600-K blackbody radiate its peak energy?
   b. If the two bodies in part (a) were the same size, what would be the ratio of the heat emitted by the hotter object to the heat emitted by the colder one?
2. a. Venus and Mars orbit the Sun at average distances of 0.72 and 1.52 AU, respectively. What is the solar flux at each planet?
   b. Venus has a planetary albedo of 0.8, and Mars has an albedo of 0.22. Using the answer to part (a), determine the effective radiating temperatures of these planets.
   c. How do the effective radiating temperatures determined in part (b) compare with the value for Earth, and why is this result surprising?
   d. The mean surface temperatures of Venus and Mars are 730 and 218 K, respectively. Using the answer to part (b), determine the magnitude of the greenhouse effect on each planet.
   e. How do the results of (d) compare with the magnitude of the greenhouse effect on Earth?
3. a. The Sun radiates at an effective temperature of 5780 K and has a radius of about 696,000 km. Remembering that 1 AU = 149,600,000 km, derive the approximate value of the solar flux at Earth's orbit.
   b. Compare your answer with the value given in the text.
4. The tropospheric lapse rate (the rate at which temperature decreases with altitude) is approximately 6°C (11°F) per kilometer. Given that the mean surface temperature of Earth is 288 K and the effective radiating temperature is 255 K, from what altitude does most of the emitted radiation derive?
5. Solar luminosity is estimated to have been 30% lower than today at the time when the solar system formed, 4.6 billion years ago.

a. If Earth's albedo was the same as it is now ($A = 0.3$), what would have been its effective radiating temperature at that time?
b. If the magnitude of the greenhouse effect had also remained unchanged ($\Delta T_g = 33$ K), what would Earth's average surface temperature have been? How does this compare with today's value?
6. For atmospheric CO_2 concentrations not too different from the present value, the radiative forcing of CO_2 can be expressed by the formula

$$\Delta F = -6.3 \ln\left(\frac{C}{C_0}\right),$$

where $C_0 = 300$ ppm is the CO_2 concentration near the turn of the 20th century, C is the CO_2 concentration at some other time, and ΔF is the change (in watts per square meter) in the outgoing infrared flux caused by the change in CO_2 concentration. The function $\ln(x)$ denotes the natural logarithm of a given number x. Any scientific calculator has this function key.
a. By how much would the outgoing infrared flux decrease if the atmospheric CO_2 concentration were increased from 300 to 600 ppm (i.e., if $C = 600$ ppm)?
b. By how much would surface temperature have to increase in order to bring the radiation budget back into balance in part (a), assuming that the planetary albedo and the amount of water vapor in the atmosphere do not change? (Hint: Use the planetary energy balance equation to calculate how much T_e would have to change to balance the radiation budget. Remember that the left-hand side of this equation represents the outgoing infrared flux. The quantity T_s will change by the same amount as T_e if the amount of water vapor is held constant.)

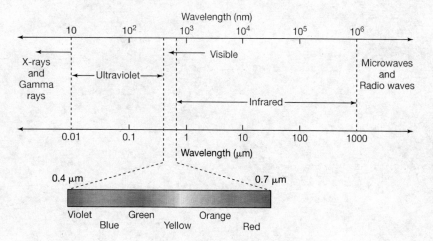

FIGURE 3 The electromagnetic spectrum.

The Atmospheric Circulation System

Key Questions

- Why does air move?
- Are the movements of the winds random across Earth's surface, or do they follow regular patterns?

- What implications do these circulatory systems have for global climate?
- What other factors govern the geographic and seasonal distributions of temperature and rainfall?

Chapter Overview

Earth's climate is a central theme of ours. We focus on the role climate plays in the Earth system and explain how Earth's climate works, how climate has changed through time, and how it may change in the future. An important element of Earth's climate is the atmospheric circulation. If we average the radiation fluxes around the globe and over a few years there is a balance. Earth emits as much energy as it receives, aside from the issue of anthropogenic increases in the greenhouse effect. If we look at regions smaller than the globe and over time periods of less than a year, however, the situation is very different. There is a significant imbalance in the distribution of energy at various latitudes: The tropics receive a surplus of radiative energy, whereas the poles run a deficit. This imbalance causes an equator-to-pole temperature gradient that results in density and pressure differences in the atmosphere. The density and pressure differences cause air to move in a global-scale pattern of wind belts, which are modified by Earth's rotation and by the distribution of land and water. The net effect is to restore the latitudinal energy balance by moving surplus energy away from the tropics to cancel out the deficit at the poles. In the process, energy is used to evaporate water from the land and ocean surfaces, water vapor is

carried by wind, and energy is released when the vapor condenses to form clouds. Thus, there are close interactions between the transport of energy and of water by means of circulating air. In other words, Earth's atmospheric circulation has a direct impact on the global distributions of temperature and precipitation.

THE GLOBAL CIRCULATORY SUBSYSTEMS

Anyone who has felt wind blow, watched clouds move, and seen rain fall is aware that large parts of the Earth system are in constant motion. Even the continents and oceans, despite their apparent permanence, are continuously moving. The island of Iceland in the North Atlantic, for example, is spreading, and its two sides are moving away from each other fast enough to be measured by today's instruments. Although these movements may sometimes appear random, they form part of a well-ordered circulation of energy and matter throughout the Earth system.

Like the circulatory system of humans (part of the cardiovascular system), Earth's circulatory subsystems work to maintain the planet in a thermal and chemical balance. The human circulatory system transports dissolved gases, nutrients, and hormones throughout the body; carries away waste products; helps regulate the acidity of body fluids; and is a vital part of the body's thermoregulatory system, carrying warm blood from one area to another. Although the human circulatory system is not an exact analogy to Earth's circulatory subsystems, these systems do have much in common. Essential gases and nutrients are transported throughout the Earth system, and waste products are removed from their area of production. All of Earth's circulatory subsystems act in some way to help regulate the global temperature: The winds and ocean currents redistribute the energy received from the Sun, and the motions of the solid Earth redistribute carbon and help regulate the CO_2 level of the atmosphere. We now will examine those circulations that occur within the fluid part of the Earth system: the atmosphere and oceans.

The purpose of this chapter is to describe the major characteristics of the atmospheric circulation, to explain why they occur, and to illustrate the way in which they affect the transport of energy and materials around the globe. Now we take that system apart and examine some of its internal workings—specifically those related to climate. In doing so, we have two primary objectives. The first is to explain why weather and climate vary across the globe. The second is to emphasize that because of the internal workings of Earth's climate system, the response to global-scale processes and changes may not be uniform around the globe. Organized movements of the atmosphere occur over many different time and space scales. These movements range from centimeter-scale swirls, or *eddies,* to global-scale motions of the wind belts. All of these are important in one way or another, but we limit our discussion to processes that are global in extent and that have the greatest influence on the transport of energy and mass through the Earth system. One of Earth's most important constituents is water. Cycling continuously among the atmosphere, the oceans, and the land surface, water carries with it energy, dissolved nutrients, and other matter—all vital for maintaining an environment suitable for life.

In the same way that the functioning of the cardiovascular system in the human body ultimately depends on the ability of the heart to keep pumping, the functioning of Earth's circulatory subsystems rely on several different pumps. Each of these pumps drives a different circulatory mechanism, and each works at a different speed. Over shorter time scales (years to decades), the most important pump is found in the tropical oceans. This pump is responsible for the movements of the air and the surface ocean over most of the globe. The energy source that drives this pump is radiation from the Sun. Over longer time scales (about 1,000 years), a second pump drives the deep-ocean circulation. The ultimate energy source is again the Sun. The pump operating over the longest time scales (millions

of years) is radioactive decay and the production of heat in Earth's interior. This pump causes the movements of the continents.

All these circulation subsystems play a vital role in the operation of the Earth system. We know that in humans the cardiovascular system can maintain stability only if the blood keeps moving. Similarly, the Earth system can maintain stability only as long as its circulatory subsystems continue to function. The long-term pump (that is, the processes of internal heat production and plate tectonics) ceased to function on Mars. The planet's inability to support an environment suitable for life may be at least partly a result of the failure of this circulation mechanism.

THE ATMOSPHERIC CIRCULATION

Recall that the troposphere is the lowermost layer of the atmosphere. Most of the processes we are interested in take place in the troposphere, so we limit our discussion here to that layer. The circulation of the stratosphere plays a role in the depletion of stratospheric ozone.

The Movement of Air

Air moves over Earth's surface because there are horizontal differences in pressure. Air also moves vertically either because it is forced to rise mechanically (e.g., when it encounters a mountain range) or because there are changes in *buoyancy.* **Buoyancy** is the tendency of an object to float in a fluid. Buoyancy is controlled by differences in *density* between the object and the fluid, where density is given by the mass of a substance within a unit volume. (The greater the mass within a given volume, the greater the density.) Ultimately, all of these horizontal and vertical movements (except those due to mechanical forces) can be attributed to differences in temperatures across the globe. To explain how these movements occur, we need to understand how pressure and density are related to temperature.

VERTICAL MOVEMENT It is easiest to picture these relationships by thinking of vertical and horizontal movements separately. Imagine the situation with a hot-air balloon. Remember that heating causes molecules to move faster. In this case, the faster the air molecules move, the more they collide with each other and with the interior of the balloon. These collisions exert a force (i.e., air pressure) on the interior surface. If the balloon was a fixed container (one that could not expand), there would be an increase in the air pressure within the container. Thus we see a connection between the temperature and pressure of a gas: As the temperature increases, the pressure increases. But the balloon *is* expandable. As the pressure starts to increase, the air pushes outward on the interior of the balloon, causing it to expand. So in a balloon, it is the volume rather than the pressure that increases (see the Box "A Closer Look: The Relationships between Temperature, Pressure, and Volumes—The Ideal Gas Law").

If we begin with the balloon partially inflated, it will contain a certain number of air molecules. As these are heated, the number of molecules does not change, but they move faster, increasing the pressure on the interior of the balloon; this causes the balloon to expand. We now have the same number of air molecules as before (the mass [m] hasn't changed), but they occupy a greater volume (V). This means that the density of the air (ρ) must decrease ($\rho = m / V$). Because the air in the balloon is less dense than the air surrounding it, the balloon becomes *positively buoyant,* and it rises. The balloon will continue to rise until the density of the air outside the balloon matches that inside (*neutral buoyancy*). If the air in the balloon is more dense than the surrounding air, the balloon would have *negative buoyancy,* and it would sink. Exactly the same processes occur in the atmosphere when we heat the surface below a parcel (column) of air. The surface heats the parcel of air at the bottom of the column; the air parcel expands, its density decreases, and the parcel rises through the air column. Cooling a parcel of air higher in the column causes it to become more dense than the surrounding air, and the parcel sinks.

HORIZONTAL MOVEMENT How do horizontal movements occur? We saw that warmer air has a lower density than cooler air. If we consider two adjacent columns of air, one warmer than the other, the cooler column would have a greater density and higher pressure than the warmer column. This difference in pressure would cause the air to move horizontally from the region of higher-pressure cool air to the region of lower-pressure warmer air—the air moves down the pressure gradient. The atmospheric pressure is a force (**F**) determined by the mass (m) of the air column and the acceleration (**a**) due to gravity (remember Newton's second law of motion: $\mathbf{F} = m\mathbf{a}$). Averaged globally and through time, the atmosphere exerts a pressure of 1013 mbar on Earth's surface. Thus 1013 mbar is considered to be one atmosphere of pressure (1 atm). The pressure decreases as you rise up in the atmosphere (because there is less air above you) until, at the top of the atmosphere, the pressure reduces to zero. The actual pressure recorded at any point on the surface or in the atmosphere, however, can be highly variable under different conditions of elevation and temperature. So, for adjacent columns of air with similar volumes, the colder high-density air has a higher atmospheric pressure. Hence, as you see on weather charts, air flows from high pressure regions to regions of low pressure.

A CLOSER LOOK
The Relationships between Temperature, Pressure, and Volumes—The Ideal Gas Law

We can see from the text discussion that we can define specific relationships among the temperature (T), pressure (P), and volume (V) of a gas. (In this case, volume refers to the space occupied by a fixed mass of gas molecules; density is the inverse of volume for a fixed mass, so we need not consider it separately here.) First, we know that if the temperature is held constant, then an increase in gas pressure results in a decrease in volume, and a decrease in pressure results in an increase in volume. In other words, pressure is inversely proportional to volume: The product of pressure and volume is a constant. Mathematically, we can write

$$P_{initial}\, V_{initial} = P_{final}\, V_{final}, \textbf{(Boyle's law)}$$

where $P_{initial}V_{initial}$ is the product of the initial pressure and volume, and $P_{final}V_{final}$ is the product of the final (new) pressure and volume. This relationship, known as **Boyle's law,** was discovered in 1662 by the British chemist Robert Boyle.

If, instead, gas pressure is held constant, then we know that an increase in temperature results in an increase in volume and that a decrease in temperature results in a decrease in volume. In other words, volume is directly proportional to temperature: The quotient of volume and temperature is a constant. Mathematically, we can write

$$\frac{V_{initial}}{T_{initial}} = \frac{V_{final}}{T_{final}}, \textbf{(Charles's law)}$$

where $V_{initial}/T_{initial}$ is the quotient of the initial volume and temperature, V_{final}/T_{final} is the quotient of the final volume and temperature, and temperature is in kelvins. This relationship, known as **Charles's law,** was discovered in 1787 by the French physicist Jacques Charles.

All gases are found to behave the same way over a wide range of conditions, and Boyle's law and Charles's law can be combined to give the ideal gas equation:

$$PV = mRT$$

where m is the mass and R is a constant called the gas constant for 1 kg of gas (the value of R depends on the particular gas concerned).

It is important to note that these relationships apply to idealized gases, that is, gases in which there are no attractive forces between molecules. In reality, gases may not respond to environmental changes exactly as described here. Nevertheless, these relationships do represent a very close approximation of how gases behave.

From this discussion we can establish two important points that will help explain why air moves:

1. Air tends to move from an area of higher pressure to an area of lower pressure until the two pressures are equalized. In other words, air (wind) will move horizontally in the lower troposphere from higher to lower pressure. Pressure differences among air masses are typically related to the distribution of surface temperatures.

2. If an air mass is heated until its density is lower than that of its surroundings, the lower-density air will rise. This phenomenon is a form of convection. Conversely, if an air mass is cooled until its density is higher than that of the underlying air, it will sink. This phenomenon is referred to as **subsidence.**

The Driving Force: The Global Energy Distribution

The average global temperature is determined by the balance between the solar energy absorbed by Earth and the infrared radiation emitted to space. However, neither the radiation received from the Sun (our primary energy source) nor the infrared emission from Earth is distributed uniformly across Earth's surface. The incoming solar energy varies with latitude and with season, whereas the outgoing terrestrial radiation depends on the temperature of the surface and atmosphere at each location.

The distribution of the incoming solar radiation changes with latitude as a result of the change in surface area presented to the Sun's rays as Earth's surface curves

(Figure 1). The energy from the Sun radiates outward in all directions; however, by the time the Sun's rays reach Earth, they are essentially parallel to each other. This means that the flux of solar energy passing perpendicularly through the plane A-B in Figure 1 will be the same at any point. For example, the three "beams" in the diagram are equal in solar flux when they pass through the plane. Because of the curvature of Earth, however, when these beams reach the top of Earth's atmosphere, the same amount of light is spread over a much larger area at the poles than at the equator. Consequently, each square meter of surface receives proportionately less energy at the higher latitudes, and the incoming solar flux thus decreases from the equator toward the poles.

The solar radiation absorbed at the surface follows the same general pattern, although the actual amount absorbed varies with cloud cover and atmospheric absorption. This equator-to-pole gradient in the energy absorbed at the surface exerts a primary control on Earth's climate. Figure 2 shows this gradient (solid curve) as a function of latitude (i.e., the amount averaged around each latitude band). As we might expect from the previous discussion, the maximum absorbed solar energy is found in the tropics, and the available solar energy decreases rapidly as we move toward the poles. This gradient in absorbed solar energy is the single most important control on temperature. More energy is generally available at the equator than at the poles, so we can assume that temperatures should be highest in the tropics and lowest at high latitudes. Figure 2 also shows the latitudinal distribution of infrared radiation emitted from Earth to space (dashed curve). The higher emissions in the tropics are a result of the high surface temperatures there and the corre-

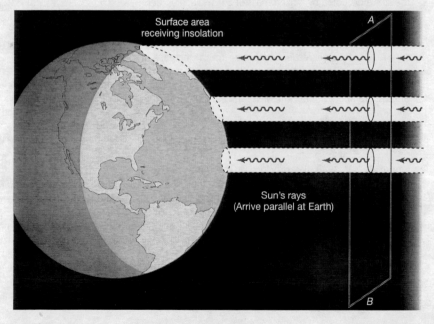

FIGURE 1 Variation of incoming solar energy with latitude. The radiation reaching Earth is spread over larger and larger areas as we move from the equator to the poles. Each square meter of the surface receives proportionately less energy as we move to higher latitudes. (*Source:* From R.W. Christopherson, *Geosystems: An Introduction to Physical Geography*, 3/e, 1997. Reprinted by permission of Prentice Hall, Upper Saddle River, N.J.)

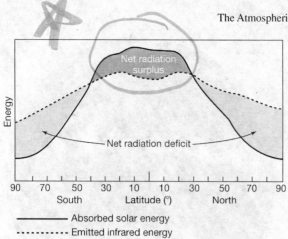

FIGURE 2   The distribution of absorbed solar and emitted infrared radiation with latitude. There is a surplus of energy in the tropics, where incoming radiation is greater than outgoing, and a deficit at high latitudes, where more radiation is emitted than is received.

spondingly high temperature in the middle troposphere, from whence the outgoing radiation is emitted.

The difference between the incoming solar radiation and the outgoing terrestrial radiation is referred to as *net radiation*. Referring again to Figure 2, note that the energy absorbed exceeds the energy emitted in the tropics (net radiation is positive); near the poles, the reverse is true (net radiation is negative). This distribution of available energy is a permanent feature of Earth's climate system. The gradient seems to imply that the tropics should get warmer while the poles get progressively colder. Clearly this does not happen; other processes must be operating to ensure an energy balance at each latitude. In reality, the latitudinal energy gradient produces atmospheric temperature and density differences that force the atmosphere to circulate, carrying warmer air toward the poles and colder air toward the equator. These circulations move energy from regions where there is a surplus to regions where there is a deficit. Most of what we experience as weather and climate is this

response of the atmosphere to the unequal latitudinal distributions of energy.

The General Circulation of the Atmosphere

From our description of the energy distribution and our discussion of how air movements occur, we can build a picture of what we would expect the global-scale circulation of the atmosphere to look like. This circulation involves several characteristic features that we will discuss in turn. Taken together, these circulation features represent a negative feedback loop as the atmosphere responds to the temperature gradient by transferring energy latitudinally to reduce the gradient and restore an energy balance. The continuous addition of energy from the sun of course means that the energy distribution is never balanced.

CONVERGENCE   We begin with the heating in the tropics. The large solar input to the tropics heats the surface (primarily ocean), which in turn heats the overlying air. As we saw earlier, when heated from below, air will rise by convection. The tropical air near the surface rises, creating a low-pressure region there. But we saw that air tends to move horizontally from an area of higher pressure to an area of lower pressure. Thus, the rising air is replaced by surface air moving equatorward into the region of low pressure from regions of higher pressure (Figure 3). The merging of air masses that are moving inward toward a low-pressure region is called **convergence**. The converging air masses that meet at the tropics and rise make up the **intertropical convergence zone (ITCZ).**

The surface heating produces evaporation in addition to convection. As the convecting air rises, it cools, and the evaporated water (water vapor) in the convecting column condenses to form clouds. As a consequence, the ITCZ is characterized by extensive areas of cloud cover and heavy precipitation. We talk more about evaporation, condensation, and rainfall later in the chapter.

DIVERGENCE   The top of the troposphere, located at about 12–15 km in the tropics, forms a barrier to further uplift.

FIGURE 3   Convergence, divergence, and the Hadley circulation in the tropics. There is a Hadley cell on either side of the intertropical convergence zone (ITCZ), located over the equator. Rising air in the ITCZ is replaced by inflowing air (convergence) at the surface. Outflowing air (divergence) in the upper troposphere sinks at about 30° N and 30° S, completing the circulations in the two cells.

FIGURE 4 Satellite image of the eastern Pacific and Central America. These images are obtained from geostationary satellites, which orbit over the equator at an altitude of about 35,000 km and at an orbital speed that keeps pace with Earth's rotation; thus the satellite appears to remain stationary over the same spot on the equator. This image was obtained by the National Oceanographic and Atmospheric Administration (NOAA) during Northern Hemisphere summer. A line of convective clouds marks the ITCZ just north of the equator. The clear areas to the north and south of the ITCZ mark the descending arms of the Hadley cells.   (*Source:* NOAA.)

Remember that temperatures generally increase in the stratosphere and that the higher temperatures produce a stable structure that limits convection from below. The air that rises in the ITCZ, upon reaching this barrier, is forced to diverge poleward. **Divergence,** in this case, refers to the movement of air outward from a region in the atmosphere. This poleward-moving air subsides at about 30° N and 30° S latitude, replacing the air that is moving equatorward at the surface (Figure 3). The air warms as it sinks, which prevents

FIGURE 5 Convective towers in the ITCZ. Solar heating evaporates large amounts of water from the tropical oceans. The air cools and condenses as it rises, releasing the energy used for evaporation as latent heat. The release of latent heat in these convective towers is the pump that drives the Hadley circulation. (*Source:* NASA.)

condensation from occurring and clouds from forming. As a result, these regions are characterized by clear skies and low rainfall amounts. If you check an atlas, you will find that such areas coincide with some of the world's largest deserts (e.g., the Sahara and Arabian deserts and the Great Australian Desert). The subsiding air also leads to an area of high pressure and divergence at the surface.

HADLEY CIRCULATION This pattern of air movement, with convergence occurring in the tropics and divergence and subsidence some 30° away in one large convection cell, is called **Hadley circulation.** This circulation pattern was named for George Hadley, the British meteorologist who first explained the phenomenon. The convection cells on either side of the equator, referred to as *Hadley cells*, represent the dominant north–south mode of circulation between 30° N and 30° S latitude. Note, however, that the Hadley cells—and the ITCZ—are not continuous around the globe. The circulation takes place in individual cells of rising and subsiding air, and the pattern is further broken up by land–ocean contrasts. The ITCZ is most obvious in the Atlantic and Pacific oceans and is readily observed in satellite images such as that shown in Figure 4. The large-scale circulation in Southeast Asia and the Indian Ocean is dominated by the monsoon, which is described later in this chapter.

The convection cells in the ITCZ result directly from surface heating in the tropical oceans. In fact, although solar heating provides the fuel for tropospheric circulation, the actual pump that drives the circulation is the release of latent heat during convection. The energy of solar radiation, used to evaporate water from the ocean surface, is converted to latent heat, and the latent heat is released to the atmosphere in huge towers of convective cloud clusters within the ITCZ (Figure 5). It is this release of latent heat that pumps the air around each Hadley cell.

FIGURE 6 Mixing of air in the midlatitudes. The lower-density warm air from the tropics rises above the colder air moving equatorward from high latitudes. These contrasting air masses do not mix very easily. This zone is characterized by large temperature contrasts over very short distances.

MIDLATITUDE AND HIGH-LATITUDE CIRCULATION

Thus far we have discussed the atmospheric circulation only between the equator and 30° N or S. What about atmospheric circulation from there to the poles? The very low temperatures at the poles, particularly in winter, result in increased air density near the surface and, thus, in higher pressures than occur in the tropics. The higher density and pressure lead to divergence and a general movement of cold air outward at the surface, that is, toward the equator. The divergence is accompanied by subsidence from above. The equatorward-moving cold air meets the warm air moving poleward from the subtropics, producing a zone of steep temperature gradients called the **polar front zone** at approximately 60° N and S latitude. The two air masses do not mix easily: The warm air is less dense than the cold air, which therefore sinks below the warm air when the two air masses meet (Figure 6). The polar front zone, therefore, slopes poleward with increasing altitude in the atmosphere. Note that, because of dynamic processes that come into play when air moves over a curved surface, this frontal zone forms a wavelike structure around the hemisphere.

The actual latitude at which the front is located, therefore, varies from place to place.

When we put Figures 3 and 6 together, we see an alternating pattern of northward- and southward-moving air at the surface (Figure 7). Such north–south movement is called *meridional* circulation. If we look at Figure 7 from above, we might expect to see a general pattern of surface winds such as those depicted in Figure 8. We would expect surface winds to blow out of the high-pressure zones at the poles and at about 30° N and S, and to blow toward the low-pressure zones at the equator and at about 60° N and S. The actual pattern, however, is more complicated because winds tend to blow in east–west directions as well. Indeed, the east–west motions are considerably greater than the north–south motions. We know that differences in solar heating cause the equator-to-pole movement we have been discussing. What causes the east–west movements?

The Coriolis Effect

East–west movements of surface winds are the result of the Coriolis effect. The **Coriolis effect** (named for Gaspard Gustav de Coriolis, the French mathematician who in 1835 proposed that the concept applies to surface winds) is the apparent tendency for a fluid (air or water) moving across Earth's surface to be deflected from its straight-line path. (Some texts refer to a *Coriolis force* in relation to this effect. This force, however, is only an apparent force due to the observer's frame of reference, not a real force due to an identifiable source, such as the gravitational pull of a planet.) Viewed from Earth, a north–south moving object appears to be deflected to the east or west. Viewed from space, the same object is in fact seen to move in a straight line. The apparent curve that we see is the result of our frame of reference—we normally view the object's movement from *within* the system.

FIGURE 7 The north–south (meridional) circulation of the troposphere. The tropical circulation is dominated by the Hadley circulation, whereas midlatitude circulation and weather are controlled by the location of the polar front zone and the mixing of cold polar air with warm air from the tropics.

FIGURE 8 A possible model of the surface winds obtained by plotting, on a globe, the pattern of surface winds that would be deduced from Figure 7. Surface winds blow out of the high-pressure zones at the poles and at 30° N and 30° S and blow toward the low-pressure zones at the equator and in the midlatitudes.

The Coriolis effect applies to any object moving on a rotating body. To visualize this, let us first consider Earth rotating on its axis. The two longitudinal lines in Figure 9a represent the distance moved in a given time interval, and the arrows represent the rotation speed of Earth's surface at different latitudes over that interval. The speed of rotation is greatest at the equator (approximately 464 m/sec), and it decreases as we move north—or south—until it becomes zero at the poles.

Now imagine an object, such as an air mass, that is apparently stationary at a point on Earth's surface. Although this air mass is not moving relative to the surface, it is traveling eastward at Earth's rotation rate for that location. (For example, an object that is stationary at any one of the points marked by the left-hand edges of the rotation arrows in Figure 9a would, to an observer in space, appear to

move along the arrow's path.) Because the rotation rate changes with latitude, an air mass moving northward from the equator—from point A to point B in Figure 9b—will appear to curve off to the right of its straight-line path, arriving at X rather than at B'. Why does this happen?

In the time it would take the air mass to travel from A to B, Earth rotates from A to A' (and B moves to B'). Remember that the air mass at A is moving not only northward but also eastward at Earth's speed of rotation (represented by the distance A-A'). As long as it is between the equator and point B, the air mass is moving from west to east faster than Earth is rotating at B. Thus, the air mass will "gain" on the ground below it and will arrive at point X instead of at B'. Although it is difficult to visualize, the air does in fact move in a straight line; if we were watching from space rather than from Earth, that is what we would see.

We have seen how an air mass (or any object) moving northward in the Northern Hemisphere is deflected to its right. Following the same reasoning, we can see that an air mass moving southward in the Northern Hemisphere also curves to its right (relative to the direction of initial movement), because now the air mass is moving eastward more slowly than Earth's surface immediately underneath. The easiest way to keep track of this is to think of the deflection direction relative to the direction of initial motion of the object—it is always to the right of the direction of initial motion in the Northern Hemisphere and to the left in the Southern Hemisphere.

What happens when the initial direction of movement is due east or due west? As it happens, the Coriolis effect still comes into play, but for a different reason. When an object is set in motion along a circular path, *centrifugal force*—another apparent force—tends to push the object away from the center of rotation. (This is the same phenomenon that forces your car off the road if you try to turn a corner too fast.) If an air mass in the Northern Hemisphere is moving eastward faster than Earth is rotating at that latitude, that air mass will experience an apparent centrifugal force that pushes it directly away from Earth's spin axis.

We can break down this apparent force into two components: one component that is acting perpendicular to the

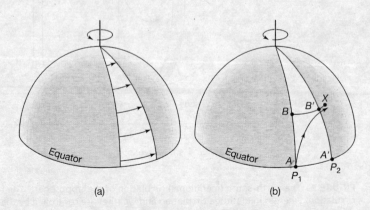

FIGURE 9 The Coriolis effect. (a) As Earth rotates, the speed of the surface is greatest at the equator and is zero at the poles. (b) At the equator, Earth has rotated from A to A'. Points A and B have moved to A' and B'. Air initially moving from A toward B would actually curve to the right and arrive at point X.

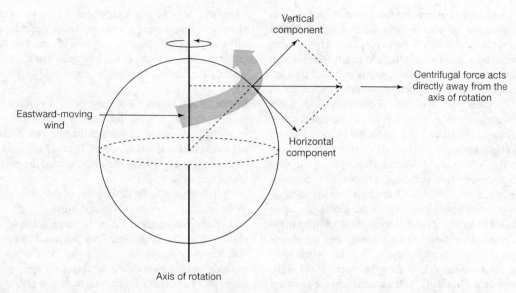

FIGURE 10 The Coriolis effect produced by the centrifugal force acting on eastward- or westward-moving winds.

surface, and one that is horizontal (parallel) to the surface (Figure 10). For an eastward-moving wind in the Northern Hemisphere, the horizontal component is to the south; the wind would curve to the south, or to the right. For a westward-moving wind, the horizontal component is to the north; the wind still curves to the right. In the Southern Hemisphere, the effects would be opposite: Both eastward-moving and westward-moving winds would curve to the left.

Although these descriptions of the deflection effect for north–south and east–west moving objects appear to be very different, mathematically the deflections are identical, and both are referred to simply as the Coriolis effect. The Coriolis effect increases as the speed of the object increases. And whereas the speed at which Earth's surface is moving due to its rotation is zero at the poles and a maximum at the equator, the Coriolis effect is zero at the equator and increases with latitude. The only place on Earth's surface where the Coriolis effect does not come into play is at the equator. An air mass moving eastward or westward around the equator is not deflected from its original path. Such an air mass is not changing latitude, so there is no Coriolis effect due to the difference in rotation rate with latitude. Nor is there a horizontal component to the centrifugal force, so again there is no Coriolis effect.

Distribution of Surface Winds

We can now modify the simplistic pattern of northward-moving and southward-moving surface winds in Figure 8 to obtain the more realistic pattern of surface winds shown in Figure 11. There the winds are deflected to the right and left of the paths of initial motion in the Northern and Southern hemispheres, respectively. This deflection of the winds due to the Coriolis effect gives rise to easterly winds at high latitudes. Meteorologists refer to winds in

terms of the direction from which they blow. In other words, an "easterly" wind is a wind that blows from east to west. The midlatitudes are characterized by westerly flow, and the tropics by easterly winds called the *northeast* and *southeast trade winds.* Winds at the equator tend to be highly variable in direction. This region where winds are light and frequently change direction is referred to as the *doldrums.*

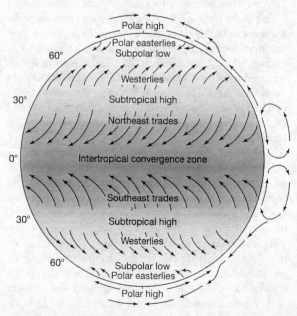

FIGURE 11 The pattern of surface winds. This shows the same general pattern of winds as Figure 8, but the wind directions have been changed to include the deflection due to the Coriolis effect. (*Source:* From T. McKnight, *Physical Geography: A Landscape Appreciation,* 6/e, 1999. Reprinted by permission of Prentice Hall, Upper Saddle River, N.J.)

Considerations of pressure differences, buoyancy, and the Coriolis effect have led us to a good first approximation of the general circulation of the troposphere. This pattern, however, is still a little too simplistic. In reality the indicated winds, for example, do not blow continuously, and they are not continuous around the globe. As we noted earlier, uplift in the ITCZ takes place in clusters of convective cells rather than in two giant cells, one on each side of the equator. The rising air moves poleward and, under the influence of the Coriolis effect, turns to the right in the Northern Hemisphere (and to the left in the Southern Hemisphere). It thus becomes a westerly flow in the upper troposphere. Some of this air subsides near 30° N or S latitude to form the subtropical high-pressure belt (Figure 11), but the subsidence too is concentrated in localized areas. The locations of these high-pressure systems vary with season, although they are always found in these approximate locations. The trade winds blow from the equatorward side of these semipermanent high-pressure systems. Similarly, poleward-moving air from the subtropical high-pressure zone curves due to the Coriolis effect, producing a generally westerly flow in the midlatitudes. The actual flow pattern, however, is highly variable from day to day.

The pressure and wind patterns in the midlatitudes depend on the location of the subtropical highs as well as on the distribution and movement of temporary areas of high or low pressure that form in association with the steep temperature gradients in the polar front zone. Small areas of low pressure (on the order of 1000 km wide) form in this zone in part due to the surface-temperature gradient, but also because of dynamic processes occurring higher in the troposphere. As air blows into these regions, it curves to the right (in the Northern Hemisphere), producing a localized circular flow pattern referred to as *cyclonic flow*. Air flowing out of a high-pressure region (referred to as an *anticyclone*) will also curve to the right in the Northern Hemisphere, creating an *anticyclonic, or clockwise, flow*. (The direction of air flow around cyclones and anticyclones is reversed in the Southern Hemisphere.)

Low-pressure systems that form outside the tropics are referred to as *extratropical cyclones*. The circular flow mixes warm air from the equatorward side of the system with cooler air from the high latitudes. As we noted earlier, the warm and cool air masses do not mix easily; hence these systems are characterized by extensive uplift as the warmer, less dense air rises above the cooler and denser air mass. As we will see later in the chapter, this rising air results in the formation of rain or snow. These circulation features move along the polar front, bringing low pressure as they move over a region, which is then replaced by higher pressure as they move past. These transient high-pressure and low-pressure systems are characteristic features of midlatitude climates and account for much of the day-to-day variability in weather in these regions. At high latitudes, the polar easterlies are most clearly developed in winter (when the coldest surface temperatures occur and

when this area of low temperatures is most extensive). However, low-pressure systems from the midlatitudes often migrate into the polar regions in summer, breaking down the surface high-pressure systems and disrupting the easterly flow.

UPPER-LEVEL FLOW Referring back to Figures 7 and 8, we see that the pressure distribution at the surface results in alternating regions of poleward and equatorward moving air. At higher levels, however, Figure 7 suggests that all of the air is moving from the ITCZ toward the poles. Why the difference?

Think back to the description of the latitudinal energy balance and the discussion of pressure, temperature, and volume relationships. On the large scale, we have a planet where the troposphere has warm air in the tropics and relatively cooler air at the poles. As the warmer air expands and the cooler air contracts, then the depth of the troposphere changes with latitude (which is also suggested by Figure 7). Consequently, we have the situation shown in Figure 12a. As the troposphere is thicker in the tropics than at the poles, then the change in pressure with height must be slower in the tropics, as shown in Figure 12b. If we join these tropical and polar pressure surfaces, we get the situation shown in Figure 12c. Notice we have given a slight slope to the pressure surfaces to reflect the decreasing temperatures toward higher latitudes.

Now, away from the surface where local temperature and pressure changes can be large, if we take any line of constant altitude in the diagram (e.g., A-A' or B-B') we see that at any point along these lines the pressure is always higher on the equatorward side than the poleward side. Air will flow down the pressure gradient from high to low pressure and, on average, the flow at higher levels in the troposphere is from the tropics to the pole. You can imagine that the wind speed will be greatest where the pressure gradient is the steepest, which happens in the upper troposphere in the midlatitudes. Belts of high wind speeds that we see in this location are referred to as *jet streams* (indicated by the J in Figure 12c).

What if we take a horizontal view? We know that if the air is moving poleward, and thus changing latitude, it must come under the influence of the Coriolis effect. Consequently, the air will curve to the right in the Northern Hemisphere and to the left in the Southern Hemisphere. In other words, there will be a westerly component to the flow in both cases. The force that is pushing the air down the pressure gradient is referred to as the pressure gradient force. This force is balanced by the Coriolis effect—such that the air actually flows at right angles to the gradient and the resulting movement is referred to as the *geostrophic wind* (Figure 13). Other forces (centripetal and centrifugal forces) come into play if the air is following a curved trajectory around centers of higher or lower pressure, where the greater the curvature, the more the flow departs from being geostrophic. Friction also plays a role, with its greatest effect being close to the surface. Friction between

A CLOSER LOOK

How Hurricanes (Tropical Cyclones) Work

Tropical cyclones (also called *hurricanes* when they occur in the Atlantic and *typhoons* when they occur in the western Pacific oceans) are strong low-pressure centers accompanied by powerful, and sometimes devastating, winds. These storms begin their lives as relatively mild, low-pressure centers overlying tropical oceans. Air from the surrounding higher-pressure regions moves inward toward the center of low pressure—at which point several different forces come into play. The flow around a hurricane is determined by the pressure gradient force and centripetal acceleration, balanced by the Coriolis effect, causing the flow to be to the right of the pressure gradient in the Northern Hemisphere and to the left in the Southern (see Box Figure 1). Note that because tornadoes are too small for the Coriolis effect to come into play, tornadoes can, in fact, rotate in either direction. The balance of forces causes the air to spiral inward in a counterclockwise direction (Northern Hemisphere) or a clockwise direction (Southern Hemisphere). The swirling winds increase the rate of evaporation of seawater, adding large amounts of moisture to the air. Because the air is converging near the surface within the hurricane, it rises in the clouds circling the storm (except, curiously, in the very center—the eye—where the air is descending). The rising air cools, causing this moisture to condense as rain and, at the same time, liberating its latent heat. This strengthens the storm, speeding up the winds and drawing in more air from outside the storm; this air rises in the clouds and the process continues in a positive feedback loop. As long as the system remains above warm tropical waters, it acts as a self-sustaining heat engine. Eventually, though, it will either move poleward, where the surface water is colder, or it will encounter land. In either case, the warm ocean water that was providing it with energy is no longer present, and the hurricane dissipates. The storm can also weaken over warm water if another weather system overpowers it.

Several conditions are necessary in order for tropical cyclones to form. One, already noted, is that they require warm ocean temperatures—generally in excess of 26 to 27°C. Because the Coriolis effect is necessary to cause the air to start to turn, then storms can't form within about 5° latitude of the equator (remember the Coriolis effect is zero at the equator and increases toward the poles). There needs to be low vertical wind shear. Wind shear occurs when the horizontal winds higher in the troposphere are moving with a much different speed or direction than the winds nearer the surface. When this happens, it tends to tear the storm apart. It also helps to have a rapid decrease in temperature with height, producing positive buoyancy and increasing convection, and also to have relatively high water vapor content in the lower and middle levels of the atmosphere. This keeps the air near the saturation vapor pressure as it rises and maximizes the amount of latent heat release (see the discussion of vapor pressure later in this chapter). Tropical cyclones also need some initial atmospheric disturbance to get them started. This can arise in various ways, such as convergence in the intertropical convergence zone, old frontal boundaries that have moved down over the subtropical oceans and, in the case of Atlantic hurricanes, the initial storm development can be caused by small disturbances in the easterly flow off Africa (referred to as easterly waves). Conditions are best for hurricanes in late summer and fall when the ITCZ has moved furthest from the equator and when sea-surface temperatures are at their warmest. Apart from the Coriolis effect, however, all these other characteristics can vary over time (from year to year or over longer time periods) causing variations in the number and intensity of hurricanes that occur.

BOX FIGURE 1 Schematic diagram of a Northern Hemisphere hurricane. The circle represents an isobar (a line of constant pressure). The arrow labeled PF represents the pressure force; the arrow labeled CF represents the Coriolis force. The winds blow counterclockwise turning to the right as they move from high to low pressure.

the moving air and the surface reduces the wind speed and counters some of the Coriolis effect. In this case, rather than flowing at right angles to the gradient (like the geostrophic wind), the air flows down the gradient at an angle less than 90°. This is why surface winds spiral into low-pressure centers and out of high-pressure centers rather than circling them (which would be the case if the flow was geostrophic). This spiraling effect is clearly seen in Figure 20.

Moving back to the upper troposphere, where friction is not an important issue, we see that the flow is close to being geostrophic. It flows normal to the gradient, but it follows a wavelike path around the globe (Figure 14). For dynamical reasons that are more complex than we want to get into here, when a fluid moves over a rotating surface, it follows a wavelike trajectory—in this case curving toward the equator and back toward the poles in several large waves that extend around each hemisphere. These waves were first described mathematically by Carl G. Rossby in 1938, and are now referred to as *Rossby waves*. The number of waves, their location, and how well developed they are varies from day to day. For those of us living

P_g = Pressure Gradient Force
C = Coriolis Force
V_G = Geostrophic Wind

FIGURE 13 The geostrophic wind results from the balance of the pressure gradient force and the force due to the Coriolis effect. The dashed lines are isobars—lines of equal pressure. The pressure gradient force (P_g) acts perpendicular to the isobars in the direction of the low pressure. This is balanced by the force due to the Coriolis effect (C), resulting in the geostrophic wind (V_G) blowing parallel to the isobars and to the right of the pressure gradient force (in the Northern Hemisphere).

FIGURE 12 Pressure change with height in the troposphere. The higher temperatures in the tropics causes the air to expand, raising the height of the tropopause compared to the poles (a). As the atmospheric pressure is the same in both regions, the decrease in pressure with height must be slower in the tropics compared to the poles (b). If the tropical and polar pressure surfaces are joined, we see the steepest pressure gradients in the midlatitudes. At any height in the atmosphere, the pressure is higher in the tropics than it is at the poles (c). As wind speeds are greatest where the pressure gradient is steepest, the highest wind speeds (the jet streams) will be found high in the troposphere in the midlatitudes—the *J* in Figure 12c.

in the midlatitudes, these waves steer the low- and high-pressure systems that produce our day-to-day weather. This is why television weather forecasts often show you the locations of the jet streams—as they control the path that low-pressure systems will follow.

SEASONAL VARIABILITY The simple pattern of global winds shown in Figure 11 is also modified by seasonal variations. As well as changing with latitude, the distribution

of solar energy varies with the seasons. Figure 15 shows the seasonal pattern of Earth's orbit around the Sun. The time when Earth is closest to the Sun is referred to as *perihelion;* Earth is farthest from the Sun at *aphelion.* This difference in distance from the Sun affects the seasonal distribution of temperature. More important to seasonality is Earth's *tilt*, or **obliquity.** Obliquity refers to the angle of Earth's spin axis relative to a line drawn perpendicular to the plane of the planet's orbit around the Sun. Each planet has a different angle of tilt. Earth's axis is tilted 23.5° from the perpendicular. On human time scales, the obliquity remains constant as Earth revolves around the Sun (Figure 15). On somewhat longer time scales, the obliquity varies by about ±1°.

For six months of each year, the Northern Hemisphere faces the Sun and the Southern Hemisphere faces away; for the other six months, it is the Southern Hemisphere that faces the Sun while the Northern Hemisphere faces away. The hemisphere that faces the Sun receives much more solar energy than does the other hemisphere. It is this factor that determines the seasons. Consider the June 21 solstice (the day with the longest period of sunlight in the Northern Hemisphere) in Figure 15. Imagine Earth spinning around its axis. The North Pole will remain in sunlight the whole time, while the South Pole will remain in darkness. The opposite is true at the solstice on December 21 (the day of shortest sunlight duration in the Northern Hemisphere). The result is six months of sunshine and six months of darkness at the poles.

The greatest heating occurs where the Sun is directly overhead. Due to Earth's obliquity, the latitude at which this occurs varies continuously throughout the year, from 23.5° S (called the Tropic of Capricorn) on December 21 to 23.5° N (called the Tropic of Cancer) on June 21. There

FIGURE 14 Northern Hemisphere mean January 300-mbar geopotential heights. The heights are in decameters (1 decameter = 10 m). Essentially, the map shows the height of the 300-mbar surface. The surface slopes down from the tropics to the Arctic and follows a wavelike structure around the hemisphere. (*Source:* Map provided by the NOAA-CIRES Climate Diagnostics Center, Boulder, Colorado, from its website, http://www.cdc.noaa.gov/)

are also two days on which the Sun is directly overhead at the equator—the *vernal equinox,* March 20, and the *autumnal equinox,* September 22. On these dates, daytime and nighttime are equal in length. (These dates vary by a day or so because the calendar is adjusted every four years to reconcile it with Earth's revolution around the Sun.) Notice, though, that within a narrow band near the equator the Sun is always close to being overhead. Hence there is a large input of solar radiation to the tropics at all times. The difference between daytime and nighttime temperatures in this region, in fact, is usually much greater than the seasonal difference there.

The seasonal variability in incoming energy shifts the atmospheric circulation patterns northward and southward as the seasons change (Figure 16). The hemisphere experiencing summer has less of a temperature gradient between the tropics and the pole than does the opposite hemisphere. The fact that the Sun shines continuously for six months at each pole compensates for the fact that the poles do not receive as much solar energy per unit area as do the tropics. This reduced temperature gradient weakens the strength of the atmospheric circulation. At the same time, because the Sun is directly overhead somewhere away from the equator, the maximum solar energy is directed somewhere poleward. Consequently, the steepest temperature gradients are shifted toward the poles, and the circulation patterns are also shifted poleward. In the winter

FIGURE 15 The seasons. The seasons are controlled by Earth's obliquity and Earth's orbit around the Sun. The hemisphere that is "tilted" toward the Sun experiences summer while it is winter for the hemisphere that is "tilted" away from the Sun. The equinoxes (when the Sun is directly overhead at the equator) mark the transition seasons: fall and spring. (*Source:* From T. McKnight, *Physical Geography: A Landscape Appreciation*, 6/e, 1999. Reprinted by permission of Prentice Hall, Upper Saddle River, N.J.)

FIGURE 16 Seasonal migration of the atmospheric circulation patterns. The ITCZ is found in the summer hemisphere, where the circulation is weaker and the patterns are shifted toward the pole. The subtropical high-pressure cells that mark the descending arms of the Hadley circulations are denoted by H.

hemisphere (with six months of darkness at the pole), the equator-to-pole temperature gradient is much stronger and the steepest gradients are shifted equatorward. As a result, the atmospheric circulation is more intense and the circulation patterns are shifted toward the equator.

The ITCZ also moves northward and southward as a result of these seasonal shifts in insolation. The ITCZ will reach its maximum northward location late in the Northern Hemisphere summer. (There is a time lag in all of these shifts between the time that the solar heating occurs and the resulting shift in the circulation pattern.) It will then migrate southward, crossing the equator in the fall and reaching its most southern location late in winter (Southern Hemisphere summer). The upper tropospheric circulation is similarly affected, with more intense wind speeds in winter and the jet streams shifting north and south with the seasons. Note that when the ITCZ is located over the equator, the poleward-moving air in the upper troposphere produces westerly winds in both hemispheres. As the ITCZ shifts northward, however, the southward-moving air will turn to the right, producing easterly winds in the equatorial region, before curving back to the west when it reaches the Southern Hemisphere. The same thing will happen in reverse when the ITCZ is south of the equator. So, while most of the upper tropospheric flow is westerly, there are frequently narrow bands of easterly winds in the equatorial regions.

GLOBAL DISTRIBUTIONS OF TEMPERATURE AND RAINFALL

In the first part of this chapter, we described some of the main features of the global-scale atmospheric circulation. For the remainder of the chapter, we look at the effect this circulation has on other parts of the Earth system, specifically, the global temperature and rainfall distributions.

As we have learned, the ultimate cause of the atmospheric circulation is the distribution of available energy. More interesting for our purposes is the fact that the interaction between temperature and circulation is not a one-way process. As we indicated earlier, the circulation itself is an important component of Earth's thermoregulatory system, transporting energy (heat) from areas where there is a surplus to areas where there is a deficit.

The transport of water is also strongly affected by the atmospheric circulation. The distribution of water about the globe is important in that organisms require a sufficient supply of water to maintain life. That distribution is also important for the transport of dissolved materials. As we will soon see, evaporation and precipitation are strongly influenced by temperature and, therefore, by the distribution of energy. Furthermore, the transport of water in its various forms (liquid, water vapor, and ice) also modifies the temperature distribution by affecting the radiation budget and thus feeds back to affect the circulation. Hence, we see that temperature, precipitation, and the atmospheric circulation are all closely linked and that interactions and feedbacks exist among all three of these components of Earth's climate.

Land–Ocean Contrasts

Beyond the latitudinal distribution of energy, global temperature patterns are also strongly influenced by the distribution of land and ocean. Recall that the albedo of the ocean surface is considerably lower than the albedo of most land surfaces. In consequence, oceans absorb more of the available solar energy than do land surfaces at the same latitude.

Land and ocean surfaces also behave very differently in what they do with that energy. An ocean surface rapidly transfers heat downward by turbulent mixing and to the atmosphere above by convection. Part of the contrast between land and ocean is due to differences in their thermal properties. The land surface rapidly loses heat to the atmosphere by convection, but it transfers heat downward relatively slowly by conduction. How easily this transfer occurs depends on the physical and chemical properties of the material; the rate at which this occurs is described by its *thermal conductivity*. More formally, thermal conductivity is the rate at which heat energy passes through a column of material that has a temperature gradient along the column of 1 K, or 1°C, per meter. Water has a high thermal conductivity, whereas land surfaces have low thermal conductivities. Furthermore, we can consider the *heat capacity* of the two types of surfaces. Heat capacity at constant volume is the energy required to raise the temperature of a unit mass of a substance by 1 K or 1°C without changing its volume. In other words, heat capacity is a measure of how much energy must be added to an object to change its temperature. The heat capacity of water is about three to four times that of dry soil. Thus, the input of a given amount of energy will raise land temperatures much more than it will raise sea-surface temperatures.

More important is that the ocean surface transfers heat rapidly downward by turbulent mixing. The surface layers of the ocean are well mixed; when the ocean surface is heated, the heat is mixed downward within the surface layers. The amount of material that must warm (or cool) is very large, so the temperature change is very slow. A further factor is differential absorption of the two surfaces. Whereas all the solar radiation falling on the land surface is reflected or absorbed right at the surface, some of the solar radiation falling on the ocean

penetrates and is absorbed below the surface. Hence, energy is transferred downward even more rapidly in water than on land.

THE SEA BREEZE Putting all this together, we see that with equal amounts of incoming energy, land surfaces will heat up much more rapidly than do ocean surfaces but will also cool down much more rapidly once the input of energy is reduced. Land surfaces heat up quickly during the day and cool quickly at night, whereas ocean surfaces warm slowly in the day, and the temperature drops very little at night. The sea breeze that occurs near coastlines is a direct result of this diurnal variability. The heating of the land surface during the day warms the overlying air and gives rise to small areas of low pressure and uplift; cooler temperatures over the ocean result in relatively higher pressures and subsidence of the cooled air above (Figure 17). Air flows down the pressure gradient (from the area of higher pressure to the area of lower pressure), creating onshore flow from ocean to land. At night this temperature structure breaks down, and the atmospheric circulation weakens. If the land cools sufficiently, the circulation pattern may reverse.

CONTINENTALITY We can see the same effect on a larger scale in terms of seasonal climate variability. As we noted earlier, the seasonal variation over midlatitudes and high latitudes is much greater than in the tropics. This variability is also much greater over land surfaces than over the oceans because of their different thermal characteristics. This property is referred to as *continentality*. The more continental the climate, the more it is characterized by seasonal temperature extremes. Land surfaces are much warmer than ocean surfaces in summer and much colder in winter. The effect of continentality on global temperatures is visible in Figure 18c. The greatest seasonal variability

FIGURE 17 The sea breeze. The heating of the land during the day causes localized convection with low pressure at the surface. This convection establishes a pressure gradient from the ocean toward the land that results in onshore wind. At night, the rapid cooling of the land (relative to the ocean) causes this circulation to break down and may even reverse the flow, causing the wind to blow from the land toward the water. (*Source:* From T. McKnight, *Physical Geography: A Landscape Appreciation*, 6/e, 1999. Reprinted by permission of Prentice Hall, Upper Saddle River, N.J.)

is found in the interior of large continental masses, and the lowest variability is over the tropical oceans. The oceans provide a moderating effect in coastal regions that reduces the temperature extremes. The temperature difference between ocean and land surfaces also affects the mean sea-level pressure distribution (again feeding back to affect the circulation). Figur 19 shows the average atmospheric pressure that would be found over land if the land surfaces were at sea level. In Northern Hemisphere winter (Figure 19a), the very cold surface temperatures of interior North America and Asia cool the lower layers of the atmosphere, producing high surface pressures over those landmasses. The North Atlantic and North Pacific are characterized by low-pressure zones produced by the low-pressure systems forming along the steep temperature gradient in the polar front zone. In summer this gradient decreases (Figure 19b). The low-pressure zones are less well developed and are displaced poleward, the subtropical highs expand, and the continental regions of high pressure are replaced by regions of low pressure.

The Southern Hemisphere (Figures 19a and 19b), with its huge expanse of ocean and very little land area, presents a less complicated picture. The midlatitude air flow is much more *zonal*—that is, the air circulation more closely follows lines of latitude—than it is in the Northern Hemisphere. The seasonal temperature change causes the air flow patterns to shift north and south slightly and causes pressure gradients to change, but the distribution of land and oceans produces much less variability of winds around the Southern Hemisphere than around the Northern Hemisphere.

We see, therefore, that the broad pattern of global temperatures is determined by the latitudinal distribution of net radiation, so higher temperatures occur in the tropics and lower temperatures at the poles. This distribution varies with season such that the seasonal range of temperatures is slight in the tropics and increases poleward. Beyond this, we see from the preceding discussion that the seasonal variability is strongly modified by land–ocean contrasts, the interior of continents having a much greater seasonal range than do coastal locations.

As we noted earlier, the circulation systems described here are very generalized; they represent averaged conditions with much of the day-to-day variability

(a)

FIGURE 18 Global temperature distributions in degrees Celsius for (a) January, (b) July, and (c) the annual range (difference between summer and winter).   (*Source:* From R. W. Christophersón, *Geosystems: An Introduction to Physical Geography*, 3/e, 1997. Reprinted by permission of Prentice Hall, Upper Saddle River, N.J.)

(b)

(c)

FIGURE 18 *continued*

(a)

(b)

FIGURE 19   Average sea-level pressure patterns: (a) January and (b) July. Units are in millibars (mbar), where one atmosphere (atm) equals 1.013 bar (1013 mbar). Low-pressure areas are designated by L and high-pressure areas by H.   (*Source:* From R. W. Christopherson, *Geosystems: An Introduction to Physical Geography*, 3/e, 1997. Reprinted by permission of Prentice Hall, Upper Saddle River, N.J.)

removed. On any particular day, the circulation and the resulting wind field will be much more complex. As an example, Figure 20 shows the surface wind field over the Pacific Ocean measured by a satellite-borne radar system on a September day. The white arrows show the wind direction. The ITCZ is clearly seen where the northeast and southeast trade winds converge just north of the equator. Note that the Southern Hemisphere trade winds are blowing from the southeast—as they move equatorward toward the ITCZ they curve to the left. As they cross the equator

FIGURE 20 [See color section] The surface wind field over the Pacific Ocean. The data were derived from a satellite-borne radar system and the white arrows show the direction of air movement at 00Z on August 1, 1999. (*Source:* NASA/Jet Propulsion Laboratory.)

(because the ITCZ is located north of the equator at this point) they move northward and, as they move away from the equator and come under the influence of the Coriolis effect again, they recurve toward the right. This is more apparent in the eastern Pacific. The subtropical high-pressure cells are also well depicted—you can clearly see the air spiraling out from the center of the cells.

MONSOONS The most extreme consequence of the seasonal variability due to differential heating of land and ocean surfaces is the monsoon regime of Southeast Asia. The **monsoon** is a seasonal reversal in the surface winds. In summer the large Asian landmass, with its high elevations in the Tibetan Plateau of central Asia, causes high surface temperatures, low atmospheric pressures, and intense convection of air above the surface. The rising air is replaced by air moving in from the high-pressure region over the Indian Ocean to the south (Figure 21a). The moist air drawn in from the Indian Ocean cools as it rises above the mountains of southwest India and over the Himalayas. In both instances the rising air produces clouds and heavy rainfall (the monsoon rains). In winter the pattern reverses: High elevations and persistent snow cover enhance the continentality, producing even lower temperatures. This results in high atmospheric pressure and subsidence of air over the continent and a southward flow of air

(Figure 21b). A similar feature, but on a much smaller scale, is found in the southwestern United States, where a "monsoonal" flow from July through mid-September brings moist air in from the Gulf of California and the eastern Pacific.

Global Precipitation Patterns

In addition to transporting energy, the circulation of the troposphere also involves the movement of material across Earth's surface. We can imagine how effective the atmosphere is at transporting material from the fact that pollution from midlatitude industrial sources has been found on both polar ice caps.

The most important substance transported in the atmosphere is water, in the form of water vapor and clouds. Both water vapor and clouds are important for several reasons: They play a dominant role in the global energy balance, they are a significant factor in determining the distribution of freshwater around the globe, and they are highly variable in time and space (making them difficult to predict).

THE GLOBAL HYDROLOGIC CYCLE Water is the most important chemical compound not only in the atmospheric circulation but also in the entire Earth system. The human

(a)   (b)

FIGURE 21 The monsoon flow over southeast Asia. (a) Summer heating of the Tibetan Plateau produces intense convection and low surface pressures, drawing in moist air from the Indian Ocean to the south. (b) The reverse occurs in winter, when low temperatures and extensive snow cover on the plateau produce high surface pressures, subsidence, and outflowing air. (*Source:* From R. W. Christopherson, *Geosystems: An Introduction to Physical Geography*, 3/e, 1997. Reprinted by permission of Prentice Hall, Upper Saddle River, N.J.)

body is 60% water by weight, and all organisms require some water in order to live. From space we see that Earth is a planet dominated by water (Figure 22). Seventy percent of Earth's surface is covered by oceans. The poles are encased in extensive sheets of ice that either float on the surface of the ocean (*sea ice*) or form glaciers several kilometers thick over land. Clouds, which are made of condensed water vapor, swirl across the surface, continuously changing in size, shape, and location but always covering about 50% of the globe at any time. The water that exists in gaseous form (water vapor) also varies in amount across the globe—from near zero over the ice caps to about 7% in the tropics.

Water is unique in the Earth system for a variety of reasons, not the least of which is that it is the only naturally occurring substance that can exist in all three phases (solid, liquid, and gas) at the temperatures found on Earth's surface. Because water changes so readily from one phase to another, it cycles easily among all the system components. In so doing, water plays a vital role in many Earth system processes. Changing from a solid to a liquid or from a liquid to a gas requires a large addition of energy. That energy is stored in the water molecule in the form of latent heat. The **latent heat of vaporization,**

FIGURE 22 [See color section] Earth, viewed from space at about 37,000 km (23,000 mi), is dominated by water. (*Source:* NASA Headquarters.)

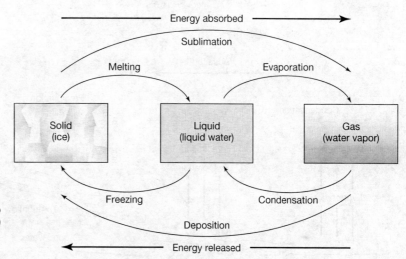

FIGURE 23 Schematic diagram of the different phases of water. Energy is absorbed as water changes from a solid to a gas (moving left to right in the diagram) and is released as water changes from a gas to a solid (from right to left).

is the energy needed to convert liquid water to water vapor, and is 2260 kJ/kg at 100°C. (This much energy must be added to each kilogram of boiling water to convert it to water vapor.) When the process is reversed and the water changes from a gas back to a liquid, this same amount of energy is released to the environment (Figure 23). The **latent heat of fusion,** or the energy needed to convert ice to liquid water, equals 335 kJ/kg at 0°C. When the process is reversed and the water changes from a liquid back to a solid, this amount of energy is again released to the environment. To raise the temperature of liquid water from 0 to 100°C requires 419 kJ/kg. To convert ice to water vapor thus takes 3014 kJ/kg (= 2260 + 419 + 335).

These values apply to water at sea level, and they will vary slightly as atmospheric pressure changes. If these conversion processes occur in different locations, then there is a net transfer of energy from one place to another. Therefore, the distribution and movement of water in its various phases has important consequences for the transfer of energy and the global pattern of surface temperatures.

Water vapor and carbon dioxide are the most important of the present-day greenhouse gases. Without them, much of Earth would be too cold to support life. We saw also that clouds have a major impact both on Earth's albedo and on the emission of terrestrial radiation to space. Water plays a vital role in breaking down rocks (weathering) and in transporting essential nutrients throughout the Earth system. *Water, in all its phases, is the primary medium by which energy and matter are circulated among the Earth system components.*

Water in the Earth system is concentrated in several major reservoirs:

1. The oceans, where the water exists in the form of seawater;

2. The land surface, in the form of ice sheets, glaciers, snow, lakes, and rivers, and the land subsurface, in the form of groundwater; and

3. The atmosphere, in the form of water vapor and clouds.

These reservoirs and the pattern of water storage and movement throughout the system comprise the global **hydrologic cycle** (Figure 24a). Most of Earth's water— about 97%—is stored in the first reservoir, the oceans (Figure 24b). Almost 3% is on or in the second reservoir, land. Of this amount, three-quarters is trapped in the polar ice sheets (in Greenland and Antarctica). Should the Greenland ice sheet melt, it would raise the global sea level by about 7 m; should all of Antarctica melt, the sea level would rise by about 57 m. A small amount of water exists in mountain glaciers as well. Most of the remainder occurs as **groundwater,** or water that penetrates through soil and rock and collects below the surface. Water stored in rivers, lakes, and the soil accounts for less than 1% of all the water found on land. Almost two-thirds of this amount is stored in lakes and reservoirs, about one-third occurs in the soil, and a tiny fraction occurs in rivers. The third reservoir, the atmosphere, contains less than 0.001% of all the water on Earth. Figure 24b also gives the annual exchange of water among the three major reservoirs.

PRECIPITATION AND SATURATION VAPOR PRESSURE. The transfer of water between the land–ocean surface and the atmosphere takes place through evaporation and *precipitation.* Precipitation occurs when atmospheric water vapor condenses to form small droplets of liquid water. When the water droplets reach sufficient size, they fall because of gravity. If they do not evaporate before they reach Earth's surface, we experience them as rain. If atmospheric temperatures are below freezing, the droplets fall instead as snow or sleet.

FIGURE 24 The global hydrologic cycle. (a) Schematic diagram of how water, in its various phases, is stored and moved throughout the Earth system. (b) The sizes of the major reservoirs of water and the rate at which water is transferred between them. (*Source:* From T. McKnight, *Physical Geography: A Landscape Appreciation*, 6/e, 1999. Reprinted by permission of Prentice Hall, Upper Saddle River, N.J.)

One way of expressing the amount of water vapor present in the atmosphere is to measure the contribution that water vapor makes to the atmospheric pressure. Air is composed of numerous different gases. Each gas exerts its own pressure. What is measured as the atmospheric pressure is the sum of all the **partial pressures** of the individual gases—that is, the pressure each gas would exert if it were the only gas present. The pressure exerted by water vapor is referred to as the *vapor pressure*.

Imagine a body of water. Water molecules at the surface that have a little more energy than do their neighbors can overcome the attractive forces that hold the molecules together and thereby escape as water vapor molecules into the air above. This is the process of **evaporation.** Some of these water vapor molecules that subsequently come in contact with the water surface would lose energy, be "caught" by the liquid water molecules, and become liquid water again. This is the process of **condensation.** Once the rate of condensation equals the evaporation rate—that is, as many molecules leave the gas as are added to it—the gas is at equilibrium. At this point, the vapor pressure of water is referred to as the *saturation vapor pressure*. In this scenario, the saturation vapor pressure depends only on the rate at which molecules are transferred from liquid to gas and back again. This rate depends on the energy of the molecules, which means it depends on temperature. (Recall that the higher the energy, the higher the temperature.) Therefore, as temperature increases, the saturation vapor pressure increases.

Figure 25 is a graph of saturation vapor pressure versus temperature for water. In general, we can think of clouds as forming when the air is at the saturation vapor pressure for water. Further evaporation adds water vapor molecules to the air, where they condense to form water droplets in clouds. When these droplets become large enough to overcome the upward motion of the air, they fall as precipitation. Assume that an air mass is at the temperature and vapor pressure indicated by point *P* in Figure 25. Point *P* is not on the curve; the air is not at the saturation vapor pressure for that temperature, hence clouds would not form and precipitation could not occur. We can bring that air mass to the *saturation point*—that is, to equilibrium at a point on the temperature versus saturation vapor pressure curve—in two ways. First, we could add more water vapor through increased evaporation from the surface and thereby increase the vapor pressure. That action would move the air mass from point *P* up along the vertical dashed line toward the curve. Second, we could reduce the air temperature, which would move the air mass from point *P* to the left along the horizontal dashed line toward the curve.

Because the saturation vapor pressure varies with temperature, knowing just the vapor pressure on a given day does not give a good indication of when clouds will form. Consequently, we normally think in terms of *relative humidity*—the ratio of the actual vapor pressure to the saturation vapor pressure at that temperature. (We are using vapor pressure as a measure of the amount of water present.) The relative humidity is usually expressed as a percentage; a relative humidity of 100% represents air at the saturation vapor pressure. In general, water vapor will condense to form water droplets and clouds when the air is fully saturated. But in fact, very clean air may have greater than 100% relative humidity (i.e., it can be *supersaturated*) without condensation taking place. Condensation is facilitated by impurities in the air—microscopic particles (solid or liquid) that are small enough to remain in suspension in the air. Such particles are known as *cloud condensation nuclei* (CCNs) when they are used in cloud formation. These nuclei can come from many sources, both natural and anthropogenic. It is likely that many of the clouds that form from CCNs over land surfaces derive from human-produced sources, such as sulfates.

We said earlier that the vapor pressure can be brought to the saturation point either by increasing the vapor pressure or by cooling the air. We can visualize both processes taking place as air moves over different surfaces: evaporation increasing as unsaturated air moves over lakes or the ocean, and temperatures decreasing as the air moves over cooler surfaces. The largest and most rapid changes take place, however, when air rises in the troposphere. Temperature generally decreases with altitude in the troposphere, where most clouds exist. Thus most rainfall situations occur with some form of **uplift**, or rising of air masses. Uplift is a general term denoting any process by which air at a given level in the atmosphere is lifted to a higher altitude.

We can get some appreciation for how precipitation is distributed around the globe, therefore, by recognizing that most precipitation takes place as air cools when it is forced to rise. We have already mentioned two of the processes that result in uplift: first, large-scale uplift that occurs with the mixing of air masses of different densities; second, uplift due to convection. Consequently, there is heavy precipitation along the polar front zone in the mid-latitudes and in the vicinity of the ITCZ (Figure 26). Convection, however, occurs not only in the tropics, but wherever there is intense surface heating. Therefore, although convection does not always produce rain, it is the dominant rainfall-producing process over warm landmasses in summer. A third process that forces air to rise is the confrontation between a moving air mass and a mountain range. Such encounters cause *orographic* precipitation on the windward (upwind) slopes of mountains. (Orography is the branch of geography that involves mountains and mountain systems.) For example, orographic precipitation commonly occurs on the western slopes of the Sierra Nevada mountain range and on the southern slopes of the Himalayas.

Under these circumstances, precipitation is enhanced due to the atmospheric circulation. Under other

FIGURE 25   Saturation vapor pressure versus temperature for water. The curve shows the temperatures and vapor pressures at which the air becomes saturated.

circumstances, precipitation is inhibited in certain areas. We call such areas **deserts,** and we can examine why they are located where they are (Figure 27). Remembering that condensation results from uplift (which cools the air) or from increasing the amount of available moisture, we would expect to find deserts in areas where uplift is suppressed or where there is an inadequate moisture supply.

In general, precipitation is low in the interior of large landmasses, simply due to the distance from moisture

MODIFIED GOODE'S HOMOLOSINE EQUAL-AREA PROJECTION

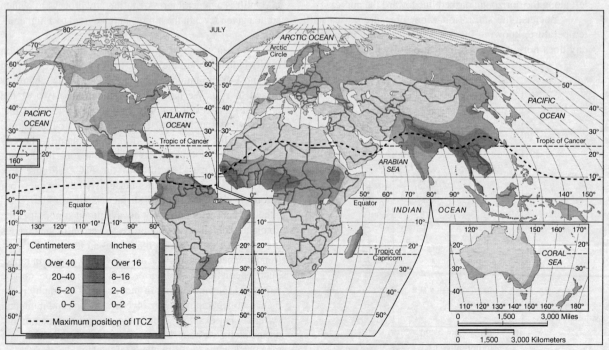

FIGURE 26 Global distributions of precipitation over land in (a) January and (b) July. (*Source:* From T. McKnight, *Physical Geography: A Landscape Appreciation*, 6/e, 1999. Reprinted by permission of Prentice Hall, Upper Saddle River, N.J.)

(a) Sonoran

(b) Taklimakan

(c) Atacama

(d) Kalahari

FIGURE 27 The distribution of the world's major deserts. (*Source:* From R. W. Christopherson, *Geosystems: An Introduction to Physical Geography*, 3/e, 1997. Reprinted by permission of Prentice Hall, Upper Saddle River, N.J.)

supplies. Deserts are located in the vicinity of the descending arms of the Hadley cells, as we noted earlier, and on the leeward (downwind) slopes of mountains. They occur also, perhaps unexpectedly, on the west coasts of large continents in areas that lie equatorward of the midlatitude low-pressure systems. These regions are characterized by cold offshore ocean currents. The cold ocean currents reduce evaporation and cool the air that moves over them, a combination that inhibits convection and precipitation over the adjacent coastline. The deserts that form in this way are called *littoral* (alongshore) deserts. In fact, one of the driest deserts in the world is the Namib Desert along the coast of southwest Africa. The desert of Baja, California (actually in Mexico), is another example. Although you generally think of deserts as being hot, some deserts are also located in the cold polar regions. The low temperatures inhibit uplift, and, where precipitation does occur, quantities are small because of the low saturation vapor pressures. The central part of Antarctica is, in fact, a desert. There is enough ice on Antarctica to raise global sea levels by almost 60 m, but the average annual snowfall on the plateau is the equivalent of less than 51 mm (2 in.) of liquid water.

Chapter Summary

1. The driving force for the atmospheric circulation is the global distribution of energy.
   a. The angle at which the Sun's rays strike Earth changes from the equator toward the poles. The result is that incoming solar radiation decreases with latitude. More solar radiation is received in the tropics than at the poles, resulting in an equator-to-pole temperature gradient.
   b. This temperature gradient drives the atmospheric circulation because of the inverse relationship between the temperature and the density of a gas: Higher temperatures produce lower densities. Differences in the distribution of global temperatures cause differences in air density and, therefore, pressure.
   c. Air tends to move from areas of high pressure to areas of low pressure. These large-scale movements of air produce the global wind belts.
   d. These wind belts are significantly modified by the Coriolis effect, which is caused by Earth's rotation.
2. The net effect of these atmospheric movements is to redistribute available thermal energy. There is a negative feedback between the energy gradient and the circulation. Energy is moved from low latitudes, where Earth is hot, toward the poles, where it is cold.
3. The atmospheric circulation exerts a major control on global temperature patterns. The movement of the air carries water vapor from one region to another. Because evaporation and condensation are largely a function of temperature, the redistribution of water around the globe is also strongly tied to temperature distributions and to the atmospheric circulation.
   a. Precipitation is enhanced wherever the circulation promotes uplift and is inhibited in areas dominated by subsidence.
   b. Precipitation amounts are also affected by continentality and the distance from moisture sources.
   c. The distribution of land and ocean affects the distribution and variability of surface temperatures. Variability increases as the distance from the ocean increases.
   d. The circulation, temperature, and precipitation distributions are modified by seasonal variations in incoming solar energy caused by Earth's obliquity and Earth's orbit around the Sun.

Key Terms

Boyle's law	divergence	latent heat of vaporization
buoyancy	evaporation	monsoon
Charles's law	groundwater	obliquity
condensation	Hadley circulation	partial pressure
convergence	hydrologic cycle	polar front zone
Coriolis effect	intertropical convergence zone (ITCZ)	subsidence
deserts	latent heat of fusion	uplift

Review Questions

1. What are the functions of the global circulatory system?
2. Explain why the distribution of solar energy varies with latitude.
3. a. Draw a graph showing the variation of incoming solar energy and outgoing infrared radiation with latitude.
   b. Indicate the regions of energy surplus and energy deficit.
   c. Explain why this distribution is important for the atmospheric circulation.
4. Explain why heating an air mass causes it to rise.

5. Use a diagram to describe Hadley cells. Why does the Hadley circulation change seasonally?

6. What is the Coriolis effect? How does the Coriolis effect help determine the global pattern of winds?

7. Explain why Earth experiences different seasons throughout the year. Which parts of Earth experience the greatest seasonal variability, and which parts experience the least? Explain why.

8. Contrast the different roles of turbulent heat transfers and conduction in modifying the thermal response of a land surface and an ocean surface.

9. Use map sketches to explain the processes that drive the Southeast Asian monsoon.

10. What is latent heat? Explain why latent heat is important for the redistribution of energy.

11. a. What is meant by saturation vapor pressure?

    b. Draw a graph that plots saturation vapor pressure as a function of vapor pressure and temperature.

    c. Explain why the information shown in the plot is useful for understanding the relationships between atmospheric circulation and precipitation.

12. Describe three processes that produce uplift in the atmosphere and are important in causing precipitation.

Critical-Thinking Problems

1. Sketch a map of India. Locate the major mountain ranges. Show which areas you think would have high rainfall and which areas you think would have low rainfall, and explain why.

2. In this chapter, we discussed several types of deserts, including polar deserts. The center of the Antarctic ice sheet, for example, receives very little precipitation each year and is regarded as a desert, although it does not match the customary idea of what a desert is. From this chapter we saw that:

- Precipitation generally decreases as temperature decreases (because saturation vapor pressure is much lower in cold air than in warm air).
- Much midlatitude and high-latitude precipitation occurs in extratropical storm systems that move along the polar front zone.
- The polar front zone is located in the latitudes where the temperature gradient is greatest. (This will be equatorward

of the ice margin, where cold air draining off the ice cap moves equatorward to meet the warm air that is blowing poleward from the subtropical highs.)

a. Put this information together in a systems diagram that has two feedback loops: one that links ice extent, albedo, temperature, and snowfall; and one that links ice extent, temperature, the location of the polar front zone, and snowfall.

b. Are these feedback loops positive or negative?

c. What implications do the feedback loops in part (a) have for the long-term growth of an ice sheet?

3. Indicate on two world maps the areas where you would expect to find relatively high rainfall and where you would expect to find relatively low rainfall, or even deserts, in (a) July and in (b) January. (c) Explain these distributions.

Further Reading

General
Robinson, P. J., and A. Henderson-Sellers. 1999. *Contemporary climatology*. 2nd ed. Harlow: Longman.

Advanced
Hartmann, D. L. 1994. *Global physical climatology*. San Diego: Academic Press.

FIGURE 20 The surface wind field over the Pacific Ocean. The data were derived from a satellite-borne radar system and the white arrows show the direction of air movement at 00Z on August 1, 1999. (*Source:* NASA/Jet Propulsion Laboratory.)

FIGURE 22 Earth, viewed from space at about 37,000 km (23,000 mi), is dominated by water. (*Source:* NASA Headquarters.)

The Circulation of the Oceans

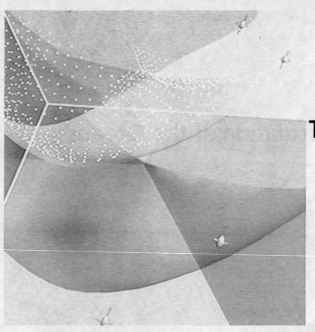

The Circulation of the Oceans

Key Questions

- Why do ocean currents form?
- How can the circulations of both the surface ocean and the deep ocean basins be driven by solar radiation and be closely

linked, yet operate at very different time scales?

- What role does ocean circulation play in the global climate system?

Chapter Overview

Here we will discuss Earth's circulatory subsystems by describing the processes that drive the circulation of the world's oceans. The movement and circulation of the oceans is tied very closely to the circulation of the atmosphere: Both are ultimately driven by the distribution of available solar energy, and their motions are linked by friction at the sea surface. There is an imbalance in the latitudinal distribution of energy that produces an equator-to-pole temperature gradient at the surface—the driving force for the pattern of Earth's surface wind. These wind patterns are responsible for the circulation of the ocean surface and the formation of the world's major ocean currents. As with the atmosphere, once the ocean starts to move, it comes under the influence of the Coriolis effect, which plays a significant role in the resulting circulation patterns. The oceans are vertically stratified, with denser water at the bottoms of the major ocean basins and less-dense water near the surface. The density is controlled by the temperature and by the salt content (*salinity*) of the water. The deep-ocean water is separated from the surface layer of the ocean by a transition zone with sharply defined density, temperature, and salinity gradients. This deep-ocean water moves as a response to small changes in density that occur over wide areas,

and the movement is largely independent of the surface-ocean circulation. Together, however, both types of ocean circulation contribute to the redistribution of available energy in the Earth system, albeit over very different time scales. And both play a major role in the distribution of nutrient supplies in the oceans.

WINDS AND SURFACE CURRENTS

The circulation in the troposphere is caused by atmospheric pressure gradients that result from vertical or horizontal temperature differences. We saw that from a global perspective, these temperature variations are caused by latitudinal differences in solar heating. But ocean surfaces are also heated by incoming solar radiation. Do the oceans, therefore, circulate for the same reason as the atmosphere? The answer is no, because the solar heating of the ocean takes place at the upper surface of the fluid, whereas the solar heating of the atmosphere occurs largely at the lower surface of the fluid near Earth's surface. Solar heating results in warmer water at the surface of most of the world's oceans. But the Sun's rays warm only the top few hundred meters of the ocean; 90% of the radiation that penetrates the surface is absorbed in the first 100 m. The warmer water is less dense than the cooler water below, which is not affected by the surface heating. This situation is inherently stable, so there is very little vertical movement. It is similar to the situation in the stratosphere. Recall that the atmosphere at this level is stable because the maximum solar heating occurs high in the stratosphere, the site of peak absorption of ultraviolet radiation by ozone. Where temperature increases with height, there is no density imbalance, and convection cannot take place. The fluid—water or air—remains well stratified. The true situation in the ocean is actually more complicated than this, as we will see, because the density of seawater is also affected by its salt content. It remains true, however, that the ocean overturns very slowly.

At the same time, temperature changes in the ocean occur slowly. Remember that the oceans have a high heat capacity—it takes a considerable amount of heat to produce just small changes in temperature. Slight differences in incoming solar radiation from place to place thus have little impact on the surface temperature of the ocean, so lateral temperature and density differences are slight over large areas. Unlike the troposphere, therefore, the surface ocean does not circulate as a *direct* response to the surface heating. Instead, surface temperature plays a more indirect role: The surface temperature influences the atmospheric circulation, and the resulting pattern of global winds determines the circulation of the upper ocean.

The movement of the wind over the ocean causes friction at the surface. As a result of friction, the wind drags the ocean surface with it as it blows, thus setting up a pattern of surface-ocean *wind-drift* currents. The force of the wind acting on the surface is referred to as *wind stress.* The water movement is usually confined to the top 50 to 100 m of the ocean, although well-developed currents such as the Gulf Stream in the North Atlantic and the Kuroshio Current in the North Pacific may extend as much as 1–2 km below the surface. The Coriolis effect influences ocean currents just as it does winds, so the water is deflected to the right of the path of the wind in the Northern Hemisphere (and to the left of the wind's path in the Southern Hemisphere). Observations show that this deflection tends to be approximately 20–25° from the wind direction. Thus, as a first approximation of what the ocean circulation should look like, we can take the surface winds and add a large ocean bounded by continents on the east and west. In doing so we obtain the surface-ocean circulation pattern shown in Figure 1. The trade winds produce westward-flowing currents in the tropics. When these currents reach the western continental boundary, they are deflected northward and southward. They then come under the influence of the westerlies, which cause the currents to flow eastward in the midlatitudes. When these currents reach the eastern landmass, some water is deflected to the pole and some toward the equator. The waters that flow toward the poles are replaced by equatorward flow along the western landmass. The waters that flow toward the equator

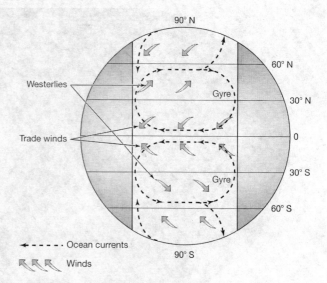

FIGURE 1 A simplified view of the surface-ocean circulation.

come back under the influence of the trade winds and are blown westward again. The currents complete a large, circular circulation pattern (called a **gyre**) in the subtropical oceans. The circulation of these gyres is clockwise in the Northern Hemisphere and counterclockwise in the Southern Hemisphere.

Compare the simplified model in Figure 1 with the observed distribution of ocean currents in Figure 2. The same general circulation features are apparent. Figure 2 shows counterclockwise gyres in the Southern Hemisphere and clockwise gyres in the Northern Hemisphere. Figure 2 identifies the world's major ocean currents and designates them as "warm" or "cool," labels that we will explain later in this chapter. The pattern in the real world is more complicated because the distribution of land and water is not as simple as it is in Figure 1. In the Southern Hemisphere, the westerlies result in an eastward-flowing current—the *West Wind Drift*—that extends around the globe because, in the real world, there is very little land in the middle and higher latitudes to deflect the water back toward the west.

Convergence

There are further differences between Figure 1 and the actual circulation of the ocean surface that are not apparent from the diagram. To begin with, although our predicted gyres are present, the explanation of their occurrence is a little more complicated than we previously suggested. To explain why they form, first we need to describe a few more processes that take place at the ocean surface. If we consider the circulation pattern shown in Figure 1, we might expect that water would pile up as it reached the coasts. In the Northern Hemisphere, therefore, we would expect to find water piling up in the northeast and southwest portions of

FIGURE 2 The major surface-ocean currents. (*Source:* From R. W. Christopherson, *Geosystems: An Introduction to Physical Geography,* 3/e, 1997. Reprinted by permission of Prentice Hall, Upper Saddle River, N.J.)

the gyre. This does not happen; rather, water piles up (or converges) in the *middle* of the gyre. This *convergence* results from the combined effects of the wind-driven surface-ocean currents, Earth's rotation, and, ultimately, friction.

The Norwegian explorer Fidtjof Nansen made a key observation that led to a better understanding of convergence during an expedition across the Arctic Ocean in the 1890s. His ship, the *Fram,* was frozen into the ice at the beginning of winter and drifted with the ice for over a year. It had long been thought that the surface-ocean currents were produced by the winds. Among many observations made during the expedition, however, Nansen noted that the ice (and the ship) did not drift *with* the wind but at 20–40° to the right of the surface wind path.

Walfrid Ekman, a Swedish physicist, first made the connection between wind-driven currents and Earth's rotation and derived a mathematical explanation of Nansen's observations. Due to friction between wind and the water surface, some of the kinetic energy of the air is transferred to the top layer of the water. As that layer moves, it drags along the water just below it, which in turn drags along the water just below that, and so on. The water appears to move as many thin, coupled layers, and kinetic energy is transferred down the water column. However, as the energy is transferred downward, friction causes some of the energy to be dissipated in the form of heat, so each level moves more slowly than the level above. At some depth below the surface, the effects of the wind-induced movement disappear. However, as each layer moves, it is again subject to the Coriolis effect. Once a layer starts to move, the water is deflected to the right of the path of the layer above (or the wind path, for the surface layer) in the

Northern Hemisphere and to the left in the Southern Hemisphere. The deeper below the surface, the farther each layer is deflected to the right or left of the surface layer, producing a spiraling effect known as the **Ekman spiral** (Figure 3a).

Ekman's theory predicts, under strong and persistent winds in the open ocean, (1) that the surface current will flow at 45° to the surface-wind path, (2) that the flow will be reversed at approximately 100 m below the surface (that is, the current at 100 m will flow in a direction opposite to the surface current), and (3) that it will also be considerably reduced in speed. In practice, there are few observations of a well-developed Ekman spiral, but observations do show that the surface flow is to the right of the surface-wind path (although usually at an angle less than 45°). The observations also bear out a further prediction from the theory—that when the movements of all the individual layers of water in the spiral are added, the net direction of transport within the water column is at a right angle (90°) to the wind direction. This net movement of water is referred to as **Ekman transport.** In a clockwise gyre in the Northern Hemisphere, the effect of Ekman transport is to push water into the center of the gyre (Figure 3b). Note that the counterclockwise gyres in the Southern Hemisphere will produce exactly the same result, because the Coriolis effect deflects the water to the left.

Divergence

Just as there are parts of the ocean where convergence occurs, there are also parts of the ocean where divergence occurs. In the equatorial Atlantic of the Northern

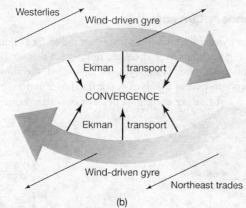

FIGURE 3 (a) The Ekman spiral. (b) Convergence in the center of a subtropical gyre due to Ekman transport.

southward-moving currents in these regions. Similar areas of divergence are found off the west coasts of South America and southern Africa, where northward-moving currents have the same effect.

Upwelling and Downwelling

In areas of convergence, the surface water piles up, the sea surface rises, and the surface layer of water thickens (Figure 4a). In areas of divergence, the surface water moves away, the sea surface drops, and the surface layer thins. Where convergence occurs, the accumulation of water causes it to sink in a process known as **downwelling.** Conversely, where divergence occurs at the surface, water must rise from below to replace it (Figure 4b). Water at depth is cooler than water at the surface. The rising of cooler water to the surface to replace warm, divergent surface water is referred to as **upwelling.** As we will see later in this chapter, these deeper waters also tend to be rich in nutrients. Upwelling, therefore, brings these nutrient-rich waters to the surface.

Geostrophic Flow

Having explained Ekman transport and convergence, we now come to the real reason why the circulation in the subtropical oceans takes the form of very distinct oceanic gyres. Areas of convergence and divergence produce slight variations in sea-surface elevation across the ocean basins, so the sea surface actually slopes from one point to another. This difference in elevation is very slight—on the order of a few meters over 10^2 to 10^5 km (that is, slopes of 1 in 10^5 to 1 in 10^8). Yet these slight elevation gradients are sufficient to cause a downslope force on the water due to gravity. If we consider the subtropical ocean in the Northern Hemisphere, for example, we have already seen that the northeast trade winds produce a westward-flowing ocean current near the equator, whereas the prevailing westerly winds in the midlatitudes result in an eastward-flowing current. The circulation is completed by the deflection of water along the coastlines at the ocean margins. Ekman transport in the surface layers causes convergence and the pile-up of water in the middle of the ocean (Figures 3b and 5a).

The sea surface is only about 50 cm higher in the center of the gyre than at the edges, but gravity acting on this pile of water results in a force (referred to as the *pressure-gradient force*) that pushes outward, down the gradient, from the center. As the water flows, however, it is deflected by the Coriolis effect until that effect balances the pressure-gradient force acting down the slope. The result of the two forces acting in opposition is to cause a flow of water off to the side—to the right in the Northern Hemisphere and to the left in the Southern Hemisphere (Figure 5b). Thus we end up with a circular flow of water around the gyre that is approximately parallel to the ocean slope (Figure 5c). Note the similarity to the description of the geostrophic wind. In this case, the resulting current is

Hemisphere, for example, the northeast trades (which, remember, blow from the northeast toward the southwest) result in a westward-flowing surface current, the North Equatorial Current. The net Ekman transport is 90° to the right of the wind, which means that the bulk of water transport is directed almost due north. Conversely, the southeast trades (in the Southern Hemisphere) produce the westward-flowing South Equatorial Current, and the net Ekman transport is to the left of the wind flow, toward the south. Hence, divergence occurs near the equator. Both divergence and convergence can also be found along coastlines where the Ekman transport may push water toward or away from the coast, depending on the direction of wind movement and the surface current. Important areas of divergence occur off the southwest coast of North America and the west coast of North Africa due to the easterly winds and

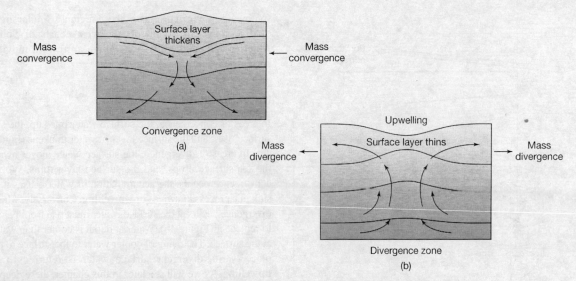

FIGURE 4 Schematic representation of zones of convergence and divergence. (a) Surface water accumulates in convergence zones, increasing the surface elevation (very exaggerated in the diagram) and thickening the surface layer. (b) The opposite happens in divergence zones—there is a decrease in surface elevation, and the surface layer thins.

called a **geostrophic current,** which flows around the gyre clockwise in the Northern Hemisphere (and counterclockwise in the Southern Hemisphere), in the same direction as the original wind-driven flow. In practice, the flow is a little less than 90° to the slope, so in fact the water tends to spiral inward as it moves around the gyre and the convergence in the gyre results in downwelling.

Boundary Currents

Ocean gyres are a prominent feature of the surface circulation. Figure 2, however, gives the impression that the flow around these gyres is not symmetric. Indeed, the flow in the western part of the gyre is confined to a narrow path with a fast-flowing current (a *western boundary current*),

FIGURE 5 (a) The subtropical gyres are formed by geostrophic currents that occur when Ekman transport from the wind-driven currents causes water to pile up in the center of the gyre. (b) There is a force due to gravity, acting down the gradient of the surface slope, that is opposed by the Coriolis effect. The net effect is a flow of water at approximately 90° to the slope. (c) The result is a geostrophic current that flows approximately perpendicular to the slope of the sea surface around the gyre.

which in the east is more diffuse, spread over a much larger area and with much-reduced current speeds (an *eastern boundary current*). Eastern boundary currents also tend to be divergent; the Ekman transport is away from the continent, thinning the surface layer along the coastline. The thinner surface layer and the divergent flow promote upwelling in these regions.

The most-studied western boundary current is the Gulf Stream in the western North Atlantic. The Gulf Stream begins as a narrow (50–75 km wide), fast-flowing stream of warm water (20°C or higher) in the Florida Current, flowing northward between Bermuda and Cuba. The current can reach depths of more than a kilometer, with surface speeds between 3 and 10 km/hr. This current follows the coast northeastward to Cape Hatteras, North Carolina, where it continues across the North Atlantic as the Gulf Stream (see Figure 2). Moving northeastward across the Atlantic, the Gulf Stream decreases in speed and the flow broadens into the North Atlantic Drift, which eventually flows into the Arctic Basin north of Norway. On reaching Europe, the North Atlantic Drift splits north and south; the southward-flowing component becomes an eastern boundary current, the Canary Current. The Canary Current moves much more slowly than the Gulf Stream, is shallower (reaching depths of only about 500 m), and is much broader—up to 1000 km across. As the water flows back toward the tropics, it comes under the influence of the northeast trade winds that push it to the west in the North Equatorial Current to complete the gyre. This elliptical flow of water essentially isolates the area in the center of the gyre, the Sargasso Sea. The Sargasso Sea is named for the extensive cover of seaweed often found in this area. Low current speeds and light, variable winds made this region difficult to traverse back in the days of sailing ships. The ancient mariners were also afraid of being entangled by the huge mats of seaweed that covered the surface.

Our discussion of wind-driven currents illustrates how wind stress, the Coriolis effect, and the pressure-gradient force serve to produce convergence, geostrophic flow, and gyres in the subtropical oceans. However, our discussion still does not account for the asymmetric nature of the gyres and the very different modes of flow in the eastern and western boundary currents. This pattern is caused by dynamic forces that operate when fluids tend to move in a rotary motion. How this happens is explained in the Box "A Closer Look: Vorticity."

Ocean Circulation and Sea-Surface Temperatures

The large-scale surface-wind pattern produces gyres in the surface layer of the midlatitude oceans. In the Northern and Southern hemispheres, the Coriolis effect and Ekman transport cause a net movement of water into the center of the gyres. The higher surface elevation in the center of the gyres causes a geostrophic current to flow around the gyres

in the same direction as the wind-driven flow, thus reinforcing the surface circulation. The shape of the gyre and the nature of the eastern and western boundary currents are then determined by the need to balance the forces that produce a tendency for water to rotate differently in different parts of the gyre.

The resulting circulation pattern has a significant impact on the redistribution of energy around the globe and on regional temperature (see Figure 2). The equatorial currents are warmed by the large input of solar radiation at low latitudes. When these currents are deflected poleward, they carry warmer water to middle and high latitudes. However, these currents lose heat as they travel poleward. When they are deflected northward and southward by the eastern landmass, the water moving poleward is warmer than the polar ocean, whereas the water moving equatorward is colder than the tropical ocean. At the same time, the surface water that originates in the polar oceans and moves equatorward is also colder than the midlatitude oceans. Ocean currents thereby aid in the latitudinal redistribution of energy: They move warmer water toward the poles and cooler water toward the equator.

Consider the warm North Atlantic Drift as an example. This northwest-flowing current brings fairly warm waters to northern Europe (see Figure 2). Due to the predominantly westerly flow of air in the midlatitude troposphere, most of northern Europe is warmed by the waters from the west and ultimately from the south. Contrast the seasonal variability and much milder conditions in southern Scandinavia with the more extreme conditions on the Labrador coast at the same latitude. Southern Scandinavia benefits from the warmth of the North Atlantic Drift. The air passing over Labrador, however, comes from the cold interior parts of Canada, and a cold offshore current (the Labrador Current) brings sea ice down to this area in winter. The result is lower temperatures and a much greater seasonal temperature range in that area. Notice that we now also have the explanation for the cold offshore currents, such as the Benguela and Humboldt currents, that are responsible for the Namib and Atacama deserts on the west coasts of South Africa and South America, respectively.

We can see that the oceans play a significant role in determining the broad patterns of Earth's present-day climate. It is also very important in controlling much of the variability we expereience in climate from year to year. Recall that the atmosphere transports heat very rapidly, and any anomalies are quickly dissipated. The atmosphere has very little "memory" of change. In contrast, the oceans absorb and store large amounts of heat, and they release this heat very slowly. Consequently, the ocean's memory of any change is much longer than the atmosphere's. Transient anomalies that develop in sea-surface temperatures can be expected to have a lingering impact on climate for some time afterward. The oceans, therefore, are the most likely place to look for processes that might cause climate anomalies on the interannual or decadal time scales.

A CLOSER LOOK
Vorticity

The text explains why large-scale gyres form in the subtropical oceans. But to explain the asymmetric pattern of the gyres and the differences between eastern and western boundary currents, we need to introduce an additional concept—that of vorticity. **Vorticity** describes the tendency of a fluid to rotate. A tendency to rotate in a counterclockwise direction is referred to as positive vorticity, whereas a tendency for clockwise rotation is negative vorticity. We refer to vorticity as being the *tendency* to rotate (rather than the actual rotary motion of the fluid) because different forces could impose both a positive and a negative vorticity on the same mass of water at the same time, and the actual amount and direction of the rotation would then depend on the net effect of the different forces.

So what produces vorticity? Imagine yourself standing exactly on the North Pole. You would be spinning around a vertical axis at the rate of one rotation every 24 hours (actually, 23 hours and 56 minutes). In other words, you would be experiencing a counterclockwise rotation about your vertical axis. At the equator you would experience no angular rotation, because you would be standing at exactly 90° to Earth's axis of rotation (Box Figure 1). Anywhere between the equator and the pole you would experience some fraction of the pole's angular rotation. This angular rotation about a vertical axis at Earth's surface,

brought about because of Earth's rotation, produces vorticity that is referred to as **planetary vorticity.** Mathematically, the planetary vorticity is identical to the Coriolis effect. Like the Coriolis effect, planetary vorticity acts in the opposite direction in the Southern Hemisphere.

A tendency for rotary motion can be created by a number of factors other than planetary rotation. Surface waters being driven by cyclonic or anticyclonic circulations in the atmosphere (i.e., low-pressure or high-pressure systems) will produce positive or negative vorticity. Similarly, *current shear,* in which the speed of the current changes across the current, will also produce vorticity. Representing the speed of the current by the length of the arrows in Box Figure 2a, for example, would produce negative (clockwise) vorticity; the faster-moving water tends to curl in toward the slower part of the current. The current shown in Box Figure 2b, conversely, would produce positive (counterclockwise) vorticity. Current shear can be quite dramatic where friction with a coastal boundary slows the edge of currents that flow parallel to the coastline. The vorticity produced by the pattern of surface winds and by current shear is referred to as **relative vorticity.** The **absolute vorticity** experienced by a body of water is then simply the sum of the planetary and relative vorticities.

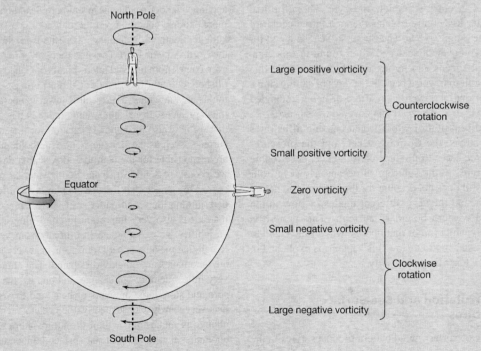

BOX FIGURE 1   Planetary vorticity, increasing from zero at the equator to a maximum at the poles.   (*Source:* Open University, *Ocean Circulation*, New York: Pegamon Press, 1989.)

(*continued*)

BOX FIGURE 2 Schematic diagram of current shear producing negative (clockwise) and positive (counterclockwise) relative vorticity. The lengths of the arrows represent relative speeds in the current.

Clockwise vorticity (a)

Counterclockwise vorticity (b)

How does this help us explain the difference between western and eastern boundary currents? The answer lies in the fact that, like mass and energy, absolute vorticity is a conserved property. In Box Figure 3, we can see the various factors that contribute to vorticity around a gyre. To begin with, the anticyclonic surface-wind pattern produces *negative relative vorticity* all around the gyre. At the eastern boundary current, this wind-supplied negative relative vorticity is balanced:

• The negative relative vorticity is balanced in part by a small increase in positive relative vorticity due to friction (current shear) along the coast. This factor is not large; because of the width of the current, only a small portion interacts with the coastline.
• Positive relative vorticity also arises from the southward flow of the water. The water is moving into an area of lower positive planetary vorticity; for vorticity to be conserved, there has to be a decrease in negative relative vorticity (or, looked at another way, a gain in positive relative vorticity).

The situation is very different on the western boundary:

• Current shear again produces positive relative vorticity.
• The change in latitude, however, leads to a gain in *negative relative vorticity* (the water is moving into regions of large positive planetary vorticity and so must acquire negative relative vorticity). This gain in negative relative vorticity reinforces rather than offsets the negative relative vorticity imparted by the surface-wind pattern.

The only way balance can be achieved in the western boundary current is by increasing the friction along the boundary, which is achieved with a narrower, deeper, and faster-flowing current. Hence the asymmetric nature of the gyre.

BOX FIGURE 3 Contributions to the changes in relative vorticity around an asymmetric subtropical gyre. (*Source:* Open University, *Ocean Circulation*, New York: Pergamon Press, 1989.)

FIGURE 6 The east–west circulation in the equatorial troposphere. The shaded areas represent heavy precipitation.

So, where do we look in the oceans? One obvious place to start is in the tropics, where we find the large convective towers of the Hadley cells that drive the atmospheric circulation over a large portion of the planet.

El Niño–Southern Oscillation (ENSO) Events

The name **El Niño** was originally given to a warm ocean current that appeared off the coasts of Peru and Ecuador. The current flowed for only a few weeks, and, because it usually occurred near Christmastime, local fishermen named it El Niño after the Christ child. The name has taken on a different meaning more recently; it is now used by researchers to describe a major shift in the oceanic circulation that occurs in this region every 2 to 10 years. This broad oceanic shift is associated with large changes in the circulation of the tropical atmosphere, which give rise to significant climate anomalies over much of the tropics and midlatitudes.

THE EQUATORIAL ATMOSPHERIC CIRCULATION Superimposed on the north–south Hadley circulation is a significant east–west circulation in the troposphere that is most prevalent over the equatorial Pacific. The western equatorial Pacific has the highest sea-surface temperatures on the globe. This region, which encompasses Australia and Indonesia, is a site of intense atmospheric convection. As is true of Hadley cells, the rising air diverges at high altitudes, but, in this case, we are concerned with a component of the flow that moves eastward and westward along the equator rather than northward and southward (Figure 6). The eastward-moving air crosses the Pacific, where it subsides off the west coast of South America. The circulation is completed by an easterly flow at the surface. This circulation is linked to other, smaller cells driven by convection over South America and Africa. Figure 6 shows the normal pattern of the equatorial east–west circulation. Figure 6 also indicates the normal pattern of precipitation, with heavy precipitation in the convective regions and drier conditions in the areas of subsidence. The circulation cells produce an oscillation in the sea-level pressure distribution between the western and the central/eastern portions of the

tropical Pacific Ocean. When pressures are low in the west, they tend to be higher in the east, and vice versa. This oscillation in sea-level pressures is referred to as the **Southern Oscillation (SO)**.

THE OCEAN CIRCULATION The persistent easterly wind at the surface in the Pacific Ocean produces a westward-flowing ocean current, which results in the water piling up in the western part of the ocean. This causes very warm water to accumulate in the western Pacific. Figure 7 shows that water piles up in the west, which causes the ocean surface to slope downward from west to east. The

FIGURE 7 The ocean surface layer in the tropical Pacific Ocean.

slope is exaggerated in the diagram; the difference in surface elevation from west to east is only on the order of a couple of meters. This east-to-west movement of water thickens the warm surface layer in the west and thins it in the east. The thinner surface layer in the east allows the upwelling of colder, nutrient-rich water from below, which promotes high levels of biological productivity and large fish populations.

We can regard this pattern of atmospheric and oceanic circulation as the norm, but in any year we see substantial differences. In some years this pattern intensifies: The sea-surface temperatures in the central and eastern Pacific are colder than normal, and convection over Indonesia is enhanced. These conditions are referred to as **La Niña** conditions—the pattern is similar to the "normal" conditions, but the circulation is enhanced. More drastic changes occur when the pattern breaks down in what is referred to as an **El Niño–Southern Oscillation (ENSO)** event. The Southern Oscillation may also be referred to as being in a "cold" phase during La Niña (or *anti-ENSO*) events and in a "warm" phase during ENSO events.

Before we describe what happens when an ENSO event occurs, let us look at this circulation again. The atmospheric convection in the western Pacific occurs as a result of the high sea-surface temperatures, but the high sea-surface temperatures are a result of the atmospheric circulation, which is driven by the convection. In other words, it is a classic chicken-and-egg situation. It is not a case of the ocean forcing the atmosphere or vice versa. Instead, it is a single integrated system with a positive feedback loop (Figure 8). If we perturb the system at any point, we should expect to see changes throughout all of its components.

ENSO EVENTS Scientists are still debating what causes ENSO events to occur. For the purposes of this discussion

FIGURE 8 Schematic diagram of the interaction between the atmosphere and ocean in the tropical Pacific Ocean.

we will simply break into the cycle in Figure 8 and ask what happens if, for some reason, there is a decline in the strength of the easterly winds.

If these winds weaken or reverse direction, which happens in some ENSO events, there is nothing to restrain the pile-up of warm water that has accumulated in the western Pacific. This water then comes sloshing back across the ocean in what is known as a *Kelvin wave*. It takes about 60 days for this wave to travel back across the Pacific. When it does, it has two major consequences. First, it shifts the pool of high sea-surface temperatures from the western to the central Pacific (Figure 9), which then completely changes the atmospheric circulation. Second, it shuts off the upwelling in the eastern Pacific, which has drastic consequences for biological productivity. The loss of the nutrient-rich water leads to a massive die-back of marine organisms and the bird life that feeds on them.

The changes in the atmospheric circulation are shown in Figure 10. The greatest area of convective activity during ENSO events lies over the central Pacific. The rising air

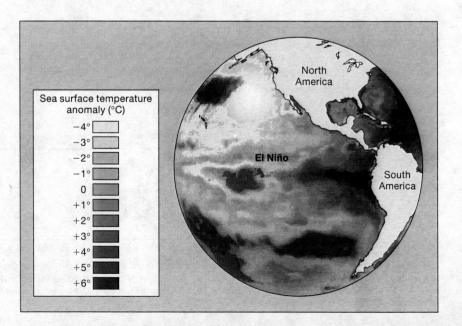

FIGURE 9 [See color section] Sea-surface temperature anomalies in the central and eastern Pacific during the 1997–1998 ENSO event.

FIGURE 10 Atmospheric circulation during an ENSO event.

diverges to the east and west, meeting and subsiding over Africa, although there is also localized uplift on the western side of the Andes. In a non-ENSO year, there is low pressure (rising air) at the surface over Australia and Indonesia and high pressure (subsiding air) at the surface in the central and eastern Pacific (Figure 6). In an ENSO year, this pattern reverses: Pressure increases over Australia and decreases in the central Pacific. We can calculate the pressure difference between these two locations (Figure 11a)

and plot this difference through time to produce the **Southern Oscillation Index (SOI)** (Figure 11b). This index is a measure of the pressure difference between the western and eastern parts of the tropical Pacific Ocean. Strong positive values indicate La Niña (non-ENSO) conditions; strong negative SOI values indicate ENSO conditions, which have occurred throughout the interval for which recorded data are available. We also find evidence from ice cores that ENSO events of various magnitudes

FIGURE 11 (a) The sea-level pressures at Tahiti and Darwin, Australia, and (b) the Southern Oscillation Index (SOI). The SOI is computed from the sea-level pressure differences. Negative values of the SOI indicate warm (El Niño) events. Note the strengths of the 1982–1983 and 1997–1998 events. (*Source:* NOAA Climate Prediction Center http://www.cpc.ncep.noaa.gov/data/indices/).

have been a feature of the climate system for at least the past 500 years.

CLIMATIC IMPACTS OF ENSO   The most dramatic impacts of ENSO events are seen in their effects on rainfall patterns. In non-ENSO years, summertime convection and rainfall occur over Australia and Indonesia. There is also convective activity and rainfall over equatorial Africa and the Amazon Basin. In contrast, there is subsiding air (dry conditions) west of the Andes. However, in ENSO years the dominant convective region shifts toward the central Pacific, and convection and rainfall over Australia and Indonesia diminish. Figure 10 shows that there is also subsidence over Africa and some localized convection over the western Andes. The result is drought in central America, Brazil, Australia, Indonesia, and southeast Africa and anomalously high rainfall amounts in the central Pacific and on the western slopes of the Andes in Ecuador and Peru. These high rainfall amounts typically result in floods and landslides, with their accompanying high levels of soil erosion. ENSO events also appear to have some effect on the monsoon circulation over India, resulting in increased rain over southern India and reduced rainfall over northern India and the Himalayas.

The impact of ENSO events is not confined to the tropics (see the Box "A Closer Look: The 1982–1983 and 1997–1998 ENSO Events"). The changes in atmospheric circulation can also influence the midlatitudes. The location and strength of midlatitude weather systems are controlled in part by the subtropical highs and in part by the sea-surface temperature gradients. Because both of these factors change during ENSO events, it is not surprising that they should have some effect on midlatitude climate. The general pattern of temperature and rainfall anomalies associated with an ENSO event are shown in Figure 12 for the Northern Hemisphere winter. In practice, each ENSO event tends to be somewhat different from others in the record. For example, the strength and location of the sea-surface temperature anomalies are not

A CLOSER LOOK
The 1982–1983 and 1997–1998 ENSO Events

The 1982–1983 ENSO event was one of the most severe of the 20th century. It developed unexpectedly. The normal early warning sign of changing tropical sea-surface temperatures was missed because of the preceding eruption of a Mexican volcano (El Chichón). The volcanic aerosols reduced the outgoing infrared radiation, resulting in lower satellite-derived sea-surface temperature measurements. The resulting pattern of climate anomalies was also slightly different from a "normal" ENSO: They were much more intense than earlier ENSO events. The impact of this particular event was considerable, with major droughts and floods occurring throughout the tropics. It is estimated that climate-related catastrophes resulting from the 1982–1983 ENSO event left more than 1,000 people dead and caused almost $9 billion worth of damage:

• Ecuador and northern Peru experienced floods and landslides that left 600 dead and resulted in crop and property losses totaling approximately $400 million. Guayaquil, Ecuador, had 20 times its normal rainfall in May 1983.
• In Indonesia, there were crop failures and starvation.
• In Botswana, the ENSO-induced drought followed two previous years of drought and eventually led to the loss of thousands of livestock.
• Eastern Australia suffered the worst drought of the century. Animal feed supplies were so diminished that thousands of sheep, dying of starvation, had to be shot. The dry conditions resulted in huge dust storms, one of which deposited 11,000 tons of topsoil on the city of Melbourne. February 1983 also saw some of the worst bushfires in Australian history that caused extensive damage and killed 75 people.

• Tahiti and French Polynesia had last experienced a typhoon at the beginning of the 20th century. The warm-water pool that formed in the central Pacific during the 1982–1983 ENSO event generated several large storms, and the islands were hit by six typhoons in five months.
• In the United States, increased rain in the Midwest resulted in the flooding of the Mississippi River. An increase in storms on the West Coast resulted in severe flooding and landslides in California, where 10,000 houses were lost or damaged and farm losses totaled half a billion dollars. There was a record snowfall in the Rockies, which, when it melted, resulted in flooding in Salt Lake City and along the lower Colorado River.

The 1997–1998 event was equally severe. Anomalous weather patterns occurred in many parts of the world, including extensive impacts in the equatorial Pacific, North and South America, and East Africa:

• Flooding, mud slides, and disease killed more than 80 people in Peru, and flooding in Ecuador resulted in 90 deaths and the evacuation of 22,000 people.
• The central Pacific had eight tropical cyclones, but only two the year before.
• Drought conditions produced hunger in Indonesia and Papua New Guinea. The extreme drought in Indonesia resulted in forest fires that burned over 1 million acres of forest.
• In the United States, this event produced heavy rains, flooding, and mud slides along the California coast but a very mild winter in the northeastern region.

FIGURE 12   Rainfall and temperature anomaly patterns associated with an ENSO event.   (*Source:* NOAA Climate Prediction Center http://www.cpc.ncep.noaa.gov/products/analysis_monitoring/impacts/warm.gif)

always the same, and ENSO events may last one year or may extend over several years. As a result, the pattern of the climate anomaly in the tropics tends to be fairly consistent, although it may vary in magnitude, but the midlatitude effects are highly variable. The western United States, for example, was very dry in the 1976 event but very wet in 1982.

THE CIRCULATION OF THE DEEP OCEAN

Salinity

In contrast to the surface-ocean circulation, which is driven by atmospheric winds, the deep-ocean circulation is driven by differences in water density. These differences are caused by variations in temperature and in **salinity**, or the salt content of a water mass. Salinity is measured in terms of the proportion of dissolved salt to pure water. The salinity of the ocean is a measure of the quantity of different elements—sodium and chlorine (Na, Cl) being the most common—dissolved in a given mass of seawater (*g* salt/*kg* seawater). Oceanographers, until recently, expressed salinity in parts per thousand (‰), or *per mil*. (Now they express it without units.) A salinity of 1‰, or 1 out of a possible 100 parts salt, is equivalent to 10‰, or 10 out of a possible 1000 parts salt. The average salinity of the world's oceans is approximately 35‰, but there is some variability from ocean to ocean.

The primary constituents of sea salt are the ions chloride (Cl^-), sodium (Na^+), sulfate (SO_4^{2-}), magnesium (Mg^{2+}), calcium (Ca^{2+}), and potassium (K^+) (Table 1). Except for calcium, which shows some variability from place to place, these elements are found in nearly constant proportions around the globe. Many of the minor constituents—but not all—show a similar uniformity.

Most of the variability occurs in those constituents that are utilized by marine organisms.

The salts contained in seawater are largely the result of the breakdown of crustal rocks, or *weathering*. Weathering occurs when rocks are altered by physical or chemical processes. When water flows over or through rocks, it removes soluble materials (ions). Rivers eventually carry the soluble ions to the ocean. In fact, it is estimated that rivers deliver between 2.5×10^{12} and 4×10^{12} kg

TABLE 1 Salt Content of the Earth's Oceans

Salt Ion	Grams per Kilogram (g/kg) of Ion in Seawater	Ion by Weight (%)
Chloride (Cl^-)	18.980	55.04
Sodium (Na^+)	10.556	30.61
Sulfate (SO_4^{2-})	2.649	7.68
Magnesium (Mg^{2+})	1.272	3.69
Calcium (Ca^{2+})	0.400	1.16
Potassium (K^+)	0.380	1.10
Bicarbonate (HCO_3^-)	0.140	0.41
Bromide (Br^-)	0.065	0.19
Boric acid (H_3BO_3)	0.026	0.07
Strontium (Sr^{2+})	0.013	0.04
Flouride (F^-)	0.001	0.00
Total	34.482	99.99

Source: P. R. Pinet, *Oceanography*, St. Paul, MN: West, 1992.

(about 4 billion tons) of dissolved salts to the oceans each year. The oceans are much saltier than the river water because, when ocean water evaporates, the salt is left behind (increasing the salt concentration) in the ocean. Some of that evaporated freshwater falls on the land and eventually runs back to the ocean. It weathers rocks along the way and thus delivers a new supply of salts that accumulate over time to increase the saltiness of the ocean.

If such great volumes of salts reach the oceans each year, are the oceans still getting saltier with time? The answer is no, because many processes also remove salts from seawater. These processes include the following:

1. Evaporation of seawater from shallow seas. The remaining salts are concentrated and precipitate from solution as **evaporite deposits,** such as halite (table salt, NaCl) and gypsum ($CaSO_4 \cdot 2H_2O$).
2. Biological processes. For example, some marine microorganisms remove the elements calcium or silicon from seawater to form their shells, some of which are eventually deposited in ocean sediments.
3. Chemical reactions between seawater and newly formed volcanic rocks on the sea floor.
4. The formation of sea spray. As small droplets of seawater become airborne, salts, especially sodium and chlorine, are removed when the spray is deposited on land. These salts are eventually returned to the oceans via rivers.

Overall, salts are removed from seawater at a rate that essentially equals the rate of input, when averaged over geologic time scales (millions of years). In other words, the present salt content of the oceans does not represent the result of continuous accumulation but simply a balance between the rates of input and output of salts (see the Box "A Closer Look: The Salt Content of the Oceans and the Age of Earth").

Variations in salinity are caused by regional differences in evaporation, precipitation, sea ice formation and melt, and river runoff. Surface salinities increase where evaporation exceeds precipitation. We see this effect in such areas as the Mediterranean Sea, the Red Sea, and the Arabian Gulf. In contrast, the Gulf of Bothnia in the Baltic Sea, which also has little exchange of water with the open ocean but experiences much greater precipitation, has relatively low salinities. A similar effect is seen in the Chesapeake Bay on the Atlantic coast of the United States.

Thermohaline Circulation

Because deep-ocean circulation depends on temperature and salinity, this circulation is referred to as **thermohaline circulation** (*thermo* is Greek for "heat," and *haline* comes from the Greek *hals,* for "salt"). In discussing atmospheric circulation, we showed that large horizontal (in particular, latitudinal) changes in temperature and pressure lead to steep pressure gradients and a relatively rapid air circulation. In the deep oceans, horizontal changes in density are small, whereas vertical changes can be larger. But the densest water is at the bottom, so the structure is very stable. Consequently, the movement of water through the deep ocean is relatively slow. Although density-driven movements are much slower than the surface currents, they are no less important in shaping Earth's climate on time scales of hundreds to thousands of years.

THE VERTICAL STRUCTURE OF THE OCEANS The vertical structure of the deep oceans is determined by water density: The highest densities tend to occur in the deepest layers, while the lowest densities are typically found near the surface. Water density, in turn, is controlled by temperature and salinity: Usually, density increases as salinity increases or as temperature decreases; density decreases as

A CLOSER LOOK
The Salt Content of the Oceans and the Age of Earth

Following ideas first expressed by British astronomer Sir Edmund Halley in 1715, Irish scientist John Joly attempted to calculate the age of Earth on the basis of estimates of the salt content of the ocean and the rate of delivery of salts to the ocean. Two hundred years after Halley, Joly calculated Earth to be 80–89 million years old. However, we now know that Earth is approximately 4.6 billion years old. So where did Joly go wrong?

Joly assumed that the ocean had simply been accumulating all the salts delivered to it by rivers at a constant rate since Earth first formed. Joly neglected the various processes that remove salts from seawater (see the accompanying text). Repeating Joly's calculations but using current estimates of ocean volumes and salinities, we obtain the following:

• The total amount of salt in the oceans is approximately 5×10^{19} kg.
• The rate at which rivers deliver salt is 4×10^{12} kg/yr.
• Therefore, the "age" of Earth is $5 \times 10^{19}/4 \times 10^{12} = 13 \times 10^6$ yr.

Thirteen million years is somewhat less than Joly calculated with his knowledge of the world's river discharge, chemical composition, ocean volume, and salt content. The "age" that we have calculated is, in fact, the average length of time salt remains in the ocean. The length of time a substance remains in a given reservoir is called the *residence time.*

salinity decreases or as temperature increases. However, water is an unusual fluid in that the density of freshwater *increases* as temperature increases from 0 to 4°C. After that point, water acts more like other fluids in that its density *decreases* as temperatures continue to increase. The temperature at which maximum density occurs varies as salinity changes. Maximum density occurs at 4°C for freshwater (0‰), 2°C for a salinity of 10‰, and at the freezing point for a salinity of 24.6‰. As salinities continue to increase, the temperature of maximum density continues to decrease (it actually stays at the freezing point, which also decreases as salinity increases).

The lower-density zone, which occurs in the top 60–100 m of the ocean, is called the *surface zone,* a layer that interacts with the overlying atmosphere. This interaction takes place through evaporation, precipitation, exchanges of kinetic energy (the effect of winds and friction), radiative exchanges (the absorption of solar radiation and the emission of long-wavelength radiation), and the exchange of heat. This zone is well mixed by wind action, and so the surface zone is often referred to as the **mixed layer.**

The transition zone between the surface zone and the deep ocean is on the order of a kilometer in thickness and is characterized by a rapid increase in density with increasing water depth. The very sharp increase in density is called the **pycnocline;** the transition zone is referred to as the *pycnocline zone* (Figure 13). In some regions this density gradient is dominated by salinity changes, and salinity rises rapidly with increasing depth. In this case, the salinity gradient is specifically referred to as the **halocline.** In most other regions, temperature changes dominate the density gradient, and temperature drops rapidly with increasing depth. There the transition is called the **thermocline.** In either case, the steep density gradient makes this layer very stable. This stability limits vertical movements and insulates the deep ocean from seasonal changes in temperature and salinity.

The deep ocean below the pycnocline (typically 1–5 km depth) contains about 80% of the volume of all oceans. Deep-ocean water is further stratified, with the highest densities at the sea floor. The water column within the deep ocean, therefore, is also stable, and little vertical movement takes place. The movement that does occur is subhorizontal, along sloping layers of equal density (*isopycnals*).

Figures 14 and 15 show temperature and salinity profiles, respectively, from the Atlantic and Pacific ocean basins. We see that the simple vertical structure outlined previously applies to most of the world's oceans, with the exception of those in high latitudes. The high-latitude seas are characterized by low temperatures and relatively low salinities at the surface, similar to the waters of the deep oceans. We will see next that there is a connection between these high-latitude surface waters and the deep oceans and that the formation of very dense surface water near the poles is, in fact, the primary driving force for the deep-ocean circulation.

BOTTOM-WATER FORMATION.   Deep-ocean circulation begins with the production of dense (cold and/or salty) water at high latitudes. This very dense water can be produced by several processes. For example, cooling and increased salinity may result from a large difference between evaporation and precipitation or from the formation of sea ice. Forming along the sea ice margin in just a few regions in the polar oceans, **bottom water** constitutes the densest water produced in the oceans. Near the poles, the surface waters are cooled below the normal freezing point (−1.9°C in some areas) by contact with the cold overlying atmosphere. (The freezing point is lower than that of pure water because of the presence of salt.) When that water freezes, it forms a layer of sea ice several meters thick that floats on the surface of the polar oceans. When the ocean surface freezes, most of the sea salt is excluded, because the salt does not fit into the crystal structure of the ice. As a result,

FIGURE 13 Generalized profiles of temperature, salinity, and density in the midlatitude ocean basins. These diagrams show the ocean to be divided into three layers: the surface zone, where there is little change in temperature, pressure, and density with depth; the pycnocline zone, where density increases rapidly (the pycnocline) and where there is an increase in salinity (the halocline) and a rapid decrease in temperature (the thermocline); and the deep ocean, where salinity generally increases slowly with depth, temperatures gradually decrease with depth, and there is little change in salinity.

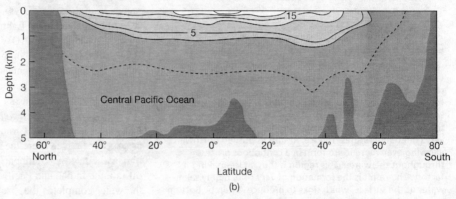

FIGURE 14 Vertical distribution of temperature in the (a) Atlantic and (b) Pacific oceans. The thermocline separates deep water from the surface layer in the tropics, but deep water extends to the surface at high latitudes. Temperature values are given in degrees Celsius.

FIGURE 15 Vertical distribution of salinity in the (a) Atlantic and (b) Pacific oceans. The salinity profiles are more complicated than the temperature distributions in Figure 7. In the deep ocean, salinity tends to increase in the deeper waters. There is a salinity maximum at the surface in the tropics, however, due to evaporation. When water evaporates, the salts are left behind. Where evaporation exceeds precipitation, there is a net loss of water from the surface layer, and the remaining water has a higher salt concentration.

FIGURE 16 The Weddell Sea. Part of the Weddell Sea is occupied by an ice shelf (a mass of ice several hundred meters thick that flows from the West Antarctic ice cap). The remainder of the sea is covered by sea ice in winter. The ice forms near the coast and is pushed northward by persistent winds blowing off the ice cap. As the ice is pushed away from the coast, open water is exposed that freezes rapidly in the very cold temperatures. This ice, in turn, is pushed northward, allowing even more ice to form in a continuous process throughout the winter. This region is thus an ice-making factory. The result is the formation of very cold, highly saline water at the surface, which sinks to produce Antarctic Bottom Water. (*Source:* W. S. Broecker and T.-S. Peng, *Tracers in the Sea,* New York: Eldigio Press, 1982, Figure 17.)

the water just beneath the sea ice becomes saltier, and an underlayer of very cold, highly saline water forms. The combination of low temperatures and high salinity results in very dense water that sinks and flows down the slope of the basin and spreads toward the equator as the bottom layer of water in the deep-ocean basins.

One of the major sites of bottom-water formation is the Weddell Sea off Antarctica (Figure 16). The water formed there, called **Antarctic Bottom Water (AABW),** circles Antarctica and flows northward as the deepest layer in all three major ocean basins (Atlantic, Pacific, and Indian). Although few direct measurements of deep-ocean circulations have been made, reconstructions using observations of the distributions of temperature and salinity have identified AABW as far north as 45° N in the North Atlantic and 50° N (at the Aleutian Islands) in the North Pacific. Typical speeds for deep-ocean currents are only 0.03 to 0.06 km/hr, yet AABW has traveled more than 10,000 km from its formation site in the Weddell Sea, a trip that has taken some 250 years.

Similar masses of cold, dense water form in the Arctic Ocean—off the coast of Greenland—and flow south at depth into the western North Atlantic. These water masses are referred to as **North Atlantic Deep Water (NADW).** The processes of NADW formation are not entirely clear.

Warm waters flowing northward in the southwest North Atlantic are evaporated and some portion of the water vapor is carried westward across Central America, where it falls as precipitation in the Pacific. This has the effect of slightly diluting (making less saline) the waters of the eastern Pacific, while producing higher salinities in the western Atlantic (the salt is left behind when the water evaporates). The Gulf Stream carries this more saline water northward where it cools, and the low temperatures and high salinities cause it to sink. At the same time, sea ice formation in the Greenland and Norwegian seas—like in the Weddell Sea—further increases the salinity and density of the surface waters in these regions. The NADW provides approximately half the input of deep water to the world's oceans, and the remainder comes from the Weddell Sea. The NADW that forms to the west of Greenland in the Labrador Sea sinks directly into the western Atlantic; the NADW that forms in the Norwegian Basin subsides and is dammed behind the *sills* (undersea ridges) that connect Greenland to Iceland and Iceland to the British Isles. This water periodically flows over the sills and cascades into the deep basins of the North Atlantic.

NADW flows southward through the Atlantic Ocean and joins the Antarctic Circumpolar Current, which flows around Antarctica. There the NADW and the AABW combine and circle the continent. They then proceed to branch off into the Indian and Pacific oceans (Figure 17). Some of the water completes the circle, reentering the Atlantic or continuing around for another circuit. The time scale over which this occurs is indicated in Figure 18, which shows the age of the water at various places in this flow. The map actually shows the change in the amount of radioactive carbon (^{14}C) present in the water masses, which represents the time since that body of water sank below the mixing layer and was no longer exchanging carbon dioxide with the atmosphere (see the two Boxes "Useful Concepts: Isotopes and Their Uses" and "A Closer Look: Carbon-14—A Radioactive Clock"). The decreasing proportions of ^{14}C indicate the pattern of flow. You can see the youngest water in the North Atlantic, getting progressively older as it flows south to the Southern Ocean. There is a further addition of young water off the Antarctic coast, and again the water gets progressively older as it flows around the Southern Ocean and up into the Indian Ocean or the northeastern Pacific Ocean. Some mixing of the deep water with surrounding water masses occurs, as does some biological addition of ^{14}C. Consequently, the ^{14}C age does not necessarily reflect the true age of the water masses. However, from these data it is possible to compute flow rates into the various basins, from which it is possible to determine the replacement (residence) time for deep water and the upwelling rates (how long it takes to get back to the surface). Taking residence times and upwelling rates into account, a parcel of Antarctic Bottom Water will reemerge at the surface in the Indian Ocean (on average) after 335 years, or in the Pacific Ocean after 595 years. The average residence time for the entire deep ocean is approximately 500 years.

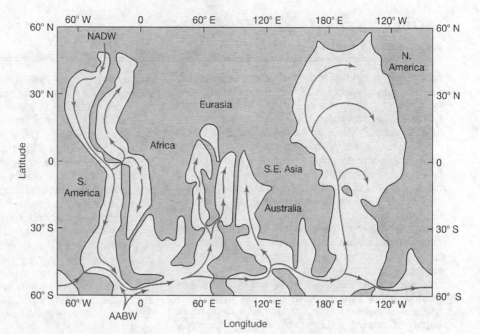

FIGURE 17 Flow pattern of the North Atlantic Deep Water and the Antarctic Bottom Water. This diagram represents the flow at a depth of 4000 m; the strange-looking continent/ocean configuration is what we would obtain if the oceans were drained to this depth. (*Source:* W. S. Broecker and T.-S. Peng, *Tracers in the Sea,* New York: Eldigio Press, 1982, Figure 12.)

Near Bottom Δ^{14}C‰ Values

FIGURE 18 [See color section] ^{14}C difference values for the near bottom waters of the world's oceans. The values represent the change in the amount of radioactive carbon (^{14}C) present in the water body compared to present-day surface waters (see "A Closer Look: Carbon-14—A Radioactive Clock"). The smallest values represent waters where the ratio of radioactive is stable carbon are most similar to the present-day ocean values (i.e., the youngest water bodies). Regions with the largest difference values show the oldest water masses. The ^{14}C acts as a tracer that shows the path of water movement in the deep oceans. (*Source:* Diagram courtesy Robert M. Key, Princeton University.)

USEFUL CONCEPTS
Isotopes and Their Uses

Much of what we know about the present, and especially the past, Earth system comes from the use of isotopes. **Isotopes** are atoms of a given element that have different numbers of neutrons in their nuclei. Isotopes have the same **atomic number**—that is, the same number of protons in the nucleus—but a different **mass number,** which is the total number of protons plus neutrons in the nucleus. Carbon is a good example because it has several isotopes that are used for all sorts of different purposes in studying Earth and its biota. All carbon atoms have 6 protons. ^{12}C also has 6 neutrons, while ^{13}C has 7 neutrons and ^{14}C has 8 neutrons. The superscript preceding the element's symbol denotes the mass number.

Some isotopes of a given element are **stable isotopes,** which means that they do not spontaneously change into other isotopes or into atoms of another element. **Unstable isotopes** spontaneously change into other isotopes or elements by a process called **radioactive decay.** ^{12}C and ^{13}C are both stable, while ^{14}C is unstable

and radioactive. Some 98.89% of all carbon is ^{12}C. ^{13}C constitutes most of the remaining carbon (~1.11%), while ^{14}C occurs only 0.0000000001% of the time. In other words, there are 10^{12} atoms of ^{12}C for every one atom of ^{14}C.

The stable and unstable carbon isotopes are both useful but for entirely different reasons. ^{13}C is used for studying the behavior of the carbon cycle over long time scales. Various microorganisms, especially photosynthetic ones, take up the different isotopes of carbon at different rates. Generally, the heavier isotope is taken up more slowly than the lighter one. This leaves a useful record for understanding rates of organic carbon burial and variations in atmospheric oxygen in the geologic past. ^{14}C is also taken up more slowly by microorganisms, but that effect is dwarfed by the fact that it is also radioactive. Thus, the main use of ^{14}C is for **radiometric age dating.** The Box "A Closer Look: Carbon-14—A Radioactive Clock" describes how this technique is used to study deep-ocean circulation.

Linking the Thermohaline Circulation and the Wind Driven Surface Flow

We have now described how surface waters in the polar regions sink and spread at depth throughout the world's oceans. Ultimately these waters must return to the surface to complete the circulation (Figure 19). Water is only slightly compressible (we cannot cram more and more of it into the same space), so if water is sinking at high latitudes, it must be rising somewhere else. There must also be some flow of surface water into the high latitudes to replace the water that is subsiding and moving equatorward. This return flow is even more difficult to monitor than the flow of bottom water. It takes place very slowly through the pycnocline over the whole ocean and more rapidly through upwelling in currents along the eastern boundary of ocean basins and other regions of upwelling and deep mixing. Once the former deep water has reached the surface, the surface circulation that we discussed earlier returns the water to the polar regions. According to Wallace Broecker, a geochemist at Columbia University, this complete cycling of ocean water that is driven by thermohaline circulation can be likened to a giant conveyor belt.

The thermohaline conveyor belt is a significant feature of the Earth system in several respects: It plays a dominant role in the recycling of ocean nutrients, and it has a major impact on Earth's climate. Much of the life that exists in the oceans can be found in the near-surface layers, utilizing sunlight for photosynthesis—phytoplankton, for example—or living off the animals that feed on phytoplankton. These plants and animals use the nutrients in ocean water, so the surface layers become relatively depleted in nutrients. When

these organisms die, they sink through the water column, decompose, and release the nutrients back into the water. The deeper ocean, therefore, is relatively rich in nutrients. The thermohaline circulation transports these nutrient-rich waters around the globe, returning the nutrients to the surface in areas of upwelling, primarily along the continental margins. Consequently, the concentrations of marine life are greatest in these upwelling regions. This is illustrated in Figure 20, a satellite image showing productivity in the oceans. The satellite measures the ocean color and the information is converted to concentrations of chlorophyll pigment in phytoplankton, so the image is showing where high concentrations of phytoplankton are found near the ocean surface. Note the high productivity in the North Atlantic and in upwelling coastal zones. In contrast, note the low concentrations in the middle of the primary ocean gyres.

Our description of the ocean circulation depicts a complex system of surface-wind-driven currents overlying a deep ocean with a relatively simple circulation driven by bottom-water formation and surface divergence. In reality, the deep oceans are much more complex. Clearly distinguishable water masses can be identified at different depths and in different geographic locations where variations in temperature and salinity impart different characteristics to the water bodies. For example, high evaporation rates and low rainfall (together with little river runoff) produce relatively warm, highly saline water in the Mediterranean Sea. This water flows out of the Mediterranean at depth through the Straits of Gibraltar and is clearly recognizable as a plume of warm, saline water spreading out into the mid-Atlantic at a depth of about

A CLOSER LOOK

Carbon-14—A Radioactive Clock

The radioactive isotope (or *radioisotope*) of carbon (^{14}C) is produced in the upper atmosphere through bombardment by cosmic rays from distant sources in the galaxy. This bombardment breaks apart atoms producing neutrons, which may then collide with other atoms. Nitrogen atoms (^{14}N) have 7 protons and 7 neutrons. When a nitrogen atom is struck with one of these "cosmic ray" neutrons, the neutron replaces one of the protons in the nucleus. The atom now has 6 protons and 8 neutrons—in other words, the ^{14}N becomes ^{14}C. The ^{14}C is unstable and so it decays back to nitrogen. Radioactive decay is exponential—half occurs in the first 5,730 years, half of the remainder in the next 5,730 years, and so on. This time period, in which half of the initial quantity of radioactive isotope decays, is referred to as the isotope's **half-life** (see Box Figure 4).

The ^{14}C is rapidly oxidized to ^{14}CO$_2$ and is distributed through the atmosphere. Production of ^{14}C occurs at a relatively constant rate, so the proportion of ^{14}C to stable carbon in the atmosphere remains constant. Living organisms take up the unstable carbon and, although the ^{14}C immediately begins to decay, it is replenished by more ^{14}C from the atmosphere, maintaining an equilibrium that matches the proportions in the atmosphere. Once the organism dies, however, metabolic activity ceases so the ^{14}C continues to decay radioactively, but can't be replenished. Knowing the rate at which this decay occurs, it is possible, by looking at

the ratios of ^{14}C to ^{12}C, to determine how long ago the organism lived. If you have a piece of wood, for example, that has half the amount of ^{14}C (in relation to ^{12}C) than we find in living trees, then we know that the piece of wood came from a tree that died roughly 5,700 years ago. This process, called **radiocarbon dating**, has been used to date materials back to 50,000 years ago and is used extensively in archeology and for reconstructing past climates.

^{14}C is also useful as a tracer of ocean circulation. Because the atmosphere exchanges CO$_2$ with the ocean surface, the surface waters of the ocean have nearly the same ratio of ^{14}C to ^{12}C as does the atmosphere. When surface waters sink, however, the ^{14}C that is present begins to decay, and it cannot be replenished. Consequently, the ratio of ^{14}C to ^{12}C in the deep waters gives a measure of how long it has been since the water was near the ocean surface: low ^{14}C/^{12}C ratios indicate "older" deep water. By measuring ^{14}C/^{12}C ratios in different localities, we can trace the time it takes for water to flow around the globe. The youngest water is found in the Weddell Sea near Antarctica and in the Norwegian/Barents Sea between Norway and Greenland. These are places where bottom water is being formed. The oldest deep water is found in the Northeast Pacific. By combining these and other data, the path and rate of the thermohaline circulation can be determined (Figure 18).

BOX FIGURE 4 The graph of radioactive decay is exponential. In other words, half of the radioactive parent is left after one half-life. After a second half-life, a quarter of the parent is left, and so on. (*Source:* From J. P. Davidson, W. E. Reed, and P. M. Davis, *Exploring Earth: An Introduction to Physical Geology*, 1997. Reprinted by permission of Prentice Hall, Upper Saddle River, N.J.)

FIGURE 19   An idealized map of the deep-water flow (solid lines) and the returning surface circulation (dashed lines). This circulation has been described as a global conveyor belt. The deep water flows out of the North Atlantic, mixing with warmer water to the south. It is recooled by mixing with the cold surface water that subsides around Antarctica. Joining with the Antarctic Bottom Water, it flows around Antarctica in the Antarctic Circumpolar Current. Branches then flow back into the Atlantic as well as the Pacific and Indian oceans, where upwelling brings the cold waters to the surface. The water eventually returns via the surface currents to the North Atlantic to complete the circulation.   (*Source:* From W. K. Hamblin and E. H. Christiansen, *Earth's Dynamic Systems,* 8/e, 1998. Reprinted by permission of Prentice Hall, Upper Saddle River, N.J.)

FIGURE 20   [See color section] The Coastal Zone Scanner carried on the Nimbus-7 satellite was one of the first instruments to record ocean color. The satellite detected the pigments from chlorophyll in phytoplankton and so measures the phytoplankton concentrations in the near-surface waters. The light shading shows the regions with the highest productivity.   (*Source:* NASA/ Goddard Space Flight Center.)

1000 m (Figure 21). We need not concern ourselves with these added complexities, but it is worth noting that our knowledge of the deep-ocean circulation is limited and that much scientific investigation remains to be done in order for us to fully understand what is going on. This understanding is particularly important because the oceans play such a significant role in global climate.

Ocean Circulation and Climate

As we discussed earlier, the ocean circulation has a strong influence on global temperatures. The transport of warm surface water toward the poles, to replace the bottom water that forms near the sea ice margin, is one mechanism by which excess solar energy is transferred poleward. Figure 22

FIGURE 21 The distribution of (a) temperature (in degrees Celsius) and (b) salinity (per mil) at 1000-m depth in the North Atlantic, showing the spread of Mediterranean Sea water. (*Source:* Open University, *Ocean Circulation*, New York: Pergamon Press, 1989.)

shows the Northern Hemisphere poleward heat transport in the atmosphere and ocean. The total heat transport data are derived by calculating the heat transfer necessary to balance the radiation budget at each latitude and estimating how much of this transfer can be accomplished by the atmosphere. The ocean heat transport is then obtained by subtracting the atmospheric transport from the total. The estimates indicate that the ocean (1) provides almost as much poleward heat transport as does the atmosphere and (2) transports more heat than does the atmosphere at low latitudes, whereas the atmospheric transport dominates at middle to high latitudes.

At the same time, the oceans represent a vast reservoir of heat, absorbing heat from the atmosphere in some areas and releasing it in others. Because water heats up and cools down relatively slowly, pools of water that are cooler than normal or warmer than normal will cool or warm the atmosphere on time periods of months to seasons or years—the time needed for the pools of water to heat up or cool down. On much longer time periods, however, the average effect of the oceans on the atmosphere is determined by the overall temperature of the oceans. Most of the water in the oceans lies in the deep oceans, and its temperature is largely determined by the process of bottom-water formation and by the transport of bottom water around the ocean basins. If the process of bottom-water formation changes, the ocean temperatures will change—and so will climate. Estimates of the rate of bottom-water formation

FIGURE 22 Poleward heat transport in the Northern Hemisphere. (*Source:* Open University, *Ocean Circulation*, New York: Pergamon Press, 1989.)

under the present climate, together with measurements of ocean volume, indicate that it would take about 1,000 years to recycle all of the deep water in the oceans. Hence, we can anticipate that the thermohaline circulation could moderate climate over time periods of about 1,000 years. However, we also have geologic evidence indicating that brief interruptions or changes in the thermohaline circulation can also have rapid and large impacts on regional climates,.

Chapter Summary

1. As with the atmosphere, the driving force for the oceanic circulation is the global distribution of energy. Unlike the atmosphere, however, the oceanic circulation is driven indirectly by temperature differences: The surface-ocean circulation is, in fact, driven by the circulation of the atmosphere.
   a. Due to friction, wind blowing over the ocean surface drags the surface waters along, producing ocean currents.
   b. The pattern of surface-ocean currents is modified by the Coriolis effect, a consequence of Earth's rotation, and by the distribution of land and oceans.
2. The thermohaline circulation of the deep oceans results from temperature and salinity variations, which control the density of ocean waters.
   a. Cold, saline water is formed in the North Atlantic and in the Weddell Sea off Antarctica.

   b. The combination of low temperatures and high salinities produces very dense water that sinks to the ocean floor and flows as bottom water throughout the world's oceans.
3. Bottom water eventually rises to the surface in zones of upwelling and returns in surface currents back to the highlatitude source regions, completing a vast oceanic conveyor belt.
   a. In combination with the atmospheric circulation, the net effect of these oceanic circulations is to redistribute thermal energy from low latitudes, where Earth is hot, toward the poles, where it is cold.
   b. The thermohaline conveyor belt and the associated zones of upwelling and downwelling play a significant role in climate and in the distribution of nutrients in the oceans.

Key Terms

absolute vorticity
Antarctic Bottom Water (AABW)
atomic number

bottom water
downwelling
Ekman spiral

Ekman transport
El Niño
El Niño–Southern Oscillation (ENSO)

evaporite deposit
geostrophic current
gyre
half-life
halocline
isotope
La Niña
mass number
mixed layer

North Atlantic Deep Water
   (NADW)
planetary vorticity
pycnocline
radioactive decay
radiocarbon dating
radiometric age dating
relative vorticity
salinity

Southern Oscillation (SO)
Southern Oscillation
   Index (SOI)
stable isotope
thermocline
thermohaline circulation
unstable isotope
upwelling
vorticity

Review Questions

1. What effects does the surface-wind pattern have on the circulation of the oceans?
2. Why do ocean currents not move in exactly the same direction as the wind?
3. What is the Ekman spiral? Explain why Ekman transport occurs.
4. What is upwelling? Where does upwelling occur?
5. What is meant by a geostrophic current?
6. Explain the different characteristics of western and eastern boundary currents.
7. Explain what happens to the atmospheric and oceanic circulations in the tropical Pacific during an ENSO event.
8. Where does the salt in the oceans originate? Are the oceans getting saltier with time? If not, then why not?
9. Define the term *thermohaline circulation*. What are the processes that drive the circulation of the deep oceans?
10. Explain the differences among the pycnocline, the halocline, and the thermocline.
11. What is bottom water? Where and how does bottom water form?
12. What is meant by the term *thermohaline conveyor belt*?
13. Explain what effects the ocean has on modifying the global temperature distribution.

Critical-Thinking Problems

1. Explain what is meant by Ekman transport and what role it plays in producing oceanic gyres in the surface waters of the subtropical oceans.
2. Use a rough map sketch to help explain the role that the oceans play in determining the climates of southern South America and southern Africa, poleward of 20° S.
3. Water is a very unusual substance in that it reaches maximum density between the freezing point and 4°C, depending on salinity. As you cool the water surface to these temperatures it becomes denser and sinks (rather than immediately freezing). This means that you have to cool the whole water body (the lake or the surface, mixed, layer of the ocean) to this temperature before you can cool the surface layer enough to freeze, which is why some lakes can remain unfrozen even when the air temperature drops well below freezing. When you have cooled the surface layer to the freezing point, water is again unusual in that its solid form (ice) is actually less dense than the liquid, so ice floats. Consider how different the world would be if water behaved like most other substances and continued to increase in density down to the freezing point, and if ice were denser than liquid water. Speculate on what this might have meant for life on the planet.

Further Reading

General

Open University. 1989. *Ocean circulation*. Oxford: Pergamon Press.
Perry, A. H., and J. M. Walker. 1977. *The ocean-atmosphere system*. New York: Longman.

Advanced

Rahmstorf, S. 2003. Thermohaline circulation—The current climate. *Nature* 421:699.
Wunsch, C. 2002. What is the thermohaline circulation? *Science* 298:1179–81.

FIGURE 9 Sea-surface temperature anomalies in the central and eastern Pacific during the 1997–1998 ENSO event.

Near Bottom Δ¹⁴C‰ Values

FIGURE 18 ¹⁴C difference values for the near bottom waters of the world's oceans. The values represent the change in the amount of radioactive carbon (¹⁴C) present in the water body compared to present-day surface waters (see "A Closer Look: Carbon-14—A Radioactive Clock"). The smallest values represent waters where the ratio of radioactive to stable carbon are most similar to the present-day ocean values (i.e., the youngest water bodies). Regions with the largest difference values show the oldest water masses. The ¹⁴C acts as a tracer that shows the path of water movement in the deep oceans.   (*Source:* Diagram courtesy Robert M. Key, Princeton University.)

FIGURE 20 The Coastal Zone Scanner carried on the Nimbus-7 satellite was one of the first instruments to record ocean color. The satellite detected the pigments from chlorophyll in phytoplankton and so measures the phytoplankton concentrations in the near-surface waters. The light shading shows the regions with the highest productivity. Note this is a false color image. (*Source:* NASA/Goddard Space Flight Center.)

The Cryosphere

The Cryosphere

Key Questions

■ What controls the distribution of sea ice over the oceans?

■ How does a glacier move and why is it important?

■ What role does the cryosphere play in the global climate system?

Chapter Overview

One of the reasons we are interested in the cryosphere is because of its importance in the climate system and, in particular, its very high albedo. Less obvious (unless you live there) is, for example, the challenge that frozen ground presents to living at high latitudes, or the importance of glaciers and mountain snow cover as a source of freshwater. In this chapter, however, we are primarily interested in Earth's major ice caps— Greenland and Antarctica—and in the ice cover of the Arctic and Antarctic oceans. We will talk about how ice forms in both environments (land and ocean), what controls ice dynamics and why it is important, and how both sea ice and the continental ice sheets interact with the climate system over different time scales.

INTRODUCTION

Looking down on Earth from space, the most obvious features of the planet are the oceans and clouds—but equally striking are the large ice masses that occupy both polar regions. Between them, the oceans, clouds, and the polar ice caps (all various forms of water) dominate the global energy balance and play a major role in shaping Earth's climate. The primary components of the cryosphere are the **continental ice sheets** and ice shelves, mountain glaciers, **sea ice**, river and lake ice, snow cover, and **permafrost** (frozen ground). These are illustrated in Figure 1 and Table 1. We include frozen ground in our definition of the cryosphere but, for the most part, when we talk about the cryosphere in this chapter we are primarily interested in various forms of frozen water at the planet's surface. (Ice particles in clouds are not usually considered as part of the cryosphere.)

The cryosphere interacts with the climate system in a variety of ways and over a wide range of time scales. Changes in the distribution of sea ice and snow cover change the albedo and feed back to regional and global temperatures. Changes in the amount of glacier ice affect global sea level, the melting of permafrost releases greenhouse gases to the atmosphere, and the process of sea-ice formation helps increase the salinity of the surface ocean at high latitudes. This, in turn, affects ocean density, bottom-water formation, and the deep-ocean circulation. Beyond these global-scale processes, sea ice and permafrost play an important role in regional ecosystems, and mountain snow cover and glaciers are an important source of freshwater. As an

FIGURE 1 Components of the cryosphere and their time scales. (*Source:* Lemke, P., J. Ren, R. B. Alley, I. Allison, J. Carrasco, G. Flato, Y. Fujii, G. Kaser, P. Mote, R. H. Thomas, and T. Zhang, 2007: "Observations: Changes in Snow, Ice and Frozen Ground." In: *Climate Change 2007: The Physical Science Basis. Contribution of Working Group I to the Fourth Assessment Report of the Intergovernmental Panel on Climate Change* [Solomon, S., D. Qin, M. Manning, Z. Chen, M. Marquis, K. B. Averyt, M. Tignor, and H. L. Miller (eds.)]. Cambridge University Press, Cambridge, United Kingdom, and New York, NY, USA.)

TABLE 1 Area, Volume, and Sea Level Equivalent (SLE) of the Cryosphere

Cryosphere Component	Area (10^6 km^2)	Ice Volume (10^6 km^3)	Potential Sea-Level Rise (SLE) (m)
Snow on land (NH*)	1.9–45.2	0.0005–0.005	0.001–0.01
Sea ice	19–27	0.019–0.025	~0
Glaciers and small ice caps			
Smallest estimate	0.51	0.05	0.15
Largest estimate	0.54	0.13	0.37
Ice shelves	1.5	0.7	~0
Ice sheets	14.0	27.6	63.9
Greenland	1.7	2.9	7.3
Antarctica	12.3	24.7	56.6
Seasonally frozen ground (NH)	5.9–48.1	0.006–0.065	~0
Permafrost (NH)	22.8	0.011–0.037	0.03–0.10

*Northern Hemisphere
Source: Lemke, P., J. Ren, R. B. Alley, I. Allison, J. Carrasco, G. Flato, Y. Fujii, G. Kaser, P. Mote, R. H. Thomas, and T. Zhang, 2007: "Observations: Changes in Snow, Ice and Frozen Ground." In: *Climate Change 2007: The Physical Science Basis. Contribution of Working Group I to the Fourth Assessment Report of the Intergovernmental Panel on Climate Change* (Solomon, S., D. Qin, M. Manning, Z. Chen, M. Marquis, K. B. Averyt, M. Tignor, and H. L. Miller [eds.]). Cambridge University Press, Cambridge, United Kingdom, and New York, NY, USA.

example, the mountain snowpack contributes about 75% of the annual surface water supply for the western United States. This moisture might still fall as rain, of course, if temperatures were warmer. However, it would not be available year-round unless it was trapped in some system of reservoirs. The mountain snowpack acts as a large regional reservoir, and this makes it extremely important to the American West and to many other parts of the world.

Like the atmosphere and oceans, the cryosphere is a dynamic system. The major components of the cryosphere (glaciers/ice sheets and sea ice) are in constant motion, and the extent of the cryosphere changes on time scales ranging from days to millennia (Figure 1). There have been times in the past when Earth was much warmer than today and there were no polar ice caps, and times when the system was colder and the ice expanded much further toward the equator. There were even times when most, if not all, of the planet was frozen at the surface. Here, we focus on the present-day distribution of snow, ice, and frozen ground.

RIVER AND LAKE ICE, SEASONAL SNOW COVER, AND PERMAFROST

The seasonal freezing and thawing of lakes and rivers plays an important role in local ecosystems and impacts a range of human activities, but plays only a minor role in the global-scale processes that are the primary object of this text. Other than to point out that they are still part of the cryosphere, we will not discuss them further. For the most part, this chapter will focus on glaciers and ice sheets and on sea ice. However, we will make brief mention of snow cover because of its interaction with the atmosphere and its possible effects on interannual climate variability, and we will discuss permafrost because of its significance as a potential source of greenhouse gas (methane) emissions.

Formation of Snow

Snow forms initially as ice crystals in clouds. In the same way that water droplets form around cloud condensation nuclei, small ice crystals also form around tiny mineral or organic particles in the atmosphere, referred to as **freezing nuclei.** At that point, the ice crystal can grow and take a variety of forms, which are largely a function of temperature. The dominant process is one of deposition: the ice forms directly from water vapor, rather than from the freezing of liquid water. The different phases of water are gas (water vapor), liquid, and solid (ice). Water can transition directly from ice to vapor (sublimation) or from vapor to ice (deposition) without going through a liquid phase in between. The conditions under which this is possible are shown in the **phase diagram** for water in Figure 2. The diagram shows the way water behaves at different combinations of temperature and pressure. The solid lines are the phase

FIGURE 2   Phase diagram for water.

boundaries and show the combinations of temperature and pressure at which the two phases can coexist in a stable state. Along the gas–liquid boundary, for example, water can exist as 100% gas or 100% liquid or any combination in between. The horizontal gray line shows the standard atmospheric pressure and the two vertical gray lines show the freezing and melting points of water at that pressure (273 K and 373K, or 0°C and 100°C).

The insert shows an enlargement of the region where all three phase boundaries come together. The curves in this case are not drawn to scale and the slopes are exaggerated to make the behavior more obvious. From the insert you can see that as pressure decreases, the melting point also decreases. Similarly, you can see that at one atmosphere (the standard pressure at sea level), if the pressure is reduced, as happens when an air parcel rises in the atmosphere, then the boiling point is also lowered. There are several other interesting features in these curves. The point at which all of the phase boundaries meet is called the **triple point;** here, water can exist in a stable state in all three phases. The point at which the gas–liquid boundary stops is called the **critical point.** At temperatures and pressures beyond this point there is no real distinction between liquid and gas. The diagram also shows that at high enough pressures ice will not melt, even at extremely high temperatures.

For our discussion of snow crystals, the relevant part of the diagram is the phase boundary between gas and solid. Once the ice crystal forms, it continues to grow primarily by deposition. In the absence of freezing nuclei, pure water will not freeze until temperatures in the cloud drop to 233 K (−40°C). This means that once temperatures drop below 273 K and some ice starts to form around freezing nuclei, the cloud will consist of a mixture of ice crystals and **supercooled water** droplets. (Liquid water that is colder than 273 K is referred to as supercooled water.) The saturation vapor pressure for ice and liquid

FIGURE 3 Characteristic hexagonal structure of a snow crystal. (*Source:* Kenneth G. Libbrecht.)

FIGURE 4 The hexagonal structure of an ice crystal. The balls represent oxygen atoms while the gray sticks represent hydrogen atoms (the two structures show different views of the same crystal). (*Source:* Kenneth G. Libbrecht.)

water are the same at 273K. As the temperature drops, however, the saturation vapor pressure with respect to ice decreases. This means that as far as the ice is concerned, the air is supersaturated and water vapor will deposit directly on the ice to grow the ice crystal. As water vapor is deposited, the vapor pressure of the air drops, which results in evaporation from the water droplets—and so the ice crystals grow at the expense of the water droplets. In other words, the ice grows by direct deposition and moves from gas to solid without going through the liquid phase first. It is this process that gives rise to the commonly observed hexagonal snowflakes such as those in Figure 3. If the ice crystal comes into contact with super-cooled water droplets, the water can freeze directly to the ice. In that case, instead of the intricate hexagonal crystal structure, one simply gets rounded ice grains (known as graupel). There is little cohesion between these grains and on the surface; if they are covered by further layers of snow, they can form an unstable layer that can lead to avalanches on slopes. A third way the ice can grow is by agglomeration, as ice crystals join together to form larger snowflakes.

Ice can take on a variety of crystalline structures, depending on the conditions of formation. The most common form at normal atmospheric temperatures and pressures is the hexagonal structure shown in Figure 4, which shows two different views of the same crystal. In this diagram, the spheres represent oxygen atoms and the gray connections represent hydrogen atoms. It is this crystal structure that gives ice the properties that make snow cover of interest to us in terms of its interactions with the climate system.

Northern Hemisphere Snow Cover

The snow cover in the Northern Hemisphere varies in area from about $2 \times 10^6 \, \text{km}^2$ to $4 \times 10^6 \, \text{km}^2$ in summer to about $45 \times 10^6 \, \text{km}^2$ to $47 \times 10^6 \, \text{km}^2$ in winter, during which it occupies about half the land area north of 20°N.

The most obvious feature of the snow cover is its high albedo (bright white color). Although individual ice crystals are clear, each crystal is a reflecting surface. When solar radiation hits the crystal, some of the radiation is transmitted through the ice and some is reflected from the surface. The large number of reflecting surfaces means that much of the radiation that falls on the surface is scattered within the snowpack and reflected back to space. A fresh, low-density snow cover has an albedo of about 80 to 90%. Most objects preferentially absorb particular wavelengths of radiation—green leaves, for example, absorb most of the visible light that falls on them—and, therefore, have a relatively low albedo. Leaves also contain pigments that preferentially absorb blue and red wavelengths; hence, they reflect more in the green part of the spectrum and appear green in color. By contrast, ice crystals absorb and scatter all wavelengths of visible light almost equally, as do water and ice droplets in clouds, which is what gives them their white color. In fact, ice does absorb slightly more at longer wavelengths (i.e., the red part of the spectrum), so the deeper one goes into the snowpack (or into a glacier), the more red has been removed, and so the snow (ice) takes on a slight blue color.

The high reflectivity of fresh snow means that it can have a significant effect on the regional energy balance. Figure 5 shows a mosaic of satellite images collected over a one-week period in February of 2002. The images show extensive snow cover over a large part of North America, and the contrast between the snow-covered and the non-snow-covered areas is very clear. The high albedo means that most of the incident sunlight is reflected and little is absorbed to heat the snowpack. This allows the snow to persist for long periods if the air temperature remains below freezing. The fact that the snow has a much higher albedo than the underlying surface also means that radiation that would otherwise warm the surface is now being reflected away, making regional temperatures lower than they would otherwise be. The snow boundary in Figure 5

FIGURE 5 North American snow cover, February 2–9, 2002. A mosaic of NASA images from the Moderate Resolution Imaging Spectroradiometer (MODIS), flying aboard NASA's *Terra* and *Aqua* satellites. (*Source:* NASA.)

extends southwestward from the Great Lakes toward New Mexico. As most of the airflow over the central and eastern parts of the United States comes from the west and northwest, much of it is coming out of this snow-covered region and, therefore, tends to be colder than it would be without the snow cover present. An extensive continental snow cover such as we find over North America or Siberia during wintertime also builds some **thermal inertia** into the climate system. The high albedo reflects energy away that would otherwise be absorbed. But recall that it takes 335 kJ of energy to convert a kilogram of ice into water. That is energy that would otherwise be warming the surface, so again it slows the temperature increase from winter to spring.

While the snow cover keeps air temperatures lower, it has the opposite effect on the underlying surface. Fresh snow is an agglomeration of hexagonal ice crystals that contain large amounts of air spaces between the crystals. This air cannot move very readily through the snowpack and so the snow is not a very efficient conductor of heat—it has low thermal conductivity. The result is that the snow cover reduces the heat loss from the ground to the overlying atmosphere. As the snow ages, the ice crystals become more spherical and more closely packed (snow density increases). This has the effect of reducing both the albedo and the insulating properties of the snow, although both are usually still higher than if no snow was present.

Permafrost

Permafrost is permanently frozen ground and is defined simply in terms of temperature. (In other words, ice does not actually have to be present.) Permafrost is considered to be present if the ground remains at or below 0°C for

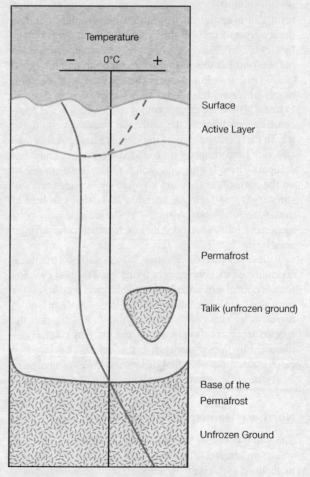

FIGURE 6 Sketch cross section of permafrost showing the temperature profile through the different layers.

2 or more years. Figure 6 gives a schematic view of what permafrost looks like in cross section. There may be pockets of unfrozen ground (Talik) either at the top of the permafrost or within the permafrost. The permafrost is heated from below and cooled from the surface, and the base of the permafrost is the depth at which the net effect produces a temperature of 0°C. Notice in Figure 6 that the temperature at some depth below the surface represents the long-term mean air temperature. Temperature changes in permafrost are slow enough that seasonal and interannual variations in air temperature are averaged out and the temperature is actually a response to the decadal and longer-term temperatures. Lower down, the temperature increases, crossing the freezing point at the base of the permafrost. Near the surface, temperatures may fluctuate widely on a seasonal basis. Surface temperatures are low in winter, but increase in summer. This upper layer, referred to as the **active layer,** freezes in winter and thaws in summer. One can imagine that if there was a long-term cooling trend at the surface, over time the temperature in the permafrost would decrease and the base of the permafrost would move downward. Conversely, if surface temperatures were to increase, then eventually the temperatures within the permafrost would increase and the base of the permafrost would move upward. Measuring the temperature profile in boreholes in the permafrost can, therefore, give an indication of long-term temperature change.

The Fourth Assessment Report of the Intergovernmental Panel on Climate Change (IPCC) assembled permafrost borehole temperature data from permafrost regions across the Northern Hemisphere. These data indicate some degree of permafrost warming across most of the region during the second half of the 20th century. Much of this is attributed to the direct effects of increasing air temperatures, while in some cases there also appears to be a contribution from the insulating effects of snow cover. The distribution of permafrost has also changed over time and, in North America, there is evidence that the permafrost is moving northward in response to long-term warming since the Little Ice Age. The IPCC Fourth Assessment Report suggests that the permafrost area in the Northern Hemisphere is likely to decrease by 20–35% by the middle of the 21st century. Much of this will be due to changes in the distribution of relatively thin and discontinuous permafrost on the high-latitude margins.

Where the permafrost has high ice content, thawing can cause the ice to melt and the surface to subside. Such pockets of subsidence result in a heterogeneous landscape of depressions and small hills—referred to as **thermokarst.** The higher areas tend to dry out while the hollows accumulate water, which affects local ecosystems, and both long-term changes in topography as well as seasonal freezing and thawing create challenges for construction and infrastructure development. In the context of this book, however, the greatest concern over melting permafrost is the potential for increasing greenhouse gas emissions to the atmosphere.

Near-surface melting of permafrost results in lakes and water-logged soil with anaerobic (low oxygen) conditions that create an environment in which methane-producing organisms can flourish. Methane is an important greenhouse gas, and the atmospheric concentration has more than doubled over preindustrial levels. The rate of increase in atmospheric concentration has slowed or stopped in recent years. This is potentially good news for greenhouse warming; however, melting permafrost could change this outlook. Methane emission from regions of melting permafrost could potentially double to over 100 million metric tons per year. However, there is considerable uncertainty in these numbers and some estimates suggest that methane emissions could go much higher. The Arctic is already warming much faster than the rest of the globe due to positive feedbacks such as the snow and ice–albedo feedback. As permafrost continues to melt, there is the potential for more methane release and a positive feedback that will increase temperatures and further accelerate melting. The potential for this is even greater when one considers methane clathrates that are found in offshore permafrost. Clathrates are solid compounds that can trap a gas molecule within them. In this case, the methane is surrounded by a lattice of water molecules and is referred to as a methane clathrate hydrate. These form at relatively low temperatures and high pressures and are found extensively on the continental shelves, not just in polar regions. They represent a large potential source of greenhouse gases. Increased atmospheric methane due to permafrost melt is not currently included in the global climate models used in the IPCC climate change assessments.

GLACIERS AND ICE SHEETS

If snow cover persists through the summer and starts to accumulate over time, the snow increases in thickness, but also undergoes various transformations. Temperature gradients in the snowpack, together with differences in the size and shape of the ice crystals (e.g., convex or concave surfaces), cause localized differences in vapor pressure that result in sublimation from some crystals and deposition on others. This tends to produce rounding of the crystals and compaction, which increases density. The compaction is further increased by pressure as the snowpack increases in thickness. The ice crystals fuse together where they contact each other and they bond through a process referred to as pressure sintering. As the snow is compacted and the ice crystals fuse together, the density increases, the volume of air between the ice grains is reduced, and the snow is transformed into glacier ice. In cold glaciers where temperatures never come close to the melting point, this process can take hundreds to thousands of years (particularly in regions—such as central Antarctica—where snow accumulation may be only centimeters per year). Where the surface is subject-ed to melting, however, the meltwater can percolate down through the pack and refreeze, considerably speeding up the process of glacier ice formation. In these conditions, with high snowfall and frequent melting–freezing cycles, the transformation from snow to glacier ice may take only a few years. New snow may have densities of about $50-70 \, \text{kg m}^{-3}$. As it goes through the transformation to glacier ice, in the intermediate step it is referred to as **firn** (which has densities of about $400-800 \, \text{kg m}^{-3}$), and once the air cavities are sealed and the ice becomes solid, it becomes glacier ice with densities of about $850-900 \, \text{kg m}^{-3}$. At this stage, the ice has low permeability and it can flow and move under its own weight. This low permeability and the ability to flow are characteristics that make glaciers, especially the large continental ice sheets of Greenland and Antarctic, particularly interesting from an Earth systems perspective.

Glacier Flow

Glaciers are broadly categorized into mountain (or alpine) glaciers and continental glaciers. (Other categorizations exist, but they are not relevant to the discussion here.) **Mountain glaciers,** as their name suggests, are found in mountainous regions such as the European Alps, the Himalayas, and the Andes. These glaciers cover relatively small areas and are largely confined to mountain valleys.

Our focus here is primarily on the large continental gla-ciers such as those that are found today on Greenland and Antarctica. These two continental glaciers cover extensive regions and are not confined by the topography. Between them, they account for about 97% of the surface area cov-ered by land ice and about 99.6% of the ice volume. As one can see from Table 6.1, most of this ice is in Antarctica. If Antarctica were to melt, global sea level would increase by about 56 m. Melting all of Greenland, by comparison, would raise sea levels by about 7 m. One thing all of these glaciers have in common, however, is that they are big enough to move.

Most of us are familiar with small blocks of ice—ice cubes that you put in drinks. That ice is brittle; when it is stressed (if you hit it with something hard) it will fracture. At higher pressures, however, deeper within a glacier, slowly applied stress causes the ice to deform more like a plastic. This stress increases as you move deeper into the ice and causes the ice to flow (see the Box "Thinking Quantitatively: Movement of Glaciers"). If the ice is frozen to the bed, then the flow at the base is zero and the maximum flow is somewhere above the influence of the bed. Similarly, friction at the sides in a valley glacier (a glacier flowing down a mountain valley) reduces the flow at the edges, and so the maximum flow is toward the center of the glacier and between the surface and glacier bed (Figures 7a and 7b). Notice in 7a that the plastic deformation does not extend up to the surface. Above a

FIGURE 7 Ice flow profile: (a) longitudinal section; (b) plane view; and (c) view including both plastic flow and basal sliding.

THINKING QUANTITATIVELY
Movement of Glaciers

Box Figure 1a shows the simplest case for a glacier, in which a large rectangular block of ice is sitting on a flat surface. As one moves deeper into the ice, the pressure from the overlying ice increases. At any point in the block, a **stress** is exerted on the ice by the ice above it. This stress is determined by the weight of ice pushing down on it. Weight is simply the force of gravity g acting on an object of a particular mass. In this case, if we think of a thin column of ice over a unit area (1m^2), then the mass is given by the density of the ice ρ multiplied by the height of the column h. The stress τ is then given by

$$\tau = \rho g\, h.$$

If we now place the block of ice on a slope (Box Figure 1b) we can see that there are two components to the stress: a **normal stress** that acts perpendicular to the slope and a shear stress that is parallel to the slope. The length of lines a and b give the relative magnitudes of these two components of the stress. As these three lines form a right angle triangle, we must have $\sin\alpha = a/b$, and $a = b\sin\alpha$. Since

b is the thickness of the ice h, so the shear stress across the base of the column (the **basal shear stress**) is equal to

$$\tau_b = \rho g\, h \sin\alpha.$$

For small angles, one can show that the effect of the bed slope is negligible, and what is important is the surface slope of the glacier. Looking at Box Figure 1c, we see that if we consider a thin column of ice, h is slightly higher on the upslope side, which means that the shear stress (force) is slightly higher on the upslope side than on the downslope side, and that difference causes the ice to deform and flow in the downslope direction (even if the bedrock is level). This deformation or flow occurs by breaking the bonds between layers in the ice crystal lattice. Looking back at the three-dimensional view of the ice crystal in Figure 4, we see that the planes are held together by hydrogen bonds. The stress breaks these bonds, causing the ice crystals to slide forward and down, where the bonds reconnect.

BOX FIGURE 1
Relationship between basal shear stress t_b and the surface slope of a glacier.

depth of about 50 m, the stress is not large enough to cause plastic deformation. In this case, the ice near the surface is simply being carried along by the ice flow at depth. Where the rate of flow changes, maybe due to a large change in the subsurface topography, then the brittle ice near the surface fractures, forming a crevasse. Where the ice isn't frozen to the bed—where there is liquid water at the base,

or where the bed is made up of unconsolidated material (particularly if that also has a high water content)—then the glacier can slide over the bed. In this case, the downslope movement has two components, one due to plastic deformation and one to basal sliding (Figure 7c).

So how does glacier movement play into the themes of this book? First, the major ice sheets such

FIGURE 8 Flow lines on an ice dome. An ice core drilled at point C will have minimal distortion due to ice movement.

as Greenland and Antarctica are an important source of information on past climates and past atmospheric gas concentrations. During the transformation of snow to ice already described, the air spaces present in the snow become sealed forming small air cavities in the ice. When we drill a core down through the ice, we can extract the gas from those cavities and determine the atmospheric gas concentrations at the time this transformation occurred. It should now be obvious, however, that we can't simply drill anywhere on the ice cap. Reconstructing the history is much easier if we know that the ice at the bottom of the core is the oldest, that the ice immediately above that was laid down in the same place and slightly later, and that there is a continuous sequence up to the present at the surface. (Note that the present isn't really the present! If it takes 50 years, for example, for the ice to form and seal off the air cavities, then the top of the ice core is actually 50 years older than when the core was obtained.) Looking at Figure 7c, we can see that these criteria certainly would not be satisfied for an ice core extracted from a rapidly moving glacier. Ice cores extracted from anywhere on the glacier can provide information on the ice structure and glacier dynamics, but for long-term climate reconstruction it is best to take the core from parts of the ice cap that are not moving. Imagine an ice dome such as that shown in Figure 8. In such a situation, the flow would be radially away from the highest point at the center of the dome. The flow would be fastest where the surface slope is greatest, and minimal where the surface slope is zero—a core drilled at point C would have minimal problems due to deformation and movement. The new deep core in Antarctica was drilled at the top of dome C at the dynamical center of the East Antarctic ice sheet.

The movement of glaciers, particularly the big continental ice sheets, has other, more direct impacts on the Earth system. A glacier is not a uniform mass. Snow falls on the glacier in winter, and some of that melts in summer. Where temperatures are cold enough that the snow persists through the summer, it will build up over time and transform into ice in the **accumulation zone** of the glacier (Figure 9). Because the ice will then flow downward, the ice will extend past the accumulation zone into regions of higher temperatures where melt (ablation) will occur in summer. The ice profile—its thickness and extent—will depend on the balance between accumulation, transport, and melt. If any of these parameters change, the profile of the glacier will change—getting thicker or thinner, retreating or advancing. Because climate tends to be highly localized in mountainous regions, it is possible for a glacier to be growing larger and advancing in one valley, while a nearby glacier is melting and retreating. With widespread

FIGURE 9 Accumulation and ablation zones on a glacier.

warming over the latter part of the 20th century, however, most mountain glaciers are retreating.

Imagine what would happen in the polar ice sheets if there was no ice flow. There would be no **ablation zone** because there would be no ice flowing from further inland, and any snow falling in that region would simply melt. Conversely, there would be no melt in the accumulation zone, and any snow that fell would build up as ice. Does this mean the ice in this region would continue to thicken indefinitely? Not really! Once it reached a depth of about 4 km, the ice at the base would start to melt as a consequence of the high pressure, along with warming provided by geothermal heat coming from below. The high pressure at the base of the ice lowers the melting point by a few degrees. But that, by itself, would not make the ice melt, as the temperature at the surface of the ice is about ($-50°C$ in the polar regions. If the ice was this cold at the base, the small freezing point depression caused by the high pressure would not make much difference. What makes the ice melt is the geothermal heat coming from below. This heat flux, which is approximately 0.03 W/m^2 in continental areas, must get out through the ice by conduction; hence, the temperature must be higher at the bottom of the ice sheet than at the top. When the ice thickness approaches 4 km, the temperature at the base approaches 0°C (or a few degrees lower), and the ice begins to melt.

In reality, ice does move, often aided by basal melting. Under any particular climatic regime, the ice will reach an equilibrium state. Even slight changes in climate, however, can have a significant impact on the ice sheet dynamics. The edge of the Greenland ice cap, for example, forms valley glaciers that end in the ocean. Although the precise mechanism hasn't been fully explained, it appears that higher temperatures during the latter part of the 20th century have caused meltwater to percolate down beneath these outlet glaciers, causing them to flow faster and to increase the rate of ablation and ice loss from the continent. Because of this, Greenland melt is occurring faster than expected. While this isn't yet enough to have a significant impact on sea-level rise or on North Atlantic salinity during this century, we also don't know whether this rate of melt will remain the same, or whether it could significantly increase as warming continues.

Other surprises could be in store when we look at what could happen to the West Antarctic ice sheet (West Antarctica is the panhandle part of the Antarctic continent). Glacial flow rates are highly variable. They depend on a range of factors such as ice structure, temperature, slope, bedrock type, and the presence or absence of water at the base of the glacier. The velocity of a glacier over its base may vary by a factor of 100 between different glaciers, but typical values range from tens to hundreds of

millimeters per day. Some glaciers, however, have been observed to "surge." Surging glaciers move episodically at velocities that may be 100 times faster than normal. If the West Antarctic ice sheet were to surge, it would deliver ice into the ocean at a much higher rate than present, causing a more rapid rise in sea level. While West Antarctica isn't known to surge, the ice sheet is inherently unstable and is held in place now by two large ice shelves at its edges. If the ice shelves were removed (if warming oceans were to melt the ice shelves at their base, for example), then much of the West Antarctic would flow rapidly out to sea.

SEA ICE AND CLIMATE

In the last part of this chapter we turn to the polar oceans to discuss the formation of sea ice and to examine climate variability induced by sea-ice effects on atmosphere–ocean interactions at high latitudes. In this section we will discuss the seasonal distribution of sea ice, and we will examine some of the ways in which changes in sea-ice cover affect the polar ocean climate. These effects are particularly interesting because they tend to dominate the high-latitude response to increasing atmospheric CO_2 levels in global climate models.

Ice–Climate Interactions

The seasonal distribution of sea ice over the polar oceans is shown in Figure 10. The seasonal range of the ice cover is extreme: The Northern Hemisphere ice cover almost doubles in size from approximately 8.5×10^6 km^2 to 15×10^6 km^2 between summer and winter; the Southern Ocean ice cover grows from 4×10^6 km^2 to 20×10^6 km^2. These are the average distributions measured during the last 30 years of the 20th century using satellite observations of the microwave radiation emitted from the ice surface. Because certain wavelengths of microwave radiation are not attenuated (absorbed or scattered) by the atmosphere and the cloud cover, we can obtain accurate measures of ice extent regardless of the weather. And, because we are measuring radiation emitted by the ice, whether the observations are made during day or night makes no difference. These same data reveal that the summer ice extent in the Northern Hemisphere has been decreasing dramatically during the first decade of the 21st century. If it continues, would we expect this reduced ice cover to have a measurable impact on climate? This is a question we ask in the "Critical-Thinking Problems" section at the end of the chapter. If you read the rest of this section, you should be able to suggest some possible answers for yourself!

Northern hemisphere sea ice   Southern hemisphere sea ice

☐ Absolute ☐ Average ☐ Average ■ Absolute
   Maximum   Minimum

FIGURE 10 The seasonal distribution of sea ice in the Northern and Southern hemispheres.

Sea ice forms when the temperature of the ocean surface drops below the freezing point (about −1.8°C for typical ocean salinities). Sea ice grows in thickness as new ice formed from seawater freezes onto the bottom of the icepack. Note that this is very different from how glacier ice forms on land, where the ice forms and accumulates at the surface. New sea ice typically reaches thicknesses of about 1 m during a single winter. The ice cover melts and freezes seasonally at the equatorward margins of the pack but lasts throughout the year at higher latitudes. This permanent pack ice in the Arctic Ocean reaches equilibrium thicknesses of about 5 m; the Southern Ocean ice is much thinner because very little of it survives through the summer melt.

Several features of this ice distribution are important to our discussion. The large seasonal range is a result of thermodynamic controls on the ice cover (that is, the ice cover is responding to the seasonal changes in temperature). The asymmetric nature of the ice margin in the Arctic Ocean, however, reflects the influence of the continental configurations and the ocean circulation: the ice margin extends well to the south in both the western North Atlantic and western North Pacific. At the eastern margins of both oceans, open water extends much farther north off Norway and Alaska. Note that the shape of the ice margin reflects the pattern of ocean currents. The warm waters of the North Atlantic Drift and the Kuroshio Current prevent the ice margins from extending farther south in the eastern oceans, whereas the East Greenland Current, the Labrador Current, and the Oyashio Current bring colder water and carry increased ice cover southward in the west.

The ice distribution helps illustrate one of the important facts about the sea-ice cover: Sea ice moves. As with the ice sheets, the ice does not simply form and melt in place; rather, it is in a constant state of motion. Indeed, it moves much faster than do the continental ice sheets. The typical pattern of sea-ice drift in the Arctic Ocean is shown in Figure 11. The map reveals two primary features of the ice circulation: a clockwise circulation, or gyre (the Beaufort Sea Gyre), in the west, and the Transpolar Drift Stream, which flows across the pole from the Siberian coast to the East Greenland Sea. This ice flows into the East Greenland Current, where it is transported southward out of the Arctic Ocean. On average it takes about 5 years for ice that forms off the Siberian coast to be transported across the Arctic Basin. Ice that forms in the Beaufort Gyre, however, may last much longer, possibly circling the western Arctic several times before melting in the summer or becoming caught in the Transpolar Drift.

Moved around by winds and ocean currents, the ice is broken into individual pieces (ice floes) that continuously join and break up. Where floes collide, large mounds of ice are thrust up into pressure ridges; where floes move apart, they produce areas of open water called leads or **polynyii** (singular, polynya). Leads are linear open-water features, and polynyii are irregular areas of open water. In winter, these open-water areas freeze very rapidly, but because the icepack is so dynamic, there is always a small amount of open water present, even in midwinter. This is important for two reasons: One, the presence of open water allows for the constant production of new ice, thus releasing salt to the upper ocean and increasing the density of the surface layer. Two, the open water has a considerable impact on the Arctic energy budget: The ocean loses heat to the atmosphere about 100 times faster from the open water than it does through the insulating ice cover. The combined effect of the positive ice–albedo feedback and the heat loss from the

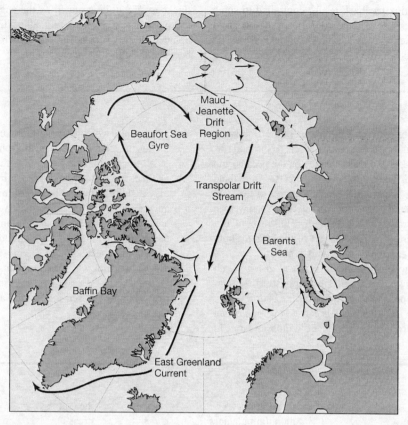

FIGURE 11 The typical pattern of sea-ice drift in the Arctic Ocean.

ocean to the atmosphere in areas of low ice concentration both have a significant influence on the high-latitude energy budget. The potential impacts of this become obvious when we look at global model projections of future global warming, where these positive feedbacks dominate the high-latitude climate response.

Ice–Atmosphere Interactions

Sea-ice cover forms as a response to ocean temperatures and that the distribution is then modified by winds and ocean currents. However, the ice cover is not simply a response to the climate: The ice cover modifies the atmospheric and oceanic circulations. We have seen that ice production in the North Atlantic contributes to the formation of North Atlantic Deep Water, which is a major factor in driving the oceanic thermohaline circulation. We have also discussed the ice–albedo feedback, whereby a change in temperature causes a change in the ice cover and the surface albedo, which further modifies the temperature. Recall that this is a positive feedback: Increasing temperature → decreasing ice cover → decreasing albedo → increasing temperature. This feedback can operate year-round near the sunlit ice margins but can play a role only in

summer at higher latitudes. (Recall that there is no solar radiation at high latitudes in winter.)

Another sea-ice feedback, however, is important year-round. The ocean surface is a source of thermal energy and latent heat for the polar atmosphere, and the most rapid heat transfer from the ocean to the atmosphere occurs through the areas of thin ice or open water. Thus, we can picture a second positive feedback (Figure 12): Increasing temperature leads to decreasing ice cover, which leads to increasing ocean heat flux to the atmosphere, which leads to increasing temperature. Both the ice–albedo feedback and the ocean heat-flux feedback are related to the ice extent and concentration (that is, the area of ice-covered

FIGURE 12 The sea-ice–ocean heat-flux feedback loop.

ocean). The heat-flux feedback is also controlled to some degree by ice thickness: The heat loss from the ocean to the atmosphere increases as ice thickness decreases. The extent of the ice cover, the ice concentration, and the ice thickness are all determined by the energy budget and the ice dynamics and these, in turn, all act to change the energy balance at the surface and the distribution of energy between the atmosphere and ocean.

Chapter Summary

1. The cryosphere represents the frozen part of the Earth system. It includes glaciers and ice sheets on the land surface, frozen lakes and rivers, sea ice on the oceans, and frozen ground. The continental ice sheets—Greenland and Antarctica—represent the largest sources of freshwater on the planet. If both Antarctica and Greenland were to melt, it would raise global sea level by a little over 60 m.
2. The cryosphere is a dynamic part of the system; both glaciers and sea ice are continuously moving.
   a. Glaciers move under the influence of gravity, with the ice flowing primarily in response to the ice-surface slope, and by sliding over the bedrock.
   b. Sea ice, on the other hand, is carried over the ocean surface through the action of winds and ocean currents, which play a significant role in determining the geographic distributions of sea ice in the Northern Hemisphere.
3. Sea ice, snow cover, and the continental ice sheets all play a significant role in determining the energy balance at high latitudes, primarily through the ice--albedo feedback. This feedback dominates the response of the climate system at high latitudes. For this reason, we would expect some of the most obvious effects of global warming to first appear at high latitudes. During the last decade we have, in fact, seen significant changes in sea-ice extent and melt from the Greenland ice cap.

Key Terms

ablation zone	freezing nuclei	shear stress
accumulation zone	mountain glaciers	stress
active layer	normal stress	supercooled water
basal shear stress	permafrost	thermal inertia
continental ice sheet	phase diagram	thermokarst
critical point	polynyii	triple point
firn	sea ice	

Review Questions

1. How does a snow cover affect overlying air temperatures?
2. How does the snow cover affect soil temperatures?
3. How do snow crystals form?
4. What is permafrost?
5. Why might melting permafrost be important for future climate change?
6. Explain how snow is transformed into glacier ice.
7. Explain how glaciers move.
8. Explain the difference between the way glaciers and sea ice accumulate ice.
9. What role do ocean currents play in the distribution of sea ice?
10. What are the two primary ways sea ice affects climate?

Critical-Thinking Problems

1. The first decade of the 21st century has been characterized by significant reductions in the extent of summertime Arctic sea ice. Given what you know of ice–climate interactions explain what effect you think continued decreases in North Atlantic ice cover may have on European climate.
2. Using the density for ice (that you can find in the text) and assuming an ice thickness of 130 m and a surface slope of 5°, calculate the basal shear stress under the glacier. The number you obtain is a typical value for a glacier. If the surface slope changes, the thickness of the ice will change. Assuming that the basal shear stress remains the same, how thick will the ice be if the slope increased to 10°? What does this tell you about the relationship between surface slope and glacier thickness?

Further Reading

General

Slaymaker, O., and R. Kelly. 2007. *The cryosphere and global environmental change*. Malden, MA: Blackwell Publishing.

Advanced

Paterson, W. S. B. 1994. *The physics of glaciers*. 3rd ed. Oxford, New York, Tokyo: Pergamon/Elsevier Science Ltd.

M. Tranter, R. Armstrong, E. Brun, G. Jones, M. Sharp, and M. Williams, eds. 1999. *Interactions between the cryosphere, climate and greenhouse gases*. IAHS Publication No, 256. Wallingford: International Association of Hydrological Sciences Press.

Circulation of the Solid Earth

Plate Tectonics

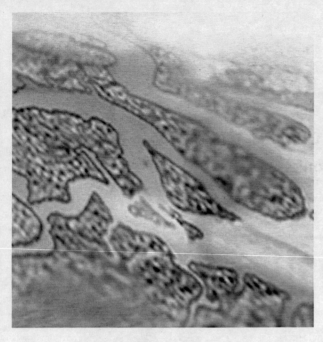

Circulation of the Solid Earth

Plate Tectonics

Key Questions

- How do the physical and chemical characteristics of Earth change with depth toward its center?

- What is plate tectonics?

- What provides the energy that drives plate tectonics?

- How can we relate the surface features of Earth to plate tectonics?

- What is the rock cycle?

- How have the geographical positions of the continents changed through time as a result of plate tectonic activity?

Chapter Overview

Our understanding of solid Earth processes has taken a great leap forward since the mid-1960s with the development of the theory of *plate tectonics*. Yet there is still much to learn about the composition and dynamics of the solid Earth. Earthquakes and volcanoes demonstrate that the interior of Earth is not a static place. Rather, like the oceans and atmosphere clinging to its surface, the solid Earth is in motion. The energy that drives the circulation of the solid Earth derives not from the Sun but from Earth's interior. Convective currents in the interior are coupled to the rigid rocks that form the continents and seafloor, putting the continents in motion. Where continents collide, huge mountain belts form; where oceanic blocks collide with each other or with continents, deep-sea trenches and volcanoes form. These plate tectonic forces join with the surface processes of rock weathering and erosion to generate landscapes and recycle elements from solid Earth reservoirs into the soils, hydrosphere, and atmosphere, making those elements available to the biota once again. Thus, plate tectonic activity is critical to the maintenance of a biologically active planet.

We will study the circulation of the solid Earth in the way we studied atmospheric and oceanic circulation. First, we explore the anatomy of the planet, from its exterior to its greatest depths. The tools used to reveal Earth's internal structure give us clues about the temperature and compositional variations in the interior, but very little direct information exists. Then we discuss how the heat flux from the interior produces the motions within the solid Earth and how these motions form and modify Earth's major surface features: mid-ocean ridges and mountains, deep-sea trenches, and transform faults. We then trace the history of these motions over the past 3 billion years, during which time the continents have drifted apart and joined together again and again in a global tectonic cycle.

INTRODUCTION

The German meteorologist Alfred Wegener is largely credited with establishing the fundamental underpinnings of the theory that we now call **plate tectonics**. According to this theory, Earth's surface is divided into rigid plates of continent and ocean floor that move relative to each other through time. (*Tectonics* is the study of Earth's crust and the processes that deform it.) Wegener was fascinated by the near-perfect fit between the coastlines of Africa and South America and by the correspondence among the geological features, fossils, and evidence of glaciers on these two separate continents. Could all the continents once have been assembled into a *supercontinent?* Wegener believed so, as had others before him. He, however, was the first to put together all the diverse evidence in support of that concept. He named the proposed landmass **Pangea**, meaning "all Earth." He proposed that Pangea began to break apart just after the beginning of the Mesozoic era, about 200 million years ago, and that the continents then slowly drifted into their current positions. This theory is called **continental drift**. Wegener's maps, produced in 1924, are remarkably similar to the best global paleogeographic reconstructions available today (Figure 1).

Although it was welcomed by paleontologists because of its consistency with the terrestrial fossil record, Wegener's theory of continental drift was not well received by the geophysicists of his day. The British scientist Sir Harold Jeffreys presented calculations in 1925 demonstrating that the continents could not possibly plow through the rigid seafloor, as the theory seemed to require. Other scientists were unconvinced because Wegener could not propose a physical mechanism for driving the motion of the continents. Indeed, many of Wegener's own calculations and proposed mechanisms were found to be in error and untenable.

The acceptance of Wegener's theory of continental drift awaited a better understanding of the structure and operation of the solid Earth. That understanding has come about largely as the result of geophysical exploration, which has revealed the complex anatomy of Earth's interior and has led to the theory of *seafloor spreading*.

ANATOMY OF EARTH

Seismic Probing of Earth's Interior

For centuries geologists have been probing Earth's surface, cataloging the variety of rocks exposed and studying the processes that have led to their formation. The study of material that has risen to the surface has given some insight into the chemical and *mineralogical* composition of the shallow interior, but virtually everything we know about Earth's deep interior has been derived by indirect methods. Paramount among these methods is the science of *seismology*, the study of earthquakes and related phenomena.

EARTHQUAKES   An **earthquake** is the sudden release of stored energy as a result of rapid movement between two blocks of rock. This energy radiates away from the earthquake in the form of vibrations. The site of energy release, known as the *focus,* can be anywhere from very near Earth's surface to as deep as 700 km below. This area, Earth's uppermost shell, is rigid; when it deforms, it does so *elastically*. This means that the material recovers its shape

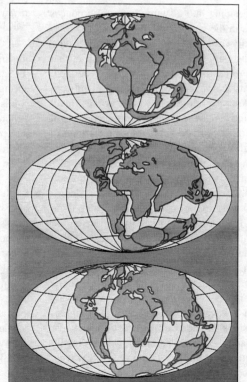

Late Carboniferous (about 300 million years ago)

Eocene (about 50 million years ago)

Pleistocene Glacial (about 1 million years ago)

FIGURE 1   Wegener's reconstructions of the positions of the continents in the geological past. (*Source:* From W. K. Hamblin and E. H. Christiansen, *Earth's Dynamic Systems*, 8/e, 1998. Reprinted by permission of Prentice Hall, Upper Saddle River, N.J.)

FIGURE 2 An earthquake's focus is located at depth. The point on the surface that directly overlies the focus is the epicenter. (*Source:* From J. P. Davidson, W. E. Reed, and P. M. Davis, *Exploring Earth: An Introduction to Physical Geology*, 1997. Reprinted by permission of Prentice Hall, Upper Saddle River, N.J.)

after the force that is tending to deform it is removed, unless it is deformed to the point of fracture and the original shape cannot be recovered. If there is differential movement on either side of the break, the fracture is called a *fault*. The *epicenter* of an earthquake is the position on Earth's surface directly above the focus (Figure 2).

Seismic Waves

Just as a person jumping into a swimming pool produces waves and ripples in the water, earthquakes create vibrations called **seismic waves** that ripple through Earth's interior, away from the earthquake's focus, as a result of that deformation. Two types of seismic waves are generated: body waves and surface waves. Both types spread outward from the focus. As we might expect, **body waves** travel through Earth's interior, whereas **surface waves** travel only across the surface. Surface waves transmit earthquake energy along Earth's surface, where movement is unconstrained vertically. The motion is much like that of a water wave, easily seen by watching a cork bobbing up and down: Particles are displaced upward, backward, downward, and then forward in a circular motion. There is no net movement of the particles, but energy is transmitted away from the center. Body waves are categorized as either P waves or S waves on the basis of their mode of propagation through Earth. **P waves**, or primary waves, result from the compression of material in Earth's interior. The material is alternately compressed and, as the wave travels away, stretched. Thus, a P wave travels as a series of compressions and expansions in the overall direction of wave movement, similar to the way sound travels or to the response of a spring or a Slinky® (Figure 3a). **S waves**, which are also called secondary or shear waves, are

FIGURE 3 The movement of seismic body waves. (a) P waves alternately compress and expand materials, like the transfer of a compressive force imposed on a spring. (b) S waves move material from side to side, perpendicular to the overall direction of wave motion, just as a spring responds to repeated side-to-side shaking. (*Source:* From J. P. Davidson, W. E. Reed, and P. M. Davis, *Exploring Earth: An Introduction to Physical Geology*, 1997. Reprinted by permission of Prentice Hall, Upper Saddle River, N.J.)

transmitted as displacements perpendicular to the overall direction of wave travel. An analogy is the movement of a spring swung from side to side (Figure 3b). Although both solids and fluids can transmit P waves, only materials with structural rigidity (solids) can transmit S waves. This fact has proved to be important in the characterization of Earth's interior, allowing us to identify particular regions as fluids rather than solids, as we will see later.

Eventually the path of all body waves intersects Earth's surface. There they can be detected and recorded by a *seismograph,* which is a sensitive instrument that detects slight vertical and horizontal displacements of Earth's surface (see the Box "A Closer Look: The Principle of the Seismograph"). The rate at which seismic body waves travel through Earth depends on the properties of the material in Earth's interior. If we know how much time it takes waves to travel from the earthquake source to a site where they are detected at the surface by a seismograph, and if we can determine the path a particular seismic wave has taken, then we can calculate an average wave speed along that path. For a single earthquake event, a seismograph near the wave source records waves that traveled very shallowly through Earth, whereas a seismograph far from the source of the earthquake receives seismic waves that may have traveled through Earth's center. Thus, by comparing several seismographic records from various places around the world for a particular event, we can construct a fairly detailed three-dimensional view of the paths along which seismic waves travel through Earth. This process is called *seismic tomography* (Figure 4).

GENERALIZED STRUCTURE OF EARTH   The gross picture revealed by seismic imaging is of a layered Earth comprising a *crust,* a *mantle* (consisting of an upper mantle and a lower mantle), an *outer core,* and an *inner core* (Figure 5), defined on the basis of contrasts in seismic wave velocities. The shallowest of these transitions is the crust–mantle boundary, first discovered by the Croatian seismologist Aa Mohorovičić, who was investigating shock waves traveling through Earth from Zagreb (the former Yugoslavia) in the early 20th century. The boundary is now known as the *Mohorovčić discontinuity,* or the **Moho**, in his honor. This boundary is defined by a sharp increase in seismic wave velocities; P-wave velocities in the crust of around 5–6 km/sec increase to uppermost mantle velocities of about 8 km/sec. Beneath the continental crust, the depth to the Moho ranges from as much as 75 km in young mountain belts to 20 km in areas undergoing extension and crustal thinning. Beneath the oceanic crust, the Moho is at a nearly constant depth of around 7 km below the ocean floor.

Below the Moho, the velocities of both P waves and S waves generally increase with depth through the mantle, although a *low-velocity zone* (or LVZ) exists at a depth of between 80 and 300 km (see Figure 5). Velocities then increase again through the transition zone between the upper and lower mantles, but the increase is not smooth: It occurs in a stepwise fashion, which indicates some sort of incremental change in mantle properties. Seismologists think that this change is related to a transformation of the minerals present to more compact, denser forms. Seismic velocities then increase more gradually with depth through the lower mantle.

The boundary between the lower mantle and the outer core, at a depth of 2900 km, is distinguished by a significant drop in P-wave velocities and by the disappearance

FIGURE 4   [See color section] Tomographic image of the mantle's S-wave velocity variations underneath North America, along the transect line shown in the insert. Blue colors indicate regions of fast seismic velocities, while reds indicate slow seismic velocities. The blue region cutting across the center of the diagram is the downgoing Farallon slab, which has been subducting under North America for 100 million years.   (*Source:* From W. K. Hamblin and E. H. Christiansen, *Earth's Dynamic Systems*, 8/e, 1998. Reprinted by permission of Prentice Hall, Upper Saddle River, N.J.)

A CLOSER LOOK
The Principle of the Seismograph

In the simplest sense, seismographs consist of a recording drum, which is anchored to bedrock and situated below a suspended weight with a pen attached. The weight has sufficient inertia to remain vertical as the ground (and the recording drum) vibrate beneath it (Box Figure 1). During an earthquake, the recording drum vibrates back and forth, allowing the seismologist to determine the amount of displacement that occurs as the seismic wave passes through the ground below.

The *amplitude,* or size, of seismic waves is related to the amount of energy released during an earthquake. Earthquake amplitudes are reported according to the

BOX FIGURE 1   A seismograph.   (*Source:* From S. Judson and S. M. Richardson, *Earth: An Introduction to Geologic Change,* 1995. Reprinted by permission of Prentice Hall, Upper Saddle River, N.J.)

(a)

BOX FIGURE 2A   Aerial view of collapsed section of the Cypress viaduct on Interstate 880, Oakland, California, after the 1989 Loma Prieta earthquake.

of S waves. Because S waves travel only through solids, geophysicists infer that the outer core is a metallic fluid. At a depth of 5150 km, P-wave velocities increase markedly. This increase in velocity measurably deflects P waves from their anticipated path, confirming that the inner core is solid. Tremendous pressure at Earth's center is thought to be responsible for converting fluids to solids there.

This description of Earth's interior structure, although essentially correct, is greatly simplified. Seismic tomography reveals a more heterogeneous distribution of seismic wave velocities (see Figure 4), perhaps related to the exchange of materials between Earth's interior and its surface. Clearly Earth's interior is a dynamic place. Plate tectonic activity has altered the chemical and thermal structure of the mantle and may have operated in response to influences conveyed through the mantle from the core. Let us explore these heterogeneities in more detail, utilizing information not only from seismology but also from *petrology,* the study of the origin and evolution of the chemical and mineralogical compositions of rocks.

The Crust

Earth's uppermost layer, the crust, is not homogeneous; rather, it varies in both thickness and composition. The most pronounced differences are between the continental and oceanic crust. *Continental crust* underlies the continents, whereas *oceanic crust* underlies the ocean basins. As delineated by variations in Moho depth, continental crust is thicker than oceanic crust. It is also less dense and

(b)

FIGURE BOX 2B Seismograms of the Loma Prieta earthquake recorded by seismographs situated on bedrock, sand and gravel, and soft mud. Notice how the amplitude and duration of ground shaking is greater in soft mud than in bedrock. (*Source:* S. Hough P. A. Friberg, R. Busby, E. F. Field, K. H. Jacob & R. D. Borcherdt, *Nature* 344, 1990, pp. 853–855; see also http://geopubs.wr.usgs.gov/fact-sheet/fs176-95.)

"moment magnitude" scale, an improved variant of the more familiar but now essentially obsolete "Richter" scale. For every tenfold increase in seismic wave amplitude (and approximately 30-fold increase in energy), the magnitude increases by one unit. Thus, an earthquake with a magnitude of 5 releases 30 times as much energy as one with a magnitude of 4.

Seismographs from around the world recorded the October 17, 1989, Loma Prieta earthquake with an epicenter 16 km northeast of Santa Cruz, California (Box Figure 2b). The earthquake had a moment magnitude of 6.9, cre-

ating the first major rupture along the San Andreas Fault since the famous 1906 San Francisco earthquake. Sixty-eight people died as a result of the Loma Prieta event, and nearly 4,000 were injured. Thousands of homes and businesses were damaged or destroyed, with an estimated dollar loss on the order of $7 billion. Structures built on mud and sand suffered larger amplitude and longer duration shaking than those on bedrock. One of the lasting images of the earthquake is the collapsed sections of the Cypress viaduct on Interstate 880 (Box Figure 2a).

on average older. The two types of crust differ in chemical and mineralogical compositions as well. To understand these differences, we must first introduce a genetic classification of crustal rocks.

IGNEOUS, SEDIMENTARY, AND METAMORPHIC ROCKS
All rocks are composed of **minerals**, defined as naturally occurring inorganic solids of definite crystal structure and chemical composition. Geologists recognize three major types of rocks: *igneous, sedimentary,* and *metamorphic.* **Igneous rocks** form by the cooling and solidification of **magma**, which is molten, or liquid, rock. If the magma solidifies beneath Earth's surface, the rocks are called *intrusive* igneous rocks. **Granite** is a well-known intrusive rock. If the magma is carried to Earth's surface at a volcano and erupts, it is called *lava* and cools rapidly, forming

extrusive igneous rocks. **Basalt** is an abundant type of extrusive igneous rock. Both intrusive and extrusive igneous rocks vary in composition, especially in the amount of the mineral quartz (SiO_2) they contain. *Felsic* igneous rocks (e.g., granite or *rhyolite,* its extrusive analogue) are quartz-rich, light-colored, and less dense than *mafic* igneous rocks (such as basalt or *gabbro,* its intrusive analogue).

Rocks (of any type) that are exposed at Earth's surface tend to decompose, or *weather,* into finer materials called **sediments**—layers of unconsolidated mineral matter that is transported by water, wind, or gravity. As new sediments are deposited on top of existing sediments, the underlying sediments become compacted, expelling water from the pores between sediment grains. The remaining pores may become filled with mineral cements precipitated from subsurface fluids. Compaction and cementation

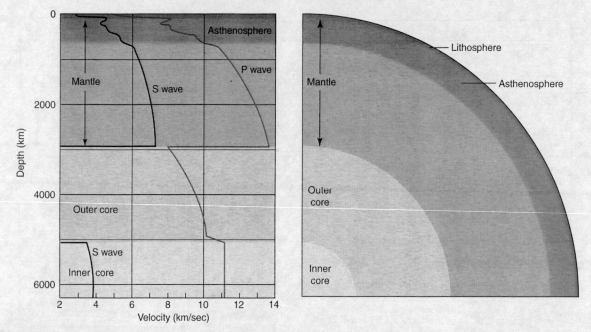

FIGURE 5 Internal structure of Earth, showing the distribution of seismic wave speeds. The speed changes with depth, defining the boundaries between the crust, mantle, outer core, and inner core. (*Source:* From W. K. Hamblin and E. H. Christiansen, *Earth's Dynamic Systems*, 9/e, 2001. Reprinted by permission of Prentice Hall, Upper Saddle River, N.J.)

are processes that contribute to **lithification**, the conversion of loose sediments into thick, cohesive, layered deposits known as **sedimentary rocks**. Sedimentary rocks formed from sand-sized grains (>63 μm in diameter) are called *sandstone,* whereas rocks composed of finer grains are called *mudstones.* Finely layered mudstones are commonly called *shales.* Sedimentary rocks may instead form chemically or biochemically. For example, some marine organisms form a shell or skeleton by precipitating calcium carbonate ($CaCO_3$) minerals. When the organisms die, the shells and skeletons accumulate on the seafloor and ultimately lithify into sedimentary rocks known as *limestones.*

Rocks (of any type) that are exposed to high temperatures, high pressures, chemically active fluids, or any combination of these agents are transformed in mineralogical and chemical compositions. As long as no melting is involved, the altered material is said to have been *metamorphosed* and is called a **metamorphic rock.** (When melting occurs, the resulting rock is igneous.) *Marble* is metamorphosed limestone, and *slate* is metamorphosed shale.

MAJOR ROCK-FORMING MINERALS Both continental and oceanic crust are composed primarily of rocks made of **silicate minerals**—that is, minerals rich in silicon and oxygen. *Feldspars* are the most abundant minerals in the continental crust. They are silicate minerals with aluminum, sodium, calcium, and potassium in their structures. Quartz also is an abundant silicate mineral in the

upper continental crust. Together with certain other minerals, feldspars and quartz form granite and *granodiorite* (a slightly less quartz-rich rock), the hard, erosion-resistant rocks that create the high peaks of many mountain ranges, including the Sierra Nevadas of California.

Magnesium and iron-rich silicate minerals such as *olivine* and *pyroxene* characterize the basalts of the oceanic crust. The Hawaiian Islands are composed of basaltic materials. The high relative abundance of these dense minerals in the oceanic crust accounts for the higher density of mafic oceanic crust in relation to felsic continental crust.

SEDIMENTARY COVER Sediments and sedimentary rocks overlie the basalts and granites/diorites of the oceanic and continental crust, respectively. The source of these materials is easy to identify in the ocean: Sediments settle through the water column and accumulate on the seafloor as a sequence of relatively flat layers. Sedimentary rocks are also abundant in the continental crust, however. Some sedimentary rocks accumulated in basins on the continents themselves, but most were originally deposited as sediments on the seafloor and may have been deeply buried. Subsequent tectonic activity transported these sediments onto the continents. There they became exposed in mountain belts where the once-flat layering has typically become highly deformed through uplift. The oldest parts of the continents were once sedimentary rocks that have become significantly deformed and altered through many cycles of tectonic activity and metamorphism.

The Mantle

Beneath the crust is the mantle, which extends from the Moho to the top of the fluid outer core. The exact structure and composition of the mantle is a hotly debated topic among geologists, largely because the mantle is very difficult to observe. The samples of deeper mantle material that are available at the surface were brought up during rare geological events, such as the formation of kimberlites. *Kimberlites* are long, pipe-shaped igneous bodies that were emplaced after having passed rapidly from the upper mantle to the near-surface. They are remarkable in that they contain diamonds that formed under the high-pressure conditions of the mantle.

Most of what we know about the mantle is inferred from seismology. The velocity structure so determined indicates that the mantle is relatively uniform in composition and formed of silicate minerals. However, as depth increases so too do pressures and temperatures, causing changes in the structural and mineralogical composition of these silicates. These changes affect seismic wave velocities.

The recognition of the seismic low-velocity zone from depths of 80–300 km in the upper mantle proves to be an important link in plate tectonic theory. Most geologists accept that the low seismic wave velocities are the result of the presence of some molten rock at this depth. There need not be much; the data can be explained if only 1% or less of the rock is molten. Yet the small amount of melt present is critical, because it allows the crust and upper mantle to move relative to the underlying mantle—a basic tenet of plate tectonics.

A transition zone of rapidly increasing seismic wave velocities from depths of 370–650 km separates the upper and lower mantles. Geologists disagree on the reason for the transition zone. Many conclude from seismic evidence and theory that the transition zone is the consequence of mineralogical changes, whereas others conclude that differences in elemental composition are the cause. We return to this controversy later in our discussion of mantle convection.

The Core

The abundance of most elements in the crust and mantle can be explained by using meteorite compositions as a basis for comparison. Meteorites are thought to be fragments of larger *planetesimals* (bodies tens to hundreds of kilometers in diameter), many of which now reside in the asteroid belt of the solar system. Their parent bodies formed at the same time that the Sun did from the solar nebula. A particular class of meteorites, the *carbonaceous chondrites*, is made of material that is thought to be essentially unaltered from the original nebular composition. Thus, carbonaceous chondrites are thought to be representative of the average abundances of elements in the solar system, including silicon, sodium, magnesium, calcium, and oxygen—all the basic rock-forming elements. Earth

contains much less water and other *volatile* (easily vaporized) *compounds* as a consequence of its high-temperature formation, but we expect that its composition should otherwise be chondritic. By comparison with chondritic meteorites, the mantle and crust are significantly depleted in iron. This deficiency is made up for in the core, which is believed to be dominated by iron, along with small amounts (about 6%) of nickel, and approximately 8–10% of some unknown light element, which could be oxygen, sulfur, hydrogen, or silicon. (The light element has to be there; otherwise, the core would be even denser than it is observed to be.) The iron–nickel core is much denser than the overlying mantle, which, together with changes in seismic wave velocity, explains why seismic waves reflect off the core–mantle boundary.

Although the core is far removed from Earth's surface, it affects surface conditions because it is the source of Earth's magnetic field. Like a simple bar magnet, Earth has a magnetic field with north and south poles. Unlike a bar magnet, though, a magnetic dynamo (Figure 6) generates Earth's magnetic field. A **magnetic**

FIGURE 6 Earth's magnetic field is like that of a bar magnet, except that this field is generated electromagnetically by convection in the outer core. Dashed arrows indicate lines of force of the magnetic field. (*Source:* From W. K. Hamblin and E. H. Christiansen, *Earth's Dynamic Systems*, 8/e, 1998. Reprinted by permission of Prentice Hall, Upper Saddle River, N.J.)

dynamo is a mechanism that transforms energy from fluid motions (convection) into electrical currents that create a magnetic field. In a dynamo, the convecting fluid (liquid iron, in Earth's case) must be a conductor of electricity. The outer core convects because a temperature gradient is established across it by heat loss from the solid, inner core.

Why does the liquid outer core convect? Thermal convection occurs when a fluid is heated from below. Our example was the troposphere, which is heated by the warm Earth's surface. The ultimate source of this energy is sunlight. No sunlight makes it down to Earth's core, of course, so we must look for a different energy source there. One possibility is radioactive decay (which we cover later in this chapter), but the elements responsible for this heat source are preferentially concentrated in the crust and mantle rather than in the core. More likely, the energy required to drive convection in the outer core is derived from the gradual growth of the inner core. As Earth's interior cools, liquid iron slowly freezes out to form particles of solid iron. This "freezing" process releases heat, just as the freezing of water to form ice does. The newly formed particles of solid iron

also heat the outer core frictionally as they settle down to join the inner core. The heat released by both of these processes is thought to be what powers outer core convection and, thus, the magnetic dynamo.

THE THEORY OF PLATE TECTONICS

Seafloor Spreading

As we discussed in the introduction to this chapter, the theory of continental drift lay more or less dormant for several decades after the publication of Wegener's ideas, largely because of the lack of acceptance by geophysicists. It is ironic that the resurgence of interest in Wegener's theory was the result of information obtained in the 1960s by geophysicists investigating the topographic and magnetic features of the seafloor. (*Topography* refers to the configuration of a surface, in particular the position and elevation of its features.) During and just after World War II, an intensive period of mapping took place that revealed intriguing details of the seafloor (Figure 7). This work gave the

FIGURE 7 Ocean seafloor and continental topography inferred from high-resolution satellite altimetry measurements and ship depth soundings. Note transform faults extending across the Atlantic, especially near the equator and across the eastern Pacific. (*Source:* National Oceanic and Atmospheric Administration/Seattle.)

world the first evidence of chains of subsea volcanic mountains running down the centers of the ocean basins; we now call these features **mid-ocean ridges**. A *rift*, or narrow valley, runs down the center of such ridges. In the early 1960s, scientists proposed that these linear volcanic chains represent new seafloor that is extruded along the mid-ocean ridges. Once it forms, the new seafloor spreads to the sides of the ridges, generating the central rift, and is replaced at the *ridge axis*—the middle of the rift—by even younger new seafloor. This process was named **seafloor spreading**. Having just crystallized from the magma, newly formed seafloor at seafloor spreading centers is hot and expanded. As it spreads to either side of the plate boundary at the ridge axis, the material cools and contracts, and the seafloor subsides. This process occurs symmetrically across the axis of spreading and so creates symmetrical undersea mountain belts some 1000–4000 km wide that rise 2–3 km from the seafloor.

The real key to the origin of these features came from a better understanding of the magnetic characteristics of the seafloor. The *magnetic* **polarity** is the geographic orientation of the North and South poles. From studies of volcanic rocks extruded on land, scientists knew that magnetic polarity has flipped numerous times in Earth's history. The reasons are not well understood, but have to do with the complex behavior of the convecting liquid outer core. As the lava that formed these volcanic rocks cooled beyond a critical temperature of about 570°C (called the *Curie point*), the rocks became magnetized in the direction of Earth's magnetic field at the time of cooling. More-recent flows record switches in the magnetic field, with the North magnetic pole roughly coincident with the South geographic pole, and vice versa (Figure 8). Radiometric age dating (see below) provided the ages of volcanic flows.

Because the basaltic rocks of the seafloor were known to be of volcanic origin, in the late 1950s oceanographic expeditions were designed to map the magnetic character of the seafloor. As a result, a startling observation was made: The seafloor has a striped magnetic pattern, with the stripes running essentially parallel to the

FIGURE 8   Magnetic reversals as recorded in volcanic rocks preserved on land for the last 75 million years. The last 4 million years of reversals are highlighted at the left. The pattern of change over a few million years is distinctive, and can be used as a signature for establishing the age of a sequence of rocks elsewhere in the world.   (*Source:* From W. K. Hamblin and E. H. Christiansen, *Earth's Dynamic Systems*, 9/e, 2001. Reprinted by permission of Prentice Hall, Upper Saddle River, N.J.)

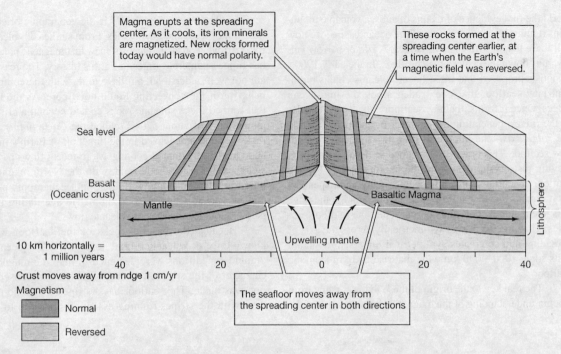

FIGURE 9 Magnetic stripes develop as new crust is added to the ocean floor at mid-ocean ridges and cools, becoming magnetized according to the magnetic field that exists at the time. As this material moves away from the axis, new seafloor is created, and its magnetization may be reversed if Earth's magnetization has reversed polarity in the intervening time. (*Source:* From S. Judson and S. M. Richardson, *Earth: An Introduction to Geologic Change*, 1995. Reprinted by permission of Prentice Hall, Upper Saddle River, N.J.)

mid-ocean ridges. The stripes reflect alternating bands of polarity. Today's magnetic polarity is considered to be *normal*, and the opposite polarity is considered to be *reversed* (Figure 8). Stripes on one side of a mid-ocean ridge were matched to others of similar width and polarity on the opposite side of the ridge (Figure 9).

Geophysicists soon concluded that this pattern of magnetic stripes must be caused by seafloor spreading. At the time of its formation, the new seafloor locks in the contemporaneous magnetic direction. It is then transported in opposite directions away from the ridge axis as new, molten rock is extruded from the volcano. Each reversal of the magnetic field produces a magnetic stripe on the seafloor. New material forming at a mid-ocean ridge is thereby differentiated from the older seafloor material that was produced during a previous magnetic interval at the same ridge and has subsequently drifted away from the ridge axis.

Seafloor spreading provided the solution to the problem plaguing geologists interested in continental drift since the days of Wegener: How could the continents drift through the rigid seafloor? The answer was that the continents do *not* plow through the seafloor. Rather, continents and segments of ocean floor are connected into plates that continuously move away from one another at mid-ocean ridges. Geologists have used a variety of types of evidence to reconstruct this drift of the continents throughout

Earth's history, largely confirming the notion of Pangea proposed by Wegener decades earlier.

Continental Drift and Paleogeographic Reconstructions

The symmetrical magnetic stripes on the seafloor increase in age to either side of the Mid-Atlantic Ridge, recording the opening of the Atlantic Ocean (Figure 10). In a sense, we can reverse time by rolling the seafloor back into the Mid-Atlantic Ridge, bringing together once again stripes of equal age at the ridge axis. In this technique, the Atlantic Ocean closes first in the Southern Hemisphere and then in the Northern Hemisphere, as South America slips into place alongside Africa. The close fit between the two continents, especially at the edges of their continental shelves, was part of what convinced Wegener in the early 1900s that the continents have drifted apart over geological time.

Seafloor magnetic stripes provide the best tool for *paleogeography*, the reconstruction of the positions of the continents in the past. However, the tectonic process of *subduction* (see below) has destroyed much of the seafloor record of the past 200 million years and all of the record older than that. So, paleogeographers turn to other sorts of evidence to determine ancient continental positions.

Sedimentary rocks prove very useful in this regard. Glacial deposits generally form at high latitudes (poleward

FIGURE 10 [See color section] The age of the ocean floor is shown as bands of different color on the basis of the magnetic striping developed during seafloor spreading. The youngest ocean floor is near the mid-ocean ridge, while the oldest is furthest away. (*Source:* From R. W. Christopherson, *Geosystems: An Introduction to Physical Geography*, 3/e, 1997. Reprinted by permission of Prentice Hall, Upper Saddle River, N.J.)

of about 45°), so we assume that glacial sediments indicate high *paleolatitudes*—that is, the latitudes at which the rocks formed. (There is an important exception to this rule—the so-called Snowball Earth episodes of the Paleoproterozoic and Neoproterozoic, for which it appears that ice sheets extended into tropical latitudes.) Similarly, because coral reefs are located in the tropics today, we assume that reef limestones indicate tropical paleolatitudes. Salt deposits indicate subtropical paleolatitudes because they form preferentially in arid regions underlying the descending branches of the tropical Hadley cells. In addition, similar fossils on two continents indicate that the continents were in close proximity, or joined, at the time the organisms lived, allowing their migration. One must be cautious, however, in applying these paleolatitude indicators, because they are based on the assumption that the present is the key to the past. There may be times, however, when this assumption does not hold. Thus, geologists are motivated to look for more reliable paleolatitude indicators. The least ambiguous paleolatitude indicator comes from magnetism in rocks. By measuring the angle of the pre-

served magnetic field with respect to the sedimentary layering of the rocks (which is presumed to have originally been horizontal), geologists are able to estimate the angle of the magnetic field with respect to the horizontal. This angle gives the latitude at which the sedimentary deposit formed (Figure 11). Rocks in which the magnetic field is nearly parallel to the bedding plane must have formed near the equator; rocks in which the magnetic field is perpendicular to the bedding plane must have formed near the poles. These inferences, of course, are based on the assumption that Earth's magnetic field has always had two poles (North and South) and that the magnetic poles have always been approximately aligned with the geographic poles. One might rightfully point out that this is also a case of using the present to interpret the past. However, in this case, the assumption seems to be well-founded. During the past several million years when the continents could not have drifted very far, the magnetic poles have remained close to the geographic poles. Magnetic dynamo theory also suggests that, far away from its source (the outer core), the magnetic field should always be more or less aligned with the planet's spin axis.

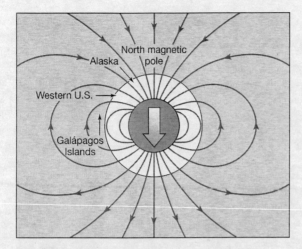

FIGURE 1 Earth's magnetic field, indicating that the angle of the field lines with respect to Earth's surface varies from horizontal at the equator to vertical at the poles. Paleogeographers use this feature to determine paleolatitudes of rocks, on the basis of the magnetic field orientation they acquired at the time of their formation. (*Source:* From W. K. Hamblin and E. H. Christiansen, *Earth's Dynamic Systems*, 8/e, 1998. Reprinted by permission of Prentice Hall, Upper Saddle River, N.J.)

Unfortunately, most of the tools paleogeographers use constrain only the latitude, not the longitude, of the continents. Longitudinal positioning is much more difficult. Similarity of fossil assemblages on adjacent continents is taken to indicate proximity, whereas large differences between the types of fossils found on two continents imply that wide oceans separated the continents and prevented the dispersal of organisms. However, features other than oceans, mountains and deserts for example, can also prevent dispersal. Thus, there are large uncertainties in the longitudinal positions of the continents prior to 200 million years ago.

The sequence of maps shown in Figure 12 shows how the continents are thought to have drifted over the past 500 million years, based on all available evidence. In the Cambrian and Ordovician periods (540–440 million years ago), the continents became increasingly dispersed from equatorial to southern high latitudes. Over the next 300 million years, the continents drifted together and collided. The collisions created large, Himalayan-style mountain ranges, including the Appalachians of the eastern United States. By 280 million years ago, the continents were assembled into the gigantic supercontinent Pangea, centered on the equator. Pangea eventually began to disassemble about 200 million years ago. The Atlantic Ocean formed as a rifting apart of continents first between North America and Africa, next between South America and Africa, and finally between North America and Europe. By 120 million years ago, Africa, Antarctica, India, and Australia had begun their separate paths. North America rotated and drifted from the

low latitudes into its present position. Most impressive was the long journey of India as it detached from Antarctica and ultimately collided with Asia some 50 million years ago. We will see that this ongoing collision between India and Asia may be responsible, at least in part, for our present, relatively cool global climate.

The paleomagnetic and geological evidence of continental positions before 600 million years ago is sparse.

FIGURE 12 [See color section] Paleogeographic reconstructions from the Early Cambrian to the Cretaceous-Tertiary boundary. (*Source:* From R. Blakey, *used with permission.*)

Available paleomagnetic data seem to indicate that between about 900 and 600 million years ago the continents were assembled into another Pangea-like supercontinent. Prior to this time the data are so scarce that paleogeographic reconstructions are not currently feasible.

New Structural Categories: Lithosphere and Asthenosphere

As Wegener learned long ago, the conventional separation of the solid Earth into the core, the mantle, and the crust on the basis of seismic wave velocities is inadequate in view of plate tectonic theory. To explain the drift of continents, the mobile plates need to be distinguished from the lubricating layer below. To do so, the mantle and crust are best recategorized according to material strength (Figure 13). The plates extend through the crust and into the uppermost mantle; we call this outermost sphere the **lithosphere.** The upper, crustal part of the lithosphere is *brittle*, that is, it fractures in response to stress. Below the lithosphere is the **asthenosphere,** a region of the upper mantle that acts more like a fluid than a solid. The asthenosphere is *ductile*—it flows plastically, or deforms easily, in response to stress. The top of the asthenosphere is coincident with the mantle's low-velocity zone. Recall that the preferred explanation for low seismic wave velocities there is the presence of a small amount of molten rock. The asthenosphere extends through the mantle's transition zone to a depth of around 700 km. Below this depth, the lower mantle is thought to be much less ductile because of the effects of very high pressure.

PLATES AND PLATE BOUNDARIES

According to the theory of plate tectonics, the lithosphere is divided into about 20 rigid plates (Figure 14). The crustal portions of some plates are entirely oceanic, whereas other plates include both oceanic and continental crusts. *Oceanic lithosphere* describes a plate that is topped by oceanic crust; *continental lithosphere* refers to a portion of a plate topped by continental crust.

We now know that tectonic activity (such as earthquakes or volcanism) is concentrated at plate boundaries; there is little activity within a plate. This activity is the result of plate motion: The plates move relative to each other at average speeds of a few centimeters per year. As a result of friction between the plates, there are alternating periods of stasis (during which stresses build) and periods of movement (when they are released) both at the plate boundary and near the surface. (Seismic and satellite measurements indicate that at greater depths or farther from the plate boundary, the motions are more continuous.) After a period of stasis, pentup energy is released suddenly as the plates jump past each other, causing earthquakes. As predicted, the distribution of earthquakes at Earth's surface follows plate boundaries quite closely (compare Figures 14 and 15).

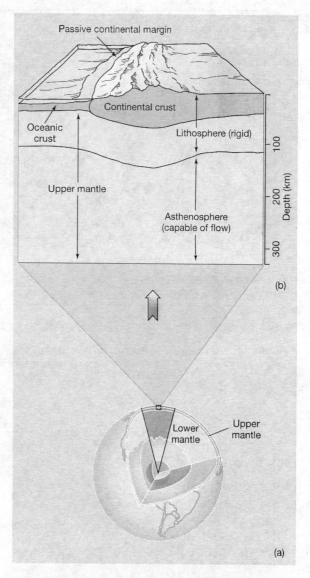

FIGURE 13 (a) Internal structure of Earth, comparing the traditional classification by seismic wave velocities with the plate tectonic classification by material strength. (*Source:* From R. W. Christopherson, *Geosystems: An Introduction to Physical Geography,* 3/e, 1997. Reprinted by permission of Prentice Hall, Upper Saddle River, N.J.) (b) A cross section of the upper mantle and crust showing the relative positions of the lithosphere (crust plus uppermost mantle) and asthenosphere. (*Source:* From J. P. Davidson, W. E. Reed, and P. M. Davis, *Exploring Earth: An Introduction to Physical Geology,* 1997. Reprinted by permission of Prentice Hall, Upper Saddle River, N.J.)

There are three types of plate boundaries (or margins): divergent, convergent, and transform (Figure 16). At *divergent margins,* lithospheric plates are moving away from each other. At *convergent margins,* plates are moving toward each other. At *transform margins,* plates are slipping past each other. Each boundary type is represented differently at Earth's surface. In other words, each type of

FIGURE 14　The lithosphere is divided into rigid plates.　(*Source:* From S. Judson and S. M. Richardson, *Earth: An Introduction to Geologic Change*, 1995. Reprinted by permission of Prentice Hall, Upper Saddle River, N.J.)

FIGURE 15　[See color section] Distribution of earthquakes of shallow, intermediate, or deep focus. Deep-focus earthquakes occur only at subduction zones.　(*Source:* From W. K. Hamblin and E. H. Christiansen, *Earth's Dynamic Systems*, 8/e, 1998. Reprinted by permission of Prentice Hall, Upper Saddle River, N.J.)

FIGURE 16 The three types of plate boundaries:
(a) divergent; (b) convergent; and (c) transform fault. (*Source:* From J. P. Davidson, W. E. Reed, and P. M. Davis, *Exploring Earth: An Introduction to Physical Geology*, 1997. Reprinted by permission of Prentice Hall, Upper Saddle River, N.J.)

plate margin is reflected in distinctive surface features: mid-ocean ridges, deep-sea trenches, and transform faults, respectively.

Divergent Margins

Divergent margins are regions where stresses are pulling apart the lithosphere. The mid-ocean ridges, already described, represent most of the divergent plate boundaries on Earth. Divergent boundaries that occur on land represent sites of continental fragmentation, or *rifting,* where the continental crust stretches. Tensional forces pull the continent apart. In the process, faulting occurs and flat-bottomed valleys called *rift valleys* form. During the

breakup of Pangea some 200 million years ago, these types of plate boundaries were much more common than they are today. Today the rift valleys of East Africa, along with the Gulf of Aden and Red Sea to the north, are our best example of a divergent continental boundary in the making (Figure 17). If one studies this area in more detail, one finds that the divergence of the African and Arabian plates has created a system of rifts that radiate from a central point. This point is referred to as a *triple junction.* The East African rift valleys are at an earlier stage of rifting than the Red Sea and Gulf of Aden, where spreading has progressed to the point that new ocean basins have been formed.

Convergent Margins

Convergent margins are regions where two lithospheric plates are forced together. Although there has been some spirited controversy in the past, most geologists now are convinced that Earth is not increasing in size. (Like Wegener, those who have suggested that Earth changes its size have no physical explanation for how this could happen. Wegener, though, turned out to be right!) But if new seafloor is produced at mid-ocean ridges, then what happens to the old seafloor? The mapping efforts that followed World War II revealed deep basins in addition to mid-ocean ridges. Deep-sea trenches are long, narrow, very deep basins that are especially common along the margins of the Pacific Ocean (Figure 18). The discovery of these trenches provided the answer: The seafloor is consumed at deep-sea trenches about as fast as it is being produced at mid-ocean ridges.

Deep-sea trenches form at two of the three types of convergent plate boundaries: those that involve two oceanic plates and those that involve an oceanic and a continental plate. A third type of convergent margin forms the world's highest mountains rather than the deepest trenches; these involve the collision of two continental plates. Let us explore each of these cases.

OCEANIC–CONTINENTAL AND OCEANIC–OCEANIC CONVERGENT MARGINS Recall that the upper portion of a lithospheric plate (the crustal section) is brittle. When oceanic plates collide, the leading edge of one plate sinks entirely beneath the other. When the leading edge of one of the plates at a convergent margin is oceanic lithosphere and the leading edge of the other plate is continental lithosphere, the denser oceanic lithosphere sinks beneath the less-dense continental plate (Figure 19a). The sinking of an oceanic plate at a convergent margin is called **subduction**, and the entire region is called a *subduction zone.* The downgoing plate, called a **slab**, subsides into the mantle. In so doing, the plate bends, creating deep, linear depressions at the surface—deep-sea trenches. These trenches are the deepest parts of the oceans. Friction between the downgoing plate and the overriding plate generates

FIGURE 17 The rift valleys of East Africa, where Africa is being uparched and pulled apart. If spreading continues, the rift system may evolve into an elongate sea like the Red Sea to the north.

a substantial amount of seismic activity near the surface (in the upper 60–100 km); other forces generate earthquakes within the subducting slab at greater depths. The earthquake foci deepen as the distance from the trench toward the continent increases (Figure 15). Inland from the trench, water released into the mantle from the heated subducted slab of lithosphere leads to melting and produces igneous activity at the surface. This activity forms a range of volcanic mountains called a *volcanic arc.*

When two oceanic plates collide at a convergent margin, one subducts beneath the other (Figure 19b). Similar to what occurs in an oceanic–continental collision, a range of volcanic mountains forms to one side of the trench, but in this case the volcanoes rise up along the seafloor rather than on land. If they reach the ocean surface, they produce volcanic *island arcs.* The Marianas Islands, off the coast of the Philippine Islands, formed in

this way. The Marianas Trench is the deepest trench of all, more than 10.5 km below sea level.

As the seafloor spreads from its place of origin at a mid-ocean ridge to its place of destruction at a subduction zone, sediment settling through the overlying water accumulates on the seafloor. Like a conveyor belt, the convergent motion of the plates in the subduction zone carries this sediment toward the trench. There the sediment may be scraped off by the opposing plate, forming wedges of deformed sediment. The rest of the sediment remains attached to the oceanic plate. The fate of this sediment is an area of active research. Part of it appears to become *underplated*—that is, attached to the base of the overlying plate—whereas some of it is carried into the asthenosphere. In the asthenosphere, it undergoes *dehydration* (loss of water) and *decarbonation* (loss of carbon) to the surrounding mantle, as well as a host of mineralogical

A CLOSER LOOK
Deep-Sea Life at Mid-Ocean Ridge Vents

The axial portion of a mid-ocean ridge is marked by volcanic activity, earthquakes with a shallow focus, and the venting of hot fluids rich in dissolved metals and hydrogen sulfide. Seawater drawn into the ridge along its flanks flows through cracks in the oceanic crust and is expelled through vents in the axis. Along the way, the seawater is heated, and chemical reactions with basalt alter its composition: Magnesium is removed and sulfate is reduced to sulfide, and calcium and trace metals are added. The circulation of seawater through the mid-ocean ridge also alters the chemical composition of the oceans. While exiting through the vents, iron sulfide minerals precipitate from the altered seawater and give the plumes a black coloration. For this reason, the vents through which the fluids exit are called *black smokers* (Figure Box 3a). They are also known as *hydrothermal vents*, because they release heated seawater.

The fluids released by black smokers sustain a unique community of organisms. These organisms synthesize organic matter with the help of bacteria that carry out **chemosynthesis** rather than photosynthesis. In other words, these bacteria utilize energy from inorganic

(a)　　　(b)

BOX FIGURE 3　[See color section] Abundant and bizarre life thriving under the harsh conditions of the deep-seafloor, in the vicinity of hydrothermal venting. (a) A black smoker chimney is shown spewing out sulfide-rich solutions that provide the energy source for this food chain. (b) Tube worms, crabs, and other organisms can be seen. (*Source:* (a) Dudley Foster/Woods Hole Oceanographic Institution and (b) American Geophysical Union.)

matter—energy released during chemical reactions between seawater and hydrogen sulfide. Chemosynthetic bacteria do not use the energy of sunlight. Feeding off these bacteria are unusual species of clams, crabs, and giant red and white tube worms (Box Figure 3b).

transformations. These reactions prove to be very important to the global recycling of elements such as carbon, because volcanoes that form in such subduction zones derive carbon dioxide gas from this sedimentary source.

CONTINENTAL–CONTINENTAL CONVERGENT MARGINS

When two continental plates meet at a convergent margin, the continents collide abruptly. Because continental crust is too buoyant to be subducted, continental collision results in the separation of the crustal portion of the lithospheric plate from the mantle portion below. Subduction of the mantle portion of one plate may occur while the continental crust on both plates becomes compressed and crumpled. As a consequence, tall mountain belts and high plateaus form (Figure 19c). Around 50 million years ago, India collided

with Asia. The collision between these two segments of continental lithosphere led to massive deformation and uplift of the continents. The tall peaks of the Himalayas and the uniformly high Tibetan Plateau bear firm testament to the awesome energetics of this collision. Older mountain belts (such as the Appalachians) are the products of collisional tectonics that occurred hundreds of millions of years ago. Subsequent erosion has reduced what were once majestic mountains into the more modest ridges we observe today.

Transform Margins

When the relative motion along a plate boundary is parallel to the boundary, lithosphere is neither created (extruded) nor destroyed (subducted); the plates merely slip past one

| ⊬⅂ | Divergent boundary | ▬▬▬ | Trench |

FIGURE 18   Distribution of oceanic trenches and mid-ocean ridges.   (*Source:* From W. K. Hamblin and E. H. Christiansen, *Earth's Dynamic Systems*, 8/e, 1998. Reprinted by permission of Prentice Hall, Upper Saddle River, N.J.)

FIGURE 19   Three types of convergent plate boundaries: (a) oceanic–continental; (b) oceanic–oceanic; and (c) continental–continental.   (*Source:* From W. K. Hamblin and E. H. Christiansen, *Earth's Dynamic Systems*, 8/e, 1998. Reprinted by permission of Prentice Hall, Upper Saddle River, N.J.)

another at a fault. Faults that form boundary-parallel margins are known as **transform faults.** The San Andreas Fault of California, which marks a segment of the boundary between the North American and Pacific plates, is a transform fault (Figure 20). Baja California and southern California (including Los Angeles) are moving slowly northward relative to the rest of California. In 50 million years or so, San Francisco and Los Angeles will be side by side, and beyond that time Los Angeles will actually be north of San Francisco. Geologists on the West Coast joke that California politics will at this time become completely reversed, with the northern part of the state being more conservative than the south.

Transform plate boundaries occur in oceanic settings as well. The jagged shape of parts of the mid-ocean ridge system is caused by offsets between ridge segments created by transform faulting (Figure 18). The Mid-Atlantic Ridge shows this type of behavior near the equator.

Overview of Plate Interactions

Figure 21 provides an overview of the types of plate interactions and the surface features they generate. The production of new oceanic lithosphere at mid-ocean ridges is matched by the destruction of older oceanic lithosphere at subduction zones, which are manifested at the surface by deep-sea trenches. Part of the sedimentary layer riding atop the oceanic plate is incorporated into the overriding plate (oceanic or continental), and the rest is subducted into the mantle.

FIGURE 20 Transform faults. Seafloor generated at the Juan de Fuca Ridge moves southeastward, past the Pacific plate and beneath the North American plate, at the Mendocino transform fault. This fault connects a divergent boundary to a subduction zone. The San Andreas Fault, another transform fault, forms the connection between two spreading centers: the Juan de Fuca Ridge and a divergent zone in the Gulf of California. (*Source:* From J. P. Davidson, W. E. Reed, and P. M. Davis, *Exploring Earth: An Introduction to Physical Geology*, 1997. Reprinted by permission of Prentice Hall, Upper Saddle River, N.J.)

As Figure 21 shows, some lithospheric plates consist of oceanic lithosphere welded to continental lithosphere. The ocean–continent boundary is not a plate boundary at all. The North American plate, for example, is made up of the North American continent and oceanic lithosphere to the east. The North American plate continues beyond the continent–ocean lithospheric boundary to the axis of the Mid-Atlantic Ridge (the mid-ocean ridge down the center of the Atlantic Ocean). In such situations, the ocean widens as the continents drift away from the mid-ocean ridge; the continental margin is referred to as passive. *Passive continental margins* consist of a broad, gently seaward-dipping continental shelf that gives way to the more steeply dipping continental slope. The continental lithosphere is welded to the oceanic lithosphere beneath the continental shelf. In other cases, such as along much of the Pacific Ocean, the ocean–continent boundary is a convergent margin and is therefore a site of subduction; such margins are said to be active. On *active continental margins,* including that off the Pacific coast of the northwestern United States, the continental shelf is narrow.

The oceanic ridge is offset in numerous places by transform faults. The relative motion across these faults is parallel to the plate boundary. Transform faults generate considerable amounts of earthquake activity. Around the globe, convergent and divergent margins are connected by transform faults.

FIGURE 21 Schematic view of the relationships among the types of plate boundaries. (*Source:* From J. P. Davidson, W. E. Reed, and P. M. Davis, *Exploring Earth: An Introduction to Physical Geology*, 1997. Reprinted by permission of Prentice Hall, Upper Saddle River, N.J.)

THE PHYSIOLOGY OF THE SOLID EARTH: WHAT DRIVES PLATE TECTONICS?

Heat from the Deep

In the simplest sense, plate tectonics is the surface expression of the mechanism by which heat escapes from Earth's interior. Although there are spatial variations, temperatures generally increase through the mantle. This heat is transported to the surface, where it escapes to the atmosphere. (The average *geothermal heat flux*, or heat transported to the surface, is $0.06 \, W/m^2$, which is trivially small compared to the net absorbed solar flux of about $240 \, W/m^2$, the energy budget. It is the only heat available, though, in Earth's interior.) Heat is transported by convection in the mantle to the base of the lithosphere, and then by conduction through the lithosphere or convection at midocean ridges to the surface.

What is the origin of this heat in Earth's interior? It comes from two major sources: (1) radioactive decay and (2) residual heat from Earth's formation. A third source, the growth of the inner core (discussed previously), drives convection of the outer core but is only a small contributor to the energy budget of Earth's interior.

RADIOACTIVE DECAY The fundamentals of radioactive decay can be applied to the decay of carbon-14. The important radioactive elements in the solid Earth are potassium, uranium, and thorium. Their *half-lives* are on the order of hundreds of millions to billions of years (whereas carbon-14, if you recall, has a half-life of only 5,730 years. Thus, the decay rates of these isotopes are quite low. However, the crust and mantle contain significant concentrations of these elements, so their radioactive decay generates a considerable amount of heat. Because radioactive decay leads to a continuous loss of radioactive materials from Earth's interior, the abundance of these materials must have been greater in the past than it is now. Similarly, the rate of heat production (and of heat loss) must have

been much higher in the past. On the basis of the abundance of potassium, uranium, and thorium in the crust and mantle, we can calculate that the amount of radioactive heat production has decreased by about a factor of 5 since Earth formed 4.6 billion years ago.

OTHER HEAT SOURCES Other sources of heat are residual; they are associated with heating events during Earth's formation. As we mentioned briefly earlier, Earth (and the other planets) was formed by the accretion of larger and larger clumps of matter into moon-sized objects called *planetesimals*. The planetesimals collided and merged, forming a large, primitive planet. A tremendous amount of energy was transferred to Earth during the accretion of the planet by collisions with planetesimals. The larger collisions probably caused widespread melting of Earth's upper mantle. The segregation of Earth into a less-dense mantle and crust and a denser core released gravitational energy in the form of heat. Convection of the outer core and mantle has been transferring this heat to Earth's surface ever since.

Convection in the Mantle

But how can a solid convect? Convection generally is thought of as a process that affects fluids. Yet solids need not be rigid; witness the flow of glaciers or the ductility of plastics. Rocks are ductile at the temperatures and pressures that occur within the mantle. When heated locally, these materials expand, become less dense, and rise buoyantly, although very slowly. Cooler, denser material sinks and replaces the buoyant material. In this way, mantle rocks can convect. Upon rising to the base of the lithosphere, the material cools as heat is transferred conductively to the lithosphere. As the material continues to cool, it travels laterally. It cools so much that it eventually becomes denser than the underlying lithosphere and descends. Thus, the material sinks back into the asthenosphere. The cycle continues as the material is again heated and becomes buoyant.

A CLOSER LOOK
Radiometric Age Dating of Geological Materials

Suppose that we have a rock sample that contains both a radioisotope and its decay product, and we know exactly how much of that isotope existed when the material formed. If we also know the half-life of that isotope, then we can calculate the age of the sample. This method, called *radiometric age dating*, has proved extremely useful in providing absolute dates for the geological time scale and for other specific events in Earth's history. The accuracy of radiometric dating drops rapidly after eight or nine half-lives. For example, the radioactive isotope of carbon, ^{14}C or *radiocarbon*, has a half-life of just 5,730 years. Thus, *radiocarbon dating* is accurately applied only to samples less than a few tens of thousands of years old.

The long-lived radioisotopes of potassium and uranium, however, are useful for determining the ages of the oldest rocks on Earth, of lunar material, and of meteorites. Especially useful are the radioactive isotopes of uranium, ^{238}U (half-life of 4.5 billion years) and ^{235}U (half-life of 0.713 billion years), which decay through a series of intermediate steps to stable lead isotopes ^{206}Pb and ^{207}Pb, respectively. The radioactivity of the uranium in these ancient rocks is not high enough to be measured directly, but we can use an instrument called a *mass spectrometer* to determine the relative amounts of the lead isotopes. From these ratios and the known half-lives, we can accurately date the rocks.

The size of mantle convection cells is unknown. Smaller cells may be generated separately within the upper mantle and within the lower mantle, or the whole mantle below the lithosphere may be involved. The nature of the mantle transition zone is the distinguishing factor between the two convection mechanisms. If this zone marks a change in chemical composition, then convection cells do not cross it because if they did, the compositional distinctions would be lost. In this case, there are likely to be separate convective cells in the upper and lower mantle (Figure 22a). Conversely, if the transition zone is the result of mineralogical rather than chemical changes, and if these changes take place quickly relative to the rate of convection, whole-mantle convection is possible (Figure 22b).

The lithosphere is an integral part of the mantle convection system. In a sense, the lithosphere is the cool upper boundary of the convective cell. However, the subduction of cool oceanic lithosphere undoubtedly perturbs the internal thermal structure of the upper mantle and the distribution of convective cells. Oceanic lithosphere is so dense that a slab of oceanic lithosphere at a subduction zone may sink to great depths within the mantle, become detached from the surface portion of the plate, and actually cool regions of the mantle from below. Such regions would become thermally stable, preventing convection locally. Lateral movements of the plates might also induce lateral movements of the underlying asthenosphere. And finally, the separation of the lithosphere at seafloor spreading centers might drive the mantle to upwell. As the asthenosphere rises, it expands and melts, which further enhances the upwelling of more magma. Thus there are a number of lithosphere–asthenosphere interactions that affect the nature of convection in the mantle.

Forces Acting on Plates

The most important lithosphere–asthenosphere interaction is that which drives the motion of the plates. When plate tectonics was first proposed, *mantle drag,* or friction between the convecting asthenosphere and the overlying rigid lithosphere, was considered to be the cause of plate motions (Figure 23). Now geologists recognize a number of other forces that act on plates. These forces include the

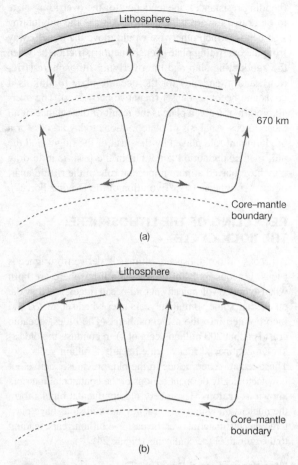

(a)

(b)

FIGURE 22   Mantle convection may (a) separate into upper and lower mantle convective cells or (b) involve the whole mantle.   (*Source:* From S. Judson and S. M. Richardson, *Earth: An Introduction to Geologic Change*, 1995. Reprinted by permission of Prentice Hall, Upper Saddle River, N.J.)

gravitational "push" generated by the high topography of a mid-ocean ridge on the rest of the oceanic plate (ridge push); the increasing density of the oceanic lithosphere as it cools, which pulls the opposite end of the plate into a subduction zone (slab pull); the elastic resistance of the oceanic plate to being bent into a subduction zone

FIGURE 23   The various forces acting on plates at their leading and trailing edges. The motion of the plates responds to the sum of these forces. See the text for a discussion of the origin of each force.   (*Source:* From W. K. Hamblin and E. H. Christiansen, *Earth's Dynamic Systems*, 8/e, 1998. Reprinted by permission of Prentice Hall, Upper Saddle River, N.J.)

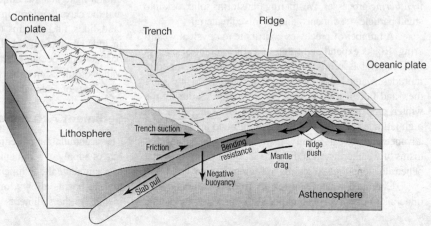

(bending resistance); the tendency for the overriding plate to be drawn toward a subduction zone as the subducting slab bends (which otherwise would move the trench away from the overriding plate (trench suction); friction between the subducting slab and the overlying lithosphere (friction); and a tendency for the oceanic plate to sink as it cools and becomes denser (negative buoyancy). The overall motion of a given plate is the result of the balance of all these forces. Analysis of plate motions today argues for a predominant role played by the push of the ridges and the pull of the subduction zone, but in the past, mantle drag may have played a more important role in the rifting apart of supercontinents (see "Evolution of the Driving Force").

RECYCLING OF THE LITHOSPHERE: THE ROCK CYCLE

All rocks of the lithosphere ultimately derive from igneous rocks. Igneous rocks of the oceanic lithosphere are born when extruded volcanically at mid-ocean ridges, and they die on average some 80 million years later when subducted and incorporated into the asthenosphere. (The oldest oceanic crust is about 200 million years old.) In contrast, the oldest-known continental rocks formed nearly 4 billion years ago. These record-setters reside in the old, previously active but now tectonically dormant regions of the continental interiors known as **cratons**. These very old continental blocks form the nucleus on which subsequent plate collisions have plastered on new material over the past 3–4 billion years, leading to the growth of the continents (Figure 24).

Weathering and Erosion

Once formed, igneous rocks are subject to a variety of processes that can alter their chemical composition and weaken their structural integrity, typically leading to complete disintegration or *dissolution* (dissolving away) of the original rock. On the seafloor, oceanic lithosphere is altered as hydrothermal solutions circulate the oceanic crust, as previously discussed, but these processes tend not to destroy the rocks. In contrast, igneous rocks that are exposed on land are subject to a variety of physical, biological, and chemical forces that tend to degrade the rock. These are referred to as *weathering* processes. Weathering transforms solid rock into small particles (sediments) and dissolved material.

A number of processes contribute to physical weathering. Rocks expand and fracture as the weight of overlying material is removed through erosion. In temperate latitudes, water seeps into these fractures in spring, summer, and fall. It then expands when it freezes during the winter, cracking the rock. Rocks exposed at the surface in high latitudes or at high altitudes are ground up as glaciers advance and retreat. Finally, there are biophysical mechanisms of weathering, including the action of plant roots that penetrate along these fractures, wedging the rock apart.

Chemical weathering results from the tendency for minerals to dissolve when exposed to rainwater and acidic

FIGURE 24   The ages of the components of the North American continent reveal that the continent has grown by the amalgamation of very old cratons, followed by accretion of younger material onto the periphery of the craton during plate collisions.   (*Source:* From J. P. Davidson, W. E. Reed, and P. M. Davis, *Exploring Earth: An Introduction to Physical Geology*, 1997. Reprinted by permission of Prentice Hall, Upper Saddle River, N.J.)

soil waters generated by bacteria, fungi, or plant root discharges. The products of these chemical reactions include dissolved materials and relatively insoluble clays that form in the soils.

The transport of the products of weathering to basins where sediment accumulates is called **erosion**. In this process, crustal materials, decomposed and loosened by weathering, and the clays that form in the soils are transported by winds, landslides, and streams to sites of deposition. These sites include lakes and flood plains on land and deltas and deeper basins in the ocean. In the process, landscapes are created: Valleys form as erodable material is removed, leaving peaks and ridges of material that are resistant to erosive forces.

Sediment Accumulation

The accumulation of sediments depends on two factors: the rate of supply of sediment and the amount of space available to accumulate the sediment. The great depth of water in deep marine basins allows for the thick accumulation of sediments. As the sediments accumulate, however, the seafloor rises toward sea level, and the amount of available space diminishes. Sedimentary deposits also form in shallow-water settings, though, such as the margins of the Gulf of Mexico, where subsidence of the seafloor (resulting from tectonic forces that stretch and thin the lithosphere, or cooling and contraction) allows for continued accumulation of sediment.

As sediments continue to accumulate in these basins, the material is compacted by the increasing weight of overlying sediments. That weight can become so great that fluids trapped between the sediment grains are expelled. Eventually, as the burial process continues, sediments may become buried to a depth of several kilometers below the seafloor. At these depths, temperatures can exceed 200°C, and the pressures can be hundreds of times the atmospheric pressure. In addition, the fluids that circulate through these buried sediments are quite distinct chemically from surface waters. As a result of these environmental changes, sediments undergo further compaction, and the small voids that remain between sediment grains become filled with mineral cements precipitated from the subsurface fluids. In other words, the sediments lithify and become sedimentary rocks.

Uplift

If the continents were at sea level, there would be virtually no driving force for weathering and erosion, and thus no rock cycle. However, continental collisions crumple the crust, producing mountains and high plateaus, and oceanic collisions produce volcanic islands. These plate collisions generate the topography that is then destroyed by erosion. The elevation of a mountain range represents the competition between uplift and erosion. Young mountain belts like Taiwan or Papua New Guinea are undergoing rapid uplift. Steep mountain slopes develop that stimulate rapid erosion as well, but uplift exceeds erosion, and elevations grow. Old mountain belts such as the Appalachians of the eastern United States are not being rapidly uplifted. Erosion is dominating, and the high peaks of the geologic past are gone, having eroded to low ridges.

Erosion promotes the recycling of sedimentary rocks before metamorphism or melting occurs. Sedimentary deposits situated along active continental margins can be entrained into the convergent plate motions and uplifted onto the continents. As soon as the sedimentary rocks become exposed at the surface, weathering and erosion commence.

Metamorphism and Melting

If instead sedimentary (or igneous) rocks are subjected to high temperatures and pressures in Earth's interior, they metamorphose. If they ultimately melt, they form magma that can itself ascend and become igneous rock. Metamorphism occurs deep in sedimentary basins along passive margins, in the deformed regions of active margins, and in other regions of the crust where igneous activity has injected hot igneous rock into what was cooler crustal rock (igneous or sedimentary). The generation of magma from crustal rocks typically occurs only where those rocks have been carried deep within Earth's interior, for example, in subduction zones.

The Rock Cycle

There are a number of alternative pathways in this process, but overall the complete regeneration of rock is called the **rock cycle** (Figure 25). The rock cycle is a consequence of plate tectonics. One complete cycle takes about 100 million years. However, the average lifetime of continental lithosphere as a whole is actually much longer (a few hundred million years), because the interiors of the continents are well insulated from the tectonic activity that occurs along their margins.

It is important to recognize that the rock cycle is not completely closed: New crustal material is produced through the emplacement of magmas derived from the mantle, and older crustal materials are taken back to the mantle at subduction zones. This slow exchange between the mantle and crust replenishes the crust, on average,

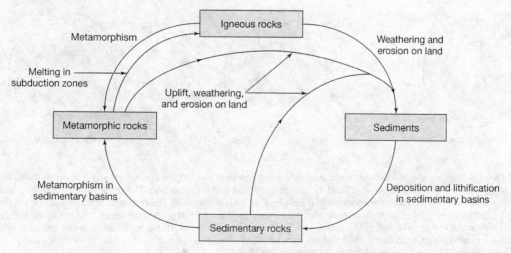

FIGURE 25 The rock cycle.

every 2–3 billion years. In other words, a large proportion of the geologic record of the early Earth's crust has not only been through the rock cycle many times, but has been ingested (perhaps once and for all) into Earth's interior. Nevertheless, averages can be deceptive: The interior parts of the continents (the cratons) can be billions of years old and represent crustal material that has never been recycled, whereas the continental margins are recycled on a time scale much shorter than a billion years.

PLATE TECTONICS THROUGH EARTH HISTORY

Evolution of the Driving Force

Earth has been losing heat throughout its 4.6 billion-year history. Although early in this history other mechanisms may have dominated, for at least the past 4 billion years heat loss has occurred by mantle convection. The rate of heat loss on the early Earth was several times the present value, presumably fueling higher relative rates of seafloor production and subduction. But the style of subduction, and the balance of forces acting on the plates, may have been somewhat different on the early Earth than they are today. Presuming that plate velocities of a few centimeters per year have prevailed over the past 4 billion years or so, the continents have moved great distances during that time.

Wilson Cycles

A pattern seems to be emerging: Continents assemble into a supercontinent, which then breaks apart; these smaller continents eventually disperse and then reassemble. This plate tectonic cycle has been dubbed the **Wilson cycle**, in honor of one of the pioneers of plate tectonics, Canadian geologist J. Tuzo Wilson. From paleogeographic reconstructions it appears that the cycle of supercontinent assembly and destruction takes about 500 million years. We can also approximate the duration of a Wilson cycle from the time it takes a plate to make its way halfway around Earth. Taking a typical plate speed of 4 cm/yr (or 40 km/million yr) and a half-circumference (at the equator) of around 20,000 km, we confirm that two continents rifting apart would meet each other again, on the far side of the planet, in around 500 million years. Accordingly, given that Pangea formed about 300 million years ago, the next supercontinent should be formed in about 200 million years as the Pacific Ocean closes, swallowed up by the subduction zones that surround it.

Why do all the continents come together into a supercontinent rather than displaying a less organized, more random pattern of collision and rifting apart? Of course, drifting continents on a finite globe are bound to collide, so larger continents are likely to form. A somewhat controversial hypothesis argues instead that the continents are drawn toward cold regions of the asthenosphere (Figure 26). Once assembled, the thick supercontinent acts as an insulator, slowing the release of heat from the mantle. Mantle temperatures rise beneath the supercontinent, modifying the pattern of convection. The resulting tension at the surface eventually rips the supercontinent apart. The continents begin to move from this region of hot upwelling mantle to a site thousands of kilometers away, where the mantle has cooled and downwelling has commenced. This hypothesis is consistent with present-day plate speeds and seismic tomography, which together suggest that the continents, with the exception of Africa, appear to be moving toward regions of cold mantle. Africa is situated above hot mantle, as evidenced by the East African Rift zone, a place where tension within the continental lithosphere is creating a rift in the continent. Africa has apparently moved little since the breakup of Pangea, and the underlying mantle still retains the heat built up during Pangea's existence.

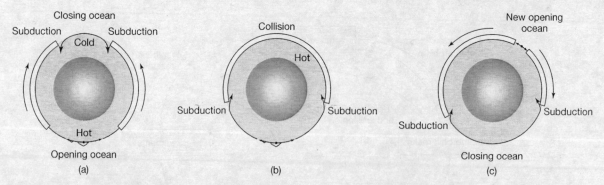

FIGURE 26   The Wilson cycle of supercontinent assembly and fragmentation. (a) The continents are drifting toward a region of cold asthenosphere. The closing ocean is lined by subduction zones and is contracting. The other ocean is opening, and the oceanic lithosphere is connected to the continental lithosphere at both margins. (b) The continental fragments have collided, forming a supercontinent. Subduction has begun along the margins of the formerly opening ocean. The insulating effects of the thick continental lithosphere lead to the buildup of heat and the initiation of rifting. (c) What once was an opening ocean has become a closing ocean, with cool asthenosphere beneath. One Wilson cycle is now complete.   (*Source*: P. Kearey and F. J. Vine, *Global Tectonics*, Oxford: Blackwell Scientific, 1990.)

Chapter Summary

1. The solid Earth is dynamic, not static. Wegener's idea of drifting continents proposed in the early 20th century has largely been substantiated.

   a. New seafloor is created at mid-ocean ridges and moves outward as ocean basins grow.

   b. Old seafloor is destroyed at deep-sea trenches in subduction zones. Earthquakes outline the surface of the slab of oceanic lithosphere being subducted beneath the continent; their foci along a continental margin become ever deeper away from the trench.

   c. Deeper probing of Earth's interior has revealed heterogeneity in composition and temperature that can be the result only of large-scale circulation in the mantle and outer core.

      i. This circulation is fueled by residual heat from the formation of the planet 4.6 billion years ago and by heat that continues to be produced as the result of the radioactive decay of potassium, uranium, and thorium in the mantle and crust.

      ii. Mantle circulation is the result of convection, not unlike that of the troposphere. Scientists continue to debate whether convective cells extend throughout the mantle or whether a dual system of upper and lower mantle convection is in operation.

2. The signature of plate tectonics is best seen at the surface, along the margins of lithospheric plates.

   a. At plate margins, divergent, convergent, and transform plate motions generate impressive topographic features: mid-ocean ridges and continental mountain belts and volcanoes, deep-sea trenches, and transform faults, respectively. These features themselves change with time.

      i. Mountains grow through plate collision but shrink through weathering and erosion.

      ii. Sediments are transported to the oceans, where they fill in deep-sea trenches as well as basins generated through subsidence.

      iii. Burial converts sediments to sedimentary rocks, but in time these rocks are likely to become reexposed as the result of plate convergence and uplift, or metamorphosed and perhaps ultimately melted.

   b. This cycle of rock production and destruction (the rock cycle), driven largely by plate tectonic processes, continuously resurfaces the planet and recycles material between the crust and mantle.

3. The movement of lithospheric plates is driven by forces at plate margins and, at the base of the lithosphere, by friction with the convecting asthenosphere.

   a. Magnetic stripes displaying mirror-image patterns across the mid-ocean ridges document the creation of seafloor at the ridges.

   b. Plate motions are slow on human time scales (on the order of centimeters per year), but over geological time they can lead to the complete redistribution of continents on the globe.

      i. These movements appear to be organized, following a pattern called Wilson cycles. These cycles consist of the alternating assembly of supercontinents (perhaps at the position of mantle downwelling) and their subsequent breakup (as the insulating effects of the supercontinent lead to sublithospheric heating and mantle upwelling).

      ii. The most recent supercontinent, Pangea, formed more than 300 million years ago. Its breakup, beginning some 200 million years ago, led to the creation of the Atlantic Ocean and the separation of North America and South America from Europe and Africa.

      iii. The Pacific Ocean is currently shrinking, and it is estimated that in another 200 million years or so the continents will again reassemble into another supercontinent.

Key Terms

asthenosphere	magma	sedimentary rock
basalt	magnetic dynamo	sediments
body waves	metamorphic rocks	seismic wave
chemosynthesis	mid-ocean ridge	silicate mineral
continental drift	mineral	slab
craton	Moho	subduction
earthquake	Pangea	surface waves
erosion	plate tectonics	S wave
granite	polarity	transform fault
igneous rock	P wave	Wilson cycle
lithification	rock cycle	
lithosphere	seafloor spreading	

Review Questions

1. Why was the theory of continental drift not immediately embraced by the scientific community in the 1920s?
2. What is the Moho?
3. What are the bases for the two major divisions of Earth's interior—one that distinguishes crust, mantle, and core and the other that distinguishes lithosphere and asthenosphere?
4. Compare and contrast P and S seismic waves.
5. Why are earthquakes focused along plate margins?
6. What are the sources of heat in Earth's interior?
7. What is magnetic polarity? What role did it play in the generation of ideas regarding seafloor spreading?
8. What are the three types of plate boundaries, and what surface features are characteristic of each?
9. What is erosion?
10. How can radioactivity be used to determine the age of a rock?
11. What are the driving forces for plate movement?
12. What is hypothesized to drive the Wilson cycle of plate fragmentation and reassembly?

Critical-Thinking Problems

1. We have seen that cooling of the oceanic lithosphere causes contraction, leading to subsidence of the seafloor away from the axis of spreading. The depth d of the ocean floor, measured in meters, increases with age t, measured in millions of years from the present, according to the following equation (valid for seafloor younger than 80 million years old):

$$d = 2500 + 350 \cdot \sqrt{t}$$

Graph a cross section of a mid-ocean ridge that is spreading symmetrically in both directions at a rate of 1 cm/yr (10 km/million yr). The age of the oldest seafloor shown should be 80 million years.

2. Duplicate Figure 10 and answer the following questions:
   a. Draw a line from the tip of Florida horizontally across the Atlantic to northwest Africa, a distance of about 6400 km. Now, graph the age of the seafloor (on the y-axis) against the distance from the ridge axis (on the x-axis). From this graph, determine the spreading rate for each geologic interval represented, averaging the two values determined for eastward and westward spreading. Graph these values (y-axis) as a function of time (in million years, on the x-axis).
   b. How has the Atlantic spreading rate varied over the last 200 million years?

Further Reading

General

Tarbuck, E. J., F. K. Lutgens, D. Tasa. 2007. *Earth: An introduction to physical geology*. 9th ed. Upper Saddle River, NJ: Prentice Hall.
Wegener, A. 1924. *The origins of the continents and ocean basins*. London: Metheune.

Advanced

Kearey, P., K. A. Klepeis, and F. J. Vine. 2009. *Global tectonics*. 3rd ed. Oxford: Wiley-Blackwell.

(a)

(b)

BOX FIGURE 3 Abundant and bizarre life thriving under the harsh conditions of the deep-seafloor, in the vicinity of hydrothermal venting. (a) Tube worms, crabs, and other organisms can be seen. (b) A black smoker chimney is shown spewing out sulfide-rich solutions that provide the energy source for this food chain. (*Source:* (a) American Geophysical Union and (b) Dudley Foster/Woods Hole Oceanographic Institution.)

FIGURE 4 Tomographic image of the mantle's S-wave velocity variations underneath North America, along the transect line shown in the insert. Blue colors indicate regions of fast seismic velocities, while reds indicate slow seismic velocities. The blue region cutting across the center of the diagram is the downgoing Farallon slab, which has been subducting under North America for 100 million years. (*Source:* From W.K. Hamblin and E.H. Christiansen, *Earth's Dynamic Systems*, 8/e, 1998. Reprinted by permission of Prentice Hall, Upper Saddle River, N.J.)

FIGURE 10   The age of the ocean floor is shown as bands of different color on the basis of the magnetic striping developed during seafloor spreading. The youngest ocean floor is near the mid-ocean ridge, while the oldest is furthest away.   (*Source: From R.W. Christopherson, Geosystems: An Introduction to Physical Geography, 3/e, 1997. Reprinted by permission of Prentice Hall, Upper Saddle River, N.J.*)

m.y. = millions of years

0–2 m.y.	58–66 m.y.
2–5 m.y.	66–84 m.y.
5–24 m.y.	84–117 m.y.
24–37 m.y.	117–144 m.y.
37–58 m.y.	144–208 m.y.

FIGURE 12 Paleogeographic reconstructions from the Early Cambrian to the Cretaceous-Tertiary boundary. (*Source:* From R. Blakey, *used with permission.*)

| Oceanic ridge | ——— Trenches | ● Shallow-focus earthquake | ● Intermediate-focus earthquake | ● Deep-focus earthquake |

FIGURE 15 Distribution of earthquakes of shallow, intermediate, or deep focus. Deep-focus earthquakes occur only at subduction zones.   (*Source:* From W.K. Hamblin and E.H. Christiansen, *Earth's Dynamic Systems*, 8/e, 1998. Reprinted by permission of Prentice Hall, Upper Saddle River, N.J.)

Recycling of the Elements
Carbon and Nutrient Cycles

Key Questions

- What determines how reservoirs (such as the atmospheric CO_2 reservoir) respond to imbalances in the flow of material to and from them?
- Which reservoirs and processes are important to the recycling of carbon and other essential nutrients in the Earth system?

- Do feedback mechanisms regulate the amount of atmospheric CO_2?
- How do nutrients limit biological productivity on Earth?

Chapter Overview

The recycling of the elements among the components of the Earth system is key to the continued functioning of Earth as a living planet. Although many elements are critical, none is more central to the workings of the Earth system than carbon. All life is based on carbon; gaseous carbon dioxide is an important greenhouse gas; the acidity of the ocean is regulated by carbon compounds; and the maintenance of an oxygen-rich atmosphere depends on the transfer of carbon to sedimentary rocks. To perform these functions, the *carbon cycle* involves a hierarchy of subcycles that operate on different time scales, ranging from decades (for the replenishment of CO_2 in the atmosphere) to hundreds of millions of years (for the recycling of carbon through sedimentary rocks and for the exchange of carbon within Earth's interior). Both biological and physical processes are involved in the recycling of carbon, and they are so closely intertwined that it becomes difficult to separate the two. In this chapter we trace the movement of carbon as it cycles through the Earth system and we develop additional systems theory notions of *steady state* and *residence time* along the way. We also discuss the *nutrient elements*, because the rate of carbon recycling depends strongly on the rate of nutrient recycling.

SYSTEMS APPROACH TO THE CARBON CYCLE

Why is Earth the only planet in our solar system that supports life? The direct answer is that Earth is the only planet that has liquid water at its surface. (Jupiter's moon Europa may have water only a few kilometers beneath its icy surface.) But part of the reason Earth is able to maintain liquid water is that our planet has natural recycling systems for the elements essential for life, including carbon, nitrogen, phosphorus, and sulfur. These recycling systems are ultimately linked with the global process of plate tectonics. The link between tectonic activity and the carbon cycle is important to the regulation of atmospheric CO_2 concentrations and thus to climate as well.

The winds and ocean currents and the moving lithospheric plates make up Earth's circulatory system: They transport energy and material to different parts of the Earth system where they are utilized in biological and physical processes. This mixing of Earth's fluid and solid parts also helps accomplish an important task: the recycling of the elements. Essential elements are released to the **biosphere** (the part of Earth that supports life, including the oceans, atmosphere, land surface, and soils) as rocks weather, volcanoes erupt, and nitrogen is made available from the atmosphere by chemical transformations stimulated by lightning discharge. Compared with the rates of utilization by the biota, these releases are very slow; they would support only very low rates of biological activity were there not highly efficient nutrient recycling mechanisms. **Nutrients** are substances, normally obtained in the diet, that are essential to organisms. Nutrient elements are incorporated into living tissue during growth and rapidly returned to the soil or ocean on death. This cycle is repeated many times before the elements are lost from the biosphere, mostly as constituents of sedimentary rocks. The situation is much like our recycling of aluminum cans: Recycling substantially reduces our dependence on the extraction of aluminum from Earth and allows us to produce aluminum products much more rapidly. Similarly, element recycling within the biosphere allows for much higher rates of biological productivity.

A number of important recycling systems operate on Earth. The cycles of the nutrient elements nitrogen and phosphorus are discussed later in this chapter. The recy-cling of carbon is especially important: As a major constituent of the greenhouse gases carbon dioxide and methane, it affects not only biological productivity but Earth's climate as well. We focus on the carbon cycle in this chapter because of its overarching importance to the Earth system.

A Journey through the Terrestrial Organic Carbon Cycle

As an introduction to just one part of the global carbon cycle, imagine that we could follow the carbon atom of a CO_2 molecule as it cycled through the terrestrial (land-based) part of the cycle (Figure 1). The carbon in CO_2 is **inorganic carbon**—it is not associated with compounds formed by living organisms and it does not contain car-bon–carbon or carbon–hydrogen bonds. After spending nearly a decade moving with the winds in the troposphere, the gaseous CO_2 molecule will have visited both the Northern and Southern hemispheres several times. Then one spring, during the annual greening of the Northern Hemisphere (Figure 2), the CO_2 molecule passes through a small opening in a leaf, the photosynthetic apparatus of a plant. Through a frenzy of collisions with other molecules and atoms, the oxygen atoms are ripped from the molecule while hydrogen, nitrogen, and other carbon atoms become

FIGURE 1   The global carbon cycle.   (*Source:* From J. P. Davidson, W. E. Reed, and P. M. Davis, *Exploring Earth: An Introduction to Physical Geology*, 1997. Reprinted by permission of Prentice Hall, Upper Saddle River, N.J.)

(a)

(b)

FIGURE 2 [See color section] Satellite image of the vegetation coverage of the land surface in the Northern Hemisphere in (a) summer and (b) winter, expressed as an index, with larger values having greater coverage by living vegetation. (*Source:* Felix Kogan/NOAA/NESDIS/ORA Climate Research and Application Division.)

attached. Our carbon atom, as part of the leaf, is now **organic carbon**. Some leaves are consumed and digested by animals. The carbon in these leaves is then released back to the atmosphere by the animals' respiration as CO_2.

Summer passes, fall arrives, and the leaf that contains the carbon atom has not been eaten. The nourishing substances and water that the leaf has received from the tree have ceased to flow. The leaf is released from the branch and settles to the ground. Other leaves fall on top, burying it in a thick mat of decaying matter. The carbon atom is part of the soil, where it will remain for about the next 50 years. By the end of that time, bacteria and fungi will have decomposed the organic matter that contains the atom. The chemical reactions that result transform the carbon atom once again into a gaseous CO_2 molecule, which escapes back to the atmosphere.

This life cycle of a carbon atom is repeated nearly 500 times on average before a "leak" occurs. Once in a while, before the organic matter that contains the carbon atom decomposes, the soil erodes and is transported by rivers to the oceans. There it settles with the other particles to the seafloor and is buried by subsequent sediments or carried with its underlying oceanic plate deep into a subduction zone. Under elevated temperatures and pressures the carbon atom may be converted into gaseous carbon atoms and escape to the surface, or be converted into a component of sedimentary or metamorphic rock.

The carbon atom may spend millions of years in the sedimentary/metamorphic rock reservoir, as mountain belts form, thrusting deeply buried rocks to Earth's surface and beyond to great elevations. Eventually our carbon

atom will be transferred from its burial place within Earth's interior to the surface. Here environmental forces, both biological and physical, will cause the sedimentary rock containing the carbon atom to disintegrate during the process of weathering. In this process, the organic carbon reacts with oxygen from the atmosphere and forms (inorganic) CO_2, which escapes as a gas to the atmosphere. The weathering process, then, is the connecting link in the long path this particular carbon atom has taken—from the atmosphere, to the plant, to the soil, to the sediment, to the sedimentary rock, and back to the atmosphere.

The path the carbon atom has taken encompasses the *terrestrial organic carbon cycle*, operating on time scales that are short (years to decades) and those that are long (centuries and millennia to multimillion years). If instead of being incorporated into a plant leaf the carbon atom had entered the ocean and been converted to organic carbon by marine algae, it would have become part of the *marine organic carbon cycle*. There are also a host of processes not involving organic carbon that compose the *inorganic carbon cycle*. These various parts of the carbon cycle are discussed below.

Carbon Reservoir Dynamics

Carbon resides in many reservoirs at or near Earth's surface (Figure 3), ranging in size from the relatively tiny amount of carbon in atmospheric methane to the tremendous amount of carbon stored in sedimentary rocks. One of our ultimate goals is to understand how this system of reservoirs responds to perturbations. We will use the response to the release of carbon dioxide from the burning of fossil

FIGURE 3 Reservoirs of carbon at or near Earth's surface circa 1995.

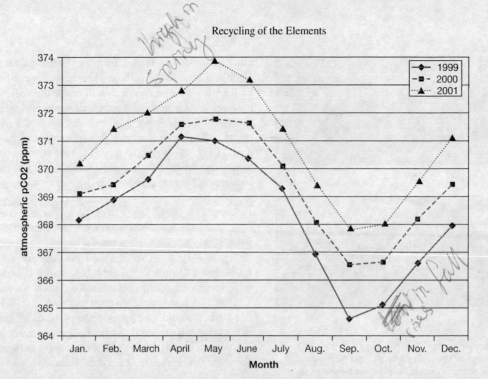

[handwritten notes: "high in spring", "CO2 high in spring, low in summers, rises in fall-winter", "from m. fall rises"]

FIGURE 4 Seasonal fluctuations in atmospheric CO_2 from the Mauna Loa Observatory for 1999–2001. The gradual increase due to fossil-fuel burning and deforestation accounts for the offset from year to year. (*Source:* Data courtesy Oak Ridge National Laboratory, http://cdiac.esd.ornl.gov/trends/co2/sio-mlo.htm.)

fuels as an example of the dynamics of the carbon cycle and of material recycling systems in general.

Figure 4 shows the seasonal fluctuations in the atmospheric CO_2 level for three years (1999–2001) measured from atop Mauna Loa, Hawaii. In Figure 4, we focus on the natural seasonal cycle rather than the gradual increase in CO_2 from fossil-fuel burning and deforestation. The CO_2 content falls during the Northern Hemisphere summer, when photosynthesis (and the growth of leaves) surpasses respiration and decomposition. It then rises during the late fall to early spring, when respiration and decomposition of the previous season's crop of leaves exceeds photosynthesis. Because Hawaii is in the Northern Hemisphere ($17°$ N), measurements made at Mauna Loa reflect the annual cycle in that hemisphere. Let us cast these observations in terms of systems theory.

RESERVOIRS From the systems point of view, the atmosphere is a *reservoir* of carbon in the form of CO_2 (Figure 5). Reservoirs are typically characterized in terms of the amount of material they are holding at any particular time.

Their sizes are commonly expressed either in mass units or volume units. (Chemists often use *moles;* refer to the Box "Useful Concepts: The Concept of the Mole" if you need a refresher.) In Figure 5, the amount of carbon is expressed in gigatons (Gt) of carbon, or Gt(C). A gigaton is 1 billion metric tons, and 1 metric ton is 1000 kg. With the notation Gt(C), we are keeping track of the mass of only the carbon atoms, not the other atoms to which they are attached.

Reservoirs are temporary repositories for material that flows through them, and their sizes change in response to imbalances between inflow and outflow, typically expressed in unit mass, unit volume, or moles per unit time. The *inflow* to the atmospheric CO_2 reservoir is the combination of the processes of respiration and decomposition. This inflow can be expressed in units of gigatons of carbon per year. The *outflow* from this reservoir is photosynthesis, and the rate of outflow is also expressed as gigatons of carbon per year.

STEADY STATE If the rates of inflow and outflow were such that the atmospheric CO_2 level remained at a constant value with time, we would say that *steady state* had been achieved. **Steady state** is a condition in which the state of a system component is constant with time. Steady state could be achieved if no inflow and no outflow existed, that is, if both processes ceased. A constant level could also be maintained if the rate of inflow of CO_2 into the atmosphere equaled the rate of outflow.

Any imbalance in these rates leads to a change in the level of atmospheric CO_2. When the inflow exceeds the outflow, the atmospheric CO_2 level rises. (This situation is analogous to the Northern Hemisphere winter condition.)

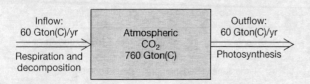

FIGURE 5 The atmospheric carbon (i.e., CO_2) reservoir, showing inflows and outflows.

USEFUL CONCEPTS
The Concept of the Mole

Atoms and molecules are typically measured in units called moles. A *mole* (abbreviated mol) of a substance is defined as the amount of that substance that contains the same number of atoms or molecules (or any other particle) as the number of atoms in 12 g of ^{12}C. There are 6.02×10^{23} atoms in 12 g of ^{12}C; this number is called *Avogadro's number*, after the Italian chemist Amedeo Avogadro. A mole of any type of particle contains Avogadro's number of these particles. In concept, a mole is no different than, say, a dozen; it simply converts a number that would be cumbersome into one that is more practical. Even when we use moles, global-scale reservoirs such as that of atmospheric CO_2 are huge. There are presently about 6×10^{16} moles of CO_2 in the atmosphere.

One mole of ^{12}C weighs exactly 12 g. However, 1 mol of H weighs only approximately 1 g, and 1 mol of ^{16}O weighs approximately 16 g. These weights are defined as the mass numbers of the given isotopes. The mass number of an isotope is the total number of protons plus neutrons in the nucleus. Equivalently, atomic weight is the weight of 1 mol of a particular isotope. For an element with more than one stable isotope, the precise atomic weight (as opposed to the mass number) of the element is determined from the relative amounts of the various isotopes.

Expressing quantities of substances in moles rather than in mass units (e.g. grams) can be useful when we are studying chemical reactions. Consider the chemical reaction for the formation of salt (sodium chloride, NaCl):

$$Na^+ + Cl^- \rightarrow NaCl$$

This equation shows that one atom of sodium (Na) will react with one atom of chlorine (Cl) to form one molecule of NaCl. Therefore, 1 mol of Na will react with 1 mol of Cl to form 1 mol of NaCl. To express this equation in mass units, we would need to use the atomic weights of sodium and chlorine. If we did, we would find that 22.99 g of Na reacts with 35.45 g of Cl to produce 58.44 g of NaCl—a more cumbersome calculation.

When the outflow exceeds the inflow, the level falls (analogous to the Northern Hemisphere summer condition).

In the record of atmospheric CO_2 variations in Figure 4, we see that one maximum and one minimum is reached each year. At these times the fluxes are in balance. The system is not really in steady state at these times, however, because the reservoir size is unchanging only for an instant. Averaged over longer times, though, the *natural* cycle of CO_2 is thought to be close to steady state, despite seasonal imbalances. Because of anthropogenic disturbances, the atmospheric CO_2 level is not currently at steady state, as demonstrated by the steady rise in CO_2 over the past several decades.

Steady state can be maintained over time only if the rates of inflow and/or outflow are sensitive to changes in the size of the reservoir. In systems terminology, this means that there must be couplings that link the reservoir size to the processes that govern inflow and outflow. Consider what would happen if a reservoir in steady state were perturbed by an addition of material. If the coupling governing inflow was negative or if that governing outflow was positive (i.e., inflow decreased or outflow increased), the reservoir would return to its original state. One such negative feedback loop exists between the photosynthetic rate of plants and atmospheric CO_2. As CO_2 levels go up, plants photosynthesize more rapidly; this effect has been called CO_2 *fertilization* (Figure 6). But as they do, CO_2 levels tend to fall, because CO_2 is consumed by plants during photosynthesis. Thus, the terrestrial biota tend to stabilize atmospheric CO_2 levels.

FIGURE 6 Effect of changes in CO_2 concentration on the photosynthetic rate of typical plants. Photosynthetic rates are relative to the value for today's atmospheric CO_2 level. Inset represents the negative feedback loop that results from this dependence.

RESIDENCE TIME   To help us monitor the recycling of elements through the Earth system, the concept of residence time can be useful. **Residence time** is defined as the average length of time a substance spends in a given reservoir that is at steady state. We can calculate the residence time by dividing the reservoir size at steady state by the inflow or outflow rate:

$$\text{residence time} = \frac{\text{reservoir size at steady state}}{\text{inflow rate or outflow rate}}.$$

If reservoir size has units of mass and the inflow and outflow rate is in mass per time, then the quotient has units of time.

We can determine the residence time of the atmospheric carbon reservoir from the size of that reservoir, which Figure 3 gives as 760 Gton(C), and from the rate of respiration and decomposition (the inflow rate) or the rate of photosynthesis (the outflow rate), both of which are given as 60 Gton(C)/yr. Thus, if we assume steady state, the residence time of carbon in the atmosphere with respect to these processes is 760 Gton(C)/60 Gton(C)/yr = 12.7 yr. This means that carbon in the atmosphere is replenished about once per decade.

We can also think about residence time as an indicator of how long a reservoir takes to respond measurably to large imbalances in inflow or outflow. In our atmospheric carbon example, if photosynthesis were to cease but respiration and decomposition were to continue at their current rate, the atmospheric CO_2 level would double in about a decade. Thus, the residence time, defined at steady state, becomes the **characteristic response time** when a system is *not* at steady state. The concept of a characteristic response time is similar to that of a half-life in radioactive decay. Stated formally, a disturbance from steady state (in a system where the rate of removal is proportional to the amount of disturbance) diminishes to 1/e (about 38%) of its original size in one characteristic response time.

Oxidized and Reduced Carbon

The many identities that carbon assumes in the Earth system can be lumped into two general categories: oxidized carbon and reduced carbon. **Oxidized carbon** is carbon that is combined with oxygen. Examples of oxidized carbon include the carbon in the skeletons of some organisms and in atmospheric CO_2. **Reduced carbon** is carbon that is combined mainly with other carbon atoms, hydrogen, or nitrogen. Organic carbon is a form of reduced carbon. Perhaps a more familiar pair of reduced and oxidized substances is metallic iron and its oxidation product, rust (iron oxide). In the presence of oxygen gas at Earth's surface, reduced substances, such as organic carbon and metallic iron, tend to be highly chemically reactive. Oxidized substances, such as CO_2 and rust, tend to be more inert.

In the next few sections, we explore the organic and inorganic carbon cycles. We begin with the organic carbon cycle as it operates on land—the terrestrial organic carbon cycle, which we already introduced in our journey through the carbon cycle. We then move to the oceans, where both oxidized and reduced carbon recycling are important on short time scales. Finally, we consider the longer-time-scale cycles, which involve geological processes.

THE SHORT-TERM ORGANIC CARBON CYCLE

The short-term organic carbon cycle involves processes ranging from those we can observe and appreciate on a daily to seasonal time scale (see Figure 2), such as the processes of photosynthesis and respiration, to processes of decomposition that are somewhat slower (Figure 7). The key step in this cycle is the conversion of inorganic carbon (atmospheric CO_2) to organic carbon by the process of **photosynthesis**. We are not so much interested in the process itself but rather in its impact on the global cycle, which is generally expressed as primary productivity. **Primary productivity** is the amount of organic matter produced by photosynthesis in a unit time over a unit area of Earth's surface. That amount depends on the population size of **primary producers**—that is, plants (or other types of photosynthesizers or even chemosynthesizers) that provide energy other organisms can use. The relationship is not simple, however, because some primary producer species are much more productive than others. In its simplest representation, primary production involves a chemical reaction between CO_2 and water to form organic matter and oxygen:

Photosynthesis: $CO_2 + H_2O \rightarrow CH_2O + O_2$

(Primary   carbon   water   carbohydrate   oxygen
production)   dioxide   gas

Here, organic matter is represented by CH_2O, the simplest *carbohydrate*, or compound of carbon, hydrogen, and oxygen. In reality the molecules making up organic matter are much larger than this simple carbohydrate, and they contain small amounts of many other elements, including nitrogen and phosphorus. For our purposes, however, this simpler representation suffices.

Photosynthesis does not occur spontaneously at Earth's surface but instead requires an input of energy from the Sun. Plants, algae, and bacteria have evolved pigments that are able to capture the energy of sunlight and convert it to chemical energy, part of which is stored in living tissues. This chemical energy is then utilized by other organisms that cannot utilize solar energy directly. Such organisms, including animals, are called **consumers**.

Most of the photosynthesis that occurs each year leads to the formation of tissue that is recycled rapidly, including the leaves of trees. This recycling is the cause of the seasonal variations observed in the CO_2 record of Figure 4. However, most of the organic carbon that makes up plant tissues has a residence time of many decades. That is because the bulk of the organic carbon in terrestrial plants

FIGURE 7 The short-term, terrestrial organic carbon cycle, showing reservoir sizes, inflows, and outflows. Dark shaded area represents the long-term cycle (see Figure 12). Reservoir sizes in Gt(C), fluxes in Gt(C)/yr.

is contained not in the leaves but in the roots and trunks of slow-growing trees. In other words, most of the biomass of primary producers on Earth is contained in tree roots and trunks. **Biomass** is the total mass of organic matter in living organisms in a particular reservoir. In terms of carbon, the total living biomass—the combined biomasses of all primary producers and consumers—is about equal to the atmospheric carbon reservoir (see Figure 3).

Consumer biomass is a small percentage (only about 1%) of the biomass of the producers. Consumers derive their metabolic energy from the chemical energy stored in plant tissues by ingesting the tissues and respiring. *Respiration* is the reverse of photosynthesis: It is the chemical reaction between oxygen and organic tissue that yields CO_2 and water:

Respiration: CH_2O + O_2 $\longrightarrow$ CO_2 + H_2O
         carbohydrate   oxygen   carbon   water
                        gas   dioxide

During photosynthesis, plants use solar energy to create tissue. But, like animals, plants produce their metabolic energy through respiration. Hence, respiration is more than just the "breathing" performed by animals. Unlike photosynthesis, respiration would proceed abiotically because it

releases rather than requires energy. However, it would do so very slowly. Organisms are able to accelerate this chemical reaction by the use of *enzymes*, chemical compounds (specifically, proteins) that they synthesize for this purpose.

On land, about half the organic material produced by photosynthesis is respired by animals and by plants themselves. The remaining material is added to the organic-rich upper layers of soil. A host of microscopic bacteria and fungi live in soil. Their metabolic requirements are satisfied through the decomposition of the large store of organic matter that is buried there, fueled by the supply of oxygen from the overlying layers. A biological process that uses oxygen is said to be *aerobic*, and an organism that carries out aerobic metabolism is an *aerobe*. The chemical reaction for this aerobic decomposition is identical to that for respiration.

Because the only source of oxygen is the air, the microorganisms that live well below the surface must be adapted to environments that are devoid of oxygen. A biological process that occurs in the absence of oxygen is said to be *anaerobic*, and an organism that carries out anaerobic metabolism is an *anaerobe*. In the O_2-free environment of deep soil live anaerobic bacteria that decompose organic matter by an overall process known as methanogenesis. **Methanogenesis** is an anaerobic form of metabolism that involves multiple steps, carried out by different bacteria. One step involves fermentation of complex organic materials into simpler forms, including hydrogen (H_2) and acetate that methanogens can then use to form both oxidized carbon (in CO_2) and reduced carbon (methane). The overall process can be represented as:

$$\text{Methanogenesis:} \quad \underset{\text{carbohydrate}}{2CH_2O} \longrightarrow \underset{\substack{\text{carbon} \\ \text{dioxide}}}{CO_2} + \underset{\text{methane}}{CH_4}$$

(Other, more complex compounds can also be used in and produced during anaerobic metabolism, but for the purposes of studying the carbon cycle, this representation is adequate.) The gases CO_2 and CH_4 can escape to the atmosphere. Once there, the CO_2 continues the short-term cycling path described earlier. Methane, however, is chemically unstable in our O_2-rich atmosphere and is destroyed by a series of oxidation reactions. The carbon contained in

CH_4 combines with O_2 to form CO_2. With an atmospheric reservoir size of 5 Gton(C) and a supply rate from fermentation of 0.5 Gton(C)/yr (see Figure 7), the residence time of CH_4 in the atmosphere is approximately 10 years.

The land surface is continuously stripped of its soil cover by the action of winds and water. On average, about 5 cm of soil is eroded from the land surface every 1,000 years and transported by rivers to the oceans. Although river systems have a substantial capacity for storing sediment in flood plains and deltas, eventually most of the sediment makes its way to the oceans and is deposited on the seafloor. These sediments contain whatever organic matter has survived the trip from land to sea. Thus, there is a transfer of organic carbon from the terrestrial to the marine realm, one that amounts to about 0.1 Gton(C)/yr. However, this transfer is small compared with the flux through the oceanic water column of organic matter produced in the ocean.

A CLOSER LOOK
Oxygen Minimum Zone

The decomposition of organic matter settling through the water column consumes oxygen, leading to oxygen depletion. Decomposition also releases nutrients to the water, so nutrient concentrations increase. The lowest oxygen concentrations are achieved at intermediate depths, about 1 km below the surface. This region is known as the *oxygen minimum zone* (Box Figure 1). In this zone, dissolved oxygen concentrations reach a minimum as a result of high oxygen demand by aerobic decomposers and low oxygen supply from the surface ocean or from below.

In the waters below the oxygen minimum zone, oxygen content increases with depth. Why is this so, if the source of oxygen is exchange with the atmosphere and production by phytoplankton in the surface ocean?

Recall that the circulation of the ocean resembles a giant conveyor belt that brings waters from the surface in the high-latitude North Atlantic and Antarctic oceans to the deep sea. This water is enriched in oxygen as a consequence of having originated at the surface in the high latitudes. Like most gases, oxygen is more soluble in cold water than in warm water. So, gas exchange with the atmosphere leads to higher gas

concentrations in high-latitude surface waters than in low-latitude surface waters. High-latitude surface waters become denser as they cool and get saltier, and sink, moving to lower latitudes at depth. Deep water therefore ends up with more dissolved O_2 than does the water above it. Thus, the oxygen minimum zone owes its existence to the combined operation of the biological pump and the global ocean circulation.

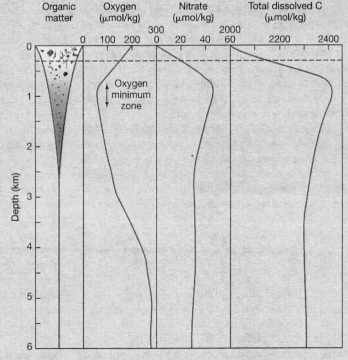

BOX FIGURE 1 The effect of the biological pump and thermohaline circulation on the chemical composition of the ocean. Typical vertical profiles of the amount of organic matter, dissolved oxygen, nitrate (a nutrient), and inorganic carbon are shown. Concentrations are in micromoles (10^{-6} mol) per kilogram of seawater.

The Marine Organic Carbon Cycle on Short Time Scales

PRODUCERS AND CONSUMERS The dominant primary producers in the ocean are the free-floating, photosynthetic marine microorganisms referred to as *phytoplankton*. (In more general terms, *plankton* are organisms with any type of metabolism that float freely in aquatic environments.) These organisms—primarily *diatoms* (Figure 8a) and other algae, such as *coccolithophorids* (Figure 8b)—live in the photic zone. The **photic zone** is the uppermost part of the oceanic water column where there is sufficient light for photosynthesis: about the upper 100 m of the water column in the open ocean, and in shallower waters near shore, where water clarity is reduced. It roughly corresponds to the "surface ocean," which, is the upper part of the ocean mixed by the winds.

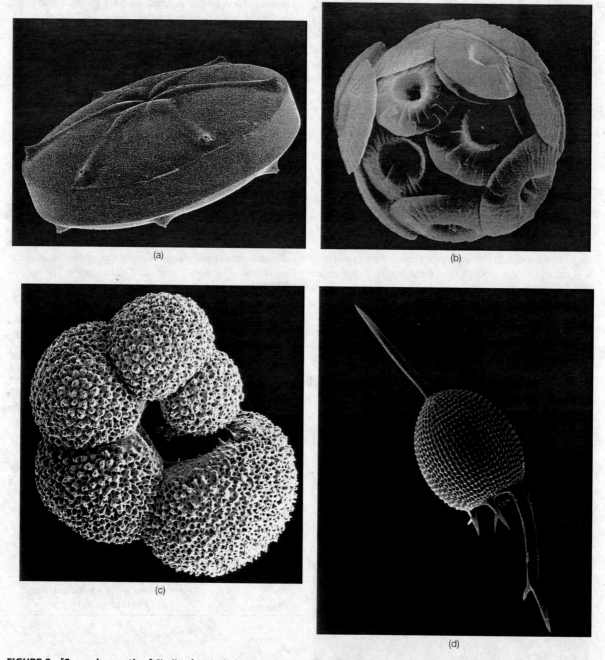

FIGURE 8 **[See color section]** Shells of typical phytoplankton: (a) diatom (SiO_2; approximately 50 μm wide) and (b) coccolithophorid ($CaCO_3$; about 10 μm in diameter). Typical zooplankton: (c) foraminifer ($CaCO_3$; approximately 600 μm in diameter) and (d) radiolarian (SiO_2; approximately 50 μm wide). (*Source:* Renate Bernstein.)

Phytoplankton consume CO_2 and produce O_2 through photosynthesis in much the same way as do land-based plants. Although the gases phytoplankton use and produce are dissolved in seawater, there is continuous gas exchange between the atmosphere and the ocean. Thus, the activities of phytoplankton affect the atmosphere as well as the ocean.

Much of the organic matter produced in the surface ocean by phytoplankton is consumed by zooplankton. **Zooplankton** are free-floating marine consumers, including small invertebrates and microorganisms such as *foraminifera* (Figure 8c) and *radiolarians* (Figure 8d), that cannot photosynthesize. Zooplankton produce fecal pellets that, together with other large particles of decaying organic matter, settle through the water column to great depths. In contrast to the flux of organic matter from treetops to the ground, though, only about 1% of this material survives the trip to the seafloor. Even then, the material is subject to efficient recycling by aerobic and anaerobic decomposers that live on the seafloor or in the uppermost layers of sediment. As a result, only about 0.1% of the organic matter that settles from the surface ocean is preserved in marine sediments.

Most marine organic matter is decomposed by animals and microbes as it settles through the water column. This decomposition releases CO_2 (the product of both oxygen-breathing animals and microbial respiration) and nutrients to the oceanic deep waters. For marine organisms, nutrients lead to high rates of primary productivity if they are available in the appropriate concentrations. Thus, it is critical to the productivity of the marine biota to get these nutrients back to the surface.

THE BIOLOGICAL PUMP The overall effect of photosynthesis in shallow waters, of the settling of organic matter, and of decomposition in deep waters is the transfer of CO_2 and nutrients from the surface waters to the deep ocean. This process is known as the **biological pump** (Figure 9). It is balanced by upwelling, which brings nutrients and carbon-rich waters back to the surface, replenishing the nutrients and carbon removed by the biological pump.

The biological pump has a profound effect on ocean chemistry. As a result of its operation, surface waters are measurably depleted in carbon and severely depleted in phosphate and nitrate (the major nutrient elements) relative to deep waters. If the biological pump were to cease—for example, as the result of a mass extinction—the ocean would assume a more uniform composition in a few thousand years, as ocean mixing homogenized the ocean.

NUTRIENT LIMITATION Some elements are classified as nutrients for marine phytoplankton because they are essential for growth and exist at suboptimal concentrations; an increase in their concentration leads to higher rates of primary productivity. Other elements are *toxic* to marine life—that is, they are poisonous to certain organisms—because their concentrations in seawater are above the optimum for growth. (Even nutrient elements can be toxic if their concentrations become too high.) There is great variability in the concentration of many elements throughout the world's oceans. Each element, depending on its concentration, can be either a nutrient or a toxic substance. For each element, there is some optimum concentration that favors biological productivity.

Marine phytoplankton incorporate many nutrient elements into their tissues in ratios that appear to be nearly identical in all species. These ratios are called **Redfield ratios,** in honor of Alfred C. Redfield, the oceanographer who first described this phenomenon. Even more remarkably, the ratios of many of these elements in seawater is nearly identical to that in phytoplankton. For example, the elemental ratio of carbon: nitrogen:phosphorus is very nearly 106:16:1 (Table 1). A chicken-or-egg question arises: Does the composition of seawater determine the composition of organisms that live in the sea, or does the composition of marine organisms determine the composition of seawater? To answer this question, we must consider the distribution of primary productivity in the oceans.

Where are rates of primary productivity greatest in the oceans? We now have a sophisticated way of answering this

Processes: Photosynthesis
           Fecal-pellet production
           Oxygen production

$$CO_2 + H_2O \longrightarrow \text{"}CH_2O\text{"} + O_2$$

Surface ocean

Upwelling of nutrients   *balanced*   Settling of organic matter

Processes: Decomposition
           Nutrient release
           Oxygen consumption

$$\text{"}CH_2O\text{"} + O_2 \longrightarrow CO_2 + H_2O$$

Deep ocean

FIGURE 9 The marine biological pump.

TABLE 1	Redfield Ratios

Element	Relative Number of Atoms in Living Phytoplankton
Carbon	106
Nitrogen	16
Phosphorus	1
Iron	0.01

question, by satellite. With a color scanner, researchers can quantify the color of seawater from space (Figure 10). The color of the ocean surface is strongly influenced by the density of phytoplankton, which contain photosynthetic pigments. In the early 1960s and 1970s, oceanographers began to study the relationship between the concentration of these pigments and the abundance and productivity of near-surface-dwelling phytoplankton. The researchers found that regions of the ocean that have low concentrations of *chlorophyll* (a green pigment that is the dominant pigment in algae) are biological deserts, with low abundances of organisms and low nutrient concentrations. In contrast, more productive waters tend to have high chlorophyll concentrations.

Although we might expect that the warm, sunny low-latitude oceans would be most conducive to phytoplankton growth, the satellite patterns reveal that the waters with the highest productivities are the cold waters of the high-latitude Atlantic, Pacific, and Southern oceans. The reason is that the thermocline is weak or nonexistent at these latitudes because surface waters are just as cold as the deep waters there. Thus, wind-driven mixing of nutrient-rich deep waters up to the surface occurs much more readily at high latitudes than at low latitudes, where mixing is inhibited by the strong temperature and density gradients. Apparently the inhibitory effects of cold temperatures and low light availability experienced by organisms that live at high latitudes are more than compensated for by an enhanced nutrient supply.

The satellite images also indicate high productivity in regions of upwelling. Many of these regions occur along the western continental margins. There the wind-driven surface currents cause offshore transport, which allows nutrient-rich waters from intermediate depths to well up to the surface. Other upwelling regions occur where surface currents diverge (for example, along the equator, due to the action of the trade winds and the Coriolis effect). Surface divergence also allows intermediate-depth waters to rise and replace the water transported away at the surface. Finally, the coastal regions of the continental shelves tend to be highly productive because of nutrient inputs from rivers (often strongly enhanced by anthropogenic inputs of nitrogen and phosphorus) and localized upwelling driven by the topography of the seafloor.

Nutrient supply therefore seems to be a major limitation on the productivity of the surface ocean. Except in upwelling regions, phosphate and nitrate concentrations in surface waters are driven essentially to zero as a result of intense uptake by phytoplankton. Deep waters begin as surface waters, depleted in nutrients, at high latitudes. These waters increase in nutrient concentration as nutrients are released by decomposing organic matter that rains down from the overlying water column (the biological pump). In the North Atlantic, the effect of this "rain" on the composition of the water is small, because the water mass is young and has not had time to build up a large supply of organic matter. Farther along the path of ocean general circulation, the aging water mass begins to show its increasing influence on the biological pump. Accordingly, the nutrient contents of deep North Pacific waters (the oldest waters in the ocean) are much greater (Figure 11a), and the O_2 contents much lower (Figure 11b), than those of the North Atlantic. Thus, the explanation for the observed similarity in nutrient elemental ratios between seawater and marine organisms—the Redfield ratios—is that the nutrient composition of the world's oceans is dominated by the production and decomposition of organic matter. In other words, the composition of marine organisms determines the composition of seawater.

THE LONG-TERM ORGANIC CARBON CYCLE

The processes we have discussed thus far affect the atmospheric CO_2 balance on time scales shorter than a century. On longer time scales, these processes must be very closely in balance: Because the fluxes involved are so large, persistent imbalances would lead to intolerable fluctuations in atmospheric CO_2. Geological processes become the important controls on atmospheric CO_2 on longer time scales (Figure 12). The fluxes of carbon involved in these processes are small, and the reservoirs involved are large. Together these two adjustments in scale mean that the importance of the geological processes affecting the sedimentary reservoir and the atmosphere are influential only on long time scales (on the order of 1,000 years to 1 million years).

FIGURE 10   [See color section] The concentration of photosynthetic pigments as determined by the Coastal Zone Color Scanner (CZCS) on the Nimbus 7 satellite. Pigment concentrations are indirect indicators of rates of primary production.   (*Source:* Gene Feldman, NASA GSFC/SPL/Photo Researchers.)

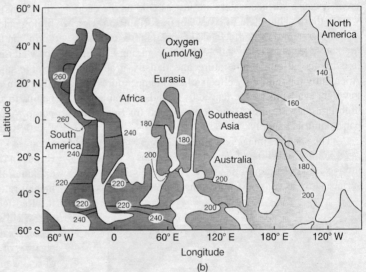

FIGURE 11 Concentrations of dissolved (a) nitrate and (b) O_2 in the deep ocean, in micromoles per kilogram of seawater. Maps are drawn for a water depth of 4000 m. At this depth the mid-ocean ridges appear as mountain ranges, and the continental outlines are substantially modified. (*Source:* W. S. Broecker and T.-H. Peng, *Tracers in the Sea*, New York: Eldigio Press, Columbia University, 1982, p. 31.)

Carbon Burial in Sedimentary Rocks

The flux of land-derived and marine sediments to the seafloor fills sedimentary basins, many of which flank the margins of the continents. The continuous supply of sediment to these basins leads to the burial of previously deposited material. Eventually, as the process continues, sediments become buried to a depth of a few kilometers below the seafloor and become lithified. The organic carbon associated with these sediments is then entombed in sedimentary rock until weathering liberates the material to the biosphere.

CARBON LEAKS AND OXYGEN REPLENISHMENT This organic carbon burial represents a leak of material from the short-term organic carbon cycle (see Figure 12). It is this leak, rather than photosynthesis alone (which is nearly balanced by respiration and decay), that maintains the O_2 content of the atmosphere. Oxygen is continuously removed from the atmosphere by chemical reactions with reduced materials (especially organic matter) that are preserved in rocks exposed at Earth's surface and with reduced volcanic gases such as hydrogen, sulfur dioxide, and carbon monoxide. The loss of O_2 is very slow, but the O_2 concentration would reach zero in a few million years if that gas were not supplied from other sources. Oxygen is replenished by the leak of organic matter into the sedimentary rock reservoir. For every carbon atom that enters this reservoir as organic carbon, one oxygen molecule is left behind. This is because the O_2 liberated during the photosynthesis of that carbon was not utilized during respiration or decomposition, and thus the gas remains in the atmosphere.

FORMATION OF FOSSIL FUELS During burial, the organic material in the sediment also undergoes significant

FIGURE 12 The combined short-term and long-term organic carbon cycles, showing the geological processes of sedimentation, burial, and weathering. Reservoir sizes in Gt(C), fluxes in Gt(C)/yr.

changes in its structure and chemistry, and fossil fuels may form. Sediments derived from land plants (especially *peat*, which forms in swamps and bogs) accumulate on land or in basins near shore. If the concentrations of terrestrial organic matter are high in these basins, burial processes under high pressures and temperatures can lead to the formation of **coal.** Similarly, high concentrations of organic matter in marine sediments can produce sedimentary rocks that, under high-pressure and high-temperature conditions of burial, serve as sources of **petroleum.** This material is fluid and tends to migrate through the basin until it becomes trapped and accumulates. If the accumulation is sufficient, the petroleum will be an economical source of fossil fuel. More commonly, however, the concentration of organic matter is 1% or less of the total sediment material. As a result, most sedimentary rocks do not represent economically viable energy sources.

THE SEDIMENTARY ORGANIC CARBON RESERVOIR

Sedimentary rocks contain by far the greatest quantity of organic carbon on Earth: approximately 10^8 Gton(C) (see Figure 3). Most of the organic carbon is found in *shales*, which are fine-grained sedimentary rocks formed by the

lithification of muds. The residence time for the sedimentary organic carbon reservoir is about 200 million years.

Weathering of Organic Carbon in Sedimentary Rocks

Weathering of the organic carbon in sedimentary rocks is an oxidation process requiring atmospheric O_2, either by direct exposure to the atmosphere or by exposure to groundwaters containing dissolved O_2. The oxidation of this material can be represented by the same schematic chemical reaction that we used previously for respiration and aerobic decomposition. The organic matter reacts with oxygen, releasing carbon dioxide to the atmosphere or groundwater.

In this sense, the mining, pumping, and combustion of fossil fuels represent merely an acceleration of the weathering process. The rocks from which humans have removed these fuels would likely have become exposed at the surface and undergone oxidation to form CO_2 some time in the distant future. Human intervention, however, has speeded up this process by a factor of a million or more for these fossil-fuel deposits. The release of organic matter from sedimentary rocks is occurring much faster than it can be replaced. Hence fossil fuels represent only a short-term energy source.

Summary of the Organic Carbon Cycle

We have now explored the entire global organic carbon cycle. Pathways exist to recycle carbon from all reservoirs (see Figure 12). Every reservoir in this cycle is directly connected to the atmosphere. Thus, the CO_2 concentration of the atmosphere changes continuously in response to changes in the flux of carbon to and from these reservoirs. The responses to these changes are rapid for the large fluxes associated with the biota, soils, and marine sediments but slow for the small fluxes from the sedimentary rock reservoir. This observation will prove to be important when we consider the fate of CO_2 added to the atmosphere from the burning of fossil fuels.

THE INORGANIC CARBON CYCLE

The photosynthesis of CO_2 to reduced carbon in organic matter, and its subsequent reoxidation to CO_2 through respiration, decomposition, and weathering, is central to the organic carbon cycle. But there are other sources and sinks for atmospheric CO_2. Carbon dioxide readily dissolves in rainwater and seawater and then undergoes rapid chemical reactions to other ionic forms of inorganic carbon. The oxidized carbon in these waters is chemically reactive and becomes involved in a number of chemical processes. Because they do not involve organic carbon directly, these processes are together referred to as the *inorganic carbon cycle.*

The important reservoirs of inorganic carbon are the atmosphere, which we have discussed at length; the ocean;

sediments; and sedimentary rocks (see Figure 3). The sediment and sedimentary-rock carbon reservoirs consist primarily of limestone. **Limestone** is a rock composed largely of *calcium carbonate* ($CaCO_3$), generally in the form of the mineral *calcite*. The magnesium-rich carbonate mineral *dolomite*, $CaMg(CO_3)_2$, is abundant in older sedimentary rocks.

Carbon Exchange between Ocean and Atmosphere

Carbon dioxide is continuously exchanged between the atmosphere and ocean. The distribution of sources and sinks of CO_2 is tied to the circulation and productivity patterns of the oceans (Figure 13). In regions of the ocean where high rates of primary productivity have created surface waters with low CO_2, CO_2 *diffuses* from the atmosphere to the ocean. In other words, the net flow of CO_2 is down the concentration gradient—from regions of higher CO_2 concentration (in this case, the atmosphere) to regions of lower concentration (the ocean). Conversely, upwelling regions, such as the equatorial Pacific surface waters, have high CO_2 concentrations because deep waters rich in CO_2 (as the result of decomposition associated with the biological pump) have risen to the surface there. In such regions, CO_2 flows from the ocean to the atmosphere. Thus, the oceans serve as both a source and a sink for atmospheric CO_2.

Before the carbon cycle was disturbed by human activity, the flux of CO_2 from oceanic CO_2 source areas was probably closely balanced by the flux to oceanic CO_2 sinks. This pattern is changing in response to the burning of fossil fuels. As we have seen, the atmospheric CO_2 concentration has been increasing. Regions of the ocean that

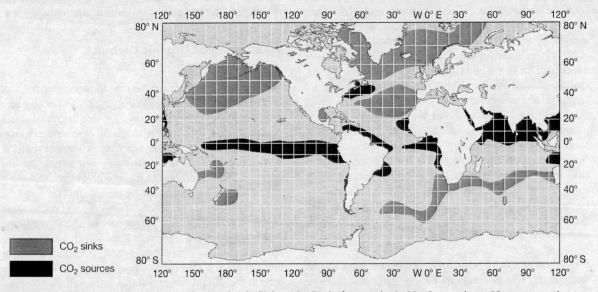

FIGURE 13 Oceanic sources (darker shading) and sinks (lighter shading) of atmospheric CO_2. Sources have CO_2 concentrations larger than those in equilibrium with the atmosphere, whereas sinks have lower-than-equilibrium CO_2 concentrations. (*Source:* T. Takahashi, *Oceanus* 32, 1989, pp. 22–29.)

were previously weak sources have now become sinks, and the ocean as a whole has become a sink for CO_2.

The Chemistry of Inorganic Carbon in Water

In the oceans, inorganic carbon exists in a number of dissolved forms. When CO_2 dissolves in water (whether it be freshwater or seawater), carbonic acid is generated:

$$CO_2 + H_2O \longleftrightarrow H_2CO_3.$$

$$\text{carbon dioxide} \quad \text{water} \quad \text{carbonic acid} \qquad (1)$$

The double arrows in this reaction indicate that the reaction can proceed both forward and backward. The rates of the forward and reverse reactions depend on the concentrations of the *reactants* (on the left-hand side) and of the *products* (on the right-hand side), respectively. If the concentration of the reactants is high, the forward reaction proceeds fast, depleting the concentration of the reactants and enhancing that of the products until the forward rate matches the reverse rate. Conversely, if the concentration of the products is high, the reverse reaction proceeds more rapidly, and the products become depleted (and reactants enriched) until the rates balance. In other words, *chemical equilibrium* is rapidly achieved in such reactions.

Like many substances that dissolve in water, carbonic acid molecules break apart, or *dissociate*, into ions. Ions are charged atoms or molecules. Ions with negative charges are referred to as **anions.** Ions with positive charges are referred to as **cations.** When carbonic acid dissociates, carbon-bearing anions and hydrogen cations are formed. The relative abundance (concentration) of the carbon anions is thus linked to the *pH* of seawater (see the Box "Useful Concepts: pH"), which is a measure of the concentration of hydrogen ions in solution.

CARBONIC ACID, BICARBONATE, AND CARBONATE ION EQUILIBRIUM   Returning to the discussion of the forms of inorganic carbon in water, we see that the dissociation of carbonic acid involves the release of one or both of its hydrogen atoms to yield carbon–oxygen anions. When the first hydrogen atom is lost, *bicarbonate ion* (HCO_3^-) is formed:

$$H_2CO_3 \longleftrightarrow H^+ + HCO_3^-.$$

$$\text{carbonic acid} \quad \text{hydrogen ion} \quad \text{bicarbonate ion} \qquad (2)$$

If the H^+ concentration were to decrease (i.e., the pH increased), more carbonic acid would dissociate to balance the equilibrium between the two forms (the reaction would proceed to the right). If, instead, seawater were to become acidic, this equilibrium would shift to the left, forming carbonic acid at the expense of bicarbonate ion.

The release of the second hydrogen ion converts bicarbonate ion in the previous reaction to *carbonate ion* (CO_3^{2-}):

$$HCO_3^- \longleftrightarrow H^+ + CO_3^{2-}.$$

$$\text{bicarbonate ion} \quad \text{hydrogen ion} \quad \text{carbonate ion} \qquad (3)$$

(Note that we have previously used the term "carbonate" to refer to calcium and magnesium carbonate minerals.) For a given hydrogen ion concentration (pH), the relative amounts of bicarbonate and carbonate ions are adjusted until equilibrium is achieved. As pH decreases from alkaline to acidic, the concentration ratio of carbonate to bicarbonate ion also decreases.

Perturbation of this equilibrium (e.g., by the diffusion of anthropogenic CO_2 from the atmosphere to the ocean) changes the pH of seawater. These changes in pH affect the relative concentrations of carbonic acid, bicarbonate ion, and carbonate ion in the following way: CO_2 dissolves, forming carbonic acid (reaction 1); the carbonic acid dissociates, forming bicarbonate and hydrogen ions (reaction 2), which causes the pH to drop. Hydrogen ion then reacts with carbonate ion, forming another bicarbonate ion (the reverse of reaction 3). The overall chemical reaction describing the uptake of anthropogenic CO_2 is the sum of these three reactions (reactions 1, 2, and the reverse of 3):

$$CO_2 + CO_3^{2-} + H_2O \longleftrightarrow 2HCO_3^-.$$

Thus, the ocean's capacity to take up CO_2 derived from fossil fuels is enhanced relative to what it would be if it simply equilibrated with the atmosphere, because it is converted to other forms of inorganic carbon. There is a limitation on the amount that can be taken up, however: the amount of carbonate ion in the ocean, which is smaller than the total available fossil fuel. If we continue to utilize fossil fuels, the oceans' capacity to take it up will become depleted, and a larger fraction will remain in the atmosphere.

Chemical Weathering

A similar chemistry applies when atmospheric CO_2 dissolves in raindrops, making them naturally acidic. As we noted earlier, the unpolluted pH of rainwater is generally between 5 and 6. Rocks exposed at Earth's surface undergo chemical attack from this rain of dilute acid, a process known as *chemical weathering*.

Crustal rocks are composed mainly of two types of minerals: carbonates and silicates. Carbonate minerals, such as calcite, contain carbon in combination with oxygen and other elements. Calcite and dolomite are the most abundant carbonates at Earth's surface, occurring as the dominant minerals in limestones and dolostones and as minor minerals in a host of other rock types. These minerals have fairly simple chemical formulas: $CaCO_3$ and $CaMg(CO_3)_2$, respectively. Silicate minerals contain compounds of silicon and oxygen. They tend to have rather complicated compositions. They are most abundant in igneous rocks but are also common minerals in sedimentary and metamorphic rocks.

In discussing the carbon cycle, we are most interested in the weathering of the calcium-bearing minerals, because calcium ions released by weathering are used by organisms

USEFUL CONCEPTS
pH

The hydrogen ion H^+ is the smallest of all cations. The small size and ionic charge make hydrogen ions extremely reactive: They tend to infiltrate solids, breaking bonds and causing the molecules that make up the solids to dissolve. Solutions (liquids with dissolved material) with high concentrations of hydrogen ions are called acids. Vinegar and hydrochloric acid are common acids. Solutions with low concentrations of hydrogen ions are called bases (or alkalis). Baking soda and lye dissolved in water are common bases.

Strong acids are solutions that completely dissociate: When dissolved in water, the anions separate completely from the hydrogen cations. This dissociation leads to high hydrogen ion concentrations. For example, the strong acid hydrochloric acid (HCl) dissociates to form hydrogen ions and chloride ions:

$$HCl \longrightarrow H^+ + Cl^-.$$
$$\text{hydrochloric} \qquad \text{hydrogen} \quad \text{chloride}$$
$$\text{acid} \qquad\qquad \text{ion} \qquad\quad \text{ion}$$

Other strong acids include nitric acid (HNO_3) and sulfuric acid (H_2SO_4). Weak acids, such as boric acid (H_3BO_3) and carbonic acid (H_2CO_3), only partially dissociate when dissolved in water.

The concentration of dissociated hydrogen ions (expressed in moles per liter of solution) determines the acidity of the solution. Acidity is commonly measured by the pH scale, which is a logarithmic scale. The pH of a solution is a close approximation of the negative of the logarithm (to the base 10) of the hydrogen ion concentration, $[H^+]$ (in moles per liter):

$$pH = -\log[H^+]$$

(We say "approximation" because chemists define pH in terms of the activity of hydrogen, which is the concentration of hydrogen ions available for chemical reaction. A small fraction of the hydrogen ions are involved in electrostatic interactions with other ions.) For example, a solution with a hydrogen ion concentration of 10^{-4} mol per liter would have a pH of 4, because the logarithm of 10^{-4} is -4. At room temperature, pure water is defined as having a neutral pH, or a pH of exactly 7. Solutions with a pH less than 7 are acids, whereas solutions with a pH greater than 7 are bases (Box Figure 2). The pH of the surface and deep oceans is slightly basic—about 8 and 7.5, respectively. Rainwater that is in equilibrium with atmospheric CO_2 has a slightly acidic pH, between 5 and 6. Most lakes, rivers, and streams range in pH from about 6 to 9, that is, from slightly acidic to mildly basic.

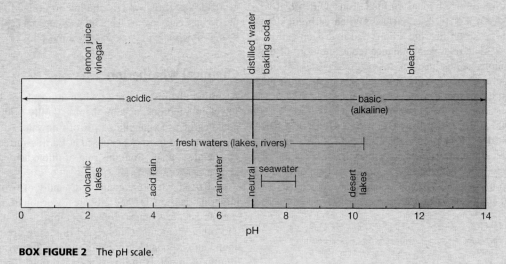

BOX FIGURE 2   The pH scale.

in the construction of calcium carbonate shells and skeletons. Important calcium-bearing silicates include *anorthite*, $CaAl_2Si_2O_8$, and *hornblende*, $NaCa_2(Mg,Fe, Al)_5(Si,Al)_8O_{22}(OH)_2$. However, we will use *wollastonite* ($CaSiO_3$), which has a much simpler formula, to represent calcium silicates. It is the relative amounts of calcium and silicate that matter to our discussion of chemical weathering, not the detailed compositions of the weathered minerals.

When exposed to rain, both carbonates and silicates weather chemically, although the carbonates dissolve much more rapidly (Figure 14). Chemical weathering neutralizes the acidity of carbonic acid in much the same way that an antacid neutralizes the acidity of your stomach:

Carbonate weathering:

$$CaCO_3 + H_2CO_3 \longrightarrow Ca^{2+} + 2HCO_3^-,$$
$$\text{calcium} \quad\quad \text{carbonic} \qquad\quad \text{calcium} \qquad \text{bicarbonate}$$
$$\text{carbonate} \qquad \text{acid} \qquad\qquad\quad \text{ion} \qquad\qquad \text{ion}$$

(a)

(b)

FIGURE 4 Differential weathering of (a) granite and (b) limestone. The granite headstone is a few years older than the limestone tombstone. (*Sources:* (a) Bill Aron/Photo Researchers and (b) Mark Burnett/Photo Researchers)

Silicate weathering:

$$CaSiO_3 + 2H_2CO_3 \longrightarrow Ca^{2+} + 2HCO_3^- + SiO_2 + H_2O.$$

wollastonite   carbonic   calcium   bicarbonate   silica   water
                   acid   ion   ion

In both weathering reactions, the products include Ca^{2+} and HCO_3^-. Silicate weathering also yields dissolved silica (SiO_2), which, together with Ca^{2+} and HCO_3^-, is transported to rivers and ultimately to the oceans. Silicate weathering consumes twice as much dissolved CO_2 (in the form of carbonic acid) as does carbonate weathering. This fact will prove important later in this chapter when we attempt to balance the carbon cycle.

Carbonate Mineral Deposition

The oceans eventually receive the products—soil particles and dissolved materials—of the chemical and physical weathering and erosion of the land surface. Most of the particulate material is deposited near the mouths of rivers in deltas, beaches, and other deposits near shore. In contrast,

the dissolved materials mix with seawater and, if their residence times are longer than the ocean's mixing time, are distributed throughout the world's oceans. The constant flux of dissolved materials from land to sea would gradually increase the saltiness of seawater by dilution were it not for processes that continuously remove material from the sea.

Some organisms, such as diatoms (Figure 8a), radiolarians (Figure 8d), and sponges, remove dissolved silica from seawater. They convert it into solid (opaline) silica as the structural part of their skeletons. Other organisms, such as foraminifera (Figure 8c), coccolithophorids (Figure 8b), corals, and shellfish, produce solid $CaCO_3$ in forming their shells and skeletons. Although these minerals can form *abiotically* (without the aid of organisms), most of the $CaCO_3$ precipitated from the ocean today is formed by such organisms.

These carbonate-producing marine organisms remove Ca^{2+} and HCO_3^- from seawater and precipitate $CaCO_3$ as a shell or skeleton. The overall chemical reaction is essentially the reverse of the carbonate weathering reaction:

Carbonate precipitation:

$$Ca^{2+} + 2HCO_3^- \longrightarrow CaCO_3 + H_2CO_3.$$

calcium   bicarbonate   calcium   carbonic
ion   ion   carbonate   acid

Calcium carbonate producers cause a shift in the ocean's carbon chemistry. By precipitating $CaCO_3$ shells or skeletons, they enhance H_2CO_3 (and, because of the equilibrium in reaction 1, dissolved CO_2) concentrations and reduce HCO_3^- concentrations, as well as pH. By increasing the concentration of dissolved CO_2 in surface waters, carbonate-producing organisms produce a CO_2 gradient between the oceans and the atmosphere. This gradient promotes the diffusion of CO_2 from the oceans to the atmosphere.

Some carbonate producers (e.g., coccolithophorids) are also phytoplankton. They photosynthesize organic matter, which tends to drive the dissolved carbon system in the opposite direction, toward lower CO_2 concentrations; hence these microorganisms have opposing effects on atmospheric CO_2 concentrations. However, the majority of phytoplankton do not produce carbonate skeletons. Thus, the overall effect of biological production in the surface ocean is in favor of reduced CO_2 concentrations: On average, the ratio of organic matter to carbonate mineral production for plankton is about 4:1.

When plankton die, their shells or skeletons sink through the water column but are less subject to destruction during the trip to the seafloor than is their organic debris. In regions where the total water depth is less than 4 km or so, carbonate particles accumulate more or less intact on the seafloor. These waters are said to be *saturated* with respect to $CaCO_3$. This shallower-water deposition of planktonic debris is part of the material that eventually becomes limestone. Other limestones form in very shallow

FIGURE 15 The distribution of CaCO₃-rich sediments on the seafloor. The pattern closely matches the areas of higher topography (shallower water) along the mid-ocean ridge system. (*Source:* W. S. Broecker and T.-H. Peng, *Tracers in the sea*, New York: Eldigio Press, Columbia University, 1982, p. 59.)

□ = Areas with > 75% CaCO₃

tropical waters, where reefs and other carbonate-producing organisms live on the seafloor. Deeper waters, however, have higher concentrations of dissolved CO_2 (carbonic acid), due to the decomposition of organic matter (Box Figure 1). As a result, these waters are corrosive to $CaCO_3$; they are said to be *undersaturated* with respect to $CaCO_3$. Carbonate particles (mostly shells and skeletons of planktonic organisms) settling through these corrosive waters dissolve slowly, and if the water is very deep, they dissolve completely. The depth below which they are completely dissolved is called the *carbonate compensation depth* (CCD). Below this depth, carbonate materials do not accumulate on the seafloor. Thus, the deep-ocean basins are devoid of the cover of plankton-derived carbonate sediments that occupy the shallower parts of the ocean, for example, along the mid-ocean ridges (Figure 15). Interestingly, carbonate sediments deposited on mid-ocean ridges are carried slowly to depths below the CCD as the seafloor spreads away from the ridge, cools, and subsides. If it weren't for a protective layer of sediments deposited above these carbonate sediments, they would dissolve as they were carried below the CCD by seafloor spreading.

Summary of the Inorganic Carbon Cycle

In the past few sections, we have discussed several processes that affect the transfer of inorganic carbon. These processes can be combined into a mass-flow diagram for the inorganic carbon cycle (Figure 16). The free exchange of CO_2 between the atmosphere and the oceans tends to keep the atmosphere near equilibrium with surface waters. During chemical weathering, CO_2 dissolved in rain and soil waters becomes converted to HCO_3^- (neutralized), which is carried to the oceans. There organisms combine it with Ca^{2+} in precipitating $CaCO_3$ shells or skeletons. Some of the $CaCO_3$ dissolves in the water column and on the seafloor. The rest is buried beneath the

seafloor, becoming part of the limestone reservoir. When tectonic uplift occurs after millions of years, the limestones become exposed at Earth's surface. There they undergo chemical weathering, and the cycle continues.

Net Removal of CO_2 from the Ocean and Atmosphere

We can combine the equations that we presented in previous sections for carbonate and silicate weathering and for $CaCO_3$ precipitation to determine the net effects of these processes on the chemistry of the oceans and on the composition of the atmosphere. To do this, we simply add the equations by adding the left-hand sides of both equations, adding the right-hand sides of both, and then canceling out terms that appear on both sides of the resulting equation—exactly as we would in adding two algebraic expressions. The net effect of $CaCO_3$ weathering on land and $CaCO_3$ precipitation in the ocean is zero, because the two processes balance each other:

Carbonate weathering:
$$CaCO_3 + H_2CO_3 \longrightarrow Ca^{2+} + 2HCO_3^-$$

Carbonate precipitation:
$$Ca^2 + 2HCO_3^- \longrightarrow CaCO_3 + H_2CO_3.$$

Net result: 0

The weathering equation is the reverse of the precipitation equation.

The situation is different for the weathering of calcium silicate minerals on land. First of all, calcium-silicate minerals do not reform under Earth surface conditions. Thus, the calcium liberated during silicate weathering ultimately leaves the ocean as $CaCO_3$. Second, recall from the silicate weathering equation that two molecules of H_2CO_3 are needed to dissolve silicate minerals, whereas only one

FIGURE 16 The global inorganic carbon cycle. Reservoir sizes in Gt(C), fluxes in Gt(C)/yr.

H_2CO_3 molecule is liberated when carbonate-bearing organisms precipitate their shells or skeletons. Thus:

Silicate weathering:

$$CaSiO_3 + 2H_2CO_3 \longrightarrow Ca^{2+} + 2HCO_3^- + SiO_2 + H_2O$$

Carbonate precipitation:

$$Ca^{2+} + 2HCO_3^- \longrightarrow CaCO_3 + H_2CO_3$$

Ocean-atmosphere CO_2 exchange:

$$CO_2 + H_2O \longrightarrow H_2CO_3.$$

Net result:

$$CaSiO_3 + CO_2 \longrightarrow CaCO_3 + SiO_2$$

(The SiO_2 liberated during silicate weathering is utilized by diatoms and radiolaria in skeleton production.) So, the combined processes of silicate weathering on land and carbonate precipitation in the sea lead to a net conversion of atmospheric CO_2 to solid $CaCO_3$. This process serves as a net outflow of CO_2 from the atmospheric reservoir, analogous to the net outflow of photosynthetically produced organic carbon that leaks out of the organic carbon cycle due to sedimentary burial.

Like the leak in the organic carbon cycle, the rate of conversion of atmospheric CO_2 to limestone by silicate weathering and $CaCO_3$ deposition is quite small: about 0.03 Gton(C)/yr. Nevertheless, if left unbalanced, this flux would apparently deplete the atmosphere of carbon in about 20,000 years. Actually, this number is misleading, because we have not accounted for the fact that the various oceanic reservoirs hold more than 50 times more carbon than the atmospheric reservoirs hold (see Figure 3). A reduction in atmospheric CO_2 creates a concentration gradient between the atmosphere and the oceans. As a consequence, CO_2 diffuses from the oceans to the atmosphere until the gradient is removed. Thus, the depletion time would be more like a million years, the time it would take for all the oceans' inorganic carbon to diffuse into the atmosphere and react with silicate rocks. Although this characteristic response time is significantly longer than the calculated 20,000 years, it is still short in terms of changes in atmospheric composition and climate over geologic time scales of many millions of years. On such time scales, then, there must be a return flux of CO_2 to the atmosphere and oceans to offset this outflow. This balance, which is in essence the long-term inorganic carbon cycle, has come to be known as the *carbonate–silicate geochemical cycle*.

THE CARBONATE–SILICATE GEOCHEMICAL CYCLE

After inorganic carbon is involved in chemical weathering and carbonate mineral precipitation and is removed by sedimentary burial, plate tectonics provides the needed return flux of CO_2 in the form of metamorphic and volcanic CO_2 inputs to the atmosphere. Mantle-derived CO_2 is released to the ocean–atmosphere system at mid-ocean ridges and along convergent margins (Figure 17). This carbon is derived from the mantle and so is, in a sense, "new."

At convergent plate margins (deep-sea trenches), some of the sediments resting on the downgoing slab are subducted along with the plate. The plate and its sediment cover are carried to depths as great as hundreds of kilometers within the mantle, where high temperatures and pressures promote chemical reactions that transform the sediments into metamorphic rock. Among these reactions is the reaction between sedimentary carbonate minerals and silica-rich sediments that forms silicate minerals and releases CO_2:

$$\underset{\text{calcite}}{CaCO_3} + \underset{\text{silica}}{SiO_2} \longrightarrow \underset{\text{wollastonite}}{CaSiO_3} + \underset{\substack{\text{carbon}\\\text{dioxide}}}{CO_2}.$$

This process is termed **carbonate metamorphism**. As before, we use the mineral wollastonite to represent the more complex silicate minerals that are typically generated by this process.

If sufficiently high temperatures are reached at depth during carbonate metamorphism, magmas are generated. These magmas may erupt in volcanoes at the surface, releasing CO_2 to the atmosphere. The CO_2 in these volcanoes probably includes some mantle-derived CO_2 and some CO_2 from the subducted crust and sediments, but scientists do not yet know the relative proportions of these two sources. Under metamorphic conditions the CO_2 produced can migrate as a fluid toward the surface. Although a substantial fraction of it reacts with minerals along the way, some CO_2 is released through springs and seeps to the atmosphere.

Together, silicate weathering, carbonate precipitation, and ocean–atmosphere exchange are the reverse of carbonate metamorphism. (Compare the equation for the net result of these processes, given in the previous section, with the carbonate metamorphism equation.) Without a fairly close balance between the inflows and outflows of carbon, the supply of this important greenhouse gas to the atmosphere and ocean would, on geological time scales, quickly be depleted. Earth would soon become a frozen ball of ice.

That may have been the fate of Mars, which appears to once have had flowing water on its surface and, perhaps, a CO_2-rich atmosphere with a stronger greenhouse effect. In contrast, on Earth the release of CO_2 after carbonate metamorphism and volcanism has essentially balanced the consumption of CO_2 during silicate weathering over the history of the planet. What has ensured this balance? We cannot call on simple chemical equilibrium, because the reactions involved are representative of a whole host of processes rather than a single chemical reaction. Rather, we must look for feedback loops that, according to the amount of CO_2 in the atmosphere, adjust the rates of CO_2 input by volcanism or of CO_2 removal by silicate weathering and thereby keep the reservoir at steady state.

Long-Term Feedbacks in the Carbonate–Silicate Cycle

Because it is driven largely by heat flow from Earth's interior, the rate of volcanism is probably not very sensitive either to the amount of CO_2 in the atmosphere or to the climate of Earth's surface. In contrast, many climatic factors affect the rate of chemical weathering. The regulation of atmospheric CO_2 on long time scales (millions of years) likely is the consequence of the feedback between climate and rates of silicate weathering. The climatic factors that help regulate the chemical weathering rates of silicate rocks include the following:

- Temperature: rates of reactions, including chemical weathering, tend to increase as temperature increases.

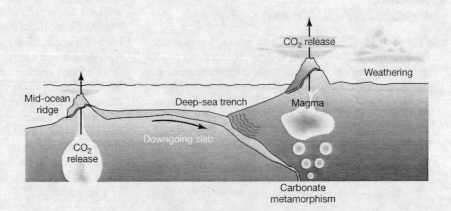

FIGURE 17 Pictorial representation of the carbonate–silicate geochemical cycle.

- Net rainfall: weathering requires water as a medium both for the dissolution of minerals and for the transport of the dissolved material to the oceans, and thus weathering rates rise as precipitation increases.

These environmental factors are responsive to atmospheric CO_2 levels. Recall that, as a result of the greenhouse effect, global temperatures rise as the atmospheric content of CO_2 increases and that rates of evaporation increase with increasing temperature. We know that water that evaporates from the ocean must fall as precipitation. For these reasons, we would expect that a warmer world would be a wetter world: Net precipitation should increase as temperature increases. Thus, the silicate weathering rate should increase as the atmospheric CO_2 level rises. Figure 18 shows a feedback loop for these processes. On the other side of the feedback loop, increased silicate weathering rates tend to reduce atmospheric CO_2 levels because silicate weathering uses up carbonic acid.

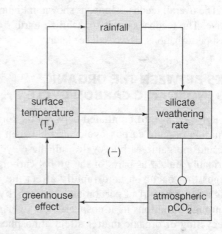

FIGURE 18 Systems diagram showing the negative feedback loop that results from the climate dependence of silicate–mineral chemical weathering and its effect on atmospheric CO_2. This feedback loop is thought to be the major factor regulating atmospheric CO_2 concentrations and climate on long time scales.

A CLOSER LOOK
Biological Enhancement of Chemical Weathering

A particularly active and controversial area of geological research centers on the extent to which terrestrial biota may enhance rates of chemical dissolution of minerals exposed at Earth's surface. Several factors are involved, including the following:

- Microbial decomposition and respiration by plant roots in soils generate large amounts of carbon dioxide. The CO_2 concentration in soils is generally 10 to 100 times that in the atmosphere.
- Microbial decomposition also releases organic acids that cause mineral dissolution. By increasing weathering rates, these biological processes enhance the release rate of essential mineral nutrients to the biota.
- Plant root development leads to the stabilization of soils on steep slopes, where erosion would otherwise strip soils away. This process creates a more stable weathering environment where mineral dissolution can take place for longer times before erosion takes place.
- Roots penetrating through fractured rock tend to enlarge the fractures, causing further disintegration of the rock and allowing water and soil acids to penetrate deeper into the rock.

Field experiments to test the hypothesis of biological enhancement of chemical weathering span environments that have huge contrasts in climate (Iceland and Hawaii) but similar types of exposed rocks (basalts). In Iceland, scientists have found that streams draining areas of plant cover have significantly higher dissolved ion concentrations than do those draining areas of bare rock.

In Hawaii, scientists are looking at rock surfaces covered with lichens (Box Figure 3) and comparing them with bare surface exposures. Underneath the lichen there generally is a

thin layer of material that is leached of the more soluble elements; bare surfaces have no such layer. These leached layers appear to be the result of mineral dissolution aided by the production of organic acids, although some scientists argue that the leached layers actually are wind-blown dust trapped by the lichens. Further research is needed to resolve this controversy.

Calculations of the extent of biological enhancement from various field studies are somewhat wide-ranging but indicate that biological activity accelerates rates of chemical weathering by at least a factor of 2. Some lichens studies have concluded that that factor is several hundred times. In any case, biological processes are very important components of the feedback loop that regulates global chemical weathering rates, and thus atmospheric CO_2 levels, on geological time scales.

BOX FIGURE 3 [See color section] The lichen *Xanthoria parietina* and other lichens on a seashore rock, England. (*Source:* Dr. Morley Read/Shutterstock.)

The overall feedback loop, as shown in Figure 18, is negative. The feedback tends to stabilize Earth's climate against perturbations, as we will see later.

LINKS BETWEEN THE ORGANIC AND INORGANIC CARBON CYCLE

Although we have differentiated between the terrestrial and marine organic carbon cycles and between the organic and inorganic carbon cycles, all these cycles are inextricably linked as parts of the global carbon cycle. Changes that occur on land rapidly affect the oceans through the transport of carbon and nutrients by rivers and through variations in atmospheric CO_2. Changes in the recycling of organic matter affect atmospheric and oceanic CO_2 and in turn the whole of the carbon cycle. Thus, the cycle divisions we have made are artificial, but they help us represent a complicated system in simple terms.

PHOSPHORUS AND NITROGEN CYCLES

Our focus in this chapter and throughout the book is on the carbon cycle because of its paramount importance to the functioning of the Earth system. However, most elements on the periodic table are recycled along with carbon on a variety of time scales. Rocks exposed to weathering contain a host of elements that are carried by rivers to the ocean, taken up by marine organisms or scavenged onto settling particles, removed to sediments and sedimentary rocks, and entrained in the rock cycle.

Two elements are of particular interest: nitrogen (N) and phosphorus (P). These two elements are required by all living organisms for the synthesis of such essential compounds as proteins and ATP (adenosine triphosphate, an important molecule in metabolism). Organisms have evolved special enzymes and metabolic pathways to facilitate the extraction of these nutrient elements from otherwise unavailable forms (e.g., *alkaline phosphatase* to release P from organic compounds, and **nitrogenase** to convert N_2 to nutrient ammonia), thus speeding the recycling of the elements. Let's take a more detailed look at the cycling of these two elements and consider how they together control the productivity of the biosphere.

The Phosphorus Cycle

Cycle of P

I put some P into the sea
the biomass did swell
But settling down soon overcame
and P went down toward Hell

From purgatory soon released
it moved up to the land
To make a perfect rose for thee
to carry in thy hand
But roses wilt and die you know
then P falls on the ground
Gobbled up as ferric P
a nasty brown compound
The world is moral still you know
and Nature's wheels do grind
Put ferric P into the sea
and a rose someday you'll find

Robert M. Garrels

This poem, by the pioneering geochemist Robert Garrels (deceased), describes a life cycle for a P atom (Figure 19) that is quite similar to that described for C previously. Phosphorus is a rock-derived nutrient, meaning that its largest repository is in Earth's interior, where it is found in igneous, metamorphic, and sedimentary rocks. It is liberated from these rocks through chemical weathering, and becomes available to terrestrial vegetation in soils. Being quite soluble, phosphorus is leached from soils and carried by rivers and groundwater to the ocean as phosphate ions, PO_4^{3-}.

Where rivers discharge to the ocean, productivity is often enhanced by the delivery of nutrients, including P. Productivity is also high in regions of upwelling because deep water is also nutrient-rich. In most other areas, the surface ocean is poor in nutrients because of aggressive uptake by plankton or attachment onto settling mineral particles, especially those containing oxidized iron minerals (the "ferric P" of Garrels's poem). These nutrients are then transferred to the deep ocean by the biological and "iron" pumps. A very small fraction of the P settling with the biological pump is transferred to the seafloor and is buried with the sediments; the rest is released to the deep ocean when the organic matter decomposes.

Over tens of thousands of years, the burial flux of phosphorus must balance the riverine input. How this balance is achieved remains the subject of active research, but it must involve a coupling between the burial rate and the amount of P in the ocean (Figure 20). If the P input from rivers were to exceed the P output to sediments, P would accumulate in the ocean. Higher P concentrations of upwelling deep waters would stimulate biological productivity, and the flux of organic detritus to the seafloor would increase. Much of this material would be recycled, but a fraction would escape decomposition and be buried. Hence, the phosphate content of the ocean would eventually stabilize, but at a higher concentration than before the increase in riverine delivery of P.

FIGURE 19 The global marine phosphorus cycle. Reservoir sizes in moles, fluxes in moles/yr.

The Nitrogen Cycle

This feedback mechanism regulating the phosphorus content of the oceans depends on the response of marine biological productivity and biological pumping to an increase in the phosphate supply. But other nutrients, especially nitrogen, are also required by organisms. Might N become limiting to biological productivity as P availability increases? If so, which element is really controlling productivity? Carbon itself is highly abundant in seawater, and unlikely to become limiting. But nitrogen does show the characteristics of a limiting nutrient: because of biological uptake, surface waters are as strongly depleted in N as they are in P (see Box Figure 1 and Figure 21). The nitrogen cycle, however, differs from the phosphorus cycle in one key attribute: the supply of N to the ocean

FIGURE 20 Negative feedback loop in the marine phosphorus cycle.

does not come primarily from the weathering of rocks and transport by rivers.

Recall that the atmosphere is dominantly composed of nitrogen gas (N_2). Vigorous gas exchange between the atmosphere and ocean provides a tremendous amount of N_2 to the ocean, but it is unavailable to the biota as a nutrient in this form because the chemical bond between the two nitrogen atoms is very strong; organisms need to have N in a reactive form such as nitrate (NO_3^-) or ammonium (NH_4^+) in order to grow. Marine biologists call the biologically available nitrogen in seawater **fixed nitrogen**. Certain types of planktonic organisms, primarily the cyanobacteria, are able to break this strong bond and "fix" nitrogen using the enzyme nitrogenase. These nitrogen fixers have a competitive edge in waters that are depleted of fixed nitrogen but that have an adequate supply of phosphorus. They photosynthesize and grow, and when they die and decompose the nitrogen they fixed becomes available to other organisms. Thus, N_2 fixers tend to increase the inventory of fixed nitrogen in the ocean by providing nutrient N at rates that greatly exceed the riverine input. Nitrogen is also fixed on land, primarily by bacteria that live in the root systems of plants, and some of this fixed nitrogen makes its way to the ocean as dissolved and particulate nitrogen in rivers.

It is fortunate for marine life that nitrogen fixers are so good at creating fixed nitrogen, because there is an equally efficient mechanism at work converting fixed nitrogen (in its predominant form, nitrate) back to N_2: **denitrification.** In environments where oxygen is scarce,

FIGURE 21 The global marine nitrogen cycle. Reservoir sizes in moles, fluxes in moles/yr. The cycle is shown as balanced, but there are great uncertainties in the numbers presented, and it is not clear that the modern cycle is balanced. (*Source:* Eky Chan/Shutterstock (left), Dean Bergmann/iStockphoto (top), Maxim Chupashkin/iStockphoto (center), Liz Leyden/iStockphoto (bottom))

such as in soils, marine sediments, and low-oxygen marine environments, bacteria use different sources of oxygen to decompose organic matter. One of these sources is the nitrate dissolved in seawater. In regions of low oxygen such as the oxygen minimum zone of the ocean (See the Box "A Closer Look: Oxygen Minimum Zone"), bacteria that can utilize nitrate thrive, converting nitrate to N_2 or the equally biologically unavailable gas nitrous oxide (N_2O), which is also a potent anthropogenic greenhouse gas and involved in the destruction of atmospheric ozone. The N_2 and N_2O they produce can be upwelled to the surface of the ocean and released to the atmosphere. Denitrification thus represents a net loss of fixed nitrogen from the ocean. Nitrogen fixation and denitrification represent the major input and output of fixed nitrogen from the ocean, respectively.

Phosphorus as the Ultimate Limiting Nutrient

Now we can return to the question of whether the proposed mechanism for phosphate regulation (Figure 20) is viable, or whether nitrogen limitation might ultimately

disable the coupling between phosphorus content of the ocean and biological productivity. The short answer is that the mechanism works, because the ocean adjusts itself to excesses or shortages of nitrogen through nitrogen fixation and denitrification. Geochemists therefore consider P to be the "ultimate" limiting nutrient. Again, consider the conse-

FIGURE 22 Feedback loop in the coupled marine phosphorus and nitrogen cycles, proposed to stabilize the N/P ratio of the oceans.

quences of an increase of phosphorus delivery to the ocean (Figure 22). The phosphate inventory of the ocean would begin to increase, and thus so would marine productivity. With no increase in the riverine nitrogen input, the fixed nitrogen inventory would fall. The N–P ratio of the ocean would fall below the Redfield ratio (see the section "Nutrient Limitation"). Nitrogen, however, would not become limiting. Upwelling deepwaters would be enriched in P but depleted in N, thus providing a competitive advantage to nitrogen-fixing phytoplankton. An increase in their numbers would then increase the global rate of nitrogen fixation, thereby restoring the ocean's N–P ratio to the normal Redfield ratio. Global rates of biological productivity and carbon, nitrogen, and phosphorus burial in sediments would all be higher. Thus, even when P input from rivers is relatively high, phosphorus retains its status as the "ultimate" limiting nutrient to biological productivity in the ocean.

Chapter Summary

1. The global carbon cycle involves processes that occur on land and in the oceans and involve both biological and nonbiological chemical reactions.
2. The terrestrial and marine organic carbon cycles operate on a variety of time scales. On the short time scale (tens to hundreds of years),
   a. carbon dioxide is removed from the atmosphere during photosynthesis on land and returned during respiration and decomposition; methane is released to the atmosphere from soils, where anaerobic metabolism is taking place.
   b. a small amount of terrestrial organic carbon survives respiration and decomposition and is buried in sedimentary basins on land or is transported to the sea.
   c. in the oceans, phytoplankton produce organic matter that is consumed by zooplankton and decomposed by aerobic and anaerobic bacteria.
   d. a small fraction of the organic matter settling through the water column is not decomposed and is instead buried in marine sediments.
3. On longer time scales (millions of years), the organic matter buried in sediments undergoes lithification with the sediments. Most of these sediments are muds, and the rocks formed are shales.
   a. When concentrations of organic matter are very high in the sediment, fossil fuels may form during burial and lithification.
   b. The sedimentary rocks may eventually undergo uplift through tectonic processes, exposure, and weathering. During weathering, organic matter undergoes oxidation, producing CO_2, which escapes to the atmosphere.
4. An inorganic carbon cycle, involving oxidized forms of carbon, is important on both short and long time scales (millions of years).
   a. Atmospheric CO_2 exchanges with CO_2 dissolved in the surface ocean on a time scale of decades. The uptake of CO_2 is enhanced by reactions among the forms of dissolved inorganic carbon in seawater.
   b. Atmospheric CO_2 dissolves into rainwater, creating an acidic solution. When the rain falls on the land surface, reactions with carbonate and silicate minerals convert carbonic acid to bicarbonate ion. The bicarbonate ion is carried by rivers to the oceans.
   c. In the oceans, carbonate-secreting organisms use the bicarbonate ion in the construction of their shells or skeletons. This material may dissolve in transit or it may become part of the sediment that covers the seafloor.
5. The regulation of atmospheric CO_2 on long time scales (millions of years) is the consequence of the feedback between climatic factors and rates of chemical weathering of silicate rocks, as part of the long-term inorganic carbon cycle, referred to as the carbonate–silicate geochemical cycle.
   a. Any disturbance in the amount of atmospheric CO_2 affects climate through the greenhouse effect. Changes in climate affect silicate weathering rates and thus the rates of CO_2 consumption.
   b. The overall feedback loop is negative, implying that on long time scales the climate system is stable against a wide range of perturbations.
6. The terrestrial and marine organic carbon cycles, the organic and inorganic carbon cycles, and the carbonate–silicate geochemical cycle are inextricably linked as parts of the global carbon cycle.
   a. Changes on land are "communicated" rapidly to the oceans by riverine transport of carbon and nutrients and through variations in atmospheric CO_2.
   b. Changes in the recycling of organic matter affect atmospheric and oceanic CO_2 and in turn the whole of the carbon cycle.
7. The cycles of phosphorus and nitrogen largely control the biological productivity of the planet on a global scale.
   a. Weathering provides the input of P to the Earth surface.
   b. In contrast, the largest supply of nutrient N comes from bacterial nitrogen fixation.
   c. P thus becomes the "ultimate" limiting nutrient.

Key Terms

acid
anion
base
biological pump
biomass
biosphere
carbonate metamorphism
cation
characteristic response time
coal
consumers

denitrification
fixed nitrogen
inorganic carbon
limestone
methanogenesis
nitrogenase
nutrient
organic carbon
oxidized carbon
petroleum
pH

photic zone
photosynthesis
primary producer
primary productivity
Redfield ratio
reduced carbon
residence time
steady state
zooplankton

Review Questions

1. Which of the following carbon reservoirs has the longest residence time: plants, the oceans, or sedimentary limestone?
2. One or more of the following processes involves organic carbon; identify it (them): the precipitation of a calcite skeleton, the exchange of carbon between the oceans and the atmosphere, dissolution at the seafloor, or oxidation during weathering.
3. Describe the biological pump.
4. Why is plate tectonics critical to the maintenance of an atmosphere–ocean reservoir rich in carbon?
5. Limestone (carbonate) weathering does not lead to the net removal of carbon dioxide from the atmosphere. Why not?

Critical-Thinking Problems

1. The key to stability is feedback between the reservoir and the fluxes into and/or out of the reservoir. Assume that the rate of outflow from a reservoir depends on the size of the reservoir according to the following relationship: outflow rate $= k \cdot$ (size of reservoir), where k is a constant.
   a. A reservoir of water has a volume of 5000 liters, and the rate of outflow at steady state is 25 liters per minute. What is k? (Give both the numerical value and its units.) What is the residence time? What is the relationship between k and the residence time?
   b. The inflow rate is 25 liters per minute. Describe graphically and in words how the reservoir size would change with time, beginning with a reservoir size of zero and continuing until the reservoir reaches steady state.
2. Use Figure 4 to answer the following questions:
   a. During which months is the rate of photosynthesis greatest, relative to the combined rate of respiration and decomposition, and during which months is it smallest? Explain your reasoning. Why aren't these coincident with the minimum and maximum CO_2 levels for the year, respectively?
   b. On the basis of your answer to part (a), estimate, for each year, the maximum net rate of photosynthesis and the maximum net rate of respiration/decomposition for each of the three years shown.
   c. Are there significant differences in these rates from year to year? If so, propose an explanation for them.
3. A giant meteor crashes into Earth, causing devastating environmental changes that kill off all life in the oceans.
   a. Describe how the vertical distribution of dissolved oxygen, carbon, and nutrients would respond over the course of the next several thousand years.

b. Would the temperature and salinity of the ocean be affected by the loss of the biological pump? Why or why not?
   c. If global warming from CO_2 released to the atmosphere from the meteor impact site caused, instead of the complete loss of marine life, the sudden cessation of thermohaline circulation in the oceans, what would be the effect on the vertical and spatial distribution of dissolved nutrients, carbon, and oxygen in the world's oceans over the next thousand years?
4. a. The atmosphere consists of 78% N_2, 21% O_2, 1% Ar, and about 0.036% (360 ppm) CO_2. What is the mean molecular weight of air? Round your answer to three significant figures, and use the following table of atomic weights:

Element	Atomic Weight
C (Carbon)	12.011
N (Nitrogen)	14.0067
O (Oxygen)	15.9994
Ar (Argon)	39.948

b. The total mass of the atmosphere is about 5×10^{18} kg. How many moles each of air, O_2, and CO_2 are present in the atmosphere? (*Note:* Calculate the latter two answers from the first one rather than by computing the masses of O_2 and CO_2. The values listed in part (a) for the various gases are abundances by volume, not by mass. This fact, and the fact that a mole of any gas takes up the same volume at a given pressure and temperature, mean that you need to work in moles.)

c. Forests contain about 600 Gton(C) in the form of wood and leaves. Suppose that all the world's forests were to burn down instantaneously. By how much would atmospheric CO_2 increase? By how much would O_2 decrease? Express your answers in percentages. Assume that the equation for burning is the same as that for respiration (given earlier in this chapter).

5. Explain why lakes and rivers have slightly basic pH values, whereas rainwater (the ultimate source of water for lakes and rivers) is slightly acidic.

Further Reading

General

Mackenzie, F. T. 1995. Biogeochemistry. In *Encyclopedia of environmental biology*. New York: Academic Press, vol. 1, p. 249.

Advanced

Hanson, R. B., H. W. Ducklow, and J. G. Field. 2000. *The changing ocean carbon cycle.* Cambridge: Cambridge University Press.

Post, W. M., T.-H. Peng, and W. R. Emanuel. 1990. The global carbon cycle. *American Scientist* 78 (4): 310.

Wigley, T. M. L., and D. W. Schimel. 2000. *The carbon cycle.* Cambridge: Cambridge University Press.

FIGURE 2 Satellite image of the vegetation coverage of the land surface in the Northern Hemisphere in (a) summer and (b) winter, expressed as an index, with larger values having greater coverage by living vegetation. (*Source:* Felix Kogan/NOAA/NESDIS/ORA Climate Research and Application Division.)

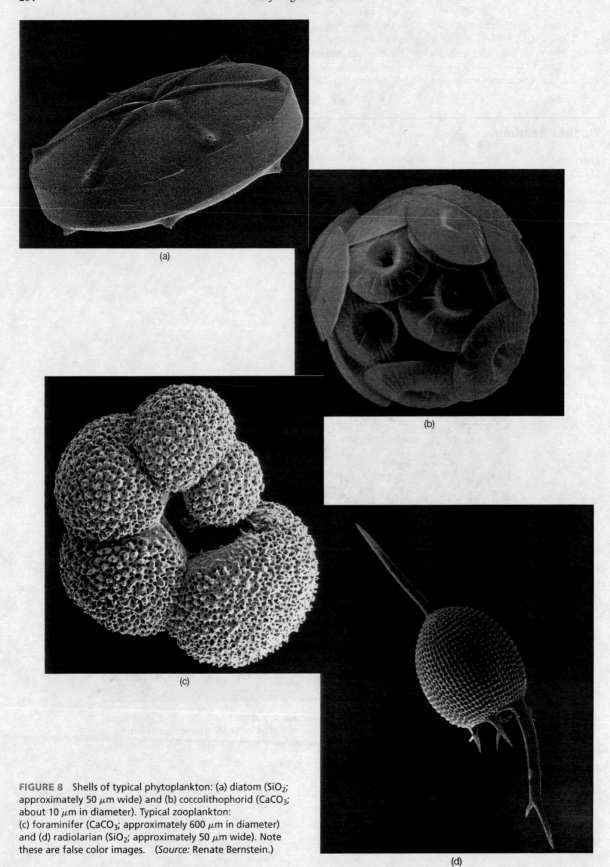

FIGURE 8   Shells of typical phytoplankton: (a) diatom (SiO$_2$;
approximately 50 μm wide) and (b) coccolithophorid (CaCO$_3$;
about 10 μm in diameter). Typical zooplankton:
(c) foraminifer (CaCO$_3$; approximately 600 μm in diameter)
and (d) radiolarian (SiO$_2$; approximately 50 μm wide). Note
these are false color images.   (*Source:* Renate Bernstein.)

BOX FIGURE 3 The lichen *Xanthoria parietina* and other lichens on a seashore rock, England. (*Source:* Dr. Morley Read/Shutterstock.)

FIGURE 10 The concentration of photosynthetic pigments as determined by the Coastal Zone Color Scanner (CZCS) on the Nimbus 7 satellite. Pigment concentrations are indirect indicators of rates of primary production.   (*Source:* Gene Feldman, NASA GSFC/SPL/Photo Researchers.)

Focus on the Biota
Metabolism, Ecosystems, and Biodiversity

Focus on the Biota
Metabolism, Ecosystems, and Biodiversity

Key Questions

- What are the characteristics of life on Earth that allow it to interact with physical processes at the global scale in such a significant way that it creates a habitable planet?
- How is the biosphere structured?
- How is energy transferred within the biosphere?

- What is an ecosystem?
- What is biodiversity and how is it measured?
- How is the diversity of interactions between the biota and the physical world related to the stability of the Earth system?

Chapter Overview

In this chapter we highlight the role that life plays in the operation of the Earth system. We begin with a general discussion of life and its unique characteristics, and then explore the varied metabolic pathways different forms of life take to grow and reproduce. Organisms interact at a variety of scales, so we find that populations of organisms group into communities, which at a larger scale interact among themselves and with their environment in ecosystems. The level of diversity of ecosystems can be expressed in a variety of ways. We can simply count the number of species or we can take into account the more complex diversity of interactions that take place between species and between organisms and their environment. This diversity of interactions, a defining characteristic of life on Earth, is important in our understanding of the feedbacks between the biota and the physical world that create a habitable planet, and helps us further understand the complexity of the Earth system.

LIFE ON EARTH
Characteristics of Life

Earth is unique among the planets in our solar system in that it apparently is the only one to support life. Earth more than supports life, it flaunts it. Life is involved in almost every process occurring at the surface of the planet. Some fundamental characteristics of life allow it to have such an influence.

- *Life spreads exponentially.* The rate of population growth depends on the number of individuals reproducing at a particular time. This characteristic leads to the phenomenon of *exponential growth.* If left unchecked, 2 individuals become 4 in one generation, 4 become 8 in two generations, 8 become 16 in three generations, and 16 become 32 in four generations. In nature, however, exponential growth ceases as resources become limiting.
- *Life needs energy.* Photosynthesizers use solar energy, *chemosynthesizers* use chemical energy, and most other organisms utilize the chemical

energy that is packaged into the material produced by photosynthesizers and chemosynthesizers.

- **Life pollutes.**   Every organism needs to metabolize, and when it does so, it releases waste products. These waste products can be of use to other organisms, and they may affect the environment (e.g., the release of the greenhouse gases CO_2 and CH_4 through respiration and decomposition).
- **Life is versatile.**   There is considerable versatility in how organisms interact with each other and with the environment. Plants and animals exist in a variety of forms and express various behaviors. But their versatility is modest compared to that of microbes. Microbes express a wide array of metabolic activities that have tremendous impact on the environment and allow them to occupy a wider range of environments than eukaryotes.

All these characteristics of life allow it to interact with the physical processes that occur on the planet in such a way that Earth is a habitable planet. Let's explore this in more detail by developing a classification scheme for life that is based on metabolic rather than genetic similarities, and is structured around the flow of energy through the ecosystem.

Autotrophs and Heterotrophs

Although life can be categorized *taxonomically* (according to species, genera, families, etc.), a classification system that focuses on the ways in which organisms obtain energy and metabolize it is more useful from an Earth systems point of view (Table 1). The most fundamental dis-tinction is between those organisms that grow using a source of energy to reduce carbon dioxide to organic carbon (primary producers or **autotrophs**) and those that require organic matter to grow (consumers or **heterotrophs**). Autotrophs include plants, algae, and a host of microbes that can photosynthesize (e.g., cyanobacteria, purple and green sulfur bacteria) or chemosynthesize (e.g., colorless sulfur bacteria). These autotrophic organisms produce organic matter from inorganic carbon sources, a process that requires energy (i.e., the chemical reactions do not occur spontaneously in nature). In the case of photosynthesis, the sun provides the necessary energy. In chemosynthesis, energy-releasing inorganic chemical reactions (those that occur even without the involvement of organisms *because* they release energy), often involving oxygen and reduced compounds, are the energy source. Chemosynthesis is the mechanism of primary production of the mid-ocean-ridge hydrothermal vent communities that exist at great depths in the ocean where sunlight does not penetrate. The organic material that autotrophs produce is a storehouse of energy, and will decompose *abiotically* (without the intervention of organisms), albeit at a slow rate, releasing that energy as heat. Heterotrophs simply accelerate these chemical reactions that would otherwise proceed at a slower pace abiotically, and in doing so, gain the energy they need to grow and reproduce.

The heterotrophic pathway that releases the most energy is aerobic respiration, which uses molecular oxygen to decompose organic matter through the process of oxidation, converting the organic carbon to carbon dioxide. In

TABLE 1   Metabolic Pathways for Life

General Method for Acquiring Energy	Specific Pathway	Subcategory	Reactants	Byproducts
Autotrophy				
	Photosynthesis		Solar energy, CO_2	
		Oxygenic	H_2O	Molecular oxygen (O_2)
		Anoxygenic	Molecular hydrogen (H_2), reduced sulfur or reduced iron	Oxidized sulfur (native sulfur or sulfate), iron oxide (solid)
	Chemosynthesis		H_2, reduced forms of sulfur, nitrogen, iron or manganese	Oxidized sulfur, nitrate, iron and manganese oxides (solids)
Heterotrophy			Organic matter	
	Aerobic Respiration		O_2	CO_2, H_2O
	Anaerobic Respiration		Nitrate, sulfate, iron and manganese oxides	CO_2 and molecular nitrogen, ammonia, hydrogen sulfide, reduced and dissolved iron and manganese
	Fermentation		Complex organic molecules	Simple organic molecules

Source: K. H. Nealson and D. A. Stahl, *Geomicrobiology, Interactions between Microbes and Mineral* (Chapter 1). Reviews in *Mineralogy* 35, 1997, pp. 5–34.

environments where oxygen isn't present (e.g., in muds on the seafloor and lake bottoms, and in the guts of animals), anaerobic heterotrophs, especially bacteria, substitute other oxidized inorganic compounds in lieu of oxygen to decompose the organic matter. Bacteria use such oxidants as dissolved nitrate (through a process known as *denitrification*) or sulfate (sulfate reduction) or particulate metal oxides of iron and manganese. Other heterotrophic organisms (certain fungi such as yeasts and some bacteria) perform fermentation, an important process that breaks down large, complex organic compounds into simpler ones that can be used by other heterotrophs. Fermenters do not oxidize organic matter, but they are able to utilize the energy that is released when complex organic materials are broken apart.

Methanogenic bacteria are an important group of organisms for our consideration of the Earth system, in particular because they may have been very significant in biogeochemical cycling on the early Earth and because they produce an especially effective greenhouse gas, methane (CH_4), through their metabolism. In fact, the word *methanogenic* means methane-producing. Methanogens can be either autotrophic or heterotrophic:

Autotrophic methanogenesis:
$$CO_2 + 4H_2 \rightarrow CH_4 + 2H_2O$$

Heterotrophic methanogenesis:
$$CH_3COOH \rightarrow CH_4 + CO_2$$

Autotrophic methanogenesis takes advantage of the energy yield of the chemical reaction between carbon dioxide and molecular hydrogen (H_2) when H_2 concentrations are relatively high, a situation that currently occurs in organic-rich muds and may have also occurred on the early Earth surface. Heterotrophic methanogens utilize the simpler carbohydrates (such as acetic acid, CH_3COOH, shown above) produced through fermentation. Both pathways produce methane, and heterotrophic methanogenesis produces both methane and carbon dioxide. Given their global abundance, it is clear that these bacteria can have a significant impact on the greenhouse effect.

Moreover, as James Lovelock pointed out long ago, the combined activity of methanogens (such as methanogenic bacteria) and oxygenic photosynthesizers (such as plants), which produce the organic matter that the fermenters convert to acetic acid, releases both oxygen and methane to the atmosphere. We can represent this chemically:

Oxygenic photosynthesis:
$$2CO_2 + 2H_2O \rightarrow 2\text{"}CH_2O\text{"} + 2O_2$$
Fermentation:
$$2\,\text{"}CH_2O\text{"} \rightarrow CH_3COOH$$
Heterotrophic methanogenesis:
$$CH_3COOH \rightarrow CH_4 + CO_2$$

NET: $\quad\quad\quad\quad\quad CO_2 + 2H_2O \rightarrow CH_4 + O_2$

The net effect of these coupled processes creates an unstable, highly reactive, far-from-chemical-equilibrium atmosphere that is as strong a signature of life on our planet as any other. Equally amazing is the dynamic stability of this reactive atmosphere. Aerobic life has persisted on Earth for hundreds of millions of years, indicating that the atmosphere has remained oxygen-rich through this interval of Earth history. Strong feedbacks must exist to maintain atmospheric compositions over geologic time intervals. As you will see in the following discussion of ecosystems, the constant and complex interaction between all living things on Earth contributes to the atmospheric conditions that are key to the stability of the Earth system.

STRUCTURE OF THE BIOSPHERE

The metabolic processes we have just described represent the main ways in which organisms interact with other species and with their environment. These interactions are not random. Rather, they make up higher levels of organization that we can recognize and study. The *biosphere* comprises that part of Earth inhabited by organisms; it includes both living and nonliving components. A simple hierarchy has been developed that subdivides the biosphere (Figure 1). The smallest subunit is the *species,* which consists of all closely related organisms that can potentially interbreed. (Note that this definition applies only to species that reproduce sexually.) All the members of a single species that live in a given area make up a **population**. In any area you will tend to find a characteristic assemblage of two or more groups of interacting species, known as a **community**. A community may include any combination of animals, plants, fungi, and microbes. A region with a characteristic plant community (such as a desert or tropical rainforest) is called a **biome**. A community of animals, plants, fungi, and microbes, together with the physical environment that supports it, is referred to as an **ecosystem**. All the ecosystems on Earth in turn make up the biosphere. Although it is usual to discuss biodiversity and extinction in terms of species, it is important to recognize that no one species exists independent of the other species around it. Species coexist and interact with a specific assemblage of other species and with their environment in ecosystems.

ECOSYSTEMS

What Are Ecosystems?

As we have said, ecosystems are subsets of the (global) biosphere, assemblages of animal, plant, fungal, and microbial species that interact with each other and their surrounding environment (see "Species Interactions," below). For terrestrial ecosystems the environment includes the topography, soils, atmosphere, and climate. For aquatic

Earth   **BIOSPHERE**

Oak-hickory forest
and all associated plants,
animals, fungi, and microbes   ECOSYSTEM
interacting together

Oak canopy,
dogwood understory,
ferns, mosses, squirrels,   COMMUNITY
and birds

Members of one species   POPULATION
inhabiting the same area

One specific kind of
plant, animal,   SPECIES
fungus, or microbe

FIGURE 1   Division of the biosphere into ecosystems, communities, populations, and species.   (*Source:* From Nebel and Wright,
Environmental Science, 4/e, 1993. Reprinted by permission of Prentice Hall, Upper Saddle River, N.J.)

FIGURE 2 Possible feedbacks between the boreal forest and climate.

ecosystems the environment includes the physical and chemical characteristics of the particular freshwater or marine water body concerned. Since each ecosystem is located in a slightly different physical environment, there is a tendency to think of the environment as determining the type of ecosystem that develops. This is true to some degree, but it is not the whole story: The organisms within a particular ecosystem interact with their environment. For example, the type of soil present may help determine which plants will grow, but the plants themselves add organic matter to the soils that changes the soil chemistry, possibly allowing different species to grow there. Certain species might tolerate only particular temperature and precipitation regimes, but those species may be capable of altering local climate, thereby promoting their own growth or the growth of other species.

We illustrate this possibility here with an example of his from the boreal forests of North America and Asia. The coniferous trees in the boreal forest hide the snow-covered ground in winter, reducing the albedo of the forested region. The reduced albedo should result in higher winter temperatures than would occur if the forest were not present. By modifying its local environment to be warmer at its northern edge, the forest may be able to push farther north beyond the point where temperatures would otherwise be too cold to allow the trees to grow. Is there any indication that this might, in fact, be happening?

Scientists at the National Center for Atmospheric Research in Boulder, Colorado, conducted a general circulation model experiment in which they changed all of the forest north of 45° N to bare ground. This is equivalent to moving the border between the boreal forest and the treeless tundra southward. The effect of this change was to produce a large increase in the wintertime albedo, because the white snow cover was revealed by the removal of the forest. The increased albedo caused a large drop in air temperatures, the greatest change in the month of April—up to 12°C (21.6°F) over the land surface. The colder winter temperatures increased the sea-ice cover, and the higher

albedo further enhanced the cooling effect. The colder temperatures were maintained through the summer, with July being as much as 5°C (9°F) colder than before the removal of the forest.

These processes are illustrated in the systems diagram in Figure 2. The solid lines indicate the interactions simulated by the model, including the ice–albedo feedback discussed in several earlier chapters. The dashed line completes another positive feedback loop implied by the model results. The forest cover is not an interactive part of the model, so we cannot see the feedback from the change in temperature to the change in forest cover. However, the model does show that the July 18°C (64.4°F) isotherm (which correlates well with the present northern limit of the forest) shifts southward far enough to prevent forest regrowth. Although the interactions are more complex than those suggested by Lovelock, we do see that the forest has a significant impact on the climate system. By keeping high-latitude temperatures from being as cold as they would otherwise be, the forest helps perpetuate an environment conducive to its own growth.

It is apparent, therefore, that ecosystems are not divorced from their environment; the environment is part of the ecosystem. As the environment changes, the types of organisms in the ecosystem and the interactions among them change, and as they do, the local environment may change. The obvious conclusion is that ecosystems are not static. Changes in climate can cause ecosystems to move gradually to new locations, such as arctic tundra and its biologic community spreading equatorward during glacial periods and retreating poleward during interglacials. This is in part a consequence of the physiological requirements of the individual organisms that make up the ecosystem's biota; each species has minimum, optimal, and maximum conditions for growth. As the environment changes, organisms may find themselves in less than optimal conditions (see "A Closer Look: Physiological versus Ecological Optima for Growth"). More interestingly, new environmental conditions could give rise to a totally new assemblage

A CLOSER LOOK
Physiological versus Ecological Optima for Growth

When studied under controlled, laboratory conditions, the growth rate of most organisms responds to environmental change. There are minimal, optimal, and maximal conditions for growth. This relationship can be clearly expressed for the response of photosynthetic rates of plants grown in greenhouses to changes in temperature (Box Figure 1a). This figure also shows a distinction between C_3 and C_4 plants. C_3 autotrophs comprise all the trees, most of the other plants, the cyanobacteria, and all algae; they are called C_3 because an important sugar produced during photosynthesis has three carbon atoms. C_4 plants are relative newcomers to the Earth system, evolving in the last 10–20 million years in response to either lower atmospheric CO_2 levels or drier climates. They include many grasses, corn plants, and pineapples, to name a few. They are called

C_4 because they produce a 4-carbon sugar during their photosynthetic cycle. C_3 plants can grow at lower temperatures, but have lower maximum temperatures for growth than do C_4 plants. C_4 plants, however, are able to very efficiently scavenge CO_2 from the atmosphere (Box Figure 1b), allowing them to spend less time with their stomata (pores) open. (Plants typically obtain CO_2 by opening their stomata.) This ability is a great advantage in arid environments because open stomata also release water vapor to the atmosphere, causing water stress in plants. It has also proven advantageous from the perspective of Earth history: Atmospheric CO_2 levels have fallen over the last several million years, falling ever closer to the break-even point for C_3 plants (~30–70 ppm) where photorespiration (respiration by plants) equals photosynthesis. As atmospheric CO_2 levels have fallen, plants that could more efficiently photosynthesize under these atmospheric conditions have presumably thrived. However, when temperatures drop, as Box Figure 1a shows, the C_3 pathway becomes favorable.

Of course, organisms have many environmental requirements, each of which may exhibit a parabolic relationship under otherwise optimal conditions (as in Box Figure 1), but nature does not provide such ideal conditions. It is important that we understand these relationships both in the laboratory and in nature so that we can establish the coupling and feedback that govern environmental change. Many of the factors that affect growth are interdependent, and can create apparent paradoxes that can only be understood when considered simultaneously. Since *interspecies* interactions are discussed in the main body of the text, let's focus here on interdependencies of *environmental* factors. In laboratory culture, algae exhibit optimal *physiological* growth rate at temperatures in the range of 20–25°C. Thus, one might predict that maximum rates of oceanic primary production would be in the tropical to subtropical ocean. Instead, what one finds are high rates of photosynthesis at high latitudes and in coastal zones irrespective of latitude, as reflected in satellite images of ocean chlorophyll concentration (Figure 10). This paradox is reconciled if we realize that the supply of nutrients to marine ecosystems is generally dependent upon upwelling of nutrient-rich deep waters to the surface. Upwelling is prevalent along west-facing coastlines (because of *Ekman pumping*) and at high latitudes, where the lack of a strong thermocline (pycnocline) allows for deep wind-driven mixing. Thus, the *ecological optimum* for algal growth is closer to 8°C, a compromise between the detrimental effects of colder water and the beneficial effects of enhanced nutrient supply. This fact will prove important to our consideration of the causes of glaciation in Earth history.

Tropical species tend to live closer to their physiological optima, and their temperature ranges (maxima–minima) are narrower than higher-latitude species. This may lead to

(a)

(b)

BOX FIGURE 1 Typical physiological responses of plants grown under greenhouse conditions to changes in some environmental conditions. (a) The response of C_3 and C_4 plants to changes in temperature. (b) The response of C_3 and C_4 plants to changes in the partial pressure of CO_2 in the atmosphere. Note that the scale is nonlinear.

(continued)

A CLOSER LOOK (*continued*)

particular vulnerability of tropical species to even small amounts of warming in the future.

Another paradox is the extremely high productivity of tropical rainforests. Perhaps contrary to expectation, tropical soils have severely depleted nutrient concentrations compared to temperate forest soils. How can they sustain such high productivities? The answer is that nutrients are very efficiently recycled in tropical forest ecosystems. Most of the nutrients are stored in the trees themselves. When a tree dies, it falls to the forest floor, which is warm and damp, the ideal conditions for decomposers (fungi and bacteria). Breakdown and release of mineral nutrients is thus quite quick. Moreover, trees in tropical forests have extensive, shallow root systems that rapidly extract nutrients as they are released by the decomposers. As a result, the residence time of nutrients in tropical soils is extremely short (Box Table 1); a typical molecule of nutrient phosphate is retained less than 2 years in a tropical soil, whereas its lifetime in a temperate

forest is closer to 6 years, and in a boreal forest, is over 300 years. The rapid recycling of nutrients in tropical soils draws down the steady-state nutrient concentration but sustains high rates of productivity. However, if the trees are removed, so too are the nutrients, and the soil left behind is infertile. This is one of the serious consequences of deforestation of the tropical rainforest.

Recognition of the distinction between physiological and ecological optima for growth is an important step in developing a deeper understanding of the Earth system. Life, including humans, is influenced by a variety of interacting factors. The overall optimal growth condition thus may be suboptimal for many if not all factors that influence growth. Thus, an environmental change that should increase primary productivity (say, warming of the high-latitude ocean in response to buildup of atmospheric CO_2 levels) may in fact diminish it. The systems approach provides the answers to these seeming paradoxes.

BOX TABLE 1 The Mean Residence Time (in years) of Organic Matter and Nutrients and the Net Primary Productivity (NPP) of Four Biomes

Biome	Organic matter	Nitrogen	Phosphorus	Potassium	Calcium	Magnesium	NPP (gc/m^2/yr)
Boreal forest	353	230	324	94	149	455	360
Temperate forest	4	5.5	5.8	1.3	3.0	3.4	540
Chaparral	3.8	4.2	3.6	1.4	5.0	2.8	270
Tropical rain forest	0.4	2.0	1.6	0.7	1.5	1.1	900

Source: From M. B. Bush, *Ecology of a Changing Planet*, 3/e, 2003. Reprinted by permission of Prentice Hall, Upper Saddle River, NJ.)

of species: an ecosystem that has not been seen before. In fact, because ecosystems and the environment interact, it may be possible for a new ecosystem to evolve without any large-scale change in the environment. In this case, the initial environmental conditions support one ecosystem but the interactions change the local environment, so the ecosystem evolves into something new.

Although Figure 1 implies an ordered hierarchy, the levels are not discrete and ecosystems themselves are not discrete units. Each level in the hierarchy interacts with all other levels, and ecosystems overlap each other. One ecosystem gradually merges into another geographically at a diffuse boundary called a transitional ecosystem or **ecotone** (Figure 3). An ecotone may include an entirely different assemblage of species that do not match those in the ecosystems on either side of the boundary (Figure 4). There is also considerable overlap between ecosystems in a structural sense: Several ecosystems may share many common physical attributes. Based on the various plant communities ecosystems support, we can identify distinct

types of terrestrial biomes. The most important are shown in Figure 5.

Species Interactions

Although ecosystems may appear to be very different from one another, they all exhibit a common biotic structure. For example, all ecosystems include autotrophs and heterotrophs. In this type of organization, primary consumers (e.g., zooplankton in the sea or rodents on land) live off the producers (algae, plants), secondary and higher-order consumers (fish, hawks) feed on lower-order and primary consumers (zooplankton, rodents), and the decomposers (bacteria and fungi) and detritus feeders feed on dead organic matter of both producers and consumers. In assisting the chemical breakdown of organic matter, the decomposers and detritus feeders return nutrients to the system that are then reused by the producers.

We can represent which organisms feed on which by means of a **food chain** that links particular organisms in an

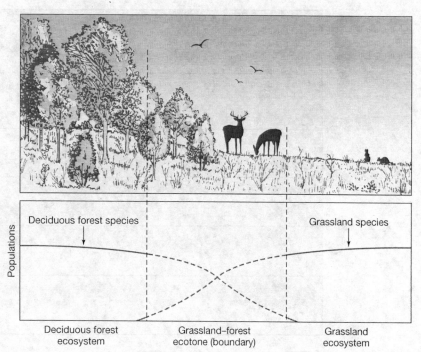

FIGURE 3 Ecosystems and ecotones. (*Source:* From Nebel and Wright, *Environmental Science, 6/e,* 1998. Reprinted by permission of Prentice Hall, Upper Saddle River, N.J.)

ecosystem. Because one organism may feed on several other types or may be eaten by several different types of organisms, food chains are usually interconnected into **food webs** (Figure 6). Despite the potential complexity of these webs, the overall structure is very simple: Each web consists of a series of feeding levels called *trophic levels*. For example, the following trophic levels range from the bottom up: producers > primary consumers > secondary consumers > higher-order consumers. There are normally no more than four trophic levels in any ecosystem.

How many organisms are there at each level? Rather than looking at the number of individuals, we can simplify the comparison between levels if we talk in terms of **biomass**. Biomass is the total combined weight of organic material in each trophic level. Each trophic level, except for the producers, ingests its food (organic matter) from the level below. The organisms utilize that organic matter for growth and to produce energy. As we move from lower-order to higher-order trophic levels, much organic matter is lost when it is converted to energy. In terrestrial ecosystems, the biomass is

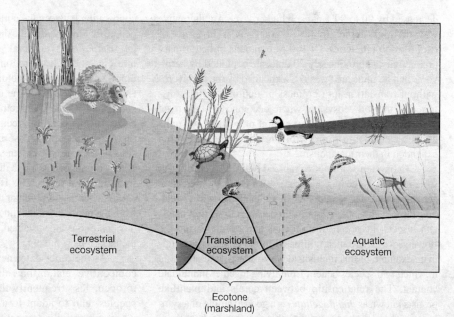

FIGURE 4 An ecotone may create a unique habitat of its own. (*Source:* From Nebel and Wright, *Environmental Science, 6/e,* 1998. Reprinted by permission of Prentice Hall, Upper Saddle River, N.J.)

60° N

30° N

0° (equator)

30° S

60° S

	Tropical rain forest		Mediterranean shrubland		Coniferous forest
	Tropical deciduous forest		Temperate deciduous forest		Tundra and alpine vegetation
	Desert		Temperate rain forest		Ice
	Savannah and tropical shrub forest		Grassland		

FIGURE 5 [See color section] World distribution of the major terrestrial biomes. (*Source:* From Audesirk and Audesirk, *Biology: Life on Earth, 5/e,* 1999. Reprinted by permission of Prentice Hall, Upper Saddle River, N.J.)

decreased by 90 to 99% at each higher level. An alternative way to think about trophic interactions is in terms of **exploitation efficiency**. Of 100 carbon units of net primary productivity, approximately 20 units are exploited by herbivores and 80 units are "wasted," expended by the herbivores without translation into biomass or unutilized and transferred to the soil ecosystem where decomposers take over. In turn, carnivores are able to exploit only about 0.2 units of the 20 available from herbivores, with the rest being expended in their metabolism.

Ecosystems are not organized entirely according to which species is feeding on whom; other forms of interaction are also found. These may include mutually supportive relationships, such as the relationship between flowering plants and insects: Insects feed on the nectar or pollen from the flowers, which are then pollinated in the process. The ultimate example of this mutualism is **symbiosis**, a relationship in which two species benefit from living together in intimate contact. The relationship between corals and plantlike protists known as *dinoflagellates* is a good example of a symbiosis. This symbiotic relationship involves a beneficial cooperation between the coral animal (*polyp*) and a dinoflagellate that lives within the digestive cavity of the coral polyp (*zooxanthalla*). The coral provides protection, inorganic nutrients through excretion, and carbon dioxide for the dinoflagellate. In turn, the dinoflagellate provides nutrition (*photosynthate*), helps the coral synthesize some organic compounds (*lipids*), and removes carbon dioxide, making it easier for the coral to precipitate its $CaCO_3$ skeleton. The dinoflagellate in this case is the coral's *symbiont*. Under stress—for example, when sea temperatures rise during El Niño climate events—the dinoflagellates may be expelled from the coral polyp. This is called a "bleaching" event because the corals turn white; their beautiful coloration comes from the pigments of the dinoflagellate symbiont. If deleterious conditions are sustained, the coral can die as a result of the lack of its symbiont.

At the other extreme are species that coexist in a competitive relationship, although this competition tends to occur less frequently than we might suppose. Most species tend to adapt to a particular habitat and, even where potentially competitive species occupy the same

Third trophic level: all primary carnivores

Second trophic level: all herbivores

First trophic level: all producers

FIGURE 6 A simple food web. Food (energy and nutrients) is transferred from one organism to another along these pathways. (*Source:* From Nebel and Wright, *Environmental Science, 6/e,* 1998. Reprinted by permission of Prentice Hall, Upper Saddle River, N.J.)

habitat, each tends to develop its own particular *niche*. An animal's niche describes not only the food it eats, but also where and when it eats, where it lives, where it nests, and so on. Specialization to this degree, in which different species occupy the same geographic location but have different living habits, reduces potential contact and helps reduce competition among species at the same trophic level.

The species in an ecosystem interact with their environment as well as with each other, and different species thrive under different physical conditions. There is usually some optimal range of conditions over which each species is best adapted. The species comes under stress as the environment moves away from that range—for example, as it becomes wetter or drier, warmer or colder, shadier or sunnier, or more or less acidic. At some point, the stress may be great enough that the organism reaches its limit of tolerance for those conditions, and death occurs.

When we throw human beings into the mix, the level of complexity and the nature of the interactions increase substantially. We then must take into account the social, political, and economic interactions among different human societies and also the dramatic effects that these societies can have on the physical environment.

Ecosystem Disturbance and Succession

Natural or human disturbances of an ecosystem that seriously disrupts the existing ecosystem structure—for example, wildfire or deforestation—initiate a response, often of

rebuilding, that in some cases follows a predictable pattern called **succession**. The job of rebuilding can be quite extensive because initial disturbances such as wildfires or deforestation can promote subsequent effects like soil erosion, nutrient loss, or microclimate changes such as aridification from the loss of evapotranspirative pumping of water into the atmosphere. The resulting arid, nutrient-poor environment is not necessarily conducive to the regrowth of the preexisting community. The first species to reinvade a disturbed environment are called *opportunists* or *pioneer* species. They tend to be fast growing, rapidly reproducing, environmentally tolerant species that can spread across the disturbed area quickly. In colonizing a previously disturbed area, these organisms tend to begin the process of repair, improving the soil or modifying the local climate in ways that can result in their replacement by other, slower growing organisms that ultimately have competitive advantages. The establishment of a mature forest can take decades to hundreds of years after disturbance; the forests of New England are still undergoing succession 200 years or more after the original logging that occurred during colonization of America. In general, succession patterns are predictable, at least in terms of the types of plants that will become prevalent at various stages of succession. If many species are equally well suited to the environmental conditions at a particular stage of succession, however, an element of unpredictability may be introduced into the succession pattern. Thus a diversity of outcomes is possible, and this diversity may be reflected in the *biodiversity* of a region subject to disturbance. Indeed, we will see in the next section that a modest level of disturbance may be required for high-diversity ecosystems to become established.

Succession is one indication that the biosphere has the capacity to "heal," that it is resilient to perturbation. In what follows we will ask a related question: is resilience a general characteristic of diverse ecosystems? Before we do, though, we need to come to a better understanding of what we mean by the term *biodiversity*.

BIODIVERSITY

How do we measure the "health" of the biosphere? By analogy to living systems, a healthy planet should actively transport nutrients from where they are not needed to where they are and should eliminate wastes. Its important environmental variables (temperature and atmospheric and oceanic compositions) should not fluctuate wildly. And it should be capable of responding to natural and anthropogenic disturbances, such as volcanic eruptions, meteorite impacts, deforestation, and pollution, in such a way as to minimize their consequences.

These characteristics of a stable Earth system are ones that we normally associate with living organisms. Indeed, it is these very characteristics that are most suggestive of an important role for the biota in the regulation of the Earth system. The biota have affected Earth's long-term climate evolution by modifying its greenhouse gas content. They have also created an oxygen-rich atmosphere. Our oxygen-rich atmosphere is a direct consequence of oxygenic photosynthesis. The evolution of this metabolic pathway has been called the greatest pollution event of Earth history. As a result of the prevalence of oxygenic photosynthesis, anaerobes, previously able to inhabit a diversity of habitats, survived only in environments such as seafloor sediments where oxygen does not penetrate. In these cases, the perturbations to which the biota has responded have been gradually imposed, perhaps over millions of years. But how has the Earth system responded to *rapid* environmental change? Is the resilience revealed over the long term also a characteristic in the short term? The answer, is yes. Earth has been subjected to insults the magnitude of which we are unable to imagine: Meteorites broader than the ocean is deep have struck Earth many times during its 3.5 billion years of inhabitation by organisms. The robustness of the planetary system is revealed by a fossil record displaced but not interrupted and by a geological and geochemical record that suggests that the long-term environmental consequences of these sudden disturbances were small.

How is the diversity of life-forms on the planet—its **biodiversity**, the number of species in an area—related to the health of the Earth system? At the local scale, if we measure "health" in terms of biological productivity, we might conclude low diversity ecosystems are the healthiest. For example, highly productive lakes that have been impacted by fertilizer additions in runoff tend to be dominated by a very few species that are highly productive under high nutrient loadings. However, we don't normally consider contaminated lakes "healthy." We might instead propose that Earth's health can be measured by the number of species it supports. This assumption is implicit in the concern over the loss of biodiversity Earth is currently experiencing as a result of deforestation and loss of habitat. But do the abilities we associate with a healthy planet depend on its biodiversity? Is global biodiversity an indicator of the functional status of the Earth system?

Measures of Biodiversity

Biodiversity can be determined in a number of different ways. Perhaps the simplest measure of biodiversity is the number of species present in a community. A community with 5 species is much less diverse than one with 100 species. There are some problems with this simple definition, however. One problem has to do with heterogeneity. Suppose there are two communities, both with two species of organisms, as shown in Table 2. According to the simple definition, the two communities are equally diverse. Community I, however, has 99 individuals of species A and 1 individual of species B, whereas community II has 50 individuals of species A and 50 individuals of species B (Figure 7). The chance of encountering species B in community I is quite remote, only 1 in 100; this community is quite homogeneous. In contrast, community II seems more diverse because there is an equal likelihood of encountering an individual of species A and of species B. Community II is thus more heterogeneous.

To capture the importance of heterogeneity, measures of diversity other than simply the number of species have been proposed. The *Simpson's diversity index* measures the likelihood that two individuals drawn from the same community will be of different species. This likelihood is expressed quantitatively as follows:

$$\text{Simpson's diversity} = 1 - [(\text{proportion of species A})^2 + (\text{proportion of species B})^2 + \dots]$$

TABLE 2   Diversity of Two Simple Communities

	Number of Individuals, Species A	Number of Individuals, Species B	Simpson's Diversity Index
Community I	99	1	0.02
Community II	50	50	0.50

Community I

Community II

FIGURE 7 Two communities comprising two species (A and B) each. Although equal numbers of species are represented, community II appears more diverse than community I.

The proportion of each species in the community is identical to the probability that an individual chosen at random will be of that species. The probability of choosing two individuals of that species in a row is in the square of the proportion, just as the probability of throwing two "heads" in a row during a coin toss is $(0.5)^2 = 0.25$, or 1/4. The value of this index for our two simple communities I and II are $1 - (0.99^2 + 0.01^2) = 0.02$ for the homogeneous community I and $1 - (0.5^2 + 0.5^2) = 0.5$ for the heterogeneous community II, as shown in Table 2. When the number of species is large and the composition heterogeneous, the maximum Simpson's diversity approaches 1.0.

The Simpson's diversity index is clearly superior to a simple species count in expressing biodiversity. Nevertheless, in most discussions of global biodiversity of the past, present, and future (to some extent, this text included), only the species count is used.

Diversity and Stability

A long-standing debate exists among ecologists about the relationship between diversity and stability. For most communities, diversity increases from the poles to the tropics: Most of the highly diverse communities exist within 10 to 20 degrees of the equator. Why are the tropics so diverse? Tropical climates tend to be stable over a range of time scales. In the short term, the lack of large seasonal variations in solar insolation leads to only small monthly contrasts in temperature and rainfall. Moreover, investigation of the geological record reveals that on long time scales, tropical temperatures have changed relatively little. Even during the Ice Ages, tropical temperatures fell only slightly while temperate to polar climates cooled substantially. The high diversity and climatic monotony of the tropics have been taken to indicate that environmental stability leads to high diversity—a premise called the *time stability hypothesis*. The persistence of uniform environmental conditions in the tropics presumably allows evolution to proceed without disruption (i.e., lower rates of extinction), leading to higher diversity. Recently it has been suggested that the tropics are also the cradle of diversity: new species evolve in the tropics and then expand into higher latitudes. If so, then higher rates of human-induced species extinction in the tropics today might have dire consequences for species at higher latitudes in the future.

In contrast, the *intermediate disturbance hypothesis* states that the high diversity of tropical ecosystems is the result of disturbances that occur with intermediate frequency and intensity. This hypothesis is in direct contradiction with the time stability hypothesis. Highly diverse tropical rainforests tend to have some species with few or no young trees (indicating that they are dying out) and other species with a very high proportion of young trees (indicating that they are increasing in abundance). This turnover is presumed to be the result of a fairly recent natural disturbance. Regions of rainforest that are known to have been relatively undisturbed over historical time tend to have lower diversities. Also, highly diverse coral reef ecosystems tend to occur at the outer edge of barrier reefs, where these ecosystems are periodically confronted with the damaging effects of waves and storms.

Both hypotheses link the diversity of life on Earth to the stability (or instability) of the environment. Another ecological consideration is the stability of the ecosystem itself: how stable (in time) are its species composition and density (the number of species per unit area)? Stable ecosystems display low variability in species density, respond quickly to perturbation, returning to their original state after the disturbance, can tolerate repeated shocks, and respond sluggishly to persistent forcings. More diverse ecosystems tend to have more stable species densities in the face of environmental variation, because decreases in some species are counterbalanced by increases of others.

DIVERSITY OF INTERACTIONS

Even the more elaborate measures of diversity, such as the Simpson's diversity index, fail to account for a characteristic of ecosystems that is important to our understanding of the feedbacks between the biota and the physical world: the diversity of interactions. A community consisting of 500 species of ants, with relatively uniform populations of each, along with a few species of plants and predators, is highly diverse according to this index. However, in terms of the diversity of roles played by these organisms, the community is extremely homogeneous.

Here the infancy of Earth system science is clearly a limitation: No diversity index has been proposed that captures the degree of interaction between biological and physical components of the Earth system. Such a diversity index should increase as the number of couplings among the biota and between the biota and the physical world increases. An ecosystem with 10 interactions and only 20 species is then not as diverse as one with 40 species interacting in these 10 ways. It should also incorporate the attribute of redundancy; the Earth system is more resilient if there are alternative ways of performing important functions, such as photosynthesis or decomposition. If one of these pathways is lost (e.g., through extinction), the others can compensate. The final attribute to incorporate into a

systems diversity index is potential diversity. Species in small abundance today may come to dominate after a disturbance. In doing so, they will ensure that some vital function of the Earth system continues with little interruption or modification. If biodiversity is defined in this way, it seems clear that a more biologically diverse world is a more stable, resilient world, that biodiversity does indeed enhance environmental stability at the global scale.

The biosphere has suffered from unimaginable catastrophes that reduced the species diversity by up to 95%, yet recovered. We also discuss how current practices of monoculture and genetic engineering may make us susceptible to the sort of widespread blight experienced by the Irish people when their monoculture of potatoes succumbed to a fungal infection in the 19th century.

Chapter Summary

1. Some of the characteristics of life that allow it to play an important role in the Earth system are its tendency toward exponential growth, its need for energy, its tendency to pollute, and its versatility.
2. Organisms can be placed into broad groups according to whether they are producers (autotrophs) or consumers (heterotrophs).
   a. Autotrophs include those that use solar energy (photosynthesizers) and those that use chemical energy (chemosynthesizers).
   b. Heterotrophs, including aerobes (use oxygen), anaerobes (use other oxidants), and fermenters (who do not oxidize organic matter), get energy from the food they consume.
3. Populations of organisms live in communities with other organisms that interact among themselves and their environment in ecosystems. Boundaries between ecosystems are typically gradational ecotones rather than sharply contrasting adjacent ecosystems.
4. The flow of energy (food) through ecosystems is often displayed as a food chain from producers to consumers and decomposers.
   a. Closer inspection of natural communities indicates that the relationships form more of a web than a chain.
   b. Exploitation efficiency is quite low; much of the food (energy) available to higher levels in the food chain is not used for growth but rather expended during metabolism.
5. Species also interact in other ways, including some that are competitive but others that are mutually beneficial (symbiosis).
6. After a disturbance, an ecosystem often responds with a predictable succession of organisms, from opportunistic, fast-growing species to slower-growing but ultimately more competitive species.
7. The diversity of life on Earth is a function not only of the number of species, but also of the degree to which the populations of those species are nonuniformly distributed (heterogeneous).
8. Environmental stability seems to lead to high biodiversity in some instances; however, modest disturbance enhances diversity in others.

Key Terms

autotrophs
biodiversity
biomass
biomes
community

ecosystem
ecotone
exploitation efficiency
food chain
food web

heterotrophs
population
succession
symbiosis

Review Questions

1. What are the characteristics of life that allow it to influence the environment at a global scale?
2. What are the two fundamental groupings of organisms based on their metabolisms?
3. Describe the two mechanisms of autotrophy. Where on Earth might you expect to find one or the other of these two pathways to dominate?
4. Describe the three mechanisms of heterotrophy. Where on Earth might you expect to find one or the other of these two pathways to dominate?
5. Why is a food web often a better description than a food chain of the way in which energy (food) is passed through an ecosystem?
6. How does symbiosis differ from other forms of species interactions?
7. Describe a typical successional sequence following a disturbance of an ecosystem. What are the characteristics of opportunistic species that allow them to rapidly repopulate a disturbed area?
8. What is the advantage of the Simpson's Diversity Index over a simple census of the number of species in quantifying the diversity of an ecosystem?
9. What do we mean by "diversity of interactions"?

Critical-Thinking Problems

1. Figure 2 presents a systems diagram of the feedbacks involving boreal forest cover, albedo, temperatures, sea ice, and the oceans. We used this diagram to show that it is possible for the northern boreal forest to have a significant impact on the larger-scale climate. Using the information you now have about the possible impacts of anthropogenically induced greenhouse climate change, expand on this diagram and discuss the implications in terms of climate and forest cover.
2. In the final section of this chapter we presented some thoughts about what a diversity index useful for Earth system scientists might include. Using these thoughts or those of your own, develop a quantitative index, similar to the Simpson's Diversity Index, that reflects the diversity of interactions at the global scale.
3. Using the information from Table 1, design a layered microbial ecosystem that could be self-sustaining with the exception of the import of solar energy from above. All of the inorganic compounds listed in the table are available for your use in building this ecosystem.

Further Reading

General

Bradbury, I. K. 1998. *The biosphere.* 2nd ed. New York: Wiley.
Wilson, E. O. 1992. *The diversity of life.* New York: Norton.

Advanced

Volk, T. 1998. *Gaia's body.* New York: Copernicus (Springer-Verlag).

Westbroek, P. 1991. *Life as a geological force: Dynamics of the Earth.* New York: Norton.

tropical rain forest	mediterranean shrubland	coniferous forest
tropical deciduous forest	temperate deciduous forest	tundra and alpine vegetation
desert	temperate rain forest	ice
savanna and tropical shrub forest	grassland	

FIGURE 5   World distribution of the major terrestrial biomes.   (*Source:* From Audesirk and Audesirk, *Biology: Life on Earth, 5/e,* 1999. Reprinted by permission of Prentice Hall, Upper Saddle River, N.J.)

Origin of Earth and of Life

Origin of Earth and of Life

Key Questions

- How old is Earth?
- How did the solar system form?
- How did the atmosphere and ocean form?
- What was the composition of the atmosphere early in Earth's history?

- When and how did life originate?
- Why did the earliest organisms show a preference for hot environments?

Chapter Overview

Earth formed some 4.6 billion years (b.y.) ago by the accretion of solid particles from a cloud of gas and dust surrounding the young Sun. Earth's atmosphere and ocean started forming as the planet itself was being built as a consequence of the release of volatile materials during impacts. The atmosphere and ocean continued to grow during the so-called heavy bombardment period between 4.6 and 3.8 b.y. ago, although new evidence suggests that the bombardment may have been a pulse, rather than an ongoing process. The composition of the atmosphere is unknown because little or no rock record survives from that time, but it probably consisted mostly of N_2 and CO_2. Life may have originated during the heavy bombardment period from reactions between organic chemicals created in Earth's surface environment or imported from space. This may explain why the last common ancestor of all extant life appears to have come from a hot environment.

INTRODUCTION

Earth is a smallish planet that orbits an ordinary star, our Sun. Earth is special, however, because it is the only planet in the universe that is known to harbor life. How was Earth formed, and how did it come to be habitable? These are questions we need to understand if we are to assess the possibility that life might exist elsewhere. We must also try to understand how life itself originated. Was it a chance occurrence, or was it a phenomenon that was almost unavoidable on a young, habitable planet like Earth? We don't know the answers to these questions yet, but scientists have made progress over the last few decades in determining how both our planet and ourselves came to exist.

Introduction to Geologic Time

One of the most important points that any geology professor makes to an introductory class is the immense amount of time represented in the geologic record. For reasons outlined below, scientists believe that Earth and the rest of the solar system formed about 4.6 b.y. ago. (See box titled "A Closer Look: Determining the Age of Earth.") The universe itself has existed for roughly 14 billion years, based on estimates of its current rate of expansion. Both the age of Earth and the age of the universe are almost inconceivably longer than a typical human lifetime of about 80 years or even the total amount of time that humanlike species have been in existence, about

A CLOSER LOOK
Determining the Age of Earth

The problem of determining Earth's age is somewhat complicated even though the basic principles of radiometric dating are straightforward . The reason is that standard parent–daughter age-dating techniques, like the uranium–lead system, yield only the crystallization ages of the minerals to which they are applied, not the age of the material itself. But, as far as geologists know, none of the rocks and minerals that composed Earth's original crust have been preserved. The oldest minerals that can be dated by standard techniques are a handful of **zircons** (a zirconium silicate mineral) that yield ages of up to 4.4 b.y. How do we deduce that Earth is actually about 150 million years older than this?

To find Earth's age, one must first answer a related question: How old are meteorites? **Meteorites** are pieces of rock and/or metal that are thought to have drifted around the solar system for billions of years before hitting Earth. They have been collected from all over the planet but are found most readily in Antarctica, where they are easily spotted on the ice. The gradual flow and melting of the ice concentrates meteorites in a few specific localities, making them especially easy to find. The most primitive meteorites (because they have not been altered by melting) are called **chondrites**. Dating of chondrites provides an upper limit on Earth's age because these objects are thought to have formed at the same time as the solar system as a whole.

Meteorites can be dated using standard parent–daughter techniques, but the most accurate method—**lead–lead dating**—involves the use of multiple lead isotopes. The reason this is useful is that the U/Pb ratio differs from one meteorite to another and even among different minerals within the same meteorite, so it is difficult to determine what the initial U/Pb ratio must have been. By using multiple isotopes, we can avoid this problem. The three isotopes used are ^{204}Pb, ^{206}Pb, and ^{207}Pb. The lead isotopes ^{206}Pb and ^{207}Pb are radiogenic isotopes that derive, respectively, from the decay of ^{238}U and ^{235}U. The half-lives of these decay processes are 4.5 b.y. and 0.713 b.y. The third lead isotope, ^{204}Pb, is a nonradiogenic isotope that is used for comparison in the measurements. By measuring the abundances of these isotopes in different meteorites and then plotting the $^{206}Pb/^{204}Pb$ ratio on one axis and the $^{207}Pb/^{204}Pb$ ratio on the other, we can construct what is known as an **isochron diagram** (Box Figure 1). If all the samples being analyzed have the same age, as is true for chondritic meteorites, then the data should (and do) all fall on a straight line. The slope of this line tells us the age of the collection of meteorites, which is accurately determined as 4.55 b.y.

Moon rocks, which were brought back by the *Apollo* spacecraft missions of the late 1960s and early 1970s, can be dated in a similar manner. The oldest Moon rocks are about 4.44 b.y. old, suggesting that the Moon formed soon after the solar system itself. The Moon could be even older than this, as there is no guarantee that we have found the oldest Moon rock.

Earth's age is more difficult to obtain because the oldest rocks are all gone. They were probably recycled back into the interior by plate tectonics. However, Earth's age can be deduced indirectly by examining lead isotope ratios in rocks containing lead minerals, that is, minerals that initially contained lead, but little or no uranium. (U–Pb dating, in contrast, is performed on minerals that initially contained uranium, but little or no lead.) The isotopic composition of lead minerals is the same as that of the magma from which they formed. Because Earth's mantle contains uranium as well as lead, the abundances of ^{206}Pb and ^{207}Pb in the mantle have increased with time, as have those of the magmas derived from it. If we plot the lead isotope ratios from rocks of different ages and then analyze the resulting curve mathematically, we can show that, 4.5 to 4.6 b.y. ago, Earth's mantle should have had the same $^{206}Pb/^{207}Pb$ ratio as meteorites. This, in turn, implies that Earth formed at the same time as the rest of the solar system, about 4.55 b.y. ago. This radiometric age scale is the fundamental underpinning to most of our theories about how Earth formed and evolved.

BOX FIGURE 1 An isochron diagram, showing lead isotope ratios from a collection of chondritic meteorites. The fact that all the data fall on a straight line shows that all the meteorites have the same age. The age of the meteorites, 4.55 b.y., is determined from the slope of the line. (*Source:* From K. K. Turekian, *Global Environmental Change: Past, Present, and Future,* 1996. Reprinted by permission of Prentice Hall, Upper Saddle River, N.J.)

4 million years (m.y.). An analogy that is sometimes made is to scale down Earth's age to a single calendar year beginning at 12:01 A.M. on January 1. In that case humans would have first appeared at about 4:40 P.M. on December 31, and the oldest human (about 120 years) would have been born less than one second before midnight later that evening.

In this chapter, we focus on events that occurred billions of years ago. The major **eons** into which geologic time is divided are the Hadean (4.6–3.8 b.y. ago), Archean (3.8–2.5 b.y. ago), Proterozoic (2.5–0.54 b.y. ago), and Phanerozoic (0.54 b.y. ago–present). The first three of these time intervals are often collectively termed the Precambrian because they come before the Cambrian period, when **shelly fossils** (fossilized remains of shelled organisms) became abundant in the rock record. Figure 1 shows some of the other major events that have occurred during Earth's history.

FORMATION OF THE SOLAR SYSTEM

How did Earth and the rest of the solar system form? This question has fascinated astronomers for hundreds of years. It is interesting to Earth system scientists as well because it sets the boundary conditions for the rest of Earth's subsequent evolution.

Formation of the Solar Nebula

The Sun is thought to have formed from a collapsing cloud of interstellar dust and gas. Such **interstellar clouds** are observed today by both optical and radio telescopes (Figure 2). The one shown in Figure 2 is a particularly spectacular one that happens to be backlit by some bright blue stars. It is a portion of the Eagle Nebula, which is sometimes referred to as the "Pillars of Creation." Interstellar clouds are concentrated in the spiral arms of our Milky Way galaxy, where the density of material is highest. If such a cloud is dense enough and cold enough (about 10 K), it will collapse under its own self-gravity and the process of star formation can begin. It may seem counterintuitive that a cold cloud is required to form a hot star, but this is indeed the case. The reason is that, according to the ideal gas law, a cold gas exerts less pressure than a warm gas of the same density. A cold interstellar cloud has less internal pressure to counteract the force of

EON		Major events in Earth's history	Billions of years ago
PRECAMBRIAN	PHANEROZOIC	First humans evolved / First dinosaurs evolved	
		First fish evolved	0.54
	PROTEROZOIC	Oldest shelly fossils	
		Rise of atmospheric oxygen	
			2.5
	ARCHEAN	Oldest microfossils (?)	
			3.8
	HADEAN	Oldest sedimentary rocks	
		Origin of Earth	4.6

FIGURE 1 The geologic time scale, showing major events in Earth's history. (*Source:* From R. W. Christopherson, *Geosystems: An Introduction to Physical Geography*, 3/e, 1997. Reprinted by permission of Prentice Hall, Upper Saddle River, N.J.)

FIGURE 2 [See color section] The Eagle Nebula viewed from the Hubble Space Telescope. (*Source:* NASA Headquarters.)

FIGURE 3 [See color section] The disk around the star Beta Pictoris, as seen from the Hubble Space Telescope. Top panel: Visible light image. Bottom panel: False color image created by image processing to highlight features in the disk structure. (*Source:* NASA Headquarters.)

gravity and is therefore more likely to collapse. Once it does so, the cloud immediately warms up because the infall of material releases gravitational energy, which is converted into heat. The innermost part of the cloud eventually becomes hot enough for thermonuclear fusion reactions to begin, and a new star is born.

The clouds that are observed in interstellar space are typically many thousands of times the mass of the Sun. As they contract, however, they produce smaller fragments that can themselves contract to form one or more stars. Whether the collapse results in a single star, or a multiple star system, depends largely on how fast the cloud fragment is rotating: the faster it rotates, the more likely it is to form two or more stars. In the case of our own Sun, a single star formed. This is fortunate for us, because a multiple star system would probably be a very difficult place to form a habitable planet like Earth. (It is difficult to identify stable orbits in such systems and probably even more difficult to form a planet in just the right place.) The cloud fragment did have a certain amount of rotation, however, and this caused some of its material to spread out into a disk. The gas and dust that made up the disk are referred to as the **solar nebula**. Astronomers have now been able to see similar disks around other Sun-like stars. Figure 3 shows the disk around the star Beta Pictoris, which was the first such disk to be discovered.

Formation of Planets

Once the solar nebula was in place, the process of planetary formation would have begun. The nebula itself would have been heated by the emerging Sun—the **proto-Sun**—so its interior would have warmed. At the same time, small particles of solid material would have begun to condense from the gas. In the hot, inner parts of the nebula, these grains consisted mainly of rocky materials such as iron and silicate minerals that can condense at temperatures as high as 2000 K. That is why Earth and the other **terrestrial planets** (Mercury, Venus, and Mars) are composed

principally of rock. In the cooler, outer parts of the nebula, icy materials such as water (H_2O), methane (CH_4), and ammonia (NH_3) would also have condensed. Thus, the giant planets (Jupiter, Saturn, Uranus, and Neptune) contain large amounts of these more volatile compounds. **Volatile compounds** are substances that have low boiling points. The particles formed by condensation were gravitationally attracted to the mid-plane of the nebula, where they clumped together to form **planetesimals**, small protoplanets. These planetesimals collided with each other, often sticking together to form larger bodies in a process called **accretion**. This process is shown schematically in Figure 4. Over tens to hundreds of million of years, the planetesimals grew to form the planets that we see today.

While Earth was growing by accretion, its core should have started to form. Recall that the innermost parts of Earth are its solid inner core and liquid outer core, both composed mainly of iron and nickel. Core formation was once thought to have been triggered by radioactive heating after Earth was fully formed. But it is now believed that core formation occurred as the planet itself was forming. Some of the planetesimals that collided with Earth during accretion were so large that they melted large portions of the crust and upper mantle. This allowed the iron and nickel to separate out and flow down to form the core.

Formation of Jupiter

Two specific events that occurred during the process of planetary accretion have special significance for surface conditions on Earth. The first was the formation of the giant planet Jupiter. Jupiter has over 300 times the mass of Earth and more than three times the mass of the next largest planet, Saturn. The reason Jupiter is so large, astronomers believe, is that its core accreted early enough to capture large amounts of hydrogen and helium from the solar nebula before the nebula dissipated. Accretion would have been rapid at Jupiter's orbit because volatiles could condense in addition to metal and silicates. To capture

(a) A slowly rotating portion of a large nebula becomes a distinct globule as a mostly gaseous cloud collapses by gravitational attraction.

(b) Rotation of the cloud prevents collapse of the equatorial disk while a dense central mass forms.

(c) A protostar "ignites" and warms the inner part of the nebula, possibly vaporizating preexisting dust. As the nebula cools, condensation produces solid grains that settle to the central plane of the nebula.

(d) The dusty nebula clears by dust aggregation into planetesimals or by ejection during a T-Tauri stage of the star's evolution. A star and a system of cold bodies remains. Gravitational accretion of these small bodies leads to the development of a small number of major planets.

FIGURE 4   The process of planetary accretion. By colliding with each other, (a) small planetesimals (b) grow gradually into (c) large planets.   (*Source:* From W. K. Hamblin and E. H. Christiansen, *Earth's Dynamic Systems,* 8/e, 1998. Reprinted by permission of Prentice Hall, Upper Saddle River, N.J.)

hydrogen efficiently, Jupiter's core must have grown rapidly to a mass several times that of Earth. Observations of young stars indicate that nebular gas and dust persist for at most a few million years, after which time they are either incorporated into planets or they spiral back into the star.

Jupiter affects surface conditions on Earth by perturbing asteroids from the asteroid belt into Earth-crossing orbits and by preventing most comets from reaching the inner solar system. The first effect makes Earth a more dangerous place to live, whereas the second one tends to make it safer. Impacts of comets and asteroids are thought to have played a major role in the evolution of life. A large asteroid impact may have caused the extinction of the dinosaurs, and this may in turn have paved the way for the rise of mammals. Thus, biological evolution might have taken an entirely different course had Jupiter not attained the size that it did.

Formation of the Moon

Another celestial event that had a profound influence on Earth's subsequent evolution was the formation of the Moon. Most of us know that the Moon's gravitational pull affects ocean tides. However, few people are aware that the Moon affects climate as well. It does so by stabilizing Earth's obliquity. Recall that it is Earth's *obliquity,* or tilt

(currently 23.5°), that gives rise to the normal progression of the seasons at middle to high latitudes. We will see that Earth's obliquity varies slightly and that these variations have influenced the glacial–interglacial cycles of the past 3 million years. Computer modeling studies have shown that, without the Moon, Earth's obliquity would vary by much larger amounts, occasionally reaching values as high as 85°. This would wreak havoc with climate because the seasonal cycles would be extremely large over much of Earth's surface. Thus, from the standpoint of planetary habitability, the formation of the Moon may be one of the most important events to occur during the formation of the solar system.

How exactly did it happen? Many theories have been advanced, including co-accretion (accreting in Earth's orbit at the same time as did Earth), fission (splitting apart of a rapidly rotating Earth), and capture (gravitational capture of a body that originated elsewhere in the solar system). Most of these theories, however, involve steps that are either physically implausible or that would produce a lunar composition different from that observed in Moon rocks. From the samples collected by the *Apollo* astronauts, we know that the Moon is depleted in volatile elements compared to the bulk Earth and that its oxygen isotopic composition is similar to that of Earth's mantle. Its density is substantially lower than that of Earth, indicating

A CLOSER LOOK

Main-Sequence Stars and the Hertzsprung–Russell Diagram

The **Hertzsprung–Russell (H–R) diagram** is a standard means of categorizing different types of stars (Box Figure 2). The horizontal axis represents the effective radiating temperature of the star, as determined by Wien's law or by some equivalent method of analyzing the star's spectrum. For historical reasons, temperature is always shown increasing to the left. The vertical axis represents the luminosity of the star relative to that of the Sun.

As Box Figure 2 shows, most stars fall along a well-defined band that runs from the upper left of the diagram to the lower right. This band is referred to as the **main sequence**. It consists of "normal" stars—that is, stars that are in the slowly evolving, middle phase of their existence. Stars are further grouped into seven classes on the basis of their spectra as O, B, A, F, G, K, or M. The brightest, bluest, and most massive (O and B) stars are referred to as

early-type stars; the dimmest, reddest, and least massive (K and M) stars are called late-type stars. Within these categories, stars are further assigned numbers ranging from 0 (early) to 9 (late).

Our Sun is an unremarkable G2 star that occupies a spot near the middle of the main sequence. In about 5 b.y., the Sun will evolve off the main sequence and become first a red giant (at the upper right in the H–R diagram) and eventually a white dwarf (at the lower left). The Sun is drifting slightly upward on the H–R diagram during its main-sequence lifetime as a consequence of the conversion of hydrogen to helium. This effect is small compared with the changes that occur before and afterward, but it has important effects on planetary climates. It is this slow, main sequence evolution that gives rise to the faint young Sun paradox and that may limit the lifetime of Earth's biota in the future.

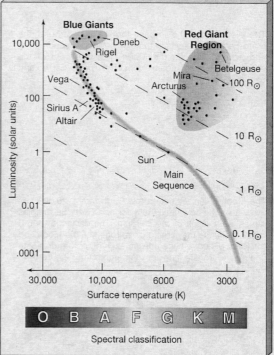

BOX FIGURE 2 [See color section] Hertzsprung–Russell diagram showing different classes of stars. (*Source:* From E. Chaisson and S. McMillan, *Astronomy: A Beginner's Guide to the Universe,* 2/e, 1998. Reprinted by permission of Prentice Hall, Upper Saddle River, N.J.)

that the Moon is also depleted in iron. Furthermore, the Moon appears to have had a completely molten surface, or **magma ocean**, shortly after it formed.

One theory that is consistent with all of the available evidence is the **giant impact hypothesis** (Figure 5). According to this hypothesis, Earth received a glancing blow from a Mars-sized planetesimal during the latter stages

of accretion, and the debris from the impact reassembled in orbit around Earth to form the Moon. This type of cosmic accident is statistically unlikely, but not so unlikely as to be implausible. We know that it is not a commonplace occurrence because none of the other terrestrial planets have large moons. (Mars has two tiny moons, Phobos and Deimos, but these are thought to be captured asteroids.) Current models

A) A Mars-sized body, 0.1 to 0.2 Earth masses, approaches the proto-Earth at an oblique angle.

B) The two bodies collide. The ejecta from the impact fly off at an angle and the proto-Earth starts spinning rapidly.

C) The ejecta from the impact form a disk around the proto-Earth. The debris in the disk collide with each other and accrete to form the Moon. The iron core of the impactor collides again with the proto-Earth and becomes part of its core.

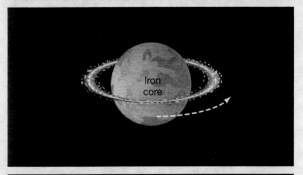

D) The Moon is initially only a few Earth radii (~20,000 km) away from the now nearly fully-formed Earth. Earth spins rapidly as a result of the collision. The daylength is 5-6 hours. Because they are so close together, the Moon and the Earth generate huge tides in each other that dissipate energy and transfer angular momentum from the Earth to the Moon.

E) Over time, Earth's rotation slows, while the Moon retreats to its present orbital distance of ~60 Earth radii (384,400 km). The Moon's current rate of recession is ~1 cm/yr.

FIGURE 5 Schematic diagram illustrating the formation of the Moon by a giant impact.

of accretion suggest that giant impacts themselves should occur fairly frequently, but that most would not have the right geometry to form a large moon. Our own Moon resulted from one giant impact that did, which is fortunate for us, because the Moon has made Earth's climate much more stable than it might otherwise have been.

FORMATION OF THE ATMOSPHERE AND OCEAN

Even after Earth had recovered from the effects of the Moon-forming impact, its surface would still have been an active and hostile environment. Continued bombardment of the surface by smaller planetesimals should have released large amounts of water and other volatile compounds directly into the atmosphere. This phenomenon is referred to as **impact degassing**. The process has been studied in the laboratory by firing high-speed bullets into targets of volatile-compound–rich material, such as carbonate rock. The shock from the bullet's impact causes the carbonate rock to release gaseous CO_2. Similar shock-induced degassing should occur when volatile-compound–rich planetesimals from the asteroid belt region or from the outer solar system collided with Earth's surface.

The energy released by the impacts, combined with the greenhouse effect of the gases given off, may have kept Earth's surface so hot that all the water would have remained in the atmosphere as steam. Alternatively, Earth's oceans may have periodically condensed and been re-evaporated many times by impacts. Any incoming object larger than about 450 km in diameter would have had sufficient energy to evaporate today's oceans. In either case, both the atmosphere and the ocean should have begun forming as the planet itself formed. This modern conception of planetary formation contrasts with older theories in which Earth was thought to have accreted as a cold, airless body, and in which the atmosphere was thought to have formed later from gases given off by volcanos. Volcanos undoubtedly contributed material to the surface, but the bulk of the atmosphere and ocean were probably formed directly by impacts.

The main period of accretion is believed to have lasted for only about 100 million years. After this time, Earth's surface would have become somewhat more quiescent. Big impacts probably continued to occur sporadically, however, until about 3.8 b.y. ago. The evidence for this **heavy bombardment period** comes from the Moon, Mars, and Mercury. All three bodies appear to have been heavily cratered during their early histories. (Venus does not provide a record of this period because, like Earth, during its history it has been resurfaced many times by volcanism.) The lunar cratering record is the best understood because some of the craters have been dated by using rocks collected near their rims. If the Moon and the other terrestrial planets were being pelted by large objects, it is almost certain that Earth was getting hit, too. The bombardment may have made it difficult for life to have originated before about 4 to 4.2 b.y. ago. We will return to this issue later in the chapter. It may also have brought additional water and other volatile compounds to Earth, particularly if the impactors were comets or volatile-compound–rich asteroids from the outer asteroid belt. So, the atmosphere and oceans may have continued to grow throughout this period.

Over the last few years, the story just told about the heavy bombardment period has come into question. Scientists have known since the days of the NASA *Apollo* manned lunar missions (1969–1973) that many of the Moon rocks are about 3.8–3.9 b.y. old. This was initially interpreted as a pulse of impacting bodies that all arrived around that time, and it was termed the *late heavy bombardment*. Subsequent theorists, though, had difficulty understanding why such a pulse of impacts should have occurred at this relatively late date in Earth's evolution, when the bulk of Earth was known to have formed by 4.4 b.y. ago, or earlier. So, the revisionists suggested instead that the impact flux declined continuously throughout the entire period between 4.5 and 3.8 b.y. ago.

Within the last 4 years, however, a new model of solar system formation has provided support for the original "pulse" theory of the late heavy bombardment. The model is sometimes termed the *Nice model* because several of the coauthors work in laboratories situated near the city of Nice, in southern France. (The name of the city is pronounced "neese," not "nice.") The Nice model provides a possible explanation for why a pulse of bombardment might have occurred at about 3.9 b.y. ago. (See the Box "A Closer Look: The Nice Model of Solar System Formation.") If this model is correct, then the heavy bombardment may have occurred essentially all at once, rather than spread out over hundreds of millions of years. And this, in turn, might have led to a very different evolutionary path for the early atmosphere and for life itself. We should bear this in mind as we discuss the early steps in biological evolution in the remaining parts of this chapter.

Composition of the Early Atmosphere

What would have been the composition and surface pressure of the atmosphere during the earliest few hundred million years of Earth's history? No one knows for sure, but we can make some educated guesses. Free oxygen, O_2, which makes up about 21% of today's atmosphere, should have been virtually nonexistent, because life—and therefore photosynthesis, the source of free oxygen—had probably not yet arisen. Nitrogen, N_2, does not participate very actively in geochemical cycles; hence, most of it should have been in the atmosphere, as it is today, at about 78% of the total. The present partial pressure of N_2 is about 0.8 bar. Nitrogen would have formed from nitrogen-rich organic compounds and ammonia ice (NH_3) in incoming planetesimals. The shock of their impact on Earth's surface should have converted much of this nitrogen to N_2.

Estimating the CO_2 concentration of the primitive atmosphere is much more difficult. On one hand, we know that Earth's total inventory of carbon is huge the equivalent of 60–80 bars if it were all oxidized to CO_2.

A CLOSER LOOK

The Nice Model of Solar System Formation

The authors of the Nice ("neese") model used a sophisticated computer code to simulate the latter stages of planetary accretion. They started their simulation with a more-or-less evenly distributed swarm of Moon-sized planetesimals, and then calculated their mutual gravitational interactions and collisions as they grew into planets. The four giant planets— Jupiter, Saturn, Uranus, and Neptune— were assumed to be fully formed at the beginning of the simulation; however, they were placed at locations that were different from where they are located today. (See Box Figure 3.) In the model, Jupiter was assumed to have started slightly farther away from the Sun than it is now, and Saturn started slightly closer in. Uranus and Neptune were assumed to have formed just beyond Saturn's orbit, with Neptune being closer to the Sun than Uranus (the opposite of the situation today). All of these assumptions are plausible, although they are by no means a unique starting point for generating the present solar system.

Once the simulation was started, the giant planets started to move, or *migrate*, from their initial orbital locations. Based on observations of Jupiter-mass planets orbiting close-in around other nearby stars, we now know that planets are able to move around during the early stages of planetary system formation. They do so by interacting gravitationally with the remaining dust and gas in the disk and with smaller planetesimals that have not yet been accreted into large planets. In the Nice model simulation, Jupiter migrated inward while Saturn migrated outward. At some time around 3.8 b.y. ago, Saturn's orbital period became exactly twice that of Jupiter. (It is just slightly greater than that now: 29.7 years versus 11.9 years for Jupiter.) The resulting *resonance* between the two planets changed the shapes of both planets' orbits, and this in turn affected the orbits of the two less-massive giant planets, Uranus and Neptune. (We will talk more about shapes of planetary orbits when we discuss the astronomical theory of Earth's Ice Ages.) Both of these planets were pushed farther away from the Sun, and Neptune moved from inside Uranus's orbit to beyond it. Although this complicated scenario may sound somewhat ad hoc, it is consistent with what we have learned about giant planet migration by studying planets around other stars. The net result of the simulation was that Uranus and Neptune were suddenly thrown into the outer solar system, which at this time was still filled with icy planetesimals that had not yet had sufficient time to accrete into larger bodies. Most of these planetesimals were subsequently scattered out of their original orbits, with some of them passing through the inner solar system, and a few of these impacting the Moon and the

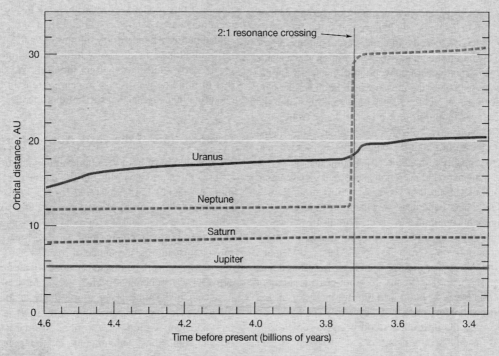

BOX FIGURE 3 Evolution of giant planet orbital distances in the Nice model. The horizontal scale shows time in billions of years before present. The vertical scale shows orbital distance in AU (1 AU = 1 astronomical unit = mean Earth–Sun distance). The vertical line shows the time at which Saturn's orbital period becomes exactly twice that of Jupiter (*Source:* Adapted from K. Tsiganis et al., Nature, v. 435, p. 459, 2005.)

terrestrial planets. If this scenario, or something akin to it, is correct, then the original interpretation of the Moon rocks as representing a pulse of bombardment may well have been correct.

The Nice model is complicated, but it may be testable at some time in the relatively near future. NASA has plans to send astronauts back to the Moon within the next 15 years. With a larger collection of Moon rocks from a wider variety of locations, it should be possible to definitively answer the question of whether the heavy bombardment was continuous, or whether it was a relatively sudden, catastrophic event. And this, in turn, will help us better understand the earliest part of Earth's history and the very early evolution of life.

Most of this carbon is presently stored on the continents in the form of carbonate rocks such as limestone and dolomite. It was originally delivered to Earth as organic carbon in incoming asteroids and comets. Following the previous discussion, much of this carbon would have been immediately released into the atmosphere by the process of impact degassing. The chemical form of the carbon is difficult to calculate: some models predict that it would have been released as CO (carbon monoxide), while other models suggest that it would have been released as a mixture of CH_4 and CO_2. In either case, most of the carbon would have ended up as CO_2 because it would have been oxidized by photochemical reactions involving water vapor. (See the Box "A Closer Look: Oxidation of the Atmosphere by Escape of Hydrogen.")

Exactly how much CO_2 would have been present in the atmosphere during this earliest period of Earth history is difficult to determine. Almost no rocks have been preserved from this time interval, and those that do exist tell us little or nothing about how much CO_2 was present. Hence, we are forced to rely on theoretical models to try to estimate the CO_2 partial pressure at that time. Unfortunately, different theoreticians get different answers depending on what they think was most important.

If, for example, the continents were originally much smaller, as some geologists believe, the process of silicate weathering on land may have been much slower than today. Because silicate weathering is the long-term loss process for CO_2, this would have tended to make the atmospheric CO_2 level higher. Some geologists have predicted that Earth could have had a 10-bar CO_2 atmosphere for the first several hundred million years of its history, until the continents began to grow. In that case, the surface temperature could have been quite hot (80–90°C), in spite of the 30% decreased luminosity of the young Sun.

On the other hand, other geologists point out that CO_2 should have reacted rapidly with the fresh seafloor and with the finely powdered **ejecta** produced by impacts. In that case, atmospheric CO_2 levels could have been quite low, and early Earth would have been very cold. For now, though, we simply acknowledge that we do not know whether the atmosphere was thick or thin during the earliest stages of Earth's history, and we are equally uncertain whether the climate was warm or cold. This might not matter much, either, except that life may have originated during this era, and some theories of life's origin depend strongly on the ambient temperature. We'll consider how that might have happened in the next section.

THE ORIGIN OF LIFE

The question of how life on Earth originated has been a topic for both religious and scientific speculation. Nearly all religions have their own creation "myths." While many of these stories have considerable moral and intellectual value, most are directly contradicted by the geologic record on Earth and by the sheer immensity of geologic time. For example, a literal reading of the Bible implies that God created Earth and all forms of life over a space of 7 days only a few thousand years ago. We saw earlier in this chapter that radiometric dating places the age of Earth at over 4.5 billion years. Unless the laws governing radioactive decay change with time themselves, an unlikely possibility, the biblical creation story cannot be true in a literal sense. A Creator or Supreme Being could indeed have played a role in the creation of both the universe and life, but if so, both events must have happened a very long time ago.

The modern scientific theory of life's origin was first formulated in the 1920s by Russian scientist Alexander Oparin and independently by British scientist J. B. S. Haldane. The *Oparin–Haldane hypothesis,* as it came to be called, postulated that life arose from chemical reactions that were initiated in a strongly reduced early atmosphere and came to completion in the early oceans. Recall that reduced carbon is carbon that is bonded to other carbon atoms or to hydrogen. A **strongly reduced atmosphere** is one that is rich in hydrogen-containing gases, such as methane (CH_4) and ammonia (NH_3). Oparin and Haldane proposed that energy sources such as sunlight and lightning caused these gases to react with each other to form organic compounds in a process termed **chemical evolution**. Ultimately, and in a manner that admittedly is still not understood today, these organic compounds assumed the characteristics of living systems. (See the Box "A Closer Look: What Does It Mean to Be Alive?")

The Miller–Urey Experiment

The Oparin–Haldane theory of life's origin received a gigantic boost from a series of laboratory experiments performed in 1953 by a graduate student at the University of

A CLOSER LOOK
Oxidation of the Atmosphere by Escape of Hydrogen

The compounds that formed Earth's primitive atmosphere were initially highly reduced. Recall that reduced carbon is carbon that is bonded to other carbon atoms, hydrogen, or nitrogen. Most of the carbon in meteorites is in the form of reduced or organic carbon, and this was presumably true of the planetesimals from which Earth formed as well. When these planetesimals impacted the young planet, much of the carbon would have been released as the reduced gases CO and CH_4. It would not have remained in those forms very long, however. In the absence of oxygen and ozone, ultraviolet radiation from the Sun would have **photolyzed** (split apart) water molecules, creating hydrogen atoms (H) and **hydroxyl radicals** (OH):

$$H_2O + UV \text{ photon} \rightarrow H + OH.$$

(A *radical* is a molecule that is highly reactive because it has an unpaired electron in its outer shell.) OH radicals play an important role in today's atmosphere, where they are responsible for oxidizing various gases, including CH_4 and CO. In the case of CO, the reaction is

$$CO + OH \rightarrow CO_2 + H.$$

For CH_4, the reaction sequence is more complicated but the result is the same: the carbon ultimately ends up as CO_2.

What makes these reactions important is the fact that they are essentially irreversible. The hydrogen atoms that are produced are light enough to escape from Earth's atmosphere. As this happens, both CO and CH_4 are converted irreversibly to CO_2. Hence, Earth's atmosphere tends to become more oxidized with time, simply because hydrogen is always being lost to space. Note, however, that this process does *not* produce free oxygen, O_2. A very small amount of O_2 can be produced by other reactions, as described later in the chapter, but almost all of the O_2 in our present atmosphere was produced by photosynthesis.

BOX FIGURE 4 Diagram illustrating escape of hydrogen to space and resultant oxidation of the early atmosphere.

Chicago, Stanley Miller, working under the guidance of famous geochemist Harold Urey. Miller and Urey filled flasks with mixtures of gases that were considered at that time to be representative of Earth's primitive atmosphere. (These gases had just recently been discovered in Jupiter's atmosphere. Because Jupiter does not lose hydrogen, its atmosphere was considered by Urey to be "unevolved." Urey reasoned, not quite correctly, that Earth's atmosphere would have been similar in composition before hydrogen had had time to escape.) The flasks contained methane and ammonia, along with water vapor and molecular hydrogen. The researchers then sparked the flasks with powerful electric discharges, simulating lightning in the prebiotic atmosphere.

After several minutes of electrification, the walls of the flasks became coated with a sticky, brownish material. When analyzed, this material was found to contain an assortment of organic compounds, including amino acids. **Amino acids** are compounds—containing an amino group (NH_2) and a carboxyl group (COOH)—that are important building blocks for proteins (see the Box "A Closer Look: The Compounds of Life"). **Proteins**, composed of one or more chains of amino acids, are key molecules in organisms. Proteins may be *enzymes* (guiding chemical reactions), structural components, *hormones* (maintaining constant body conditions), or transport molecules.

The Miller–Urey experiment, as it is now called, made headlines around the world. It was indeed a revelation

A CLOSER LOOK

Prebiotic O$_2$ Concentrations

How much O$_2$ would have been present in the atmosphere prior to the origin of life? We already know that most of Earth's O$_2$ was produced by photosynthesis. This, of course, is a biological process. We would like to know the prebiotic atmospheric O$_2$ level for two reasons: (1) free O$_2$ would have poisoned the chemical reactions leading to the origin of life, as discussed in the text; and (2) if prebiotic O$_2$ levels were low on Earth, then the presence of O$_2$ in another planet's atmosphere may be a useful indicator that life is present. Scientists hope to eventually look for the presence of O$_2$ in the atmospheres of planets around other stars to determine whether such planets might be inhabited.

How could O$_2$ have been produced in the absence of photosynthesis? Probably the most important mechanism for producing O$_2$ abiotically is the following. First, water vapor is photolyzed by a UV photon, producing atomic hydrogen (H) and a hydroxyl radical (OH):

$$H_2O + UV \text{ photon} \rightarrow H + OH.$$

Then, another UV photon splits a CO$_2$ molecule, producing carbon monoxide (CO) and atomic oxygen (O):

$$CO_2 + UV \text{ photon} \rightarrow CO + O.$$

The OH and O radicals then combine to form O$_2$:

$$O + OH \rightarrow O_2 + H.$$

If the hydrogen atoms produced in these reactions escape to space, which they can do because they are light, then a net production of O$_2$ has occurred.

This does *not* necessarily imply that O$_2$ will build up in the atmosphere of an abiotic planet, however, because there are also loss processes for O$_2$ that tend to remove oxygen as fast as it is produced. The most important of these is oxidation of reduced volcanic gases, such as H$_2$ and CO. These gases do not react directly with O$_2$ at room temperature (unless one provides a flame to get them started!). However, they can react with oxygen indirectly by way of reactions that involve the by-products of water vapor photolysis. The net result is

$$2 H_2 + O_2 \rightarrow 2H_2O$$
$$2CO + O_2 \rightarrow 2CO_2.$$

Thus, the oxygen reacts with these reduced gases to form H$_2$O and CO$_2$. When one studies these processes with detailed models, one finds that such reactions will quickly use up almost all of the O$_2$ produced by the photolysis of H$_2$O and CO$_2$, followed by the escape of hydrogen to space. The net result is a **weakly reduced atmosphere** with a composition similar to that shown in Box Figure 5. (Evidently, the amount of free O$_2$ generated by photochemical reactions in an early Earth-type atmosphere is extremely low. Hence, the presence of O$_2$ in a planet's atmosphere is a strong indication of the presence of life.)

BOX FIGURE 5 Vertical profiles of H$_2$ and O$_2$ in a weakly reduced primitive atmosphere.

to discover that many of the basic compounds on which life depends can be synthesized by a straightforward process that could have occurred in nature. Many scientists working in this field thought that we might be close to understanding how life itself began.

Today, the Miller–Urey experiment is still held in high regard scientifically, but researchers are less certain that it represents a critical step in the origin of life. One reason is that just mentioned: Current theories of the early atmosphere suggest that it was not as strongly reducing as the gas mixtures in Stanley Miller's flasks. Methane and ammonia, if they were present at all, would probably have been held to relatively low concentrations because they are photolyzed by solar UV radiation. The hydrogen then escapes to space, and the carbon and nitrogen atoms left behind are converted into CO$_2$ and N$_2$. Furthermore, modern volcanos do not emit much methane or ammonia. Early volcanic gases might have been more highly reducing; however, even this was probably not enough to produce a Miller–Urey-type atmosphere.

The RNA World

A second way in which our ideas about the origin of life have changed is that most biologists now believe that proteins were not among the earliest structural elements of life. Rather, life might have relied exclusively on RNA or some simpler variant of RNA. (See Box "A Closer

A CLOSER LOOK

What Does It Mean to Be Alive?

Almost anywhere we go on Earth today, we can see things that we know are alive: plants, animals, insects, people, and other **organisms**. How do we know that these various, extremely different things are alive?

It is surprisingly difficult to come up with a good definition of life. The ability to move, for example, is not an identifying characteristic of life because while animals move, plants do not. Also, many inanimate objects, cars for example, move under their own power. At a chemical level, all organisms that we know of consist of organic (carbon-based) compounds and are reliant on the presence of liquid water during at least part of their life cycles. However, we cannot be certain that this is true of life in general. Carbon is particularly well suited for making long chains and big, complex molecules, so it may well be that all life is carbon based. However, biologists still seek some more general definition.

The definition of life that is generally quoted by biologists is based on Charles Darwin's theory of evolution. According to this theory, organisms evolve by way of the combined processes of **replication**, **mutation**, and **natural selection** (Box Figure 6). As the name suggests, *replication* is the process by which an organism reproduces itself. Given that all organisms have a finite (and relatively short) life span, life obviously could not exist for very long if organisms were unable to replicate. *Mutation* simply means that the replication process is not exact, that is, the organisms that are produced can in some instances be different from the original organisms. If not for mutation, organisms could not evolve into different and more complex forms. *Natural selection* refers to the process by which certain, better-adapted organisms survive in greater numbers than do others. Thus, a favorable mutation can lead to a new type of organism that may gradually replace the old organism or, alternatively, to an organism that is capable of living in some different environment. Through this combined process of replication, mutation, and natural selection, life has evolved into a myriad of different forms that have successfully colonized nearly all parts of Earth's surface.

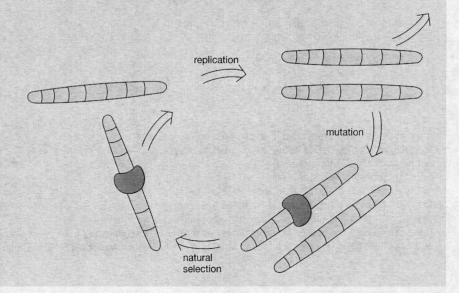

BOX FIGURE 6 Cartoon illustrating the processes of replication, mutation, and natural selection, by which life is defined.

Look: The Compounds of Life" for a description of what RNA, DNA, and proteins consist of chemically.)

The evidence that RNA preceded proteins was discovered in the mid-1980s by Thomas Cech of the University of Colorado and Sydney Altman of Yale University, and it earned them the 1989 Nobel Prize in chemistry. Cech and Altman discovered that one particular type of RNA molecule was capable of cleaving (cutting) itself into smaller pieces. This capability meant that it was theoretically possible for an RNA molecule to replicate (duplicate) itself without help from any other molecule. DNA-based organisms cannot do this. The DNA molecule can replicate only with the aid of complex enzymes made of proteins. An **enzyme** is a biological molecule that speeds up, or *catalyzes*, a particular biochemical process.

Life depends on a complex interaction among DNA, RNA, and proteins. The DNA carries the basic genetic information (the blueprint for the organism); the RNA is used to transfer this information to other parts of the cell, where proteins are made; and the proteins perform many different cell functions, including the replication of DNA and RNA.

A primitive, RNA-based organism could have been much simpler than today's organisms. RNA itself could have been the molecule in which the genetic information was stored. RNA is less stable than DNA, but it carries

A CLOSER LOOK

The Compounds of Life

Life depends on a complex array of organic (carbon-containing) compounds that organisms use to perform different tasks. Perhaps the most fundamental of these compounds are amino acids and nucleic acids. Amino acids are the building blocks of proteins, which are essential to many different cell functions. Nucleic acids, which include both ribonucleic acid (RNA) and deoxyribonucleic acid (DNA), are the carriers of genetic information. DNA stores this information, and RNA transfers the information to different parts of the cell and makes proteins and other compounds.

Chemically, an amino acid is an organic compound that contains an amino group (NH_2) and a carboxyl group (COOH). The two simplest ones are glycine and alanine (Box Figure 7). These compounds are similar except for the side chain: The hydrogen atom, H, in glycine is replaced by a methyl group, CH_3, in alanine. Other amino acids have more complicated side chains containing oxygen, nitrogen, or sulfur. Twenty different amino acids are found in naturally occurring proteins, but many other amino acids are chemically possible.

RNA and DNA are more complicated compounds that consist of chains of molecules called **nucleotides**. Each nucleotide consists of three parts. In RNA, these include a phosphate molecule, a ribose (sugar) molecule, and a nitrogen-containing base. The base can be any of four molecules: adenine (A), guanine (G), cytosine (C), or uracil (U) (Box Figure 8). The nucleotides in RNA are linked together in a long, single strand.

A DNA nucleotide is similar to an RNA nucleotide except that the sugar molecule is deoxyribose instead of ribose and that one of the four bases, uracil, is replaced by thymine (T). The DNA nucleotides are strung together in two chains that form a double helix. This double-stranded, twisting structure was discovered in 1953 by James Watson and Francis Crick. The sequence of bases in DNA carries information in the form of the genetic code. Groups of three individual nucleotides code for specific amino acids. For example, the sequence CCA codes for glycine and CGA codes for alanine.

BOX FIGURE 7 Two of the simpler amino acids found in proteins.

BOX FIGURE 8 Structural diagrams of the components of (a) DNA and (b) RNA. (*Source:* G. S. Kutter, *The Universe and Life,* Boston: Jones and Bartlett, 1987.)

essentially the same information. And because it can cleave itself, RNA could have reproduced without the aid of enzymes. The elegance and simplicity of this idea has led biologists to suggest that DNA-based life was preceded by an **RNA World**, in which only RNA-based organisms were present.

Even if this idea is correct, it does not solve the problem of life's origin. We still need to make the basic compounds of which RNA is composed and then assemble them into a self-replicating molecule. The required phosphate molecules were probably present in the primitive ocean as a result of weathering of rocks, but ribose and the four nitrogen-containing bases have more complicated structures that may or may not have been easy to form.

Prebiotic Synthesis of Organic Compounds

In the Miller–Urey experiment, the investigators found that they could synthesize amino acids by starting from gaseous mixtures that contain methane and ammonia. If RNA-based organisms came first, the first requirement for originating life would have been to synthesize ribose and the four bases adenine, guanine, cytosine, and uracil. Alternatively, the earliest organisms could have used simpler compounds that later evolved into RNA, but this scenario presents the difficult problem of how life could have switched from one molecular basis to another. (Switching from RNA to DNA is not considered difficult from an evolutionary standpoint because the molecules are so similar. Indeed, the first step in synthesizing DNA within a cell is to form the corresponding RNA molecule.)

Could ribose and the bases have formed from compounds present in the primitive atmosphere and oceans? We can get a clue by looking at chemical formulas. The molecular formula for ribose is $C_5H_{10}O_5$. (The corresponding structural formula, which shows how the atoms are arranged, is shown in Box Figure 8b.) Simple division shows that ribose can be formed from five molecules of H_2CO—the compound *formaldehyde,* which is commonly used to preserve dead animals. (If you dissected a frog in high school biology class, you may recall its distinctive smell.) The molecule H_2CO should not be confused with the shorthand notation for organic carbon, CH_2O, that we have used elsewhere in this book. Whereas H_2CO is an actual molecule, CH_2O merely represents complex hydrocarbons that have approximately the same relative ratios of C, H, and O atoms.

Thus, the first step in forming ribose is to synthesize formaldehyde. This step, it turns out, is easily accomplished. Photochemical reactions in weakly reducing, CO_2-rich atmospheres are predicted to produce large quantities of formaldehyde. Because formaldehyde is soluble in water, much of it should have dissolved in rainwater and been transported into the early ocean. Converting formaldehyde into ribose is also not difficult, because formaldehyde spontaneously reacts to form sugars in water solution. The problem for life's origin, which we will not discuss here, is

that lots of other sugars form in addition to ribose and that these molecules might have interfered with the synthesis of RNA. What we can say is that the necessary starting material for forming ribose should have been available.

What about the four bases—could they have been formed on the prebiotic Earth? Let us take the same approach and begin with chemical formulas. For simplicity, we consider only the simplest base, adenine. Its molecular formula is $C_5H_5N_5$. Evidently, adenine can be formed from five molecules of HCN, *hydrogen cyanide.* Hydrogen cyanide is an extremely deadly poison to most higher organisms. To prebiotic chemists, however, it is considered an essential building block for life.

Forming hydrogen cyanide in the prebiotic atmosphere is more difficult than forming formaldehyde. In a Miller–Urey-type atmosphere containing methane and ammonia, HCN would have been generated by lightning. In a weakly reduced, CO_2–N_2 atmosphere, lightning would not have sufficed because the carbon and nitrogen atoms produced by the lightning would have combined with oxygen atoms from the CO_2. However, the primitive atmosphere might have contained a few tens of parts per million of methane, CH_4. Methane photolysis in the stratosphere produces molecular fragments that can combine with N atoms that flow down from the ionosphere, forming HCN. The N atoms are produced from the breaking apart of the ion N_2^+ when it recombines with an electron.

The key to this mechanism is to identify a source for atmospheric methane. The methane in today's atmosphere is almost entirely of biological origin. However, some abiotically generated methane is released in fluids coming from hydrothermal vents at mid-ocean ridges. These vents, which are described in more detail below, are places where hot, mineral-laden water flows into the deep ocean. The water contains dissolved carbon compounds, including both CO_2 and CH_4. The fluids emanating from the hottest vents contain mostly CO_2, but the cooler, off-axis vents on certain, slow-spreading ridges (e.g., the Mid-Atlantic Ridge) are rich in CH_4 and H_2. These gases are thought to be produced by a process called **serpentinization**, a chemical reaction in which seawater reacts with **ultramafic rocks** (rocks rich in magnesium and iron) to form compounds called *serpentine minerals.* We will return to this topic in the next chapter because it may bear on the rise of atmospheric oxygen. For now, though, we simply point out that some abiotically produced methane should have been available on the early Earth even if the highly reduced, Miller–Urey-type atmosphere never existed.

Other Theories of Life's Origin

Some researchers remain skeptical that life could have formed on Earth's surface or in its oceans. Although the fundamental building blocks of life, H_2CO and HCN, were probably available, the chance that they would have been concentrated sufficiently to allow further reactions to occur might have been small. And the more complex organic compounds that might have formed in this way would not have lasted long in the surface-ocean environment, because they would have been destroyed by photochemical and thermal (heat-driven) reactions. Therefore, researchers have sought alternative ways of forming complex organic compounds.

One possibility is that the relevant organic compounds were formed in space and brought to Earth by asteroids or comets or as tiny dust particles. **Interplanetary dust particles (IDPs)** are small particles recovered from the stratosphere that are known to be of extraterrestrial origin. We know that organic compounds, including amino acids, exist in IDPs as well as in some meteorites. Indeed, amino acids and many other complex organic compounds have now been identified in interstellar dust clouds (Figure 2). They are believed to form from reactions between ions and neutral molecules that occur at very low temperatures. Typical temperatures in interstellar dust clouds are on the order of 10 K, not much above absolute zero. It may seem surprising that organic chemistry could occur in this environment, but it is precisely the extremely low temperatures involved that allow complex organic molecules to exist. The organic molecules form from reactions between other molecules and ions (charged particles), and then they live for long times because temperatures are too cold to allow them to decompose.

Some of the molecules formed in the interstellar environment are thought to have survived the collapse of the cloud that formed our own Sun and solar nebula. They would have been incorporated into solid materials that condensed out of the nebula and accreted to form asteroids and comets. Such materials might have been delivered to Earth in great quantities during the heavy bombardment period of solar system history, between 4.5 and 3.8 b.y. ago.

A third theory of life's origin is that it took place in or around **hydrothermal vents** in the mid-ocean spreading ridges. Recall that mid-ocean ridges are places where new seafloor is being created. The ridges are cooled by seawater that flows a kilometer or more down through cracks in the rock, is heated, and then rises rapidly back to the surface. In the process, the water picks up reduced substances such as hydrogen (H_2), hydrogen sulfide (H_2S), and dissolved ferrous iron (Fe^{2+}). *Ferrous iron* is a reduced form of iron that is soluble in seawater. When it hits the cold water, the hot (350°C) vent water produces a dark plume of precipitating material called a **black smoker** (Figure 6). The majority of the dark material is iron sulfide, FeS, produced by the reaction between ferrous iron and hydrogen sulfide.

Are submarine hydrothermal vents a likely place for life to have originated? The vent systems are rich in the types of reduced materials from which organic molecules can be synthesized. They contain liquid–solid interfaces that some researchers think are needed to organize organic molecules into specific patterns. One model suggests that life originated on the surface of *pyrite* (FeS_2) mineral grains, which are abundant in hydrothermal vent systems.

FIGURE 6 [See color section] Picture of a black smoker. (*Source:* Ken MacDonald/SP/Photo Researchers.)

However, complex organic molecules are not stable at the high (350°C) temperatures observed in vents located directly on the ridge axes. If life did originate at the mid-ocean ridges, it probably did so in cooler, off-axis vents. Some researchers argue that even the off-axis vents are too warm and that the best place for life to have originated would be in some near-freezing surface environment. The debate as to whether life originated in a hot or cold environment is likely to continue until we have a better idea of how the process actually occurred.

When Did Life Arise?

Thus far, we have discussed how life may have arisen but we have not talked about when this event occurred. The question of when life originated is currently the topic of much debate. Until about the middle of the last century, **paleontologists** (geologists who study fossils) believed that life originated only about 540 m.y. ago at the dawn of the Cambrian period. Fossils of this age or of more recent time periods are easy to find because the organisms that formed them were large enough to see with the naked eye and because many of them formed shells of silica or calcium carbonate that became preserved within sedimentary rocks. In the 1940s, though, paleontologists such as Elso Barghoorn at Harvard University began to discover **microfossils**. As their name implies, microfossils are the fossilized remains of tiny, single-celled organisms (or, in some cases organisms formed of chains of individual cells). Unlike **macrofossils** (the remains of multicellular organisms), microfossils are difficult to find and even more difficult to classify. And it is easy to be confused between bonafide microfossils and structures that look like microfossils but are formed abiotically. During the early 2000s, a vigorous debate occurred over what had been thought to be the world's oldest microfossils (see Figure 7). These specimens were collected from the Apex Chert, which is part of the 3.5 b.y.-old Warrawoona Formation in Australia, by paleontologist J. William Schopf from the University

FIGURE 7 Apex Chert "microfossils." These structures are from the 3.5 b.y.-old Warrawoona Formation in Australia. A debate is currently raging as to whether they are biogenic or not. (*Source:* J. William Schopf.)

of California, Los Angeles, and they do indeed look remarkably like some modern bacteria. But British paleontologist Martin Brasier and his colleagues argued that these structures are not biological at all. Rather, they think that these are bits or chains of organic carbon that formed abiotically within fluids emanating from a hydrothermal vent. The jury is still out as to whether the organic carbon is or is not biological in origin. However, most researchers would probably agree that these microfossils are not what they were originally interpreted to be.

Regardless of who turns out to be right about the Apex Chert microfossils, it does appear that life had originated by 3.5 b.y. ago or slightly thereafter. Many more structures that are plausible microfossils have been found in slightly younger rocks, along with macroscopic structures called *stromatolites*. More interesting is the question of whether life had originated even earlier. *Isotopically light* organic carbon has been found in 3.85 b.y.-old rocks from Isua, West Greenland, and from nearby Akilia Island. By "isotopically light," we mean that the organic carbon is depleted in the heavier ^{13}C isotope compared to the normal ^{12}C isotope. As we will discuss in more detail in the next chapter, metabolic processes such as photosynthesis tend to discriminate against the heavier carbon isotope, so "light" organic carbon is usually considered to be evidence for biological activity. However, some abiotic processes can also favor one isotope over another. Furthermore, some (but not all) of the rocks in which this organic carbon has been found have

recently been reclassified as being of igneous, rather than sedimentary, origin. It is difficult to imagine how biologically generated carbon could end up trapped within a rock that formed from a molten magma. So, the jury is still out on this question as well. But it is certainly possible, even likely, that life was already around by 3.8–3.9 b.y. ago.

The Universal Tree of Life

Some of the most useful information concerning the origin of life comes from studying modern organisms. Over the past two decades, molecular biologists have learned to sequence both RNA and DNA. Sequencing a molecule of nucleic acid means determining the order of the individual nucleotides. Recall that a nucleotide consists of one of four bases attached to a ribose molecule for RNA, or deoxyribose, for DNA, which in turn is connected to other nucleotides by phosphate linkages. (See the Box, "A Closer Look: The Compounds of Life.") By using powerful new techniques such as **polymerase chain reaction (PCR)**, biologists have been able to unravel the genetic code of all sorts of different organisms, including humans. Both DNA and RNA are extremely large and complicated molecules that contain information about every facet of an organism. Particular parts of these molecules can be used to look way back into early evolutionary history. The particular molecule that has been found to be most useful is the RNA found within **ribosomes**. The ribosome is a part of the cell in which proteins are manufactured. All organisms have ribosomes and ribosomal RNA, which makes this molecule useful for making comparisons. Protein manufacture is also an extremely ancient and slowly evolving metabolic capability, so sequencing ribosomal RNA provides a way of looking deeply into evolutionary history. Because PCR acts on DNA, not RNA, this is actually done in practice by sequencing the part of the DNA molecule that codes for ribosomal RNA, but it is essentially the RNA sequences that are being compared.

The results of comparing sequences of ribosomal RNA from various organisms can be used to draw an evolutionary "tree" (Figure 8). This tree was first constructed by Carl Woese at the University of Illinois and his graduate student, George Fox. It shows that organisms can be divided into three main categories, or **domains**: **Bacteria**, **Archaea**, and **Eukarya**. The Bacteria and Archaea are both composed entirely of single-celled organisms that we commonly refer to as *bacteria*. The Eukarya contain some single-celled organisms as well, such as the intestinal parasite *Giardia,* but they also include all higher plants and animals, including humans. As Figure 8 shows, humans (*Homo*) and corn (*Zea*) are closely related to each other by comparison to the very deep divisions that occur between the three different domains of life.

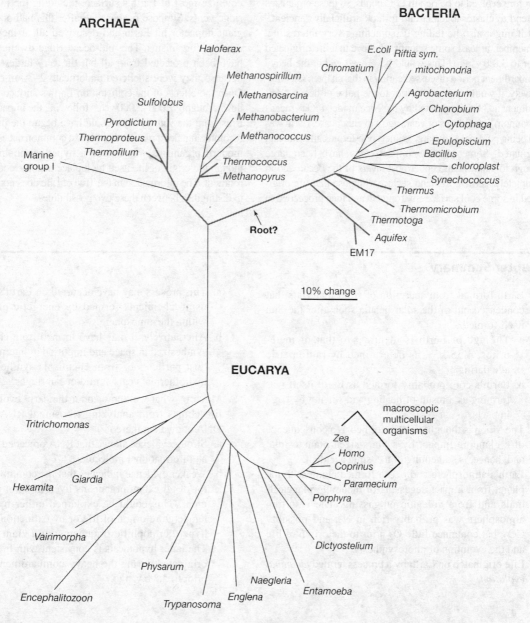

FIGURE 8   The Universal Tree of Life derived by sequencing ribosomal RNA.   (*Source:* Courtesy Norman Pace, University of Colorado.)

A Hyperthermophilic Last Common Ancestor?

All sorts of interesting information can be derived from this Tree of Life, and we shall take advantage of some of it in the next chapter when we discuss the rise of oxygen. For now, though, let us concentrate on the shaded branches near the point at which the Archaea and Eukarya split from the Bacteria. This point is thought to lie close to the common ancestor of all life.

The shaded branches represent **hyperthermophilic bacteria**—organisms that live at temperatures above 80°C.

Surprisingly, nearly all of the organisms near the "root" of the tree are hyperthermophiles. Today, by contrast, hyperthermophiles are restricted to a few unusual environments, such as the mid-ocean ridge vent systems and geothermal hot spots like Yellowstone National Park.

What is the Tree of Life telling us? Does this imply that life originated in a hot environment like the mid-ocean ridge hydrothermal vents? Maybe. But there are other possibilities as well. Some biologists believe that this is merely an artifact of the fact that guanine-cytosine (G-C) bonds in DNA are slightly more stable at high temperatures than are adenine-thymine (A-T) bonds. The DNA of hyperthermophiles has therefore evolved to be rich in G-C bonds, so these organisms all tend to cluster together and to look artificially "ancient." But it might also be telling us something very interesting. Remember, at least some scientists believe that life originated prior to 3.8 b.y. ago. This would have been within the heavy bombardment period discussed earlier in this chapter. Or, alternatively, it would have been prior to the pulse of heavy bombardment at 3.8 Ga predicted by the Nice model. ("Ga" means "gigannum," or billions of years ago.) In either case, Earth was still being pummeled by large comets or asteroids after life had originated. Some of these impacts may have been large enough to vaporize the uppermost layers of the ocean and to completely sterilize the land surface. Suppose that life originated in some cool surface environment and then proceeded to colonize most of Earth's surface, including the mid-ocean ridge vents. Suppose further that, after this had occurred, a giant impactor hit Earth and destroyed all of the surface-dwelling organisms. The mid-ocean ridge dwellers would have been protected from all but the very largest impacts because they were sheltered underneath 2–3 km of ocean. Once the effects of the collision on Earth's surface had died down, roughly 1,000–2,000 years following the impact, organisms from the vent systems could have begun the process of recolonizing. So, it may be that the last common ancestor of all modern organisms was indeed a hyperthermophile, even though the origin of life itself took place in some cooler environment. The information in the Tree of Life does not allow us to distinguish between these two possibilities.

Chapter Summary

1. Earth formed from accretion of solid materials that condensed out of the solar nebula soon after the Sun itself formed.
    a. The age of Earth is identical to that of meteorites, 4.55 b.y., as determined by radiometric age dating.
    b. Earth's core probably formed as Earth itself was forming as a result of heating and stirring by large impacts.
2. The Moon is thought to have formed as a consequence of a glancing impact by a Mars-sized planetesimal and, hence, is something of a cosmic accident.
3. Earth's atmosphere and ocean formed along with the planet from impact degassing of incoming planetesimals and from volcanic outgassing. The resulting atmosphere was probably rich in N_2, and possibly CO_2, but contained little O_2 prior to the origin of life and the evolution of photosynthesis.
4. Life originated on Earth by a process termed *chemical evolution*.
    a. This process may have occurred on Earth's surface using chemicals formed by energetic processes within the atmosphere.
    b. Alternatively, it may have formed from chemicals synthesized in space and imported in interplanetary dust particles or from chemicals synthesized in hydrothermal vents at mid-ocean ridges.
5. Much of what we know about the early evolution of life comes from analyzing ribosomal RNA, or the DNA equivalent thereof.
    a. Strong evidence shows that RNA preceded DNA as an informational molecule.
    b. Weaker evidence indicates that the common ancestor of all extant organisms lived in a hot environment. This could be explained either by a high temperature origin of life or by extinction of non-hyperthermophilic organisms by a giant impact. The latter hypothesis is consistent with life having originated during the heavy bombardment period prior to 3.8 b.y. ago.

Key Terms

accretion	Eukarya	isochron diagram
amino acids	giant impact hypothesis	lead–lead dating
Archaea	heavy bombardment period	macrofossils
Bacteria	Hertzsprung–Russell (H–R) diagram	magma ocean
black smoker	hydrothermal vents	main sequence
chemical evolution	hydroxyl radicals	meteorites
chondrites	hyperthermophilic bacteria	microfossils
domains	IDPs	migration
ejecta	impact degassing	mutation
enzyme	interplanetary dust particles (IDPs)	Nice model
eon	interstellar clouds	natural selection

nucleotides
organisms
paleontologists
photolyzed
planetesimals
polymerase chain reaction (PCR)
proteins

proto-Sun
replication
ribosomes
RNA world
serpentinization
shelly fossils
solar nebula

strongly reduced atmosphere
terrestrial planets
ultramafic rocks
volatile compounds
weakly reduced atmosphere
zircon

Review Questions

1. How old is the solar system, and how is this age determined?
2. How is the age of Earth determined if no rocks older than 4.1 billion years have been preserved?
3. How do Jupiter and the Moon affect the habitability of Earth?
4. How and when did the atmosphere and ocean form? Which gases are thought to have been present in the early atmosphere?

5. In what types of environments might life have originated?
6. Why is RNA thought to have preceded DNA in evolution?
7. How is the Universal Tree of Life constructed?
8. Into what three different domains are modern organisms divided?
9. List two possible reasons why organisms near the base of the Tree of Life are hyperthermophilic.

Critical-Thinking Problems

Write a one- to two-page typewritten essay on the following question:

1. What do you feel is the best theory for how life originated? Do you think that life might exist elsewhere besides Earth?

Further Reading

General

Lovelock, J. E. 1988. *The ages of Gaia: A biography of our living Earth.* New York: Norton.
Lunine, J. 1999. *Earth: Evolution of a habitable world.* Cambridge: Cambridge University Press.

Advanced

Brack, A. 1998. *The chemical origins of life: Assembling the pieces of the puzzle.* Cambridge: Cambridge University Press.

Sullivan, W. T. III, and J. A. Baross. 2007. *Planets and life: The emerging science of astrobiology.* Cambridge: Cambridge University Press.
Wong, J. T.-F., and A. Lazcano, eds. 2008. *Prebiotic evolution and astrobiology.* Austin, TX: Landes Bioscience.

FIGURE 2 The Eagle Nebula viewed from the Hubble Space Telescope. (*Source:* NASA Headquarters.)

FIGURE 3 The disk around the star Beta Pictoris, as seen from the Hubble Space Telescope. Top panel: Visible light image. Bottom panel: False color image created by image processing to highlight features in the disk structure. (*Source:* NASA Headquarters.)

FIGURE 6   Picture of a black smoker.   (*Source:* Ken MacDonald/SP/Photo Researchers.)

BOX FIGURE 2   Hertzsprung–Russell diagram showing different classes of stars.   (*Source:* From E. Chaisson and S. McMillan, *Astronomy: A Beginner's Guide to the Universe,* 2/e, 1998. Reprinted by permission of Prentice Hall, Upper Saddle River, N.J.)

Effect of Life on the Atmosphere
The Rise of Oxygen and Ozone

Effect of Life on the Atmosphere
The Rise of Oxygen and Ozone

Key Questions

- What were the earliest forms of life, and how did they affect atmospheric composition?

- When and why did atmospheric O_2 become abundant?

- When did the ozone layer form, and how did its formation affect Earth's surface environment and the evolution of the biota?

- By how much has atmospheric O_2 varied over the last 540 million years?

- What controls the atmospheric O_2 concentration today?

Chapter Overview

Earth's present atmosphere is rich in molecular oxygen and has a well-developed ozone layer that shields the planet's surface from harmful solar ultraviolet radiation. This oxygen is produced by photosynthesis and, hence, would not have been present prior to the origin of photosynthetic life. The first organisms to evolve were probably not photosynthesizers. Rather, they lived in other ways, for example, by converting carbon dioxide and hydrogen into methane. Oxygenic photosynthesis originated at or before 2.4 b.y. ago, the time when atmospheric O_2 levels first rose. Indeed, photosynthesis was probably occurring for several hundred million years prior to this time, but the initial rise of O_2 was delayed for reasons that are not entirely understood. Atmospheric O_2 has varied by modest amounts for the past few hundred million years because of changes in the rate of organic carbon burial. The fluctuations in O_2 are small, however, because of a negative feedback mechanism that appears to involve the oxygenation of the deep oceans and the availability of dissolved phosphorus.

INTRODUCTION

The prebiotic Earth probably had an atmosphere dominated by carbon dioxide and molecular nitrogen (N_2). But we also saw that life probably originated very early—within the first 700 m.y. of Earth's history—even though some of the evidence in favor of this idea has been questioned. As soon as life had evolved, it began to be a force that could change the composition of the atmosphere and eventually the surface as well. What was the nature of these earliest organisms, and how did they alter atmospheric composition? We can gain some insight into these questions by studying the structure of the ribosomal RNA tree and deducing which modern organisms look most "primitive."

An even bigger change in atmospheric composition occurred when organisms evolved that were capable of oxygenic photosynthesis. The production of oxygen by such organisms eventually led to the establishment of our modern, O_2-rich atmosphere. But this change from reduced to oxidized atmospheric conditions appears to have occurred well after the invention of photosynthesis, for reasons that are poorly understood. What other nonbiological changes in the planet were needed in order to allow atmospheric O_2 to accumulate?

A related change in atmospheric composition that has affected both microbial and advanced life has been the development of a protective ozone layer. We have already seen that ozone is important because it blocks out harmful solar ultraviolet (UV) radiation. But, if the concentration of atmospheric O_2 was initially very low, there must have been a time when the ozone layer did not exist. How did life cope with the solar UV flux at that time? When was an effective solar UV screen established? These are also questions that we address in this chapter.

EFFECT OF LIFE ON THE EARLY ATMOSPHERE

We still do not know how life originated on Earth. We also do not know exactly when it originated because both the 3.5 b.y.-old Apex Chert microfossils and the 3.85 b.y.-old carbon isotopic evidence for life have been

FIGURE 1 Stromatolites from the 3.5 b.y.-old Warrawoona formation in Australia. (*Source:* Princeton University Press.)

called into question. Starting at about 3.5 Ga, geologists have also found layered structures called **stromatolites** that are believed to be the fossilized remains of bacteria that form layered, sedimentary mats (Figure 1). The organisms that formed them are thought to have been similar to communities of photosynthetic bacteria that inhabit the shallow, salty waters of Shark Bay on the coast of western Australia (Figure 2).

FIGURE 2 [See color section] Shark Bay in western Australia. These "living stromatolites" are formed by communities of microbes and may be an analog to early microbial life. (*Source:* Robin Smith/Photo Library/Getty Images.)

How did the presence of life affect the composition of the atmosphere? The organisms that formed stromatolites were almost certainly photosynthetic—the fact that they lived in layers implies that they needed sunlight. However, this does not necessarily imply that they were producing oxygen. "Normal," **oxygenic photosynthesis** is carried out by higher plants and algae today. But some bacteria make their living by a related process called anoxygenic photosynthesis. In **anoxygenic photosynthesis**, H_2S or H_2 is used instead of H_2O to reduce CO_2 to organic carbon; this process does not yield O_2. Finally, certain bacteria called **cyanobacteria**, formerly referred to as blue-green algae, can perform both oxygenic and anoxygenic photosyntheses. In practice, some cyanobacteria switch back and forth between these two metabolic processes in response to changes in their local environment. When hydrogen sulfide, H_2S, is present, these cyanobacteria photosynthesize anoxygenically; when H_2S is absent, they generate O_2.

Until just recently, it was widely believed—based on their relatively large sizes—that the Apex Chert microfossils were the remains of cyanobacteria. The new evidence from Brasier's group, however, indicates that the environment in which they were living was similar to the modern, hydrothermal vents in the deep ocean. No light penetrates to these depths, so if these fossilized structures were indeed organisms, they are unlikely to have been photosynthetic. Instead, they probably survived on the energy produced from chemical reactions. Such organisms are termed **chemosynthetic**. Today, many organisms that live near the hydrothermal vents derive energy from reacting H_2S from the vent fluids with O_2 dissolved in the surrounding ocean water. On the early Earth, free O_2 is unlikely to have been present. How might these organisms have been making their living?

Production of Methane

To get some idea of what types of organisms may have been living on the primitive Earth, we can turn once again to the "Universal" Tree of Life derived from sequencing of ribosomal RNA. Many of the organisms near the root of the tree appear to be *hyperthermophiles*—organisms that live at high temperatures. Only slightly further away from the root, along one branch of the Archaea, are the methanogenic bacteria (Figure 3). **Methanogenic bacteria**, or **methanogens** for short, produce energy from chemical reactions that generate methane. The simplest of these is

$$CO_2 + 4\,H_2 \rightarrow CH_4 + 2\,H_2O$$

Both CO_2 and H_2 are abundant in modern vent fluids and in surface volcanic gases. On the early Earth, they would have been abundant in the atmosphere as well. CO_2 may have built up to very high levels and probably played an important role in keeping Earth warm, despite reduced solar luminosity. The abundance of H_2 can be estimated by balancing the rate of escape of hydrogen to space with the rate at which hydrogen and other reduced gases were outgassed from volcanos. Such a calculation predicts that hundreds to thousands of ppm of H_2 should have been present (possibly even more if hydrogen escape was slower than it is today because the upper atmosphere was colder). Many methanogens can survive at these H_2 concentrations, although most require about 1% H_2 (0.01 bar) to reproduce. Methanogens can also metabolize other reduced substances, such as formate ion ($HCOO^-$), which is formed when carbon monoxide (CO) dissolves in water. CO, like H_2, is thought to have been an important constituent of the early atmosphere. Thus, there is good reason to believe that methanogens were widespread on the early Earth. If primitive methanogens produced methane at the same rate that it is produced biologically today, the atmospheric methane concentration could have exceeded 1000 ppm, more than 600 times its present level (1.6 ppm). The higher abundance results from the fact that methane would have been destroyed less rapidly in a low-O_2 atmosphere.

The presence of high concentrations of methane may have caused the early atmosphere to look quite different from today's atmosphere. We can get some idea of what it might have looked like by observing Saturn's moon, Titan. Titan has a dense (1.5-bar) atmosphere that consists of about 98% N_2 and 2% CH_4. But the most striking feature of Titan is that it is enveloped in an orangish haze layer that completely obscures the surface (Figure 4). This haze layer is thought to consist of hydrocarbon aerosols formed from photolysis and charged particle bombardment of atmospheric CH_4. Although Titan is not a perfect analog for early Earth—its surface temperature is only 94 K—computer models predict that the same type of haze could have formed in Earth's early atmosphere if CH_4 was more than about one-tenth the abundance of CO_2.

Although this discussion is highly speculative, the geologic record provides indirect evidence that something like this actually happened. In particular, some of the sedimentary organic carbon from the Late Archean (around 2.7 b.y. ago) is highly depleted in ^{13}C (Figure 5)—more so than can be explained by photosynthesis alone. This depletion is thought to be an indication of widespread methanogenic activity. The methane produced by methanogens is depleted in ^{13}C relative to ^{12}C. If this methane was taken up by other organisms, its low-^{13}C carbon may have made its way into sediments and could account for the low-^{13}C carbon preserved in the geologic record. Other indirect evidence from sulfur isotopes, discussed later in this chapter, also suggests that a methane-based organic haze could have been present at around this time.

Cycling of Atmospheric Nitrogen

A second way in which organisms might have affected the atmosphere is by cycling nitrogen through the atmosphere–ocean system. Organisms need nitrogen for

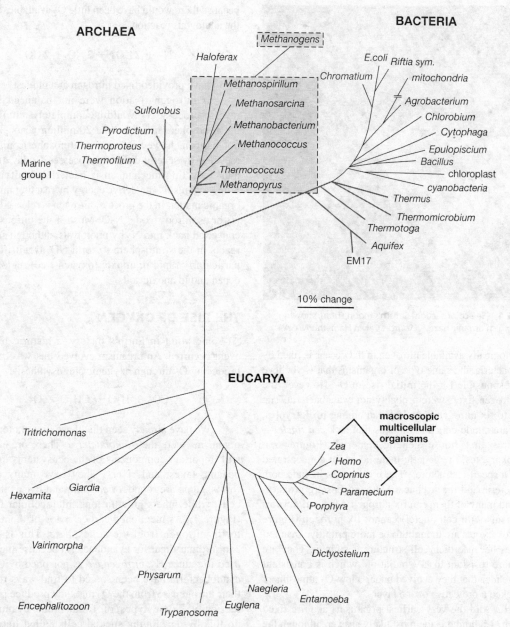

FIGURE 3 The ribosomal RNA tree, showing where methanogens and cyanobacteria fit into the picture. (*Source:* Courtesy Norman Pace, University of Colorado.)

making proteins and nucleic acids as well as for other biochemical functions. However, most of them cannot use nitrogen in its normal molecular form, N_2. Instead, they require **fixed nitrogen**, in which nitrogen atoms are bonded to other types of atoms. Ammonia (NH_3) and nitrate ion (NO_3^-) are two examples of fixed-nitrogen compounds.

Modern marine organisms acquire fixed nitrogen in two ways. One of these is from lightning. In the high-temperature region surrounding a lightning discharge, nitrogen and oxygen react to form nitric oxide, NO:

$$N_2 + O_2 \rightarrow 2\,NO$$

Nitric oxide is a radical that plays an important role in ozone photochemistry. In today's atmosphere it is eventually oxidized to nitric acid, HNO_3. Nitric acid is soluble in water and, thus, is quickly rained out of the troposphere. In solution, it **dissociates** (comes apart) to form hydrogen ions and nitrate ions:

$$HNO_3 \leftrightarrow H^+ + NO_3^-$$

The resulting nitrate ion can be directly used by organisms as a source of fixed nitrogen.

Some marine organisms can make their own fixed nitrogen by a process termed **nitrogen fixation**. Most of

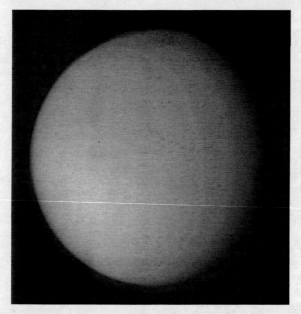

FIGURE 4 [See color section] Saturn's moon, Titan, showing the orangish organic haze. (*Source:* Calvin Hamilton/NASA.)

the biologically available nitrogen in the oceans is fixed by cyanobacteria, the same type of organisms that we believe were responsible for the initial rise in O_2. However, the first nitrogen-fixers were probably not cyanobacteria. The ability to fix nitrogen is widespread among **prokaryotes**, which are single-celled organisms that lack *cell nuclei*— structures that house genetic material (Figure 6a). (In prokaryotes, the genetic material is not concentrated within a specific structure.) The prokaryotes include both the Bacteria and the Archaea. Methanogens are prokaryotes, and many of them can fix nitrogen. Most **eukaryotes** (organisms with cell nuclei) cannot fix nitrogen (Figure 6b). Prokaryotes are thought to be more primitive than eukaryotes because their cell structure is simpler. They are also more resistant to UV radiation, which is consistent with the idea that they evolved under a low-O_2 atmosphere that lacked a protective ozone layer.

How did the very earliest organisms acquire fixed nitrogen? Lightning is the most likely answer, although the reaction between N_2 and O_2 could not have been the source

because there would have been little O_2 available. However, the analogous reaction

$$N_2 + 2\,CO_2 \rightarrow 2\,NO + 2\,CO$$

could have provided fixed nitrogen at a modest rate.

If nitrogen fixation were not balanced by some reverse process, N_2 would be completely removed from the atmosphere in only about 20 million years. This does not happen, however, because atmospheric nitrogen is recycled by several different processes. Today, the dominant recycling mechanism is bacterial **denitrification**. Some organisms can derive energy by reacting nitrate with organic matter. In the process, nitrogen is released as either N_2 or as nitrous oxide, N_2O. Most of the nitrous oxide is converted back into N_2 by photolysis, although some of it reacts in the stratosphere to form NO. Denitrification is particularly rapid in **anoxic** (oxygen-free) regions of the ocean and in anoxic soils.

THE RISE OF OXYGEN

At some point in Earth's history, a historic biological event occurred. An organism evolved that was capable of producing O_2 through oxygenic photosynthesis:

$$CO_2 + H_2O \rightarrow CH_2O + O_2$$

We have already seen that these first photosynthetic organisms were the *cyanobacteria*. These organisms are still important components of the ecosystems in modern oceans, lakes, and rivers. They have many different forms: some are round, or *coccoid*, and live as individual cells, while others grow in long, multicellular filaments (Figure 7). As mentioned earlier, many of them are able to fix nitrogen from the atmosphere. This is quite an extraordinary feat for cyanobacteria because the enzyme used to reduce N_2, *nitrogenase,* is poisoned by O_2. Thus, cyanobacteria have been forced to find ways to protect their nitrogenase from the O_2 that they produce photosynthetically. Some types of filamentous cyanobacteria do this by developing special cells called **heterocysts** that are devoted to fixing N_2 (see Figure 7c). No O_2 is

FIGURE 5 Carbon isotope values from organic carbon (kerogen) in ancient rocks. Organic carbon produced by oxygenic photosynthesis typically has $\delta^{13}C$ values near −25‰ to −30‰. The extremely "light" (−50‰ to −60‰) values around 2.7–2.8 b.y. ago probably require cycling of carbon through methane. (*Source:* A. A. Pavlov et al., *Geology* 29, 2001, pp. 1003–1006.)

(a)

(b)

FIGURE 6 [See color section] (a) Prokaryotes have no nucleus, and the DNA is dispersed within the cell. (b) Eukaryotes have their DNA enclosed within a cell nucleus. (*Sources:* (a) A. B. Dowsett/SPL/Photo Researcher and (b) Eric V. Grave/ Photo Researchers.)

produced within a heterocyst, so the inside of the cell can be kept virtually oxygen-free. Other types of cyanobacteria photosynthesize during the day and fix nitrogen at night, so they protect their nitrogenase in a different way. Still others, for example the abundant tropical marine species *Trichodesmium*, fix nitrogen in the morning and photosynthesize in the afternoon. Clearly, even though they are "simple" prokaryotes, cyanobacteria are very advanced organisms in a metabolic sense.

Cyanobacteria are important for yet another reason. Most photosynthesis today is carried out by eukaryotic algae or by higher plants. But we are virtually certain that these organisms did not reinvent photosynthesis on their own. A glance at the universal, ribosomal RNA tree (Figure 3) shows why. As the diagram shows, cyanobacteria are closely related to the chloroplasts in higher plants. **Chloroplasts** are the parts of plant cells in which oxygenic photosynthesis takes place. Chloroplasts

contain their own DNA, which is why they can be placed on the Tree of Life along with free-living organisms. As biologist Lynn Margulis of the University of Massachusetts pointed out more than 30 years ago, this shows conclusively that all higher plants (including algae) acquired their ability to produce oxygen by way of an **endosymbiotic** event: some eukaryotic organism ingested, or enveloped, a prokaryotic cyanobacterium without killing it. After that, the two organisms lived together in a mutually beneficial arrangement. The eukaryotic host cell provided nutrients to the cyanobacterium, and the cyanobacterium in turn provided O_2 to the host. This O_2 could then be used as an energy source (via respiration) by the host cell.

When Did Cyanobacteria Evolve?

A critical question from the standpoint of understanding Earth history is: when did the cyanobacteria evolve? Or, to be more precise, the question could be phrased: When did cyanobacteria evolve the capability of producing O_2? We have seen that organisms, or at least structures, resembling modern cyanobacteria were already present by 3.5 b.y. ago. But, even if they were indeed alive, these organisms could not have been producing oxygen by photosynthesis because they lived in a deep-ocean, hydrothermal vent environment where light levels were extremely low.

Somewhat better evidence for the existence of cyanobacteria comes from organic chemicals in 2.7 b.y.-old sedimentary rocks from the Fortescue Group in western Australia. (Western Australia is a haven for Precambrian geologists because it contains very old rocks *and* it is extremely dry, so that these rocks are not covered up by vegetation.) These rocks contain organic carbon that has not been as highly degraded as most organic material of that age. In essence, they contain 2.7 b.y.-old oil. In this oil are compounds called *2α-methylhopanes* (Figure 8). These compounds are thought to derive from the breakdown of *lipid* molecules that are present in the cell walls of modern cyanobacteria. If the oil in these rocks formed at the same time that the rocks were deposited, rather than migrating in at some later date, then cyanobacteria may have been around by this time. However, this argument has recently been shown to be inconclusive, because the precursors to 2α-methylhopanes have now been found in other organisms, specifically, two different strains of purple nonsulfur bacteria. These are phototrophic ("light-loving") organisms that do not produce O_2. They live in lakes and streams today, rather than in the oceans, so they may not have been the source of the methylhopanes in ancient rocks. But this shows that our understanding of when cyanobacteria evolved is far from certain.

Even if the methylhopanes are indeed from ancient cyanobacteria, the geochemical evidence does not by itself prove that those cyanobacteria were producing oxygen.

a)

c)

b)

FIGURE 7 [See color section] Three different types of cyanobacteria: (a) *Chroococcus* (coccoid), (b) *Oscillatoria* (filamentous), (c) *Nostoc* (heterocystic). (*Source:* (a) Tom Adams/Visuals Unlimited, (b) Dr. Gernot Arp, and (c) Susan Barns and Norman R. Pace.)

Like the Apex Chert microfossils discussed earlier, these organisms may have resembled modern cyanobacteria—in this case by having a similar cell wall—but they did not necessarily have the same metabolism. We mention this because the first evidence for the presence of free O_2 in the atmosphere does not come until almost 300 m.y. later. Thus, if O_2 was being produced photosynthetically 2.7 b.y. ago, it must have been entirely consumed by reactions with reduced substances.

Additional evidence that O_2 was being produced at this time comes from the presence of other organic compounds called **steranes** in these same 2.7-b.y.-old sediments. Steranes derive from the breakdown of organic compounds such as **cholesterol** that are thought to be produced exclusively by eukaryotes. (Cholesterol is familiar to us as the fatty substance that builds up in one's arteries as one gets older and that can lead to heart attacks.) Most eukaryotes use O_2 for respiration and, hence, require at least 1 percent of present dissolved oxygen in the water in which they are living. And the biochemical synthesis of sterols requires free O_2 during one key step of the process. So, the presence of steranes in ancient rocks implies that O_2 was being produced within the water column, presumably by cyanobacteria. The presence of O_2 in surface water does *not* necessarily imply the presence of O_2 in the atmosphere because the rate at which oxygen (or any gas) can flow between the surface ocean and atmosphere is limited by diffusion through the gas–liquid interface, and so the atmosphere and surface ocean need not have been in chemical equilibrium.

To determine when O_2 first rose to appreciable concentrations in the atmosphere, we must turn once again to the geologic record. Until a few years ago, the question of when O_2 first rose was hotly debated. The reason is that most of the

2α(Me), 17α(H), 21β(H)-hopane

FIGURE 8 A 2α-methylhopane molecule, thought to be an indicator for cyanobacteria. (*Source:* Courtesy Jen Eigenbrode, Pennsylvania State University.)

FIGURE 9 [See color section] A banded iron-formation, or BIF. (*Source:* J. William Schopf.)

geologic evidence bearing on the O_2 rise is difficult to interpret. As we will see, new evidence from sulfur isotopes may have finally resolved this long-standing question. Let us begin, however, by discussing the various types of geologic evidence that have been used to try to track atmospheric O_2.

Banded Iron-Formations

One type of geologic evidence that bears on the rise of oxygen is the occurrence of banded iron-formations. **Banded iron-formations (BIFs)** are laminated sedimentary rocks that consist of alternating, millimeter-thick layers of iron-rich minerals and chert (Figure 9). Such minerals include *magnetite* (Fe_3O_4) or *hematite* (Fe_2O_3), and *chert* (SiO_2). They are of enormous economic importance today. Much of the iron that is used in making steel and automobiles come from BIFs in Canada and Australia. But these deposits do not form today; nor have they done so at any time in the recent past. Radiometric age dating shows that almost all BIFs formed prior to 1.9 b.y. ago. The only exceptions are a few BIFs that formed in the Late Proterozoic, about 0.6–0.8 b.y. ago. As we will discuss

further in the next chapter, the Late Proterozoic is unusual for several reasons, the most intriguing of which is the evidence of low-latitude glaciation. Some researchers have suggested that the two phenomena are linked: extensive ice cover inhibited oxygen transfer between the atmosphere and ocean, and this led to the reappearance of BIFs. This is one piece of evidence that the so-called Snowball Earth events actually occurred.

The reason that BIFs are useful as oxygen indicators is that iron can exist in more than one oxidation state. The **oxidation state** of an atom, molecule, or compound is its degree of oxidation. Substances with a low oxidation state have a large number of available electrons; substances with a high oxidation state do not (see the Box "Useful Concepts: Oxidation States of Iron"). We have already mentioned one oxidation state of iron, **ferrous iron** (Fe^{2+}). A second, more oxidized state is termed **ferric iron** (Fe^{3+}). Iron ions in these two oxidation states have very different chemical properties: Fe^{2+} is soluble in seawater, whereas Fe^{3+} is not. Because iron switches from Fe^{2+} to Fe^{3+} when oxygen is present, it can provide indirect information about past O_2 levels.

To make use of this information, we need to understand the process by which BIFs formed. Although no consensus has been reached regarding the precise mechanism, there is general agreement on some parts of the story. To explain the voluminous quantities of iron deposited in BIFs, large portions of the deep oceans must have been anoxic. This condition would have allowed iron to be transported as dissolved Fe^{2+}. The iron was probably supplied originally from continental weathering and from mid-ocean ridge hydrothermal vent fluids. Trace element patterns in BIFs, especially those of the **rare earth elements** (atomic numbers 57–71 in the periodic table), show that at least some of the iron must have come from the vents. What happened next is not well understood. We know that BIFs did not form on the floor of the deep ocean. If they had, they would have been destroyed when the seafloor was subducted. Instead, the dissolved iron must have been transported to the margins of

USEFUL CONCEPTS
Oxidation States of Iron

Iron occurs in three oxidation states in nature: elemental (or metallic), ferrous, and ferric. The elemental form is located mostly in Earth's core, which is composed largely of iron–nickel alloy. Ferrous and ferric iron occur in the mantle and crust. They exist in dissolved form as Fe^{2+} and Fe^{3+} ions, respectively. The positive charges arise because these ions are missing electrons: Fe^{2+} is missing two electrons, and Fe^{3+} is missing three. We say that these two ions are in the 2+ and 3+ oxidation states. Elemental iron, by comparison, has an oxidation state of zero.

When iron reacts with oxygen, the oxidation state of the iron atom determines the number of oxygen atoms

with which it combines. Oxygen, when it reacts, can be thought of as having a valence of −2. It has six electrons in its outer shell, and it wants two more in order to complete the shell. Thus, to produce a neutral molecule, one Fe^{2+} ion combines with one O_2^{-2} ion to form the mineral FeO (wüstite). Two Fe^{3+} ions combine with three oxygen ions to form Fe_2O_3 (hematite).

Most of the iron in BIFs consists of magnetite, Fe_3O_4. This is equivalent to one molecule of FeO bonded to one molecule of Fe_2O_3. So, BIFs contain a 1:2 mixture of ferrous iron and ferric iron.

the continents, where it was deposited on stable continental shelves. To be precipitated, the iron must first have been oxidized from Fe^{2+} to Fe^{3+}.

Exactly how this occurred is still a subject of debate. One suggestion is that the iron was brought to the surface by wind-induced upwelling of the type that occurs in some modern coastal settings. The fine, millimeter-scale banding observed in the BIFs could have been caused by seasonal changes in winds that produced upwelling at certain times of the year but not at others. Iron-rich sediments would have formed when the upwelling was strong; silica-rich sediments would have formed when upwelling was weaker. Once the dissolved ferrous iron was brought to the surface, it could have been oxidized by dissolved O_2 produced by photosynthetic cyanobacteria. Alternatively, the iron could have been oxidized abiotically. Laboratory experiments have shown that dissolved Fe^{2+} can be oxidized to Fe^{3+} by UV radiation. (In the process, H_2O is reduced to H_2.) A third possibility is that Fe^{2+} could have been oxidized by **phototrophic** bacteria (bacteria that use sunlight) that did not produce O_2. Whether the iron in BIFs was oxidized by UV radiation or by biologically generated O_2 is still unresolved.

Because the oxygen in BIFs could have come from several sources, we cannot use them directly to infer the O_2 content of the atmosphere. We can, however, safely conclude that the deep oceans must have been anoxic prior to 1.9 b.y. ago, during the time that BIFs formed. This in turn implies that the atmospheric O_2 concentration was lower than it is today. So, BIFs are a strong indicator that the atmosphere has changed during recorded geologic history.

Detrital Uraninite and Pyrite

More direct information on atmospheric O_2 levels can be obtained from other types of geologic indicators. Elements other than iron are also capable of changing their oxidation state. Uranium, for example, has two common oxidation states: U^{4+} and U^{6+}. As with iron, these two ions differ in their solubilities. In this case, however, it is the oxidized (6+) form that is soluble and the more reduced (4+) form that is not.

The U^{4+} ion combines with oxygen to form **uraninite**, UO_2. This mineral occurs in rocks today, but it is normally oxidized to the soluble, 6+, state during weathering. (Notable exceptions to this rule occur in some of the rivers that drain the Himalayas, where the eroded sediments are redeposited very quickly, before the uranium can be oxidized.) Dissolved uranium is transported to the oceans, where it diffuses into anoxic sediments, is reduced, and precipitates as UO_2.

This modern cycle of uranium weathering and deposition does not seem to have operated early in Earth's history. Sedimentary rocks older than about 2.4 b.y. contain uraninite in *detrital* form (Figure 10a). A **detrital mineral** is a mineral that survived the weathering process and was transported to the site of deposition as a solid particle rather than in solution. Such a mineral can often be identified by its

appearance, which closely resembles the texture of the source rock. These minerals also have rounded edges, produced by grinding as they were transported down streams as pebbles. The presence of the detrital form implies that, at the time when the source rock was weathered, the atmospheric O_2 content was too low to oxidize uraninite. Quantitative analysis suggests that the O_2 concentration during this time was less than 10^{-3} bars, or 0.005 PAL. (*PAL* means "times the present atmospheric level.") Unfortunately, this is only an upper bound. The actual O_2 concentration prior to 2.4 b.y. ago could have been much lower than this. Indeed, in most places it might have been essentially the same as on the prebiotic Earth, where the surface O_2 concentration is thought to have been on the order of 10^{-13} PAL (see the Box "A Closer Look: Prebiotic O_2 Concentrations" in the previous chapter). But during the Late Archean, this largely anoxic atmosphere may have been punctuated by plumes of free O_2 rising from productive areas of the surface ocean. O_2 was a pollutant in the anoxic Archean atmosphere, just as the educed gas CO (carbon monoxide) is a pollutant in today's oxidized atmosphere.

A second mineral that was deposited in detrital form prior to about 2.2 b.y. ago, but not since then, is **pyrite**, FeS_2 (Figure 10b). It tells essentially the same story as uraninite. When pyrite is weathered under today's oxidizing atmospheric conditions, the sulfur is oxidized to sulfate, SO_4^{2-}, and the iron is oxidized to Fe^{3+}. But this oxidation apparently did not happen on the early Earth. Eroded grains of pyrite were transported long distances by streams and rivers, as evidenced by the rounded appearance of some samples, and were deposited in chemically unaltered form. This evidence is another indication that atmospheric O_2 was low during the Archean eon.

Paleosols and Redbeds

Other geologic indicators that have been used to study the rise of atmospheric O_2 include **paleosols** (ancient soils) and **redbeds** (reddish-colored sandy and silty sediments). Heinrich Holland, now retired from Harvard University, has conducted chemical analyses of numerous Precambrian paleosols. He has found that most paleosols older than about 2.2 b.y. have lost significant amounts of iron, whereas paleosols younger than 1.9 b.y. have retained it. This finding is consistent with the story outlined previously, although the age dates in Holland's study (which are old ones) may need to be revised. Prior to 2.2 (or, more likely, 2.4) b.y. ago, atmospheric O_2 was low, so the iron released during weathering remained as soluble Fe^{2+} and was carried away by groundwater. The resultant paleosols are iron-poor. After 1.9 b.y. ago, atmospheric O_2 was relatively abundant, so the iron released by weathering was oxidized to insoluble Fe^{3+} and was retained in the soil. Holland's detailed calculations predict that atmospheric O_2 was less than 0.01 PAL before 2.2 b.y. ago and greater than 0.15 PAL after 1.9 b.y. ago.

(a)

(b)

FIGURE 10 [See color section]
Samples of the detrital form of
(a) uraninite and (b) pyrite. (*Source:*
(a) and (b) J. William Schopf.)

Redbeds are sandy sediments that were deposited on land by rivers or as windblown dust (Figure 11). They form today in arid regions, such as the American Southwest. The reddish color of these deposits comes from a thin layer of **hematite**, Fe_2O_3, that coats the surfaces of the sediment grains. The iron in hematite is of the oxidized, Fe^{3+}, variety, so redbeds indicate oxidizing atmospheric conditions at the time of their formation. The earliest confirmed redbeds are thought to have formed about 2.2 b.y. ago, which is consistent with the other evidence for a rise in atmospheric O_2 at about this time.

Even better evidence for the rise of atmospheric O_2 comes from sulfur isotopes. The arguments here are more complex, so the reader who doesn't care about the details may choose to bypass this discussion. For those who are interested, though, the data are described in the Box: "A Closer Look: Mass-Independent Sulfur Isotope Ratios and

FIGURE 11 A sequence near Uranvan, Colorado, showing Triassic redbeds overlying Upper Jurassic sandstones. (*Source:* Estate of Preston Cloud.)

A CLOSER LOOK

Mass-Independent Sulfur Isotope Ratios and What They Tell Us about the Rise of Atmospheric O_2

As mentioned earlier, new evidence from sulfur isotopes may have clinched the question of when atmospheric O_2 first rose. Sulfur is unusual in that it has four stable isotopes that occur naturally: ^{32}S, ^{33}S, ^{34}S, and ^{36}S. These isotopes can be separated, or **fractionated**, by a variety of physical and chemical processes. In such processes, the lighter sulfur isotopes typically react faster than do the heavier isotopes. For example, **biological sulfate reduction**, in which certain bacteria use sulfate to oxidize organic matter, discriminates strongly against the heavier isotopes. Scientists usually measure just the two most abundant isotopes, ^{32}S and ^{34}S. The reduced sulfur that is formed from this reaction is preserved as pyrite (FeS_2), which we have just discussed. The pyrite produced by bacterial sulfate reduction is strongly depleted in ^{34}S relative to ^{32}S. Indeed, such "isotopically light" pyrite is considered evidence for biological activity. (We say that the pyrite is "light" because it is enriched in the light isotope of sulfur compared to the heavier one.)

If one examines modern, sulfur-bearing rocks, one observes that the four sulfur isotopes are distributed in a highly predictable manner. ^{33}S is fractionated relative to ^{32}S by about half as much as is ^{34}S, and ^{36}S is fractionated by about twice as much. This is because the mass difference between ^{33}S and ^{32}S (1 atomic mass unit) is half that between ^{34}S and ^{32}S (2 atomic mass units), whereas the mass difference between ^{36}S and ^{32}S (4 atomic mass units) is twice as much. We say that all of the sulfur isotopes fall along the normal *mass fractionation line (MFL)*. But if one examines sulfur isotopes in Archean sediments, the results are quite different (Box Figure 1). In Box Figure 1, the pyrite sediments have more ^{33}S than would be expected and the barite ($BaSO_4$) sediments have less.

The units used in Box Figure 1 deserve some explanation. Isotopic abundances are measured in parts per thousand (‰), also called "parts per mil." The standard way of expressing isotope abundances is to use *delta (δ) notation*. For ^{34}S, for example, we write

$$\delta^{34}S(‰) = \left[\frac{(^{34}S/^{32}S)_{sample} - (^{34}S/^{32}S)_{standard}}{(^{34}S/^{32}S)_{standard}} \right] \times 1000$$

Negative $\delta^{34}S$ values mean that the sample is depleted in ^{34}S relative to the standard. The standard employed is FeS (the mineral *troilite*) from the Canyon Diablo meteorite. Hence, sulfur isotopes are said to be measured on the *CDT* scale.

Box Figure 1 by itself does not tell us when atmospheric O_2 first rose. However, if one replots these data in terms of the ages of the various samples, adding new datapoints that have been obtained during the past few years, a very clear result appears (Box Figure 2). In Box Figure 11-2, $\Delta^{33}S$ represents the deviation of the measured $\delta^{33}S$ values from the normal mass fractionation line. The solid bar through $\Delta^{33}S = 0$ represents 73 samples of Phanerozoic age, that is, younger than 540 m.y. old. The data show that so-called mass-independent fractionation of sulfur isotopes is observed in sedimentary rocks older than about 2.4 b.y. of age but not in younger rocks. This marked change in the sulfur isotope distribution occurs

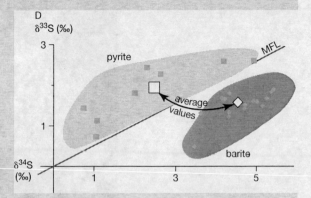

BOX FIGURE 1 Diagram showing sulfur isotope concentrations measured in Archean rocks. Barite is $BaSO_4$; pyrite is FeS_2. (*Source:* J. Farquhar et al., *Journal of Geophysical Research* 106, 2001, pp. 1–11.)

at exactly the same time that other, conventional types of geologic evidence indicate that oxygen levels first rose.

The data in Box Figure 2 also show more complicated patterns that were not obvious until just a few years ago. Between about 2.8 and 3.2 b.y. ago, the $\Delta^{33}S$ values are much smaller than before or after that time, but are still distinctly non-zero. Exactly what this means is a topic of current debate. Some researchers have suggested that atmospheric O_2 increased transiently during this time (see the following discussion), then went back down again, only to rise for good at 2.4 b.y. ago. Alternatively, this decrease in $\Delta^{33}S$ may have been caused by the buildup of high-altitude organic haze, which prevented solar ultraviolet radiation from reaching the lower atmosphere.

How are sulfur isotopes in sediments affected by atmospheric O_2? Laboratory experiments show that isotopes can be fractionated in a mass-independent manner by photochemical reactions occurring in the atmosphere. In particular, photolysis of sulfur dioxide (SO_2) fractionates sulfur isotopes in this unusual way. The reason is probably related to slight shifts in the absorption lines of SO_2 molecules containing different isotopes of sulfur. This causes SO_2 molecules containing the most abundant isotope, ^{32}S, to be photolyzed at higher altitudes than those containing minor sulfur isotopes. Today, SO_2 is not photolyzed in the atmosphere because the ultraviolet radiation needed to cause this reaction is absorbed by O_2. Much lower O_2 levels would be needed in order to allow this reaction to occur. Even more importantly, today all the sulfur that enters the atmosphere is eventually oxidized to sulfur dioxide or to sulfuric acid (H_2SO_4). These gases are soluble in water; hence, they are removed by rainout and end up in the ocean as dissolved sulfate ($SO_4^=$). Even if some photochemical reaction within the atmosphere did cause mass-independent fractionation of sulfur isotopes, the effects would disappear because all of the byproducts of the reactions would be recombined as oceanic sulfate before they entered into sediments.

By contrast, in a low-O_2 atmosphere, sulfur photochemistry is much more complex (Box Figure 3). Here, the horizontal scale represents the oxidation state of sulfur,

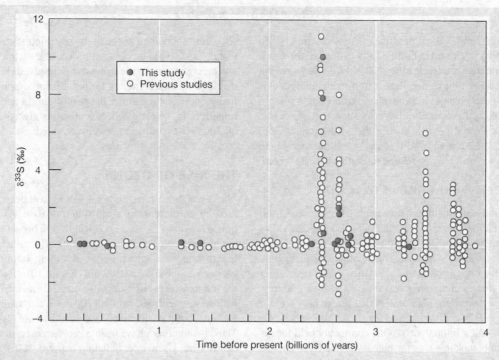

BOX FIGURE 2 Diagram illustrating the deviation of $\delta^{33}S$ from the normal mass fractionation line. Phanerozoic samples fall close to zero on this scale. (*Source:* Domagal-Goldman et al., *Earth Planetary Science Letters* 269, 2008, pp. 29–40. Data courtesy J. Farquhar and D. T. Johnston.)

which ranges from –2 for hydrogen sulfide (H_2S) to +6 for sulfuric acid. Because of the absence of O_2, sulfur photochemistry can proceed in both directions, left and right in the figure. Sulfur outgassed as SO_2 can be reduced to elemental sulfur (S_8) or to H_2S. Conversely, sulfur outgassed as H_2S can be oxidized all the way to H_2SO_4. The important point is that sulfur can leave the atmosphere in a variety of different oxidation states, and it does not all end up as

dissolved sulfate in the ocean. Hence, mass-independent fractionation patterns produced in the atmosphere can, in theory, be preserved in sediments. Detailed photochemical modeling shows that atmospheric O_2 concentrations must have been at least 10^5 times lower than today in order for this type of chemistry to occur. Hence, the new data on sulfur isotopes provide strong evidence that the Archean atmosphere was essentially anoxic.

BOX FIGURE 3 The atmospheric sulfur cycle in an anoxic, Archean atmosphere. The horizontal scale represents the oxidation state of sulfur. (*Source:* J. F. Kasting, *Science* 293, 2001, pp. 819–820.)

What They Tell Us about the Rise of Atmospheric O_2." To geochemists interested in Earth's early evolution, these sulfur isotope data are fascinating. Not only do they confirm the basic story told earlier, they also provide indirect evidence of other changes in atmospheric composition prior to the rise of O_2. In particular, they may show that an organic haze was indeed present during the Mid-Archean eon, around 2.8–3.2 b.y. ago. We'll return to this question in the next chapter, as it may be related to Earth's climate record.

What Delayed the Rise of Oxygen?

When combined with the other geologic evidence bearing on the rise of atmospheric oxygen, the sulfur isotope data tell us fairly conclusively that O_2 first rose to appreciable levels some time close to 2.4 b.y. ago. This creates a puzzle, though, because the organic biomarker evidence mentioned earlier suggests that cyanobacteria had evolved at least 300 m.y. before this time. Hence, a question that researchers are still working on is this: What delayed the rise of atmospheric O_2 by almost half a billion years? One commonly held idea is that it simply took this long for photosynthetic O_2 to remove all the reduced ferrous iron that was initially present in the oceans. This idea is probably incorrect, however, because if oxygen was produced at today's rate, it would have oxidized all the dissolved iron in the oceans in only a few thousand years. Something else must have been suppressing O_2. Several possibilities have been suggested. Perhaps the organisms that generated the 2.7 b.y.-old 2α-methylhopanes were merely the precursors to cyanobacteria, or entirely unrelated organisms like the purple nonsulfur bacteria, and were not generating oxygen. Or, perhaps cyanobacteria were indeed generating oxygen at this time, but they had not yet learned to fix nitrogen simultaneously, and so their production of O_2 was extremely limited. (We saw earlier that modern cyanobacteria have evolved complicated mechanisms for protecting their nitrogenase from the O_2 that they produce.) A third idea is that volcanic gases were more reduced prior to 2.4 b.y. ago, and that this additional sink for oxygen kept atmospheric O_2 levels suppressed. But there is no evidence

for a corresponding change in the oxidation state of Earth's mantle, and so the mechanism for causing such a change in volcanic gas composition remains unresolved. We will not dwell on this problem any further, except to point out that many questions regarding the rise of atmospheric oxygen remain to be investigated. Scientists, as always, find new questions when old questions are answered.

THE RISE OF OZONE

The rise of atmospheric oxygen would have been accompanied by an increase in stratospheric ozone. As we mentioned previously, ozone is critical for life because it shields out harmful solar ultraviolet radiation. The principal wavelength region in which ozone shielding is important is between about 200 and 300 nm (Figure 12). (Recall that 1 nm [nanometer] = 10^{-9} m = 10^{-3} μm.) Ultraviolet radiation with wavelengths shorter than 200 nm is also harmful to organisms, but it is effectively absorbed by both O_2 and CO_2. Thus, it should not have been a problem even in an anoxic atmosphere. Ultraviolet radiation between 300 and 400 nm is much less harmful to organisms and is not considered to be a threat, even though a substantial flux of such radiation reaches Earth's surface today.

The amount of UV radiation absorbed by ozone depends on the ozone *column depth*, that is, the total amount of ozone between the surface and the top of the atmosphere. The column depth is usually measured in *Dobson units*. One Dobson unit (DU) is equivalent to a layer of pure ozone 0.01 mm thick at the ground. The average ozone column depth today is about 320 DU, equivalent to a 0.32-cm-thick layer of pure ozone at 1 atm pressure.

How much ozone would have been present if the atmospheric O_2 concentration were lower than it is today? **Photochemical models** can be used to address this question: From a model calculation that is capable of reproducing today's average ozone column depth, O_2 is gradually removed from the model atmosphere. The results of one such calculation are shown in Figure 13. The calculation

FIGURE 12 The wavelength region where absorption by ozone is important.

FIGURE 13 Ozone column depth at different atmospheric O_2 levels, as calculated by a photochemical model. "PAL" stands for "times the present atmospheric level."

shows that the ozone column depth increases nonlinearly with atmospheric O_2 level: Even a small amount of O_2 produces a substantial ozone column depth. The reasons have to do with the details of ozone photochemistry. Exactly when a biologically effective UV screen would have been established is not clear because organisms differ greatly in their tolerances for UV radiation. However, examination of the calculated UV fluxes shows that most of the harmful UV radiation would already have been absorbed once the ozone column depth exceeded about 100 DU, or roughly one-third of today's value. As Figure 13 demonstrates, this column depth would have been reached at an O_2 level of only 0.01 PAL. For comparison, the paleosol evidence discussed earlier indicates that atmospheric O_2 was greater than 0.15 PAL by 1.9 b.y. ago. So, we can infer that a reasonably effective UV screen was already established by this time.

VARIATIONS IN ATMOSPHERIC O_2 OVER THE LAST 2 BILLION YEARS

The initial rise of atmospheric oxygen and ozone occurred over 2 b.y. ago. This does not necessarily imply, however, that O_2 concentrations immediately jumped up to the modern value of 21% by volume. Indeed, although the available evidence is far from conclusive, we have reason to believe that O_2 concentrations remained well below the present level until shortly before the dawn of the Cambrian period. One line of reasoning is the following. Recall that eukaryotes (organisms whose cells have nuclei) had already evolved by 2.7 b.y. ago, according to organic biomarker evidence. Recall also that the same Archean "oil" that

contained 2α-methylhopanes from cyanobacteria contains *steranes*. These compounds are formed by the breakdown of cholesterol, which is thought to be manufactured only by eukaryotes. Most eukaryotes are aerobes, that is, they require oxygen, so their presence at 2.7 b.y. ago implies that free O_2 was present in their immediate environment, most likely the shallow surface ocean or lakes. Free O_2 was not present in the atmosphere, however, because this is conclusively ruled out by the geologic evidence just described.

The Ediacaran Fauna

The curious thing is this: multicellular organisms did not appear in the fossil record until about 560 m.y. ago during a time period referred to as the Vendian. Until then, all eukaryotic organisms were single-celled. Why did the evolution of multicellular organisms take so long if eukaryotes were already present by 2.7 b.y. ago? One possible answer is that atmospheric O_2 levels were too low to support them. A study performed more than 30 years ago by Donald Rhoads and John Morse showed that animal life disappears below a few tens of meters depth in the anoxic Gulf of California. Their results indicate that modern multicellular organisms need at least 10–20% of present dissolved oxygen in order to survive. The evolution of multicelled animals could have been delayed because atmospheric O_2 concentrations and, hence, dissolved O_2 concentrations as well were below this level prior to the Vendian.

Another clue that atmospheric oxygen levels were still low in the Vendian period comes from the nature of the multicellular organisms that did evolve at that time. The animals of the Vendian period, termed the *Ediacaran fauna* because they were first discovered in the Ediacaran hills

FIGURE 14   The Ediacaran organism, *Dickinsonia*.   (*Source:* Simon Conway Morris.)

of Australia, have flattened bodies that may have been designed to maximize surface uptake of oxygen. For example, the Ediacaran fossil *Dickinsonia* (Figure 14) was about 30 cm in length but only 1 or 2 cm in thickness. Bruce Runnegar of the University of California, Los Angeles, has argued that *Dickinsonia* lacked a circulatory system, so that it had to acquire all of its oxygen through its skin. His analysis of this fossil organism indicates that O_2 concentrations had to be above 0.1 times the present level in order for *Dickinsonia* to survive. However, oxygen levels were probably not much higher than this, if O_2 limitation was the reason for this animal's flattened shape.

Variations in Atmospheric O_2 during the Phanerozoic

The Phanerozoic eon—the time during which advanced, multicellular life has thrived—began 542 m.y. ago with what is often termed the *Cambrian explosion*. At about this time, organisms acquired the capability of making hard shells. As a result of this invention, the fossil record becomes much more detailed after this time. Figure 15 shows a sample of the early Cambrian fauna collected from the famous Burgess shale in western Canada. These organisms almost certainly required high levels of atmospheric oxygen, perhaps approaching those of the modern

Earth. Indeed, numerous researchers, beginning with Lloyd Berkner and William Marshall back in the 1960s, have suggested that the Cambrian explosion was triggered by an increase in atmospheric O_2. This speculation remains unproven, but it remains a leading hypothesis for why multicellular life diversified so rapidly beginning at that time.

The record of atmospheric O_2 variations since that time is almost as poor as it is during the Proterozoic. However, we can make some estimates of how much O_2 has varied by looking at carbon isotopes. Carbon, like sulfur, has more than one stable isotope, and these isotopes behave differently in chemical reactions. For carbon, the two isotopes of interest are ^{12}C and ^{13}C. During photosynthesis, plants consume CO_2 that contains both of these carbon isotopes. The lighter isotope, ^{12}C, reacts faster, however; thus, the organic matter that is formed is depleted in ^{13}C. For typical rates of photosynthesis, the depletion in ^{13}C is about 25 parts per mil. (Carbon isotope concentrations are expressed using "delta" notation as well. For carbon, the standard is carbonate from the Peedee belemnite, a fossil cuttlefish which is related to modern squid. Hence, the carbon isotope scale is referred to as the *PDB* scale.)

Carbon isotopes can be used to estimate the rates of O_2 production in the following way. It is burial of photosynthetically produced organic carbon that results in net production of O_2. The organic carbon

FIGURE 15 Early Cambrian fauna from the Burgess shale. (*Source:* (a) Chip Clark and (b) A. J. Copley/Visuals Unlimited.)

that is buried is isotopically light, that is, it is depleted in ^{13}C. Hence, the carbon that remains in the atmosphere and in the ocean as dissolved bicarbonate and carbonate ion becomes isotopically heavy. The carbonate sediments that are formed are in equilibrium with dissolved carbonate and bicarbonate; thus, they are isotopically heavy as well compared to the buried organic carbon. And the faster

that organic carbon is buried, the heavier the carbonates become.

Figure 16 shows the carbon isotope composition of carbonate sediments during the last 540 m.y. Today, carbonate sediments are at about 0 per mil on the PDB scale. It can be shown from mass balance arguments (see the Box "Thinking Quantitatively: Carbon Isotopes and Organic

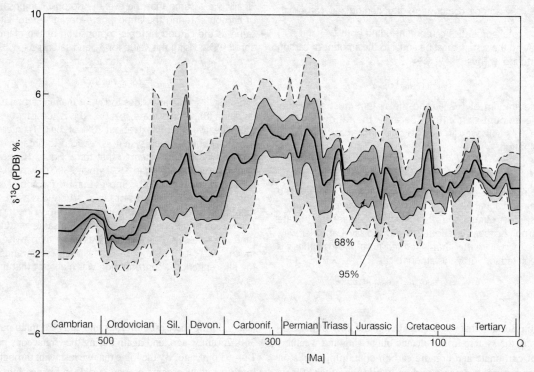

FIGURE 16 The carbon isotope record from carbonate rocks deposited during the Phanerozoic. Solid curve is the running mean. Shaded areas include 68% and 95% of all the data. (*Source:* J. Veizer et al., *Chemical Geology* 161, 1999, pp. 59–88.)

THINKING QUANTITATIVELY
Carbon Isotopes and Organic Carbon Burial

Carbon isotopes provide a useful way of analyzing the behavior of the organic carbon cycle in the distant past. The reason is that organisms fractionate carbon isotopes when they convert CO_2 into organic matter during photosynthesis. As described in the text, ^{13}C is taken up faster during photosynthesis than is ^{12}C. By measuring the $^{13}C/^{12}C$ ratio in carbonate sediments, we can determine how fast organic carbon was being buried and, hence, how fast O_2 was being produced.

We can analyze the carbon isotope record mathematically by keeping track of the total amount of ^{12}C and ^{13}C flowing through the system. For the purposes of this analysis we can treat the atmosphere and oceans as one combined reservoir. Carbon enters the atmosphere–ocean system in two different ways: (1) outgassing of CO_2 from volcanoes, and (2) weathering of carbonate rocks and sedimentary organic carbon (**kerogen**) on land. Carbon leaves the system in the form of sedimentary organic carbon and carbonates. Let

F_{in} = flux of carbon into the atmosphere— ocean sysytem

F_{carb} = burial rate of carbonates

F_{org} = burial rate of organic carbon

δ_{in} = isotopic composition of carbon entering the sysytem

δ_{carb} = isotopic composition of buried carbonate carbon

δ_{org} = isotopic composition of buried organic carbon

The total amount of carbon (including both ^{12}C and ^{13}C) leaving the system must be equal to the amount of carbon entering it. Thus

$$(1) \qquad F_{in} = F_{carb} + F_{org}.$$

The amount of ^{13}C leaving the system must also equal the amount that enters. Because the ratio of ^{13}C to ^{12}C is small, we can express this mathematically by the equation

$$(2) \qquad F_{in}\delta_{in} = F_{carb}\delta_{carb} + F_{org}\delta_{org}.$$

To make use of this system of two equations, we need one additional piece of information. During photosynthesis, most plants (and photosynthetic algae) fractionate carbon isotopes by about 25‰. Or, to say it another way, the organic matter that is formed from photosynthesis is depleted in ^{13}C by this amount. Let

$$\Delta_B = \delta_{carb} - \delta_{org} \approx 25‰$$

To simplify things still further, let

$f_{carb} = F_{carb}/F_{in}$ = fraction of carbon entering the system that is buried as carbonate

$f_{org} = F_{org}/F_{in}$ = fraction of carbon entering the system that is buried as organic carbon.

Dividing equation (1) by F_{in} yields the relationship

$$(3) \qquad 1 = f_{carb} + f_{org}.$$

This just tells us an obvious result: all of the carbon entering the system must leave either as carbonate carbon or organic carbon. Meanwhile, dividing equation (2) by F_{in} yields

$$(4) \qquad \delta_{in} = f_{carb}\delta_{carb} + f_{org}\delta_{org}.$$

Now, we can make use of equation (3) to write: $f_{carb} = 1 - f_{org}$. Thus,

$$(5) \qquad \delta_{in} = (1 - f_{org})\delta_{carb} + f_{org}\delta_{org}$$
$$= \delta_{carb} - f_{org}(\delta_{carb} - \delta_{org}).$$

But the quantity $(\delta_{carb} - \delta_{org})$ is just Δ_B, the average fractionation produced during photosynthesis. Thus

$$(6) \qquad \delta_{in} = \delta_{carb} - f_{org}\Delta_B,$$

or, rearranging terms and solving for f_{org}

$$(7) \qquad f_{org} = (\delta_{carb} - \delta_{in})/\Delta_B.$$

Finally, we assume that the average isotopic composition of carbon entering the atmosphere–ocean system is the same as the carbon isotopic composition of the mantle, about −5‰. Using this value for δ_{in} and setting $\Delta_B = 25‰$ gives

$$(8) \qquad f_{org} = (\delta_{carb} + 5)/25.$$

When $\delta_{carb} = 0‰$, as it does today for marine carbonates, equation (8) predicts that $f_{org} = 0.2$. This is consistent with the value given in the text: about 20% of the CO_2 entering the atmosphere–ocean system is reduced to organic carbon and leaves the system in that form. Figure 16 shows that δ_{carb} was greater than +5‰ around 300 m.y. ago. According to equation (8), this implies that the fraction of carbon leaving the system as organic carbon was >0.4, or more than twice the modern value. If the carbon input rate from weathering and outgassing was the same as today, then the rate of O_2 production was more than twice as much. So, it would not be at all surprising if the atmospheric O_2 concentration was higher at that time as well.

Carbon Burial") that this implies that about 20% of the CO_2 entering the system from volcanic outgassing and weathering of carbonate and organic carbon-containing rocks on land is buried as organic carbon, while the other 80% is buried as carbonates. Figure 16 shows, however, that this has not always been the case. Carbonates were isotopically heavy during the Carboniferous and early Permian periods, 360–250 m.y. ago, and again during the Cretaceous period, 144–65 m.y. ago. By the logic that we just went through, this implies lots of organic carbon burial, and hence lots of O_2 production during both time periods. The biggest excursion in the carbon isotope record and, hence, the biggest increase

FIGURE 17 Calculated variation in atmospheric O_2 during the Phanerozoic. (*Source:* R. A. Berner and D. Canfield, *American Journal of Science* 289, 1989, pp. 333–361.)

in organic carbon burial, was during the Mid-Carboniferous period. Carbonate sediments were about 5‰ heavier at that time, indicating that organic carbon was being buried about twice as fast as today. It is not hard to understand why if one considers what was happening at that time. The Carboniferous period gets its name from the extensive coal deposits that were formed during this time interval. The peak of this long-lived period of coal formation was during the Pennsylvanian epoch, 318–299 m.y. ago. The coal formed during that time has been the basis for the coal mining industry of western Pennsylvania and West Virginia.

Robert Berner and Donald Canfield of Yale University put these carbon isotope data into a model of the global carbon cycle and used them to estimate atmospheric O_2 levels. Their results are shown in Figure 17.

Atmospheric O_2 concentrations were probably higher than today during both the Carboniferous and the Cretaceous periods. The predicted variations in O_2 are not as large as one might anticipate from Figure 16 because the actual situation is more complicated than just described. Some of the excess oxygen that was produced was taken up by the sulfur cycle in oxidizing sulfide to sulfate. One can see evidence for this from sulfur isotopes, which covary with carbon isotopes in just the manner one would expect if oxygen was shuttling back and forth between the two reservoirs. However, Berner and Canfield's prediction is probably at least qualitatively correct. Other researchers have picked up on this idea and have suggested that the giant dragonflies of the Carboniferous (Figure 11-18) and the dinosaurs of the Mesozoic may both have been breathing an enriched blend

FIGURE 18 [See color section] A Carboniferous dragonfly with a wingspan of 60 cm (2 ft.). (*Source:* John Weinstein/ The Field Museum.)

of air. Like the Ediacaran organism *Dickinsonia* mentioned earlier, insects take in O_2 through their "skin"; thus, some paleontologists have suggested that it was the higher O_2 levels during the Carboniferous that allowed them to achieve their gigantic size. On the other hand, other researchers have pointed out that the level of biological competition was not as great then as it is today. One wonders how long 2-foot dragonflies would have survived in the presence of modern eagles or falcons. The gigantic pterosaurs of the Mesozoic would probably have made short work of them as well. So, the giant dragonflies of the Carboniferous could have existed simply because there was no one around to eat them. If this was true, they are not very reliable oxygen indicators.

MODERN CONTROLS ON ATMOSPHERIC O₂

Let us now turn our attention to the modern system. We have offered some suggestions for why atmospheric O_2 concentrations may have increased when they did. A related question, which we might hope would be somewhat easier, is this: What controls the atmospheric O_2 concentration today?

The answer, surprisingly, is that we do not know for sure, although researchers do have a number of ideas. Whatever the oxygen control mechanism is, it appears to be very efficient. The modern atmospheric O_2 level is 21% by volume, or 0.21 bar. It seems unlikely that the O_2 concentration has strayed from this level by more than ±50% since the late Devonian period, about 360 m.y. ago. The evidence is that forests have existed since that time and, while they have always been able to burn, they have never disappeared entirely.

Forest Fires and Atmospheric Oxygen

Fires burn more intensely when the oxygen content of the air is increased. A graphic, and tragic, illustration of the phenomenon occurred in the mid-1960s, when an *Apollo* space capsule burned up on its test pad in Houston with three astronauts aboard. At that time, NASA was using pure O_2 in its spacecraft to minimize launch weight. After the fire, the space agency returned to using normal air because they realized, belatedly, that pure O_2 was too flammable.

A similar problem could occur globally if the atmospheric O_2 content got too high. Forest fires, ignited by lightning or other mechanisms, might rage out of control and burn everything within reach. It is difficult to determine the exact O_2 level at which this would occur, but laboratory experiments using wet matchsticks and shredded paper suggest that an O_2 concentration of 35% by volume would be enough to destroy most of the global biota (Figure 19). A catastrophe of this magnitude may actually have taken place in the aftermath of the K–T impact event, 65 m.y. ago. But, this was a very special event in which fires may have been

FIGURE 19   The oxygen "fire window," showing proposed minimum and maximum atmospheric O_2 levels consistent with the continuous record of charcoal deposition since the Devonian period.   (*Source:* T. P. Jones and W. G. Chaloner, *Global and Planetary Change* 97, 1991, p. 39.)

ignited all over the globe by finely dispersed ejecta reentering Earth's atmosphere. Other than that scenario, there is no evidence that such widespread forest fires have occurred. We can infer that the atmospheric O_2 concentration has probably remained below 35% by volume ever since forests first appeared.

Forest fires can also be used to place a lower bound on atmospheric O_2 levels. Fires will not ignite when the O_2 concentration falls below about 13% by volume. This limit is somewhat firmer than the upper bound on O_2 because it depends on simple physics: At O_2 concentrations below 13%, a flame loses heat by convection more rapidly than it gains heat by combustion. Sedimentary rocks preserve a more-or-less continuous record of charcoal since the late Devonian period. Charcoal is produced from the incomplete combustion of organic matter by fire, so forest fires must have burned on and off throughout this period. Hence, we conclude that the atmospheric O_2 concentration has not fallen below 13% by volume during the last 360 m.y.

What mechanism could have stabilized atmospheric O_2 within the "fire window" during the past few hundred million years? The main loss processes for O_2, surface weathering and the oxidation of reduced volcanic gases, are thought to be independent of O_2 concentration within this range. The control mechanism must therefore act on the O_2 source—namely, photosynthesis followed by burial of organic carbon. Let us consider the factors that affect the organic carbon burial rate.

Oxygenation of the Deep Ocean

Most of the organic matter being buried today is deposited in marine sediments rather than on land. The same seems to have been true during most of the past few hundred

FIGURE 20 The vertical profile of dissolved O_2 in the (low-latitude) ocean.

million years, except during the Carboniferous period, when the great coal beds were forming. Thus, the control of organic carbon burial appears to lie in the ocean.

For many years, researchers have believed that the feedback mechanism that stabilizes atmospheric O_2 involves the deep oceans. The deep oceans today contain relatively high concentrations of dissolved O_2. Indeed, over much of the globe, the dissolved O_2 content of deep water is higher than that of surface water (Figure 20). The reason is that the water in the deep ocean originates at the surface at high latitudes, where temperatures are very cold. Like most other gases, O_2 increases in solubility as the temperature goes down. Thus, cold, high-latitude surface water contains more dissolved O_2 than does surface water at lower latitudes. This high O_2 content is passed on to the deep ocean when the cold surface water sinks as part of the global thermohaline circulation.

Oxygen concentrations in the deep ocean would drop dramatically, however, if the atmospheric O_2 concentration were lowered. Even today, over much of the ocean a pronounced **oxygen minimum zone** exists at a depth of about 1 km (see Figure 20). The low O_2 concentrations at this depth are caused by the decay of organic matter that falls from the surface ocean. In some regions—the Black Sea, for example—the rate of vertical mixing is slow enough to cause the deep ocean itself to become anoxic. If the atmospheric O_2 concentration were to decrease from its present level, the area covered by such **anoxic basins** would expand. The lower O_2 content of deep water could, in principle, allow more organic carbon to be buried on the ocean floor because the organic matter would decay less quickly. This, in turn, could provide a negative feedback that might stabilize atmospheric O_2. Unfortunately, however, measurements do not support this idea. There is no direct correlation between the concentration of dissolved O_2 and the organic carbon content of marine sediments. Evidently, organic carbon in sediments can be oxidized

quite efficiently by bacteria that utilize either sulfate or nitrate rather than O_2.

Dissolved Oxygen and Sedimentary C:P Ratios

The actual O_2 control mechanism appears to be slightly more complicated than that outlined above. Marine productivity is usually limited by the availability of key nutrients, especially nitrogen (N) and phosporus (P). Of these, P is thought to be the most critical, because N can be fixed by organisms such as cyanobacteria. The concentration of P in seawater is controlled by the rate of supply of P from the weathering of rocks on the continents and by the loss of P due to incorporation in sediments. The C:P ratio in sediments is related to the dissolved oxygen concentration in seawater. Sediments overlain by well-oxygenated water have lower C:P ratios (i.e., they contain more phosphorus) than do sediments overlaid by anoxic water. The reasons are complex: Apparently, bacteria in sediments store phosphorus when oxygen is available and use this stored material as an energy source when oxygen levels become too low. Phosphorus also tends to be bound up with iron compounds in sediments when oxygen is present. Both processes tend to create higher C:P ratios in sediments deposited under anoxic conditions.

The existence of such a relationship means that the dissolved O_2 content of deep water can affect the burial rate of organic carbon indirectly by altering the availability of phosphorus. This effect creates a negative feedback loop that may stabilize atmospheric oxygen (Figure 21). If atmospheric O_2 were to decrease for some reason, deep-ocean O_2 would decrease, and the C:P ratio in sediments would increase. This change would allow more organic carbon to be buried without removing any additional phosphorus. Increased burial of organic carbon would result in increased O_2 production, which would help restore atmospheric O_2 to its original level.

FIGURE 21 A likely feedback loop for controlling atmospheric O_2, involving dissolved O_2 concentrations and the C:P ratio in marine sediments.

Although this mechanism may help stabilize atmospheric O_2, it does not imply that O_2 levels have remained constant. Atmospheric O_2 levels can be affected by changes in the rate of organic carbon burial on land, such as those that occurred during the Carboniferous period. Furthermore, the degree of deep-ocean oxygenation may depend on the details of ocean circulation. Periods such as the Mesozoic, when the poles were much warmer, are unlikely to have had the same type of thermohaline circulation that operates today. Data from oxygen isotopes indicate that during most of this time deep water was 10–15°C warmer than it is today. Warmer deep water would have contained less dissolved O_2. Thus, anoxia should have tended to be more prevalent if other factors had remained the same.

If the oxygen control mechanism suggested is correct, however, the atmospheric O_2 concentration should have responded to this change. Larger areas of anoxia would have promoted the deposition of sediments with high C:P ratios. This deposition in turn should have led to increased oxygen production and higher atmospheric O_2 levels. So, as suggested earlier, the dinosaurs may have breathed a somewhat enriched mixture of air. The possible connection between deep ocean circulation and atmospheric O_2 concentration illustrates yet another interesting linkage in the highly intertwined Earth system.

Forest Fires and C:P Ratios in Sedimentary Organic Matter

Although the control mechanism described previously is attractive, it leaves one important question unanswered: If the control of atmospheric O_2 lies in the oceans, why have O_2 levels always remained within the fire window for forests? Either this is just a coincidence, or forests themselves must have something to do with regulating O_2. But forests are not part of the control mechanism outlined earlier.

The answer to this question may also involve sedimentary C:P ratios. The C:P ratios of marine sediments and terrestrial sediments are very different. The C:P ratio of typical marine organisms is 105:1, whereas organic matter derived from trees has a characteristic C:P ratio of about 1,000:1. Thus, the burial of terrestrial organic carbon removes much less phosphorus than does the burial of an equivalent amount of marine organic matter. And, although the burial rate of organic matter on land is relatively low,

FIGURE 22 A possible feedback loop by which forests might help control atmospheric O_2. The link between forest fires and the C:P ratios in near-shore marine sediments is not well established. Some such control mechanism may be required to keep atmospheric O_2 levels within the "fire window."

some of the organic matter produced there is carried away by rivers and buried in river deltas.

Could this mechanism create a feedback loop that keeps atmospheric O_2 within the fire window? Suppose that atmospheric O_2 levels were to become so high that the forests all burned down. The phosphorus that was being utilized by terrestrial vegetation would go directly into rivers and, thence, to the oceans, where it would be utilized to make low C:P marine organic matter. The burial of this marine organic matter would generate less oxygen than would the burial of the same amount of terrestrial organic matter. Oxygen production would go down, causing atmospheric O_2 levels to decrease. The net result would be a negative feedback cycle, which could conceivably help to keep atmospheric O_2 within the limits acceptable to terrestrial vegetation (Figure 22).

For reasons that are not entirely understood, however, the C:P ratio of river delta sediments collected to date does not appear to be much higher than that of normal marine sediments. Either other plants and algae with low C:P ratios provide most of the terrestrial organic material, or else sufficient reprocessing of material occurs during sediment deposition to smooth out the C:P differences between terrestrial and marine organic matter. Most of the work done so far has been on passive margins, though, where reprocessing times are long. Current work on active margins, where terrestrial organic matter is rapidly buried, may reveal the site of high C/P organic matter burial.

Chapter Summary

1. Evidence from ribosomal RNA, combined with our knowledge of the early environment, suggests that methanogenic bacteria were among the earliest organisms. Once methanogens evolved, they changed the composition of the atmosphere by converting hydrogen into methane. The biota should also have increased the rate at which nitrogen was cycled between the atmosphere and ocean.

2. The first O_2-producing organisms, the cyanobacteria, are thought to have originated at or prior to 2.7 b.y. ago, based on the presence of organic biomarkers (2-methylhopanes) in ancient rocks, along with the

presence of steranes from eukaryotes. Nevertheless, the geologic record indicates that atmospheric O_2 did not become abundant until sometime after 2.4 b.y. ago. Prior to that time, O_2 levels were suppressed by reaction with reduced volcanic gases. A variety of different types of geologic evidence, including mass independently fractionated sulfur isotopes, show when the initial rise in O_2 took place.

3. Accompanying the rise in atmospheric O_2 was a corresponding rise in the abundance of ozone. A reasonably efficient UV shield should have developed once the O_2 concentration exceeded about 1% of its present level. Based on the geologic evidence, this threshold should have been passed by 1.9 b.y. ago, or perhaps a few hundred million years earlier.

4. Atmospheric O_2 levels have probably fluctuated over the last 2 b.y. as a consequence of changes in the rate of organic carbon burial. O_2 concentrations may have increased markedly just before the beginning of the Cambrian period, 542 m.y. ago, perhaps triggering the explosion of multicellular life at that time. O_2 levels were probably also higher during the Carboniferous and Cretaceous periods, based on evidence from carbon isotopes. The formation of the Carboniferous coal beds created the largest positive excursion in atmospheric O_2 during the Phanerozoic era.

5. Despite these changes in the rate of organic carbon burial, atmospheric O_2 concentrations have probably not changed by more than $\pm 50\%$ during the past 360 million years, as evidenced by the continuity of the fossil charcoal record. The most plausible control mechanism involves the degree of oxygenation of deep water and the C:P ratio of marine sediments. Less-oxygenated deep water promotes a higher sedimentary C:P ratio that, in turn, allows more organic carbon to be buried for a given burial rate of phosphorus. The burial of terrestrial organic matter in river deltas may also influence the C:P ratio of sediments, allowing forests to exert some control over ambient O_2 levels.

Key Terms

anoxic
anoxic basin
anoxygenic photosynthesis
banded iron-formation (BIF)
biological sulfate reduction
chemosynthetic
chloroplasts
cholesterol
cyanobacteria
denitrification
detrital mineral
dissociate
endosymbiotic

eukaryotes
ferric iron
ferrous iron
fixed nitrogen
fractionated
hematite
heterocysts
kerogen
methanogenic bacteria
methanogens
nitrogen fixation
oxidation state
oxygen minimum zone

oxygenic photosynthesis
paleosols
photochemical models
photochemical reactions
phototrophic
prokaryotes
pyrite
rare earth elements
redbeds
steranes
stromatolites
uraninite

Review Questions

1. To which domain of life do methanogens belong? Why are they thought to be evolutionarily ancient?

2. What is the difference between prokaryotes and eukaryotes? Which are seen first in the fossil record?

3. What types of organisms have heterocysts and what are they used for?

4. Which organisms were the first to produce O_2?

5. What types of geologic evidence are used to study the rise of atmospheric O_2?

6. How did plants and algae acquire their ability to photosynthesize?

7. When did the ozone layer become thick enough to provide an effective UV screen?

8. What do carbon isotopes tell us about the rise of atmospheric O_2?

9. What does the fossil charcoal record tell us about atmospheric O_2 levels?

10. How is the atmospheric O_2 content maintained at its current level?

Critical-Thinking Problems

1. a. The atmosphere consists of 78% N_2, 21% O_2, 1% ^{40}Ar, and about 350 ppm CO_2. What is the mean molecular weight of air? Round your answer to three significant figures. (*Note:* The atomic weights of N and O are 14 and 16, respectively.)

   b. The total mass of the atmosphere is about 5×10^{18} kg. How many moles of air does it contain? How many moles of O_2 and CO_2 are present? (*Note:* Calculate the latter two answers from the first one, not by computing the mass of O_2 and CO_2. The concentrations listed for the various gases are percentages by volume, not by mass, so you need to work in moles.)

   c. Forests and soils contain roughly 2160 Gton of carbon in the form of wood, leaves, and humus. (The actual value is not known this accurately, but this choice makes the numbers work out well.) Suppose that all of the world's forests were to burn down instantaneously and that all of the soil carbon was oxidized as well. By how much would atmospheric CO_2 increase? By how much would O_2 decrease? Express your answers in percentages. Assume that the burning equation is the same as that for respiration and decay: $CH_2O + O_2 \rightarrow CO_2 + H_2O$.

2. The combined burial rate of organic carbon in marine sediments and in coal is approximately 0.05 Gton(C) per year. This burial is the net source of atmospheric O_2. In steady state, this source of oxygen is balanced by the weathering of reduced materials in rocks (kerogen, sulfides, and iron). If the weathering rate were to remain constant following the disaster in Problem 1c, and if all photosyntheses were shut off (in the oceans as well as on land), how long would it take for atmospheric O_2 to disappear?

Further Reading

General

Cloud, P. 1988. *Oasis in space: Earth history from the beginning.* New York: Norton.

Advanced

Canfield, D. E. 2005. The early history of atmospheric oxygen: Homage to Robert M. Garrels. *Annual Review of the Earth and Planetary Sciences* 33:1–36.

Catling, D., and J. F. Kasting. 2007. Planetary atmospheres and life. In *Planets and life: The emerging science of astrobiology,* ed. W. T. Sullivan III and J. A. Baross, 81–116. Cambridge: Cambridge University Press.

FIGURE 2 Shark Bay in western Australia. These "living stromatolites" are formed by communities of microbes and may be an analog to early microbial life. (*Source:* Robin Smith/Photo Library/Getty Images.)

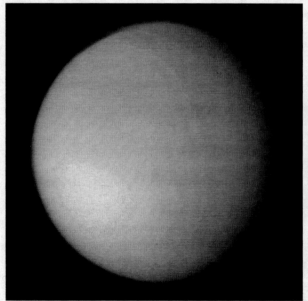

FIGURE 4 Saturn's moon, Titan, showing the orangish organic haze. (*Source:* Calvin Hamilton/NASA.)

(a)

(b)

FIGURE 6 (a) Prokaryotes have no nucleus, and the DNA is dispersed within the cell. (b) Eukaryotes have their DNA enclosed within a cell nucleus. (*Source:* (a) A. B. Dowsett/SPL/Photo Researcher and (b) Eric V. Grave/Photo Researchers.)

(a)

(c)

(b)

FIGURE 7 Three different types of cyanobacteria: (a) *Chroococcus* (coccoid), (b) *Oscillatoria* (filamentous), (c) *Nostoc* (heterocystic). (*Source:* (a) Tom Adams/Visuals Unlimited, (b) Dr. Gernot Arp, and (c) Susan Barns and Norman R. Pace.)

FIGURE 9 A banded iron-formation, or BIF. (*Source:* J. William Schopf.)

(a)

(b)

FIGURE 10   Samples of the detrital form of (a) uraninite and (b) pyrite.   (*Source:* (a) and (b) J. William Schopf.)

FIGURE 18   A Carboniferous dragonfly with a wingspan of 60 cm (2 ft.).   (*Source:* John Weinstein/The Field Museum.)

Long-Term Climate Regulation

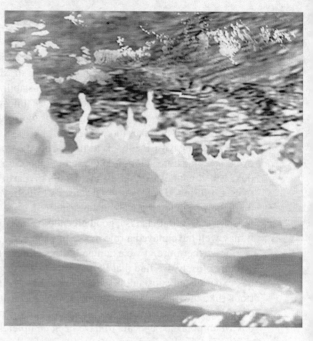

Key Questions

- Why was Earth's climate warm despite reduced solar luminosity in the distant past?
- Was Earth's surface ever totally frozen?
- Has Earth's climate generally been warmer or colder than today's climate?

- Why was the climate warm during the time of the dinosaurs, and why has it cooled over the past few tens of millions of years?

Chapter Overview

Solar evolution models predict that the Sun was about 30% dimmer when it first formed and that its luminosity has increased more or less linearly since then. Nevertheless, Earth appears to have had liquid water at its surface for as far back as the geologic record extends, roughly 4.2 b.y. Warm temperatures on the early Earth were maintained by a combination of powerful greenhouse gases, especially CO_2 and CH_4. CH_4 concentrations fell abruptly around 2.4 b.y. ago when atmospheric O_2 levels rose, throwing Earth into its first major glaciation. Indeed, this glaciation appears to have been the first of three or more "Snowball Earth" episodes, during which times Earth's surface was entirely covered with ice and snow. Earth recovered from this climatic catastrophe because volcanic CO_2 accumulated in the atmosphere, thereby increasing the greenhouse effect and eventually melting the ice. As the Sun gradually brightened, atmospheric CO_2 concentrations diminished, maintaining the climate within the limits favorable to life. This decrease in CO_2 was not accidental; rather, it was a natural consequence of a negative feedback in the carbonate–silicate cycle. Over the past few hundred million years, Earth's climate has fluctuated between warm and cold conditions, primarily as a result of changes in atmospheric CO_2 induced by plate tectonics and the carbonate–silicate cycle.

INTRODUCTION

Earth has been in existence for billions of years and has been inhabited by organisms for most of that time. All known organisms require water during at least part of their life cycles (although some can do without water for extended periods). This implies that Earth's surface temperature has remained warm enough to support liquid water throughout this entire time. But we have already seen that the Sun was approximately 30% less bright early in the solar system's history. Why did the climate remain relatively warm despite such a large change in solar heating?

The solution to the "faint young Sun paradox" probably involves either a stronger atmospheric greenhouse effect or a lower planetary albedo, which is what is needed to balance the planetary energy budget. When we last looked at this problem, we had no good reason to believe that either of these factors should have changed in the needed direction. A strong negative feedback exists between atmospheric CO_2 concentrations and the rate of silicate weathering. This feedback has a tendency to stabilize climate over long time scales because it causes atmospheric CO_2 levels to increase when the climate gets too cold or to decrease when it becomes too warm.

This negative feedback in the carbonate–silicate cycle is a plausible solution to the faint young Sun paradox. But it cannot explain all the details of Earth's climate evolution. There are good reasons to believe that methane was much more abundant prior to the rise of atmospheric O_2. Methane is a good greenhouse gas; hence, it may well have played a role in keeping the early Earth warm. Furthermore, if we examine Earth's climate history more closely, we find that Earth's surface temperature has experienced substantial swings: there have been periods (like the present) when the polar regions have been covered with ice, and there have been other, longer periods when polar ice appears to have been completely absent. There have even been periods, like the Neoproterozoic era (about 700 million years ago), when continental ice sheets may have existed in the tropics! In this chapter, we examine the question of just how stable Earth's climate has been, and we look at how plate tectonics and biological evolution may have caused large climatic shifts.

THE FAINT YOUNG SUN PARADOX REVISITED

Let us return now to the problem of the faint young Sun paradox. We have already mentioned that the Sun gets brighter as it ages. The luminosity increase is a direct consequence of the density change caused by the conversion of hydrogen into helium. As such, it is considered to be a *robust* prediction of solar evolution models, meaning that it does not depend sensitively on the details of the model. Thus, even if physicists are wrong about precisely how fusion occurs in the Sun's core, the faint young Sun problem is not likely to go away.

How Well Do We Understand Solar Evolution?

Recently, our faith in solar evolution models was increased by an important new observation. Physicists had been bothered for years about the apparent underabundance of neutrinos emitted by the Sun. **Neutrinos** are nearly massless particles emitted during nuclear reactions. The word "nearly" here is important. Until just recently, it was not known whether they had any mass at all. Like photons, they could have been totally massless. However, researchers at two new underground neutrino detectors, one in Sudbury,

Canada, and another in northern Japan, have shown that this cannot be true. Neutrinos come in three different "flavors," only one of which was able to be measured by earlier detectors. These detectors measured only about one-third as many neutrinos as they should have, based on our theories of what is happening in the solar interior. However, if neutrinos have mass, then they can convert to the other two forms of neutrinos on their way from the Sun's core to Earth. The Super-Kamiokande detector in Japan measured all forms of neutrinos, whereas the Sudbury detector measured only one type. By comparing the numbers in the two experiments, the researchers were able to show that the total number of neutrinos emitted by the Sun agrees with the number that is predicted theoretically. Thus, solar physicists have renewed faith that they understand how the Sun produces energy.

There is one way in which the faint young Sun paradox could be avoided or, at least, modified. If the Sun was a few percent more massive in the past, it would have been brighter than it is now. But this would imply that it must have lost large quantities of material during its lifetime. The Sun does lose mass by way of the **solar wind**, an outflow of charged particles from the Sun's **corona** (the hot, outermost layer that is visible during a solar eclipse; see Figure 1). But the solar wind mass flux is about 10,000 times too small to account for a 1% change in the Sun's mass over geologic time. Rapid mass loss does occur in young stars that are spinning rapidly. The rapid rotation, combined with the presence of the star's magnetic field, heat up the star's corona, and this drives a much stronger stellar wind. However, observations of nearby young stars by Brian Wood and his collaborators at the University of

FIGURE 1 The solar corona, as revealed during a solar eclipse. (*Source:* UCAR/NCAR/High Altitude Observatory.)

Colorado have shown that these strong stellar winds persist for less than 200 m.y. After that, the stars spin more slowly because they have been slowed by the drag from their magnetic fields. Once the star's mass has stabilized, its luminosity rapidly approaches that predicted by standard stellar evolution models, implying that stars like our Sun are significantly less bright than they will be when they reach the Sun's age. Thus, the faint young Sun paradox appears to require an Earthbound explanation.

Defining the Faint Young Sun Problem Mathematically

Let us see if we are any closer to resolving this paradox now that we have examined the Earth system in more detail. A 30% reduction in solar luminosity would have led to a 22° decrease in mean surface temperature, T_S, if Earth's albedo and greenhouse effect remained unchanged. As T_S is 15°C today, this would make the surface temperature at 4.5 b.y. ago equal to about –7°C, well below the freezing point of water. The actual surface temperature could have been even colder because of the positive feedback provided by water vapor and ice cover. A climate model calculation that includes the water vapor feedback (by assuming fixed relative humidity) is shown in Figure 2. The lower dashed curve represents the effective radiating temperature, T_e, calculated using the principle of planetary energy balance. The upper dashed curve is the mean surface temperature calculated by the climate model. The shaded region between the two curves represents the greenhouse effect, ΔT_g; this increases with time because of the water vapor feedback. A constant atmospheric CO_2 concentration of 340 ppm and a constant surface albedo are assumed.

Under these assumptions, T_S falls below the freezing point of water prior to 1.9 b.y. ago and reaches a chilly 255 K (–18°C) at 4.6 b.y. ago. This prediction is at odds with geologic evidence, which shows that liquid water was present at 3.8 b.y. ago and that life has probably been present since that time as well.

Possible Solutions to the Problem

How can the faint young Sun problem be resolved? According to the planetary energy balance equation, three types of solutions exist. Either the planetary albedo must have been lower in the past, the greenhouse effect must have been larger, or additional heat sources besides the Sun must have been present.

One additional heat source that is sometimes suggested for warming the early Earth is **geothermal heat** from Earth's interior. Some of this heat is produced by the decay of radioactive elements in Earth's crust and mantle and some is left over from Earth's formation. Both heat sources should have been larger in the distant past, so it is not unreasonable to ask whether geothermal heat might have helped keep Earth warm.

The problem with this suggestion is that the geothermal heat flux is simply not big enough to supply the required energy. A deficit of 30% in the solar flux is equivalent to a loss of about 70 W/m² of heating, averaged over Earth's surface. The modern geothermal heat flux is only about 0.09 W/m². Theoretical models of Earth's interior evolution suggest that the geothermal heat flux at 4 b.y. ago was higher than the present value by a factor of 3 or 4, so the available heat flux should have been approximately 0.3 W/m². The release of this much heat at the seafloor would have prevented the oceans from freezing to the bottom, but they should still have been covered with an ice layer several hundred meters thick if no additional surface warming was present. Little or no light would have penetrated such an ice layer, so this would be hard to reconcile with the evidence for ancient photosynthetic life. (Recall that stromatolites provide evidence that some type of photosynthetic bacteria were already extant by 3.5 b.y. ago.) The early Earth was not a global iceball.

It is also difficult to solve the faint young Sun problem by simply changing Earth's albedo. The current planetary albedo is about 0.3, so the factor $(1 - A)$ in the energy balance relation is equal to 0.7. If the solar luminosity, S, were 30% lower, A would have to be near zero to keep T_e constant. It is difficult to imagine how a water-covered planet could have an albedo near zero, because clouds, which are highly reflective, would almost certainly have been present. If the surface was actually as cold as predicted

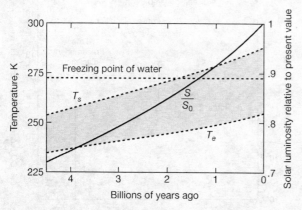

FIGURE 2 The faint young Sun paradox. The scale on the right applies to the solar luminosity curve, labeled S/S₀; the scale on the left applies to temperature curves. The shaded area represents the magnitude of the atmospheric greenhouse effect. (*Source:* From J. F. Kasting et al., How Climate Evolved on the Terrestrial Planets. *Scientific American* 256[2]:90–97, 1988. Used with permission, © George V. Kelvin/*Scientific American*.)

by Figure 2, sea ice would likely have been present also, even if continents and continental ice sheets were not. So, although Earth's albedo may have changed with time, it is unlikely that this by itself could have kept the planet warm.

The most likely solution to the faint young Sun problem is that Earth's greenhouse effect was larger in the past. If so, though, which greenhouse gases would have been more abundant? As we have seen previously, water vapor is the strongest greenhouse gas in the modern atmosphere. However, water vapor cannot solve the faint young Sun problem by itself because it is close to saturation and, hence, acts as a feedback on climate rather than as a forcing. Sagan and Mullen, who pointed out the faint young Sun problem in the first place, suggested that ammonia, NH_3, might be the solution. Ammonia is a good absorber of infrared radiation and it is also a **reduced gas**, that is, one that combines with oxygen to form stable compounds. As discussed in the previous chapter, reduced gases should have been much more abundant prior to the rise of atmospheric oxygen around 2.4 b.y. ago. That is why Sagan and Mullen thought that ammonia might be a good candidate for warming early Earth. After their paper was published, however, other researchers demonstrated that ammonia would have been rapidly destroyed by ultraviolet radiation. Hence, it is unlikely to have been abundant enough to have provided the necessary warming.

A CO_2-Rich Early Atmosphere?

One greenhouse gas that could have kept early Earth warm is carbon dioxide. There are several reasons for suspecting that atmospheric CO_2 levels were originally much higher. Smaller continents would have reduced the amount of land available on which to weather silicate rocks and to store carbonate rocks; thus, the CO_2 sink should have been smaller. Impact degassing of late-arriving planetesimals, along with enhanced volcanism on the hot, young Earth, would have created a larger CO_2 source. All these changes would have favored higher atmospheric CO_2 concentrations. On the other hand, weathering of the seafloor itself could have drawn down CO_2 levels by converting silicate minerals in carbonates and allowing these minerals to be subducted into the mantle. So, it is difficult to say whether atmospheric CO_2 concentrations would have been high or low during the first several hundred million years of Earth's history. There is also little geologic evidence with which to test one's theories. Climate during the earliest part of Earth's history remains largely a mystery.

Beginning about 3.8 b.y. ago, the geological record improves and one can draw inferences about climate with somewhat more confidence. As we have seen, the presence of liquid water and (possibly) of life suggests that additional greenhouse gases were present. CO_2 is among the most likely of these for the following reason. The carbonate–silicate cycle, which affects atmospheric CO_2 levels over

long time scales, contains a strong negative feedback. If Earth's surface temperature were lower as a result of low solar luminosity, the rate of silicate weathering should have been slower, thereby lowering the CO_2 loss rate. CO_2 emitted from volcanos would have accumulated in the atmosphere until the global rate of silicate weathering balanced the volcanic outgassing rate. If Earth had ever become entirely ice-covered, silicate weathering would have ceased entirely and volcanic CO_2 should have accumulated in the atmosphere until the associated greenhouse effect became large enough to melt the ice. Thus, the Earth system has a natural way of recovering from global glaciation. Most of the time, the feedback is strong enough that global glaciation is avoided. When it does happen, however, the system apparently recovers in exactly the manner described.

How much atmospheric CO_2 would have been required to keep the early oceans from freezing? If CO_2 and H_2O were the only important greenhouse gases, then the minimum CO_2 level needed to compensate for a 30% reduction in solar luminosity is 0.3 bar—about 1,000 times the amount of CO_2 in the atmosphere today (Figure 3). Although this sounds like a lot, this amount of CO_2 is not large compared to the total amount of carbon available. The CO_2 stored in carbonate rocks today would produce a partial pressure of some 60 bars were it all present in the atmosphere. Only a small fraction (0.5%) of this CO_2 is needed to resolve the faint young Sun problem. Indeed, atmospheric CO_2 levels may initially have been much higher than this, as mentioned earlier. The upper limit of

FIGURE 3 Atmospheric CO_2 concentrations needed to compensate for changing solar luminosity if CO_2 and H_2O were the only important greenhouse gases. The vertical bars at 2.5 and 0.65 b.y. ago show limits estimated from climate model calculations during glacial periods. (*Source:* Reprinted with permission from J. F. Kasting, *Science* 25:920–926. Copyright 1993 American Association for the Advancement of Science.)

10 bars shown in Figure 3 corresponds to the amount predicted on an ocean-covered early Earth. Climate model simulations show that such a CO_2 concentration would produce a global average temperature of 80–90°C. While we do not consider such a situation to be very likely, it is difficult to rule it out entirely. This would provide an alternative explanation for the prevalence of hyperthermophiles near the base of the evolutionary tree.

Effect of Methane on Archean Climate

CO_2 was probably not the only greenhouse gas that affected Earth's early climate. We saw in the previous chapter that CH_4 could also have been relatively abundant prior to 2.3 b.y. ago, when atmospheric O_2 levels were low. This CH_4 could have come from a variety of biological and abiotic sources. Prior to life's origin, CH_4 could have been produced by impacts and by *serpentinization* of rocks on the seafloor. Serpentinization is a process by which various *serpentine* minerals are formed from reaction of water with iron- and magnesium-rich basalts. In the process, ferrous iron is oxidized to magnetite (Fe_3O_4) and water is reduced to molecular hydrogen (H_2). If CO_2 is present in the water, CH_4 is formed instead. These processes could have introduced modest amounts (10–100 ppm) of CH_4 into the prebiotic atmosphere. We saw earlier that this may have helped in the synthesis of the key biological precursor molecule, HCN.

Once life evolved, the source of methane to the atmosphere should have increased greatly. Methanogenic bacteria were probably among the earliest organisms. These bacteria would have converted much of the H_2 in the atmosphere into CH_4 by way of the reaction $CO_2 + 4$ $H_2 \rightarrow CH_4 + 2 H_2O$. They could also have generated CH_4 from organic matter created by photosynthetic bacteria. Theoretical models suggest that atmospheric CH_4 concentrations of 1000 ppm or more are likely to have existed during the postbiological Archean and early Paleoproterozoic eras, 3.8–2.3 b.y. ago.

If atmospheric CH_4 was indeed present at these concentrations, it would have had a strong warming effect on global surface temperatures. The greenhouse effect of CH_4 would have been supplemented by warming from *ethane*, C_2H_6, produced from CH_4 photolysis. However, this greenhouse warming may have been offset to some extent by cooling caused by the presence of organic haze. Haze particles can produce an *anti-greenhouse effect*, as described further in the following text. The net result of these rather complex interactions is shown in Figure 4. The horizontal axis of the figure represents the atmospheric CO_2 partial pressure in bars (1 bar ≅ 1 atm). Recall that the partial pressure of a gas is just the pressure that it would exert if it was present by itself, with no other gases present. If the surface pressure is 1 bar, as it is in Figure 4, then a CO_2 partial pressure of 10^{-4} bar corresponds to a concentration of 100 ppm. The labels on the curves show the CH_4 *mixing ratio*. Mixing ratio is just fractional abundance, so a mixing ratio of 10^{-3} is equal to 1000 ppm. The solid curves show global average surface temperatures calculated with a one-dimensional radiative-convective model, or RCM. The calculations were performed for an assumed solar luminosity of 80% of the present value, which is the value expected 2.8 b.y. ago.

What these curves demonstrate is the following: If CH_4 was *not* present in the atmosphere at that time, a CO_2

FIGURE 4 Average surface temperature as a function of atmospheric CO_2 and CH_4 concentrations. The total assumed surface pressure is 1 bar. The dashed curves show the freezing point of water and the published upper limit on Late Archean CO_2 derived from paleosols. The arrow at the top right shows a more generous upper limit on CO_2 derived from the paleosol data. (*Source:* J. Haqq-Misra et al., *Astrobiology*, v. 8, 2008, p. 1127.)

concentration of about 0.02 bar, or about 60 times the present level, would have been needed to keep Earth's surface from freezing at that time. If, however, CH_4 was present at a mixing ratio of 10^{-3}, as expected on the basis of biological considerations, then the surface temperature could have remained above freezing at a CO_2 concentration of 0.005 bar, or about 15 times present. Keeping the early Archean climate as warm as that of today (288 K) would require about 0.03 bar of CO_2, or about 100 times the present value. This point is marked by a star in Figure 4.

These attempts to model the climate of the early Earth are constrained to some extent by data. The nearly vertical dashed curve represents a published upper limit on atmospheric CO_2 levels derived from *paleosols* (ancient soils). Robert Rye and colleagues from Harvard University examined several paleosols of Late Archean age and noticed that none of them contained the mineral *siderite* ($FeCO_3$). Siderite is formed from the reaction between ferrous iron and carbonate ion ($CO_3^=$). Their analysis indicates that siderite should have formed in these soils if atmospheric CO_2 concentrations were higher than those indicated by the dashed curve. (Their limit is temperature-dependent because the chemical reactions involved in siderite formation depend on temperature.) All of the solid curves fall to the right of this line; hence, none of these solutions is able to satisfy this constraint. However, if the paleosols being studied were formed in tropical regions where the surface temperature was higher than average, then the upper limit on CO_2 partial pressure increases to 0.03 bar (100 times present), in agreement with the CO_2 concentration estimated previously. Thus, the study by Rye and colleagues is consistent with an Archean atmosphere in which CH_4 was an important greenhouse gas.

A Pink Sky during the Archean?

As mentioned in the previous chapter, high CH_4 concentrations could have made the Archean atmosphere appear very different from today's atmosphere. Today, the skies are blue as a consequence of scattering of sunlight by gas molecules (predominantly N_2 and O_2). **Scattering** is when a photon interacts with a particle (or molecule) and is sent off in a different direction. Gas molecules are smaller than the wavelength of visible light, so their interaction with sunlight is termed **Rayleigh scattering**. In Rayleigh scattering, the shorter wavelengths of light are scattered preferentially compared to longer wavelengths. Thus, if you are looking away from the Sun, the blue rays are scattered into your line of vision more effectively than are the red ones, giving the sky its bluish appearance. Conversely, when one looks directly at the Sun near sunrise or sunset, the blue rays are scattered out of your line of sight during their long pathlength through the atmosphere, and the Sun appears reddish-orange.

In the Archean, the interaction of sunlight with the atmosphere may have been quite different. When CH_4 becomes about one-tenth as abundant as CO_2 in an atmosphere, photochemical models predict that it can **polymerize** to form particles of higher hydrocarbons. Higher hydrocarbons are molecules in which carbon atoms are attached to each other in long chains. Planetary scientists believe that polymerization of CH_4 accounts for the orangish haze in Titan's atmosphere. The reason that Titan's atmosphere appears orange is that the particles are approximately the same size as the longer (red) wavelengths of solar radiation. Scattering by particles that are comparable in size to the wavelengths being scattered is called **Mie scattering**. Mie scattering also predominates in Mars's atmosphere because of the large amount of suspended dust. Thus, the martian atmosphere looks pinkish, particularly during or after a global dust storm.

Earth's Archean atmosphere may have looked pinkish as well if the methane greenhouse story is correct. Indeed, there is a positive feedback that may have pushed Earth's climate system into a state in which organic haze would have started to form. Most methanogens are either **thermophiles** or hyperthermophiles. Recall that hyperthermophiles are organisms whose optimum growth temperatures are 80°C or above. Thermophiles are organisms with optimum growth temperatures between 40° and 80°C. Laboratory culture experiments have shown that the methanogens with higher optimum growth temperatures also have faster growth rates and shorter doubling times. Hence, a positive feedback loop exists whereby higher surface temperatures should have favored faster-growing methanogens. This, in turn, would have led to increased methane production, a bigger greenhouse effect, and hence still higher surface temperatures.

Climate Regulation by the "Anti-Greenhouse Effect"

The previous discussion makes it appear as though the early Earth should have become hotter and hotter until temperatures became too high for even the hyperthermophilic methanogens. (The highest temperature at which life has been found today is 121°C. Such temperatures can be reached without having the water boil if the overlying pressure is greater than one bar.) Well before this happened, however, another phenomenon would have occurred. As the methane content of the atmosphere increased, organic haze should have started to form. Both methane and the haze that it produces are strong absorbers of visible radiation. Methane itself absorbs in the red part of the visible and in the near-infrared. (This is why Uranus and Neptune appear blue. The red wavelengths of the incident sunlight are absorbed by the 2% methane in their atmospheres, so only the blue light is reflected.) Absorption of sunlight by methane and organic haze could have produced an **anti-greenhouse effect**, as occurs on Titan today. Indeed, the term "anti-greenhouse" was coined by Christopher McKay of NASA Ames Research Center in a paper about Titan's climate. In the anti-greenhouse effect, sunlight is absorbed high in the atmosphere and is reradiated back to space as infrared energy without ever reaching the planet's surface. This cools the surface, which is why it is called the "anti-greenhouse" effect. On Earth, the organic haze layer could not have been too thick, or it would have cooled the surface below the freezing point of water. Once this happened, the methanogenic bacteria that were producing the CH_4 would have died off, and the haze layer would have thinned.

All of this suggests that Earth's climate at this time may have been regulated by a negative feedback loop between surface temperature, atmospheric CH_4 and CO_2, and the organic haze layer (Figure 5). Higher temperatures would have led to an increase in CH_4 (for reasons described above) and to a decrease in CO_2. The decrease in atmospheric CO_2 with surface temperature is because of the well-known feedback involving the silicate weathering rate, which we have just been studying. As CH_4 levels went up and CO_2 levels went down, methane would have begun to polymerize and an organic haze layer would have begun to form. As soon as it became thick enough to block out sunlight, however, the anti-greenhouse effect would have set in and the surface would have begun to cool. The overall effect of this negative feedback loop should have been to stabilize Earth's surface temperature somewhere above the freezing point of water. Whether this would have kept the Archean Earth hot, or merely warm, depends on a variety of factors (e.g., continental size) that are difficult to determine. So, this hypothesis does not tell us what the Archean climate was like, but it does suggest why it may have been stable for long periods of time.

We note parenthetically that the Archean climate stabilization mechanism that we have just outlined is quite "Gaian" in nature—much more so than the present climate system. If methanogens truly were keeping the early climate warm, and if they themselves depended on this

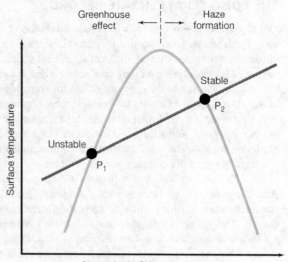

FIGURE 6 A "Daisyworld"-type diagram of the Late Archean climate system. See text for explanation. The diagram shows how the biota—methanogenic bacteria, in particular—may have helped stabilize the climate system at that time.

warmth in order to flourish, then they were clearly modifying climate in such a way as to benefit themselves. Indeed, we can emphasize the Gaian nature of the Archean climate system by redrawing the feedback loops (Figure 5) in the form of a Daisyworld-type diagram (Figure 6). In this diagram, surface temperature has been plotted on the vertical axis. The solid curve in the figure shows the effect of surface temperature on atmospheric CH_4. Higher temperatures lead to increased CH_4 production and, hence, to increased atmospheric CH_4. The parabolic curve in the figure shows the effect of atmospheric CH_4 on surface temperature. At low CH_4 concentrations, increased CH_4 causes an increase in surface temperature because it increases the greenhouse effect. At higher CH_4 concentrations, however, increased CH_4 causes a *decrease* in surface temperature by increasing organic haze formation and creating an anti-greenhouse effect.

The possible solutions to this Daisyworld-like diagram of the Archean climate system are the points P_1 and P_2. Point P_1 is unstable, however. Point P_2 is the stable equilibrium point in this model. Because P_2 lies on the right side of the diagram, this model predicts that the Archean climate system should have stabilized at a point in which a thin organic haze was present in the atmosphere. So, in this case, "Gaia" has some predictive power! But is there any way of knowing whether this prediction is correct? To answer that question, we must examine more carefully the long-term geologic record of Earth's climate. The next section summarizes what we know, and do not know, about this intriguing subject.

FIGURE 5 Feedback diagram showing a possible climate control mechanism that may have regulated Earth's surface temperature during the Archean era.

THE LONG-TERM CLIMATE RECORD

Our discussion to this point has been focused on the very early Earth and on processes that may have contributed to climate stabilization. After all, the most significant characteristic of Earth's climate on long time scales is that it has remained conducive to the presence of life for something close to 4 b.y. If one examines the geologic record in more detail, however, one finds that climate is anything but stable. A variety of different geologic indicators, discussed in the following text, show that **paleoclimate** (past climate) has actually varied in a complex manner, with long periods of warmth separated by shorter periods of intense cold. And there may have been several "Snowball Earth" episodes, when Earth's surface actually did freeze over entirely. This suggests that other factors that we have not yet talked about affect long-term climate as well. Determining what those other factors might be occupies the last two sections of this chapter. Before discussing them, let us examine some of the different types of geologic evidence that are used to study paleoclimate and see if we can piece them together to determine the broad outlines of Earth's climate history.

Geological Indicators of Paleoclimate

The types of geological indicators that are useful for determining paleoclimate depend on the time scale being considered. For recent periods of Earth history, it is possible to obtain a reasonably accurate estimate of ocean temperatures by measuring oxygen isotopes in carbonate sediments obtained from *deep-sea cores*. This technique is used to identify the glacial–interglacial cycles of the past 3 m.y. This method works only for time periods more recent than about 200 m.y. because most of the seafloor older than this has been subducted.

For more ancient time periods, including the Precambrian, it is possible to look at oxygen isotopes in carbonate rocks and in cherts (SiO_2) preserved on the continents. If one takes these isotopic data at face value and analyzes them, one obtains a very curious result: Earth's mean temperature appears to have been about 70°C during the Archean eon and still 55–60°C throughout most of the Proterozoic! Some biologists are quite happy with this result, as it corresponds nicely with the biological evidence for a thermophilic or hyperthermophilic last common ancestor for extant life. These results, however, are difficult to understand, given the dimness of the young Sun. More importantly, they are in glaring contradiction with evidence (discussed below) for glaciation at several different times during the Precambrian. Hence, some researchers hypothesize that these isotopic data have been influenced by other processes, for example, by a change in the oxygen isotopic composition of seawater. The ongoing argument among scientists concerning these isotopic data is not one that is

well suited for discussion in an introductory textbook. We mention it, though, simply to warn the reader that our understanding of the climate of the early Earth is still developing and that different researchers may have different opinions.

During the past 540 m.y. (the Phanerozoic era), we can learn about paleoclimate by examining the fossil record. Species of plants and animals that are known to live in certain climates can be used to estimate surface temperatures in the localities where their fossils are found. In doing so, we must account for the fact that the continents have drifted over Earth's surface as a consequence of plate tectonics. This technique is of limited use in the Precambrian era, however, because the single-celled organisms that were the only extant forms of life during most of this time could have survived under a wide range of climatic conditions.

Evidence of Past Glaciations

The best available evidence for climate change on billion-year time scales comes from geologic deposits formed by glacial ice. Three such types of deposits are shown in Figure 7. **Tillites** (Figure 7a) are mixtures of cobbles, pebbles, sand, and mud that have been packed together to form rocks. They are formed from debris produced when glaciers grind up surface rocks. The debris is carried along by the glaciers as they move and is deposited in piles of rubble called **moraines** along the margins of the ice sheets. (Moraines mark the terminal points or flanks of the glaciers.) In association with tillites, geologists sometimes find rocks with long, parallel scratches, or **glacial striations**, formed when moving glaciers drag other rocks across their surfaces (Figure 7b).

A third signature of glaciation is **dropstones**, "misplaced" chunks of rock that occur in otherwise finely laminated marine sediments (Figure 7c). They form when rocks trapped in glacial ice are carried out to sea by icebergs, a process termed **ice-rafting**. When the iceberg melts, the trapped debris falls to the bottom of the ocean and becomes incorporated into sediments.

The Long-Term Glacial Record

Geologists who have studied the long-term glacial record have concluded that Earth's climate history has been marked by six main periods of glaciation (Figure 8). The first such period occurred at approximately 2.9 b.y. ago. This "Mid-Archean glaciation" is known from only two localities in South Africa and has not been studied as well as the later glacial intervals. The next glaciation, at 2.4 b.y. ago, is the time from which the tillite and dropstone pictured in Figure 7 derive. Because these deposits were first identified near the banks of Lake Huron in North America, this early cold period is sometimes called the "Huronian glaciation." The Huronian glaciation was

(a)

(b)

(c)

FIGURE 7 Geological indicators of glaciation:
(a) a tillite from the 2.4 b.y.-old Gowganda formation
in Canada; (b) glacial striations from the 0.65 b.y.-old
Smalfjord tillite in Norway; (c) a dropstone from the
Gowganda formation.   (*Source:* (a), (b), and
(c) J. William Schopf.)

followed by over 1 billion years of ice-free conditions during the Late Paleoproterozoic and Mesoproterozoic.

Why did Earth experience these major glaciations in the midst of what was otherwise an extended, ice-free stretch of its history during most of the Precambrian? Let's consider the Huronian glaciation first because that one is the easiest to understand. Indeed, the discussion we have just been through offers a convenient explanation. Suppose that methane *was* an important component of the atmospheric greenhouse during the Late Archean and early Proterozoic. The rise of atmospheric O_2 around 2.4 b.y. ago would have eliminated most of this methane, throwing climate into a temporary deep-freeze. And indeed, the geologic record is entirely consistent with this story. Figure 9 shows a stratigraphic section from the Huronian sequence of southern Canada. This particular section was deposited from 2.2–2.45 b.y. ago, based on radiometric age dating. The three bluish layers, G1, G2, and G3, represent glacial deposits (tillites), indicating that there were three separate episodes of glaciation. Beneath the lowermost glacial layer one finds rocks containing *detrital uraninite*. As discussed in the previous chapter, such deposits are indicative of a low-O_2 atmosphere. Above the uppermost glacial layer is the Lorraine *redbed* formation, which must have formed under a high-O_2 atmosphere. As pointed out over 40 years ago by Canadian geologist Stuart Roscoe, it appears as if the Huronian glaciation (or glaciations) is contemporaneous with the rise of O_2.

The Mid-Archean glaciation at 2.9 b.y. ago is not as easy to explain. One possibility is that atmospheric O_2 increased just before this time, then went down again just afterward. This could have destroyed the methane greenhouse and thereby caused the glaciation, just as proposed for the Huronian. This might also explain the smaller $\Delta^{33}S$ values seen at this time. However, this explanation is inconsistent with other geologic evidence bearing on atmospheric O_2 levels. For example, detrital uraninite and pyrite are found in the Witwatersrand Basin of South Africa at essentially this time. As we saw in the previous chapter, such minerals are formed only under low-O_2 conditions. So, it seems more likely that the Mid-Archean glaciation was triggered by other factors.

Another idea is that both the low $\Delta^{33}S$ values between 2.8 and 3.2 b.y. ago and the glaciation at 2.9 b.y. ago were caused by the presence of organic haze. Such haze could have blocked SO_2 photolysis, leading to low $\Delta^{33}S$, while at the same time creating an anti-greenhouse effect that might have triggered the glaciation. Although this idea is admittedly speculative, it would probably be easier to understand than would a transient rise of O_2. More detailed studies of sulfur

FIGURE 8 The major cold and warm periods during Earth's history. (*Source:* From W. K. Hamblin and E. H. Christiansen, *Earth's Dynamic Systems*, 8/e, 1998. Reprinted by permission of Prentice Hall, Upper Saddle River, N.J.)

isotopes, looking at [36]S as well as [33]S, may help to show whether this hypothesis might be correct.

Let us move forward now to the early Proterozoic eon. Following the Huronian glaciations at 2.45–2.2 b.y. ago, the climate became warm again, as evidenced by the complete absence of evidence for ice. Why, one might ask,

should the climate have warmed back up when the methane that was keeping it warm originally had largely disappeared? The carbonate–silicate cycle provides one possible explanation. CO_2 should have been outgassed from volcanos at about the same rate after the rise of O_2 as it had been before. Hence, it had to have been removed by

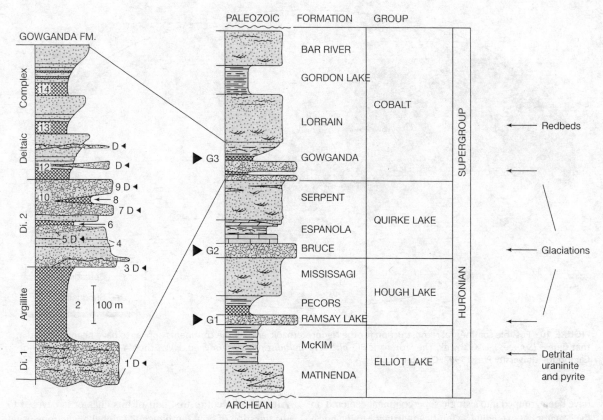

FIGURE 9 A stratigraphic section from the Huronian sequence in southern Canada. The bluish regions show the three glacial layers. (*Source:* G. M. Young, *Stratigraphy, Sedimentology, and Tectonic Setting of the Huronian Supergroup.* Field Trip B5 guidebook, joint meeting Geol. Assoc. Canada, Mineral. Assoc. Canada, Soc. Econ. Geol., Toronto, 1991.)

silicate weathering at that same rate. The silicate weathering rate is largely a function of surface temperature; thus, after the glaciation, the surface temperature had to recover to approximately its original value in order to keep the rate of silicate weathering the same as before. To accomplish this, atmospheric CO_2 could have jumped to a substantially higher concentration. This prediction remains speculative for the time being, but it might eventually be tested if more paleosol data become available to constrain past CO_2 concentrations.

There is another possibility for the extended warmth of the middle Proterozoic that climatologists have begun to think about only recently. It may be that after disappearing briefly just prior to the Huronian glaciation, atmospheric methane recovered and again reached levels much higher than today. Why, one might ask, should it have done so? A possible answer is that both atmospheric O_2 and dissolved oceanic sulfate levels may still have been much lower than today. This model for the Mid-Proterozoic has been championed by Donald Canfield and his colleagues from the University of Southern Denmark. Today, most of the organic matter that reaches the seafloor is recycled back to CO_2 either by aerobic bacteria that cause decay or by **sulfate-reducing bacteria**. (This is the process of bacterial

sulfate reduction that was mentioned in the previous chapter.) If neither O_2 nor sulfate was present in appreciable concentrations, then much more organic matter may have decayed by the combined processes of fermentation and methanogenesis. (Methanogenesis is the biological production of methane.) These processes occur in modern marine sediments today, but only at depths below which the O_2 and sulfate are exhausted. So, today, little or no methane is released from marine sediments. But in the lower-O_2 Proterozoic, methane may have come out of marine sediments in large enough amounts to warm the atmosphere significantly and help keep Earth's surface ice-free.

Low-Latitude Glaciation: The Snowball Earth

Eventually the climate became cool once again. Indeed, the Late Proterozoic, between 0.75 and 0.6. b.y. ago, was so cold that it is considered a great mystery. Evidence for glaciation during this time interval is found on all seven present-day continents. The reconstruction shown in Figure 10 suggests that the continents were at that time grouped into two supercontinents, one of which was centered near the equator. Alternatively, the continents may

FIGURE 10   Possible continental reconstruction for the Neoproterozoic era. All the continents appear to have been glaciated at that time.   (*Source:* J. L. Kirshvink, *The Proterozic Biosphere: A Multidisciplinary Study*, ed. J. W. Schopf and C. Klein, Cambridge: Cambridge University Press, 1992, Chapter 12.1.)

have been grouped into a single supercontinent centered on the equator but extending a significant distance to the north and south. In all continental reconstructions of this time period, one feature remains constant: The continent of Australia is situated at or near the equator. This is considered remarkable because the geologic evidence indicates that at this time Australia was glaciated from one end to another. The evidence includes tillites, glacial striations, and dropstones, the latter demonstrating that ice sheets extended right to the margins of the paleocontinent. Today, in contrast, there *is* glaciation in the tropics but it is confined to high mountain ranges like the Andes of South America. There, the glaciers never make it down below about 5 km elevation.

How could Earth have possibly gotten cold enough to glaciate the tropics? In one sense, it's not that difficult.

Why are geologists convinced that Australia was situated in the tropics at this time? Recall that past north–south continental positions are determined from paleomagnetic data. In Australia, glacial deposits are found mixed in with rocks in which the remnant magnetic field lines are parallel to the original bedding plane of the rock. If Earth's magnetic field was approximate to a dipole field, as it is today, this implies that these rocks formed near the equator. Many different geologists have looked at the paleomagnetic data from the Neoproterozoic rocks in Australia and have concluded that the evidence for low-latitude glaciation is real. The Huronian sequence described earlier also shows evidence for low-latitude glaciation; hence, it too may represent a "Snowball Earth" episode.

After all, the entire first half of this chapter is devoted to the question of how Earth *avoided* global glaciation during the earlier parts of its history. If the Sun was less bright in the distant past, then the atmospheric greenhouse effect had to be larger, or else global glaciation would be expected. Conversely, if CO_2 and CH_4 levels were low at some time in the past, then the lower solar luminosity would ensure that Earth's climate was very cold.

Let us take the Neoproterozoic glaciations as an example because they are the ones that have been best studied. Fieldwork in Namibia, West Africa, by Paul Hoffman and his colleagues at Harvard University has shown that there were two main episodes of glaciation: one at ~730 m.y. ago and a second at ~610 m.y. ago. Consider the more recent of these two episodes. In the recent past, solar luminosity has been increasing at a rate of about 1% every hundred million years. Thus, the Sun should have been about 6% less bright at the time of the second glaciation. Under these reduced luminosity conditions, GCM climate modeling by William Hyde and colleagues from Texas A&M University indicates that CO_2 concentrations would have to have been more than twice the preindustrial level (i.e., 2×280 ppm) in order to avoid global glaciation. Other GCMs yield slightly different critical CO_2 levels, but all of them agree that there is some CO_2 level below which global ice cover cannot be avoided.

How exactly would a Snowball Earth glaciation proceed? To understand in detail, see the Box "A Closer Look: How Did Life Survive the Snowball Earth". The general outline, however, is as follows. For one reason or another, atmospheric CO_2 concentrations were drawn down to relatively low values. (We will not consider the Huronian glaciation here. That one appears to have been caused by the rise of atmospheric oxygen.) Hoffman and his colleagues originally suggested that increased organic carbon burial on newly created continental shelves was the cause, but it appears likely that other factors were operative as well. Perhaps the most important of these is that a significant fraction of the continental area was situated in the tropics. This allowed silicate weathering to proceed even though Earth was growing colder and colder, so that atmospheric CO_2 could continue to be drawn down. This first step in initiating global glaciation is counterintuitive because the conventional wisdom regarding glaciations has been that they occur when a continent drifts near or over one of the poles. Global glaciations are different. They probably require continents at low latitudes. This may also explain why they have occurred only at certain times in Earth's history. When the continents are not concentrated at low latitudes, the silicate weathering feedback prevents global glaciations from occurring.

An alternative mechanism for triggering Snowball Earth, if one postulates that methane was still abundant during the Mid-Proterozoic, is that atmospheric O_2 may have increased near the end of this time period. Such an increase has been suggested for other reasons, as discussed in the previous chapter. (Increases in atmospheric O_2 are a possible trigger for the Cambrian explosion.) If atmospheric O_2 went up, the methane flux from marine sediments may have gone down, thereby reducing the methane greenhouse effect and making the climate colder. Such a change could conceivably have occurred faster than the carbonate–silicate cycle could regulate atmospheric CO_2. So, this again might have circumvented the normal processes that keep Earth's climate stable.

The rest of the sequence may have gone like this: As the Neoproterozoic climate became colder, for whatever reason, the polar ice sheets gradually crept down to lower latitudes. Once they reached approximately 30 degrees, however, something spectacular happened. All of a sudden, within a few decades perhaps, the oceans froze all the way down to the equator. The reason is that the positive feedback loop between ice albedo and surface temperature became so strong that it made the system unstable. This result can be demonstrated quantitatively using climate models. (See the Box "Thinking Quantitatively: Energy Balance Modeling of the Snowball Earth.") Once the ocean surface had frozen entirely, Earth's surface would have become extremely cold, $-50°C$ or lower, because the albedo would have been very high (> 0.6, as compared to 0.3 today) and most of the incident sunlight would have been reflected back to space. However, as soon as the surface froze, silicate weathering on the continents would have virtually ceased, and volcanic CO_2 would have begun to accumulate in the atmosphere. In approximately 10 m.y., given modern volcanic outgassing rates, the atmospheric CO_2 partial pressure would have

reached 0.1 bar (300 times the current level) and, all of a sudden, the ice would have begun to melt. The positive ice–albedo feedback loop would now have worked in the other direction: increased melting would have led to decreased albedo, which would in turn have led to increased surface temperature and more melting. Models predict that the ice cover would have disappeared entirely within a few thousand years. At this point, Earth would have had a dense, CO_2-rich atmosphere and a low albedo, and so it would have become very hot, with an average surface temperature as high as $50–60°C$. Silicate weathering would now have proceeded rapidly, drawing down atmospheric CO_2 levels and eventually restoring the climate system to its original state.

Additional Geological Evidence for the Snowball Earth: BIFs and Cap Carbonates

To some, this story of an ice-covered Earth sounds simply too extraordinary to be true. Is there any additional evidence that such a sequence of events actually occurred? The answer is yes. A number of other observations are consistent with the Snowball Earth model. Of these, two features in particular stand out. The first is the reappearance of banded iron-formations (BIFs). Recall that most BIFs were deposited prior to 1.8 b.y. ago and that their formation was linked to anoxic conditions in the deep ocean. Surprisingly, BIFs reappear briefly during the Neoproterozoic at exactly the time of the glaciations. This reappearance is explained by the Snowball Earth hypothesis because the global ice cover would have cut off the ocean from the large reservoir of atmospheric O_2. The dissolved O_2 in the oceans, or at least in some ocean basins, was used up by oxidation of organic matter in sediments. Ferrous iron emanating from the hydrothermal vents in the mid-ocean ridges accumulated in the ocean and was ultimately upwelled on continental shelves (after the ice had melted) and deposited as BIFs.

The other piece of evidence is even more telling. Directly above each of the two Neoproterozoic glacial deposits in Namibia is a layer of carbonate rock approximately 400 m thick. These carbonate deposits are often termed **cap carbonates** because they "cap" the glacial layers. The bottom parts of these caps are fine-grained and show evidence of having been deposited very rapidly, as would be expected in the immediate aftermath of a Snowball Earth episode. This close association between glacial deposits and carbonates has puzzled geologists for many years because glaciers typically form at high latitudes, where it is cold, whereas carbonates typically form at low latitudes where the surface ocean is warm and, hence, carbonate minerals are less soluble. The Snowball Earth hypothesis explains this association naturally; indeed, the model *predicts* that such carbonate deposits should have been formed. Thus, there is compelling evidence to indicate that the Snowball Earth model is correct.

THINKING QUANTITATIVELY
Energy Balance Modeling of the Snowball Earth

Although detailed modeling of the Snowball Earth climate requires a general circulation model, or GCM, much can be learned from simpler climate models. Indeed, much of the theoretical framework for understanding runaway glaciation was developed independently in the late 1960s by Soviet climatologist Michail Budyko and English climatologist William Sellers using what were later termed "energy-balance climate models," or EBMs. In a typical EBM, Earth's surface was divided into 18 different latitude bands, each 10 degrees wide. In their simplest form, these models calculated the annually averaged solar heating in each latitude band, along with the average outgoing infrared radiation flux. Heat transport between different latitude bands was parameterized as *diffusion*. Diffusion of heat is usually called *conduction*. We know, of course, that the atmosphere does not really transfer heat in this way. Rather, it does so by the complex system of winds and ocean currents. Budyko and Sellers did a clever thing, however: they adjusted their diffusion coefficients so that their models matched the observed equator-to-pole temperature gradient. Thus, their models were capable of reproducing the average latitudinal distribution of temperature and, most importantly, they could estimate the size of the polar ice caps. This allows such models to be used to study the phenomenon of runaway glaciation.

Results from a more up-to-date version of an EBM are shown in Box Figure 1. The figure is somewhat complicated, so let us go through it carefully. The horizontal axis is the effective solar flux (S_{eff}), that is, the solar flux divided by the modern value. Thus, $S_{eff} = 1$ corresponds to the modern solar constant. The vertical scale is the sine of the ice-line latitude. This marks the extent of the polar ice

caps. (The model is symmetric in each hemisphere.) Recall from trigonometry that sin 30° = 0.5, so a point halfway up the vertical scale corresponds to a latitude of 30°. Exactly half Earth's surface area is located poleward of 30°; the other half is located equatorward of this point.

The lines and curves in Box Figure 1 represent the ice-line extent as calculated by the EBM climate model. Solid curves represent stable solutions; dashed curves represent unstable solutions. The three different curves shown correspond to three different atmospheric CO_2 levels. The curve furthest to the right is for a CO_2 partial pressure of 3×10^{-4} bar, which corresponds to a CO_2 concentration of 300 ppm, close to today's value. The points where the curves (or lines) intersect a vertical line at $S_{eff} = 1$ represent stable climate solutions for the modern Earth. Surprisingly, there are three different, stable solutions. The one that actually corresponds to the modern climate is the "small ice cap" solution. The sine of the ice-line latitude is ~0.95, which puts the boundary of the polar ice cap at about 72°. But there are two other stable solutions as well: an ice-free solution (no polar cap) and an ice-covered solution. The ice-covered solution corresponds to the Snowball Earth. It is stable because the high albedo of the ice causes most of the incident sunlight to be reflected back to space.

The most interesting features of Box Figure 1, however, are the unstable solutions (dashed curves). As one can see, all solutions in which the ice line is equatorward of ~30° are unstable. If the polar ice caps ever reached this latitude, the ice–albedo feedback would have become completely unstoppable: increases in ice cover past this point would cause more sunlight to be reflected back to space, which would result in decreased surface temperatures and further increases in ice cover. Very quickly, within a few decades, the ocean surface would have frozen all the way down to the equator. This is thought to have been how the climate system became trapped in the Snowball Earth.

Box Figure 1 also shows how the system could have recovered from the Snowball Earth. Once Earth's surface was totally frozen, silicate weathering would have ceased and volcanic CO_2 would have accumulated in the atmosphere. One can see that when the CO_2 partial pressure reaches 0.12 bar (12,000 ppm), the unstable solution intersects the equator (sine ice-line latitude = 0) at $S_{eff} = 1$. Physically, this means that the ice-covered solution is no longer stable. Instead, the system would transition spontaneously (and rapidly) up to the ice-free solution. The climate would become extremely warm, 50–60°C, and would remain that way until silicate weathering was able to remove the excess CO_2 from the atmosphere. As described in the text, it looks as if this is exactly what happened during the Late Precambrian Snowball Earth episodes 610 m.y. and 730 m.y. ago.

BOX FIGURE 1 Energy-balance climate calculations for the Snowball Earth model. Solid curves represent stable solutions; dashed curves represent unstable solutions. Dots show equilibrium solutions for today's solar flux. (*Source:* K. Caldeira and J. F. Kasting, *Nature* 359, 1992, pp. 226–228.)

A CLOSER LOOK
How Did Life Survive the Snowball Earth?

Perhaps the most interesting question regarding the Snowball Earth is: How did life manage to survive through it? One can estimate the thickness of the ice cover over the oceans by means of a fairly simple calculation. (See "Critical-Thinking" Problem 1 at the end of the chapter.) The thickness of the ice is limited by the geothermal heat flux that must be conducted upward through it. If you do the problem correctly, you should find that the sea ice during the Neoproterozoic glaciations was over a kilometer thick on average. This is far too thick to allow sunlight to penetrate. Very little sunlight makes it any deeper than 5 or 10 m even in very clear ice. And, yet, we are certain that photosynthetic life survived these two catastrophes, as well as the earlier Huronian glaciation, which may also have been a Snowball Earth episode. How can one resolve this apparent paradox?

One solution that has been suggested by William Hyde and his colleagues from Texas A&M University is that the tropical ocean may not have been entirely frozen. In their model (published in the journal *Nature* in May 2000), the tropical oceans remained ice-free, but at least some tropical continents were ice-covered. They suggested that the ice sheets formed at high elevations where the local temperatures were below freezing and that they flowed down to the continental margins before they melted. In this way, they could account for the occurrence of dropstones in Neoproterozoic marine sediments around Australia. Their model has been termed a "Slushball Earth" because the planet was never entirely ice-covered, if they are correct. However, their model has difficulty explaining the reoccurrence of BIFs and the presence of cap carbonates (see the next section); hence, it does not appear to us that their solution is the right one.

Another idea is that life survived in geothermally heated environments in which liquid water remained even as the rest of the surface froze. The hydrothermal vents of the mid-ocean ridges are one obvious refuge. As most mid-ocean ridge vents are over 2.5 km deep, they would have been well beneath the ice layer, and organisms living within them would have been essentially unaffected by a global glaciation. Such organisms are not photosynthetic, however. Continental geothermal areas such as Yellowstone Park in the United States are another possibility. However, the water in Yellowstone's geysers and hot pools ultimately derives from rainwater. During a Snowball Earth event, the hydrological cycle would have virtually shut down and such areas should have dried up. A few geothermal areas that are well connected to the ocean, the island of Iceland, for example, might have remained habitable for photosynthetic life. However, there are very few such areas in the world. If life had been restricted to only a few such locations, biologists believe that the Universal Tree of Life would show evidence for this. So, they think that photosynthetic life must have remained more widespread.

A third idea is that the ice may not have been as thick in all locations as simple models predict. Christopher McKay from NASA Ames Research Center near San Francisco has suggested that the ice could have been thin enough in the tropics to allow some sunlight to penetrate. Climate modeler David Pollard at Penn State has worked on this problem as well, along with one of the authors of this book (JK). McKay has spent several field seasons studying ice-covered lakes in the so-called dry valleys of Antarctica. The lakes there are covered with about 5 m of exceptionally clear ice, beneath which is found a thriving photosynthetic biota. The ice is clear because it forms very slowly and, hence, excludes air bubbles, which would otherwise give it a cloudy appearance. Box Figure 2 shows the fraction of light transmitted through such clear ice as a function of its thickness. If the ice in the tropics was as thick as predicted previously, then obviously very little light would make it through. But, if the ice was only a few meters thick, then as much as 10% of the incident sunlight might penetrate it. This energy would have to get out by conduction through the ice, just like the geothermal heat from Earth's interior. If you work "Critical-Thinking" Problem 2 at the end of the chapter, you should be able to show that a stable solution can exist with ice as thin as 2 m in the tropics. Approximately 10% of the incident sunlight could make it through this ice, according to Box Figure 2. This problem has now grown complicated, as one needs to also consider the possibility that thick ice near the poles—"sea glaciers," in the climate modeling lingo—would have flowed toward the equator. There is now a debate in the scientific literature as to whether or not this would preclude a "thin-ice" Snowball Earth. If such a solution is possible, however, this would readily explain how the photosynthetic algae made it through this catastrophe. So, perhaps this thin-ice model is indeed the solution to the Snowball Earth paradox.

BOX FIGURE 2 Visible light transmissivity (400–700 nm) versus depth for clear ice. (*Source:* C. P. McKay, *Geophysical Research Letters* 27, 2000, pp. 2153–2156.)

VARIATIONS IN ATMOSPHERIC CO$_2$ AND CLIMATE DURING THE PHANEROZOIC

Although the most spectacular extremes in climate appear to have occurred during the Precambrian, climate has varied over the past 542 m.y. as well. Three of the six glacial periods shown in Figure 8 have occurred during the Phanerozoic eon: a brief one during the Late Ordovician period (about 440 m.y. ago), a long series of glaciations near the boundary between the Permian and Carboniferous periods (about 280 m.y. ago), and the most recent episode, which is here called the Pleistocene glaciation. This name is something of a misnomer because Antarctica began to be glaciated some 15–30 million years ago, well before the Pleistocene epoch began, and because both Antarctica and Greenland continue to be ice-covered today. So, a better name for this glaciation (but one which would likely not be as widely understood) is the Late Cenozoic glaciation. To qualify as a long-term "glacial period," it is only necessary that ice be present over part of Earth's surface for an extended period of time. This is different from common usage, whereby the term "glacial period" refers to one of several episodes of maximum ice extent during the last 3 m.y. These shorter-time-scale climate fluctuations, can be thought of as modulations of an overall climate that is basically "glacial."

CO$_2$ and Climate during the Paleozoic Era

The first part of the Phanerozoic eon, which extended from about 542 m.y. ago until 251 m.y. ago, is called the Paleozoic era. From this time on, considerable information is available to tell us about climate because the fossil record is much more detailed. By examining the types of plants and animals that existed and determining where they lived, scientists can deduce not only whether the climate was warm or cold, but also how wet it was and by how much it varied between the pole and equator. The general results of such studies are shown in Figure 11. Following the intense cold of the Neoproterozoic, the climate warmed. The Cambrian period was decidedly warmer than today, and the ensuing three geological periods were mostly ice-free as well, except for a brief (and poorly understood) spike of glaciation during the Late Ordovician. Climate cooled markedly, however, during the Carboniferous period, culminating in a series of glaciations that spanned almost 80 m.y. and are termed the "Permo-Carboniferous glaciations."

Why did climate get cold at this time? We have already seen that, on long time scales, climate is largely determined by a trade-off between solar luminosity and the atmospheric greenhouse effect. By this time, the atmosphere was well oxygenated, so we can assume that CH$_4$ concentrations were modest and that the greenhouse effect was mostly attributable to CO$_2$ and H$_2$O. Thus, the cooling in Earth's climate was probably caused by a decrease in atmospheric CO$_2$ levels.

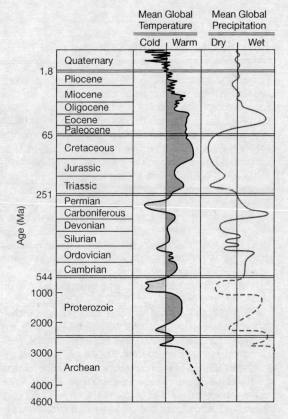

FIGURE 11   Estimated change in surface temperature during the Phanerozoic eon.   (*Source:* From K. C. Condie and R. E. Sloan, *Origin and Evolution of Earth: Principles of Historical Geology*, 1998. Reprinted by permission of Prentice Hall, Upper Saddle River, N.J.)

Why should CO$_2$ levels have declined during the Late Paleozoic? On long time scales, atmospheric CO$_2$ is largely controlled by the carbonate–silicate cycle, but the organic carbon cycle cannot necessarily be neglected. Consider the carbonate–silicate cycle first. How might that have changed? As we saw in the previous section, the rate of silicate weathering is enhanced when continents move toward the equator. So, perhaps changes in continental positions were once again the key. But, biological innovations could have been important as well. Plants and microorganisms are thought to accelerate weathering by increasing the CO$_2$ partial pressure in soils and by releasing organic acids that help dissolve rocks. **Vascular plants** have a well-developed stem or trunk for transporting water and nutrients from the ground up to their leaves, and typically a well-developed root system that takes up water and nutrients and helps support the plant. So, one might expect that the spread of vascular plants would have lowered atmospheric CO$_2$ (Figure 12). Unfortunately for this idea, the timing is not right. Vascular plants originated in the Late Silurian and spread widely during the Devonian period, well before the climate

CO₂ + H₂O $\xrightarrow{\text{Photosynthesis}}$ CH₂O + O₂

$$CO_2 + H_2O \xrightarrow{\text{Photosynthesis}} CH_2O + O_2$$

Solar energy

Heat energy

Decay

$$CH_2O + O_2 \longrightarrow CO_2 + H_2O$$
Respiration and decay

Heat energy

Decay

FIGURE 12 Land plants enhance the partial pressure of CO_2 in soils through root respiration and decay. (*Source:* From T. McKnight, *Physical Geography: A Landscape Appreciation*, 6/e, 1999. Reprinted by permission of Prentice Hall, Upper Saddle River, N.J.)

began to cool. So, let us consider other factors that might have affected atmospheric CO_2.

A strong clue as to what might have happened is suggested by the carbon isotope record. Carbon isotopes indicate that the organic carbon burial rate nearly doubled during the Carboniferous as a result of the formation of large coal beds. This may have led to an increase in atmospheric O_2. However, it could have led to a decrease in atmospheric CO_2 as well. Robert Berner from Yale University has included this information in a model that tries to predict CO_2 levels during the Phanerozoic (Figure 13). As expected, the increased burial of organic carbon during the Carboniferous leads to a substantial drop in atmospheric CO_2 levels. As partial confirmation of Berner's results, the CO_2 concentrations predicted by his model are in approximate agreement with CO_2 levels estimated from paleosol data. This gives us some confidence that the basic idea is correct: during the latter half of its history, Earth's climate has been tightly coupled to atmospheric CO_2 levels.

The Warm Mesozoic Era

The Mesozoic and Cenozoic eras span the past 251 m.y. of Earth history. The Mesozoic, the age of the dinosaurs, is thought to have been considerably warmer than today (Figure 11). Because large animals existed during this

FIGURE 13 Phanerozoic atmospheric CO_2 levels predicted by the geochemical cycle model of R. A. Berner. Solid bars represent constraints on CO_2 from paleosol data. (*Source:* R. A. Berner, *Science* 261, 1993, pp. 68–70.)

time, the fossil evidence relating to Mesozoic climate is quite extensive. For example, during the Mid-Cretaceous period, around 100 m.y. ago, lush ferns and alligators resided in what is now Siberia. Dinosaur skeletons have

FIGURE 14 Estimated limits on longitudinally averaged surface temperatures during the Mid-Cretaceous period, 100 m.y. ago, as compared with today. (*Source:* E. J. Barron and W. M. Washington, "The Carbon Cycle and Atmospheric CO_2," *Geophysical Monograph* 32, AGU, Washington, DC, 1985.)

been recovered from north of the Arctic Circle in Alaska. These and other pieces of evidence indicate that the Mid-Cretaceous climate was on the order of 2 to 6°C (3.6–11°F) warmer at the equator and 20 to 60°C (36–110°F) warmer at the poles (Figure 14).

A second type of evidence that indicates that the Mesozoic climate was warm comes from measurement of oxygen isotope ratios in carbonate sediments recovered from deep-sea cores. Oxygen isotopes provide information both on the temperature of the water in which they formed and on the amount of water stored in the polar ice caps. The measured isotope ratios tell us that Mesozoic ocean water was much warmer than today. This is especially true of the deep ocean, which currently has an average temperature of only 2°C. Deep-ocean temperatures during the Mesozoic era were as high as 15°C. Furthermore, the polar ice caps, which today hold enough water to raise sea level by nearly 80 m, appear to have been absent throughout the entire Mesozoic and during the early Cenozoic as well.

What factor or combination of factors was responsible for the extreme warmth of the Mesozoic? In keeping with the discussion of the previous section, suspicion currently centers on higher atmospheric CO_2 levels. Climate models suggest that an increase in CO_2 by a factor of 4 from the present value could explain the warm climate of the Mid-Cretaceous period. This hypothesis is bolstered by paleomagnetic evidence that indicates that the seafloor was spreading faster at that time than it has in the more recent geologic past. Recall that the spreading rate can be estimated by looking at magnetic patterns in the seafloor. Faster spreading rates would have led to faster rates of subduction of carbonate sediments and this, in turn, should have led to increased rates of CO_2 production from carbonate metamorphism. More CO_2 may also have been released by outgassing at the mid-ocean ridges themselves. And

higher sea level at that time, itself caused by faster sea-floor spreading as well as the absence of polar ice, would have meant that there was less land area available on which to weather silicate rocks. These factors have been included in Berner's models and account for the high atmospheric CO_2 levels predicted for this time period (Figure 13).

Carbon Isotopic Evidence of High Mesozoic CO_2 Levels

Our discussion of paleo-CO_2 levels and climate has thus far been based mostly on theory. It has recently become possible, however, to test the theory with data for at least a few time periods in Earth history. Several different methods have been employed. One example, discussed earlier in the chapter, is based on the mineralogy of paleosols. That particular method is not applicable to more recent times because siderite ($FeCO_3$) is not stable under an oxygenated atmosphere. However, a similar type of analysis can be performed on some paleosols using trace carbonates found in the mineral goethite, $Fe(OH)_3$. The paleosol data shown in Figure 13 were obtained by this technique.

Another technique for inferring past CO_2 concentrations is based on carbon isotopes. Photosynthetic organisms tend to take up ^{12}C faster than they take up ^{13}C. But they do this to a greater extent if CO_2 is relatively abundant in the organism's environment. So, photosynthetically produced organic matter created under high-CO_2 conditions tends to have a low $^{13}C/^{12}C$ ratio, or negative $\delta^{13}C$. If CO_2 is scarce, organisms use whatever isotope is available and the relative isotopic abundances do not change as dramatically.

Carbon isotope abundances have now been measured in sediments of various ages by a number of different research groups. Figure 15 shows the difference in $\delta^{13}C$ values between carbonates and organic carbon. The story that has emerged is consistent with that told above: organic matter from sediments of Mesozoic age contains less ^{13}C than organic matter from sediments deposited during the last 20 m.y., indicating that atmospheric CO_2 levels were probably higher at that time. Although there is still considerable disagreement concerning how much CO_2 has decreased, the idea that CO_2 is a main driver of climate on these time scales has received additional support.

Other Possible Influences on Mesozoic Climate

Although higher atmospheric CO_2 levels can account for the overall warmth of the Mesozoic climate, this mechanism cannot by itself explain the extremely small latitudinal temperature gradient at that time. The equator-to-pole temperature contrast during the Mid-Cretaceous period was only 20–30°C, as compared to 50–60° today. Part of this difference can be explained by the absence of polar ice at that time. Recall that ice cover interacts with climate

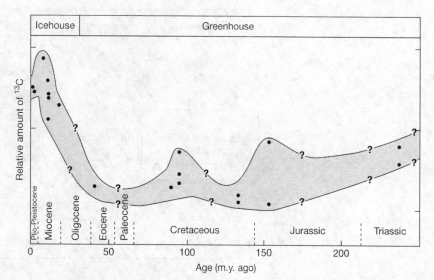

FIGURE 15 Carbon isotope data for the past 150 m.y. The vertical scale is a measure of the difference in ^{13}C content between carbonates and organic carbon. Large differences in ^{13}C correspond to lower atmospheric CO_2 values. The data are consistent with a decrease in CO_2 since the Mid-Cretaceous period. (*Source:* B. Popp et al., *American Journal of Science* 289, 1989, pp. 436.)

by way of a strong, positive feedback loop. Removal of the ice caps would cause a large decrease in the albedo of the polar regions that, in turn, should cause them to warm significantly.

Calculations with climate models suggest, however, that ice–albedo feedback alone is not sufficient to explain the extreme warmth of the Mid-Cretaceous poles. It seems likely that the atmosphere–ocean system was for some reason more effective in transporting heat from the equator to the poles than it is today. One possibility is that the thermohaline circulation of the oceans ran backward at that time: warm, but highly saline, deep water formed at low latitudes welled up near the poles, where it then warmed the climate through evaporation. Unfortunately, no one has yet demonstrated that this mechanism could work. A second possibility is that the tropical Hadley circulation extended further poleward than it does today. Because Hadley cells are very efficient at transporting heat, this mechanism could explain the low latitudinal temperature gradient. Moreover, it could explain the apparent absence of sub-freezing temperatures in continental interiors (Siberia, for example) during the long polar night. Again, however, no one has demonstrated that this mechanism is dynamically feasible.

One of the authors of this text (LK), together with David Pollard (mentioned earlier), have proposed yet another mechanism for additional warmth during these already warm periods: reduced biological production of the cloud condensation nucleus dimethyl sulfide, leading to fewer and thinner clouds. Warm intervals would be less biologically productive because of reduced nutrient supply by upwelling; the strong thermocline (warmer surface waters above cool deep waters) would provide an effective barrier to upwelling by stabilizing the water column density structure. This mechanism leads to overall amplification of global warming and an intensification of warming near the poles. Perhaps the Cretaceous sky not only contained

higher greenhouse gas concentrations but was less cloudy as well!

Cooling during the Cenozoic Era

Starting about 80 m.y. ago, Earth's climate began to cool (except for a short-lived warming during the early Eocene period). The initial decrease may simply have been caused by a decrease in mid-ocean ridge spreading rates, leading to a reduction in atmospheric CO_2. However, the cooling trend accelerated around 30 m.y. ago during the Oligocene epoch in a way that does not correlate with the spreading-rate data. Thus, paleoclimatologists have searched for other explanations for the observed cooling. One intriguing theory, suggested by Maureen Raymo, then at the Massachusetts Institute of Technology, and William Ruddiman of the University of Virginia, is that the carbonate–silicate cycle was perturbed by plate tectonics, but by a mechanism that differs from those discussed previously.

During the Mesozoic and early Cenozoic eras, India was a separate continent drifting slowly toward Asia. The two continents collided around 40 m.y. ago, a process that is still continuing today. The collision created a gigantic chain of mountains (the Himalayas) and a huge area of uplifted terrain called the Tibetan Plateau (Figure 16). The Himalayan Mountains provided fresh, readily erodable surfaces on which silicate weathering could proceed rapidly. At the same time, the uplift of the Tibetan Plateau created seasonal rainfall (the southeast Asian monsoon), which provided the water needed for weathering to occur on the face of the Himalayan range. The combination of these factors may have accelerated silicate weathering rates over a substantial portion of Earth's surface, thereby helping bring atmospheric CO_2 concentrations down to the relatively low levels that prevail today.

The point to be drawn from this discussion is that plate tectonics probably does influence climate over long

FIGURE 16 The collision of India with Asia, shown in a series of paleogeographic maps for the Paleocene (60 m.y. ago), the Eocene (40 m.y. ago), and the Miocene (20 m.y. ago) eras. (*Source:* E. J. Barron, *Paleogeography, Paleoclimatology, Paleoecology* 50, 1985, p. 45.)

time scales, but not necessarily in the way that geologists have traditionally imagined. Continental-scale glaciers can indeed grow when landmasses drift close to the poles but only if climatic conditions are ripe for such a development—specifically, if atmospheric CO_2 concentrations are relatively low. The main influence of plate tectonics on climate appears to be indirect: by changing the way in which the carbonate–silicate cycle operates, plate tectonics helps modulate atmospheric CO_2 levels. This, in turn, affects climate by way of the greenhouse effect. Such changes, in combination with the long-term increase in solar luminosity, can account for the main features of the long-term climate record.

Chapter Summary

1. During the early parts of Earth's history, the faintness of the young Sun must have been offset by higher concentrations of greenhouse gases in the atmosphere.

   a. CO_2 may have dominated at first, but CH_4 was probably an important greenhouse gas as well, once it was being produced by methanogenic bacteria.

   b. The combination of CO_2 and CH_4 kept Earth's climate relatively warm until the early Paleoproterozoic era.

   c. The rise of atmospheric O_2 at ~2.4 b.y. ago eliminated most of the CH_4 and thereby triggered the Paleoproterozoic glaciation.

   d. That said, CH_4 could still have remained an important greenhouse gas during much of the Proterozoic eon, provided that the deep oceans remained anoxic. A decrease in CH_4 toward the end of this eon, perhaps triggered by a corresponding rise in atmospheric O_2, could have provided the trigger for the Neoproterozoic Snowball Earth glaciations.

2. During Earth's more recent history, climate has been largely determined by the balance between increasing solar luminosity and decreasing atmospheric CO_2.

   a. During most of this time, climate has been kept within moderate bounds by the negative feedback associated with the carbonate–silicate cycle.

   b. This stabilization mechanism has broken down temporarily, however, at least three times, resulting in global glaciations near the beginning and the end of the Proterozoic. Life survived these Snowball Earth episodes by mechanisms that are currently being debated.

3. During the last 500 m.y. of Earth's history, climate has alternated between periods of warmth (the Mid-Cretaceous) and periods of cold (the Late Ordovician, Permo-Carboniferous, and Pleistocene glaciations). Earth is currently in a moderately cold state—a brief interglacial period within the Pleistocene glacial epoch. Variations in atmospheric CO_2 levels caused by changes in plate tectonics and by biological innovations can explain the broad features of Phanerozoic climate history.

Key Terms

anti-greenhouse effect
cap carbonates
corona
dropstones
ethane
geothermal heat
glacial striations
ice-rafting

methanogenesis
Mie scattering
moraines
neutrinos
paleoclimate
polymerize
Rayleigh scattering
reduced gas

scattering
solar wind
sulfate-reducing bacteria
thermophiles
tillite
vascular plants

Review Questions

1. Why does the Sun get brighter with time?
2. How might the carbonate–silicate cycle have helped solve the faint young Sun problem?
3. Why is methane thought to have been an important greenhouse gas during the Archean era?
4. What triggered the Huronian glaciation at 2.4 b.y. ago?
5. What types of geologic evidence are used to infer past glaciations?
6. How many separate episodes of glaciation have occurred during Earth's history?
7. What types of geologic evidence support the Snowball Earth model for the Late Precambrian glaciations?
8. How are carbon isotopes used to infer past atmospheric CO_2 concentrations?
9. How are atmospheric CO_2 levels affected by the presence of land plants?
10. What mechanisms might explain the warm climate of the Mesozoic era? How might the equator-to-pole temperature gradient have been reduced?
11. Why did climate cool during the past 40 million years?

Critical-Thinking Problems

1. Evidence for low-latitude glaciation is found at both 0.6 Ga and 2.4 Ga. These are two of the three possible Snowball Earth events mentioned in the text. (We will neglect the event at 0.75 Ga because it is similar to the first one.) Your job is to estimate how thick the ice was at those times.

   a. The variation in solar luminosity with time can be approximated by the following formula (derived by fitting the results of a computer model of the Sun's evolution):

$$S = \frac{S_0}{1 + 0.4(t/4.6)}$$

where S = solar flux at time t

$S_o = 1370 \ W/m^2$ = present solar flux
t = time in Ga (billions of years before present).

Calculate the solar flux at 0.6 and 2.4 Ga both in W/m^2 and as a percentage of its current value.

b. As we have learned previously, the effective radiating temperature of Earth can be found from the formula

$$\sigma T_e^4 = \frac{S}{4}(1 - A),$$

where A is the planetary albedo and $\sigma (= 5.67 \times 10^{-8} \ W/m^2/K^4)$ is the Stefan–Boltzmann constant. Calculate T_e at 0.6 and 2.3 Ga, assuming an albedo of 0.65 (the value for clean ice and snow). Then, calculate the global average surface temperature, T_s, assuming that the atmospheric greenhouse effect, ΔT_g, was the same as today (33 K). Recall that $T_s = T_e + \Delta T_g$.

c. The conductive heat flow through ice is given by

$$F = \frac{\lambda \Delta T}{\Delta z},$$

where λ (= 2 W/m/K) is the thermal conductivity of ice, ΔT is the temperature difference between the top and bottom of the ice layer, and Δz is the thickness of the layer. We know that the current geothermal heat flux, F, is about 0.09 W/m^2. Assume that F had this same value at 0.6 Ga, but was twice as high at 2.4 Ga. Assume also that the top of the ice is at temperature T_s and that the water below the ice has a temperature of $-2°C$ (the freezing point of seawater). What is the thickness of the ice at both 0.6 and 2.4 Ga?

2. Suppose now that the ice is transparent enough so that some sunlight makes it through. Let's see how that would change the ice thickness.

a. Calculate the globally averaged solar flux incident on Earth's surface during the Neoproterozoic glaciation (0.6 Ga).

b. The solar flux at the equator is about 20% higher than the global average value. Suppose that 10% of this incident sunlight makes it through the ice. How thin must the ice layer be in order to conduct this heat back out so that the water temperature remains constant? (Use the formula from Problem 1c.)

c. Is the ice thickness calculated in part (b) consistent with the assumption that it would transmit 10% of the sunlight through it? Determine this by consulting Box Figure 2.

Further Reading

General

Gribbin, J. 1990. *Hothouse Earth: The greenhouse effect and Gaia*. New York: Grove Weidenfeld.

Lovelock, J. E. 1988. *The ages of Gaia: A biography of our living Earth*. New York: Norton.

Advanced

Crowley, T. J., and G. R. North. 1991. *Paleoclimatology*. New York: Oxford University Press.

Haqq-Misra, J. D., S. D. Domagal-Goldman, P. J. Kasting, and J. F. Kasting. 2008. A revised, hazy methane greenhouse for the early Earth. *Astrobiology*, v. 8, pp. 1127–1137.

Biodiversity through Earth History

Key Questions

- How and why has the diversity of life changed over the history of Earth?
- How can the fossil record be used to elucidate this history?

- What caused the massive losses of global diversity that have occurred at least three times over the past half-billion years of Earth history?

Chapter Overview

This chapter discusses changes in biodiversity, the variety of life forms, through geologic time. *Paleontologists* (scientists who study ancient life) use many methods to reconstruct this history. Shelly marine organisms (those with the most robust fossil record) appeared abruptly about a half-billion years ago. Their diversity rose rapidly (geologically speaking), reaching a level that persisted for a few hundred million years. Then, about 252 million years ago, Earth experienced a dramatic loss of species diversity: perhaps 95% of all species living at that time went extinct. A subsequent event, occurring some 65 million years ago, led to the extinction of the dinosaurs. A rich body of evidence supports the theory that this most recent mass extinction was a direct result of the collision of a 10-km-diameter meteorite with Earth. (We use the term *meteorite* liberally to mean a comet or asteroid that impacts Earth. Formal usage, however, would require us to refer to such objects as *meteoroids* until they strike Earth, at which point the materials that remain are referred to as meteorites.) The environmental consequences of this event were severe and clearly capable of annihilating most life on Earth at the time. Evidence for asteroid or comet impact at the other extinction boundaries is equivocal; during these events, extreme volcanic activity and its environmental consequences may have played a direct role. Nevertheless, there is a distinct periodicity in the extinction record that suggests extinction has an extraterrestrial pacemaker.

THE FOSSIL RECORD OF BIODIVERSITY

The diversity of life is one of its key indicators of the health of the planet. In anticipation of the forthcoming discussion of how human activity is impacting global biodiversity, we here explore how the diversity of life has changed over Earth history, what the causes of those changes have been, and, in particular, how the Earth system has responded to sudden reductions in global biodiversity.

Phanerozoic Diversity Patterns

The best evidence for past changes in global biodiversity comes from the fossil record. Biologists have traditionally defined species on the basis of the ability of individuals to interbreed. This criterion obviously cannot be applied to fossils nor to organisms such as bacteria that do not reproduce sexually. Thus, paleontologists have used similarities in *morphology* (body shape) to group fossils into species. More than a hundred years of paleontological research have been laboriously compiled in an effort to determine how the diversity of life has changed over Earth history. This effort was undertaken in the 1970s and 1980s by the late Jack Sepkoski of the University of Chicago. Although the compilation has recently been updated and reanalyzed (see the following text), many of the fundamental features revealed in his compilation remain.

Paleontologists have cataloged the presence or absence of thousands of species of fossilizable organisms (primarily those with hard parts, i.e., skeletons, shells, or teeth). These observations reveal that, to the extent that fossil diversity reflects the diversity of all forms of life, global biodiversity has generally increased over the past 500 million years but there have been significant fluctuations (Figure 1a and bias-corrected curve Figure 2; see below). Note that in Figure 1a the number of species has been normalized to what we would find if rocks representing exactly 1 million years of Earth history were investigated. This normalization has been done because the geological periods are of uneven duration. Longer periods would otherwise appear to be overly diverse. Diversity rose rapidly in the Cambrian (Camb.), an event that has been called "The Cambrian Explosion." Diversity stabilized in the Ordovician (Ord.) and remained stable for much of the rest of the Paleozoic (the era from the Cambrian through the Permian), with drops at the end of the Ordovician and in the Late Devonian (Dev.). The greatest diversity drop of the entire Phanerozoic occurred in the Late Permian (Perm.), when up to 95% of all species went extinct (best seen in Fig. 2). Following this event, diversity recovered rather gradually, beginning an upward trend that continued for the rest of the fossil record, with two abrupt interruptions at the end of the Triassic and at the end of the Cretaceous.

Biases in the Fossil Record

Unfortunately, paleontologists don't have great confidence in the species-level diversity curve shown in Figure 1a. The upward trend certainly is consistent with our realization that diversity must have increased over the past 3.5 billion years. However, our confidence in these data is weakened by the observation that the outcrop area (the area of rocks exposed at Earth's surface; Figure 1b) and the volume of sedimentary rocks (Figure 1c) that contain the fossils of various ages display essentially the same pattern. Particularly troubling is the anomalously high abundance of Devonian and Tertiary species, outcrops, and sediment volume. Geologists recognize that these patterns, especially the increased volume and outcrop area of the youngest rocks, are consequences of erosion: older rocks have been subject to a longer interval of erosion, so their volumes and outcrop areas are reduced. Because the number of species discovered by paleontologists depends on the availability of rocks to study, we are

(a) Apparent Species Diversity

(b) Geologic Map Area

(c) Estimated Volume of Sediment

FIGURE 1 (a) The fossil record of apparent species diversity of marine organisms, compared with the (b) outcrop area and (c) the volume of sedimentary rocks of the same age. All values are normalized to a million-year interval of Earth history. (*Source:* P. W. Signor, *Annual Review of Ecology and Systematics* 21, 1990, pp. 509–539.)

forced to conclude that the fossil record of species diversity is not a true reflection of the trend through Earth history. The higher species diversity of more recent times could be more apparent than real. In particular, the marked apparent increase in species diversity toward the modern is likely largely an artifact of the higher abundance of rocks and outcrops, a phenomenon called *the pull of the recent*.

A strategy paleontologists have adopted to minimize this sampling bias is to group their fossil data into increasingly higher levels of taxonomy. **Taxonomy** is the systematic organization of living or fossil organisms into a hierarchy (see the Box "Useful Concepts: Taxonomy"). The occurrence of a single specimen of a species confirms the existence of its higher taxonomic levels: *genus, family, order, class, phylum* (for animals and some protists) or *division* (for bacteria, fungi, plants, and some protists), *kingdom,* and

USEFUL CONCEPTS
Taxonomy

Given the millions of species that exist on Earth today and the thousands of distinct fossils recognized in the geologic record, a system of organization is clearly needed. Hence the field of taxonomy (from the Greek *taxis*, meaning arrangement or order) was born. Two approaches are possible: one based on evolutionary, genetic relationships, and the other based on discernible physical similarities. The former is theoretically more satisfying, but the latter is usually more practical, especially for extinct organisms observable only as fossils. Species of extant (currently living) organisms are differentiated on the basis of their inability to interbreed. Higher levels of groupings (Box Figure 1) into genera (the plural of genus), families, orders, classes, phyla (the plural of phylum) or divisions, kingdoms, and domains are based on the degree of dissimilarity in all detectable characteristics between taxa (plural of **taxon**, an individual taxonomic group). For example, all families within an order should share some similarity that is distinct from all other orders.

Biochemists and evolutionary biologists are currently working feverishly to reveal the genetic sequences of a number of organisms, including both humans and bacteria. These investigators are finding that the established taxonomy based on morphology is in need of revision. Organisms that once seemed distant relatives are now surprisingly closely related on the "Tree of Life". Moreover, there has been considerable transfer of genetic material across lineages, making the distinctions among groups a bit fuzzy. Finally, we have long known that the genetic makeup of the mitochondria of eukaryotes (including us) is distinct from the rest of the body's genetic sequences, probably indicating that eukaryotes evolved from an early symbiotic relationship among different bacteria (the "endosymbiosis" hypothesis of the origin of eukaryotes).

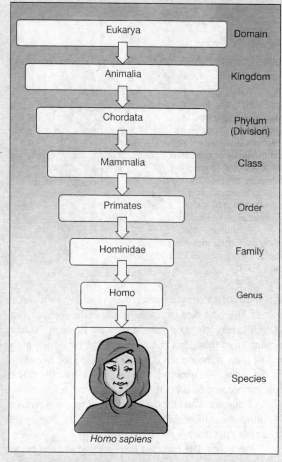

BOX FIGURE 1 A taxonomic tree for our species, *Homo sapiens.*.

domain. No other species in any of these other taxonomic levels need be found. Thus, it is less likely that a higher taxonomic level will be unrepresented in the fossil record of a time when it did indeed exist. Paleontologists generally agree that the diversity record at the genus level and above, for marine organisms with well-preserved skeletons and shells and for data for which sampling biases have been removed, is reasonably robust.

Fossil Biodiversity with Bias Removed

In the most recent compilation of the fossil diversity data (Figure 2), paleontologists have gone to great lengths to rid the data of various biases that are associated with the processes of fossilization, subsequent erosion of the rocks hosting the fossils, and sampling. The new data are presented at the genus level and are lumped into bins with an average duration of 11 million years. This record, published in 2008 by scientists associated with the Paleobiology Database initiative (http://paleodb.org), differs significantly from earlier compilations and has yet to be fully interpreted. It displays some trends that have been recognized for a long time, including the large increase in biodiversity throughout the Cambrian (Cm) and Ordovician (O) periods. (Note the most of the genera shown in the earliest Cambrian bin arose during the earliest Cambrian, so there is an abrupt increase, not shown, during the earliest Cambrian.) The data also show major decreases in biodiversity in the latest Permian (P) and at the end of the Triassic (Tr); these decreases are associated with well-known extinctions. However, unlike the data in previous compilations (Figure 1a), the Cm–O diversification continues well into the Devonian (D), and then declines

FIGURE 2 The fossil record of marine organism biodiversity at the genus level of classification. These data have been corrected for a number of sampling biases by the Paleobiology Database project and collected into bins that average about 11 million years in duration. (*Source:* Study published in J. Alroy et al., *Science* 321, 2008, pp. 97–100.)

into the Early Permian, rather than reaching any sort of plateau. Diversity then increases rapidly in the Permian, only to decline abruptly once more in the Late Permian. Notably missing from these data is any sign of the extinction at the end of the Cretaceous (K), which heralded the demise of the dinosaurs. The unbinned data do indeed show the extinction, but because biodiversity recovered within a few million years of this event and the data are binned into approximate 11-million-year increments, the graph does not display this severe but brief diversity drop (see below).

The fossil data can also be compiled at even higher taxonomic levels to reveal more fundamental features of the evolution of biodiversity on the planet. Like the species-level curve in the Paleozoic (Figure 1a) and the genus-level diversity curve in the Mesozoic and Cenozoic (Figure 2), the order-level diversity curve (Figure 3a) reaches a plateau early in the Phanerozoic that is sustained for the rest of Earth history (although there is a marked Silurian high and Permian low). Early in the Cambrian period, as organisms evolved fossilizable hard parts, new species evolved rapidly as they developed new ways to utilize their environment. Common morphologies such as particularly shaped shells or skeletons arose that were related to form or function required by their particular ecological **niche** (the role a particular organism plays in the ecosystem: decomposer, surface grazer, etc.). For the paleontologist, these common features allow the species to be grouped into higher taxonomic levels. As these ecological niches were filled and the opportunities for new lifestyles diminished, the rate of appearance of novel body shapes for marine organisms (as reflected in the number of new orders) diminished. The rest of the Phanerozoic had slower

rates of origination of new orders (Figure 3b), and this slowdown was very nearly balanced by the loss of orders (steady state was achieved).

Evolution, Extinction, and Origination

What drives these trends in biodiversity through time? The biological diversity of Earth today has been acquired through the process of biological evolution. **Evolution** can be defined as the change from one generation to the next of inherited characteristics of a population of organisms. Variability in the genetic makeup of a population of organisms arises through *genetic mutation*—damage to the DNA of organisms that occurs as a result of such processes as exposure to ultraviolet radiation (from the sun), natural radioactivity in the environment, and exposure to certain chemicals. Mutations can also result from mistakes made in DNA replication during reproduction. Usually, mutated genes are detrimental to the organism, reducing its prospects for reproduction or survival, but occasionally they are beneficial. Organisms with these desirable traits (termed **adaptations**) have a higher likelihood of reproduction and/or survival under given environmental conditions, allowing them to pass on the trait to their descendants. This process, **natural selection**, is the major driver for evolution. If a population of organisms becomes isolated from the rest of the members of its species and acquires favorable adaptations through natural selection, it may eventually become a new species, unable to breed with the original species; this process is called **origination**. **Extinction** is the loss of all individuals within a species. It can occur because the species has become unfit or

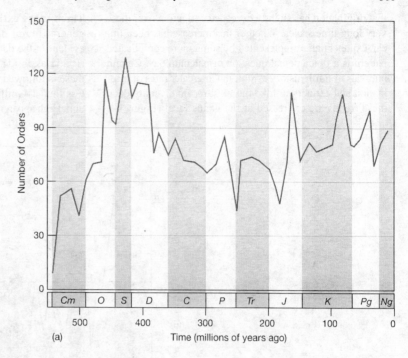

(a)

Time (millions of years ago)

(b)

Time (millions of years ago)

FIGURE 3 (a) The apparent diversity of fossilized marine organisms through geological time, grouped at the order taxonomic level. (b) The number of new orders of marine organisms that first appear in sedimentary rocks of a given age. The Cambrian and Ordovician were clearly a remarkable time of origination of a variety of new body shapes (which allow paleontologists to recognize the appearance of the various taxonomic groups). (*Source:* Courtesy John Alroy, Paleobiology Database, National Center for Ecological Analysis and Synthesis.)

uncompetitive in its (often changing) environment, or it could result from an external stress that affects a particular species or many species simultaneously.

Diversity is best thought of as a dynamic characteristic of the biota:

$$\frac{\text{rate of change in number}}{\text{of species on Earth}} = \frac{\text{origination}}{\text{rate}} - \frac{\text{extinction}}{\text{rate}}$$

Researchers estimate that 10 to 25 species originate every year, and 10 to 25 go extinct. These are considered to be the average rates of origination and extinction as a result of natural selection, which was first described by Charles Darwin. We can safely presume that, through evolution by natural selection, the total number of species has increased over the 3.5-billion-year history of life on Earth, indicating that origination has slightly exceeded extinction over these very long time scales. Whether this increase has been linear, exponential, or represented by some more complicated pattern is a fundamental question of paleontology. Certain intervals of Earth history exhibit much greater rates of origination and extinction. Like the most recent diversity data, these trends are expressed at the genus level (Figure 4).

Three **mass extinctions**, in which 50% or more of the genera (plural of genus) go extinct during one bin, are evident in the data: these occur at the ends of the Permian (P), Triassic (Tr), and Cretaceous (K) periods. Each of these is followed "immediately" (in the next data bin, or in less than 10 million years) by enhanced rates of origination. High apparent rates of extinction in the Cambrian (Cm),

(a)

FIGURE 4 Rates of origination and extinction of genera during the Phanerozoic. Extinction is defined as the percentage of genera present in a bin that are absent in the next bin. Bin length averages 11 million years. Origination likewise is expressed as the percentage of genera appearing during an interval of time that weren't present in the previous bin. The five major Phanerozoic extinctions are those that exhibited greater than 50% genus loss. (*Source:* Courtesy John Alroy, Paleobiology Database, National Center for Ecological Analysis and Synthesis.)

(b)

Late Ordovician (O), the Late Devonian (D), the latter two commonly identified as mass extinctions in the literature, may be artifacts of uncorrected biases in the record. The biodiversity drop in the Late Devonian in the new dataset seems to be brought about as much by a failure of origination (Figure 4b) as by a peak of extinction (Figure 4a). Another biodiversity drop, at the end of the Ordovician, has been well studied as a mass extinction but here doesn't appear to be particularly anomalous. The three undisputed mass extinctions are at one extreme of a continuum of origination and extinction rates from the small to the extremely large. Thus, origination and extinction, like other natural phenomena (floods, earthquakes), are likely to be the result of a variety of causes occurring on many different time scales and over a range of magnitudes.

The time period from the Triassic to the Recent exhibits a plateau in genus-level diversity (Figure 2) despite very high rates of turnover of the biota on geologic time scales: origination and extinction rates typically range from 20 to 40% per bin interval (~11 million years), meaning that the genera that make up one bin are quite different from those of the next bins. Thus, the diversity curve could be considerably more variable than it actually is. The fact that it does not vary that greatly may reflect feedbacks that tend to stabilize diversity over time. According to the fossil data, extinction rates tend to be highest when diversity is high (tending to suppress unrestrained growth of biodiversity; a negative coupling), and origination rates tend to increase markedly following large extinction events. Presumably, mass extinction empties ecological niches that newly evolved species can fill. Although the response is geologically rapid, it takes up to tens of millions of years. The fossil record shows that if modern species diversity continues to decrease, it will be a long time before the system recovers.

Causes of Mass Extinction

The largest of all known mass extinctions occurred at the end of the Permian period, 252 million years ago. It occurs near the beginning of a series of huge volcanic eruptions in Siberia, suggesting that these events could be causally related. The eruptions created massive basalt flows that are known today as the **Siberian Traps**. The volcanic eruptions also appear to have permeated a gigantic coal bed that had been previously emplaced. Heating of this coal could have led to a rapid buildup in atmospheric carbon dioxide, extreme global warming, and loss of oxygen from the oceans, leading to an "anoxic" state that would be inhospitable to oxygen-dependent organisms. One hypothesis suggests that toxic hydrogen sulfide (H_2S) built up in the anoxic oceans and was released suddenly to the atmosphere, causing extinctions on land and in the surface ocean. However, all of these explanations are still considered speculative, and the end-Permian extinction remains a topic for research and debate.

In contrast, the Cretaceous–Tertiary (K–T) mass extinction (65 million years ago) has been the focus of a tremendous amount of research in the past few decades. It has also captured the attention of the general public, because it is the event at which the dinosaurs went extinct. And, it appears that the killer has been identified. For these reasons, we end this chapter with a detailed discussion of the K–T event.

THE CRETACEOUS–TERTIARY MASS EXTINCTION

It has been estimated that 75% of all species went extinct in a very short interval of geologic time at the end of the Cretaceous period. The species affected included both marine- and land-based organisms. The most well known, of course, were the dinosaurs.

Two important questions arise concerning the K–T mass extinction: What caused it? And, how did the Earth system respond to and recover from it? The first of these has been one of the most thoroughly studied questions in Earth science and has perhaps engendered more hypotheses than the origin of life itself. The second question is of particular importance to us because it returns us to our discussion of the resiliency of the Earth system to perturbations.

Possible Causes of the K–T Mass Extinction

As many as 20 hypotheses on the cause of the mass extinction at the end of the Cretaceous period have appeared in the scientific literature. Add to that a similar number of wild speculations appearing in the tabloids (including invasions by extraterrestrial life-forms), and you have the sort of scientific enigma that is certain to stimulate discussions in all forums for some time to come. Of these, only four survived the scrutiny of scientists working on the problem in the late 20th century: (1) sudden sea-level changes, (2) sharp temperature fluctuations, (3) volcanic eruptions, and (4) meteorite impacts.

A central tenet of the scientific method is that hypotheses cannot be proved, only disproved. A hypothesis that continues to be consistent with observations may be elevated to the status of theory. Eventually, however, even well-established theories may be disproved as new observations are made that are inconsistent with theory. The debate about the causes of mass extinctions, especially that at the K–T boundary, provides a good example of how theories rise and fall from general acceptance within the scientific community.

SEA-LEVEL CHANGE AND CLIMATE CHANGE Until quite recently, changes in sea level or climate were the generally accepted theories for explaining mass extinctions including the K–T. Major drops in sea level are known to have contributed to extinctions of marine life by exposing vast regions of the continental shelves to the atmosphere, leading to the loss of habitat for shallow-marine organisms (which tend to dominate the fossil record). Climate excursions, especially glaciations or periods of extreme warmth, have also severely stressed marine communities, especially those in the tropics, which are especially temperature-sensitive, causing substantial losses of biodiversity.

However, some of the largest known sea-level drops were not associated with mass extinctions. It is also unclear how sea-level changes could have exterminated land-dwelling organisms, such as the dinosaurs. As for climate change, the best studied of the glaciations, those of the Pleistocene epoch, were associated with only a modest level of extinction, despite rapid climate swings and sea-level fluctuations. Glacial sea-level fall seems to be the best explanation for the Late Ordovician mass extinction, though.

METEORITE IMPACT AND VOLCANIC ERUPTIONS. Astronomical explanations for mass extinctions have long existed but have suffered from lack of substantiation. One such hypothesis called for a nearby supernova, which would have destroyed Earth's ozone layer, leading to high levels of exposure to ultraviolet radiation. On similar, purely theoretical footing was the idea that a large meteorite impact caused the K–T extinction.

Anomalously high concentrations of **iridium**—an element that is rare at Earth's surface but is concentrated in Earth's interior and in extraterrestrial materials—were found in 1979 in unusual, fine-grained sediments deposited at the end of the Cretaceous (the K–T boundary clays of Gubbio, Italy). This iridium anomaly was the piece of evidence needed to establish meteorite impact as the currently accepted theory for the cause of the K–T extinction. However, a minority of scientists were still convinced that widespread volcanism was to blame. These scientists argued that volcanism would lead to many of the same environmental changes as a meteorite impact would have. We will examine this controversy as an example of how theories compete for acceptance by the scientific community.

Proponents of the meteorite-impact theory made a number of predictions, any of which, if invalidated, would disprove the theory. Luis Alvarez, one of the discoverers of the iridium enrichment layer, has enumerated predictions to test the theory and the ways in which previously made and new observations are consistent with the theory:

1. *An iridium enrichment should be found in K–T boundary sediments worldwide.* The K–T iridium anomaly has been documented in more than 75 localities around the globe in both marine- and land-based sediments. A 10-km-diameter meteorite is required to account for the amount of iridium deposited in all these regions.
2. *This enrichment should always be found within the same interval of geologic time.* All iridium layers found near the K–T occur in an interval defined by magnetic polarity reversals known as *polarity chron C29R,* which has been precisely dated to span the interval from 65.6 to 64.9 million years ago. The K–T

boundary is placed at 65.0 million years ago by these researchers.

3. *Large meteorites strike Earth sufficiently frequently to explain the extinction record.* The late Eugene Shoemaker of the U.S. Geological Survey (a codiscoverer of the Shoemaker–Levy comet that collided with Jupiter in 1994) demonstrated that a strong relationship exists between the frequency and size of impacts (Figure 5). The data he used span time and size scales ranging from observations of the rate of space shuttle pitting (one dust-sized impact every 30 μsec on average) to the frequency of large cratering events (every 10,000 years for 100-m-wide impactors). Recent satellite observations confirm the left side of the figure (objects smaller than 10 m in diameter), and near-Earth asteroid tracking studies confirm the diagram up to ~200-m-diameter objects. According to this relationship, a meteorite 10 km in diameter should strike Earth on average every 100 million years. This is a rare event, but many such events have occurred since the origin of life. Five or six such events should have occurred since the beginning of the Phanerozoic. Impacts of the sort that caused the widespread devastation of Tunguska, Siberia, in 1908 occur about once every thousand years. In this event the bolide exploded in the atmosphere, flattening trees over hundreds of square kilometers (the area of a large city).
4. *On shorter time scales, such events should be rare.* In polarity chron C29R, there are no other iridium enrichments. In a study of a 34 million-year interval surrounding the K–T event, it is the only known anomaly. In fact, no iridium anomalies of comparable size have been detected anywhere else in the geologic record. According to prediction 3, several iridium layers should be lurking in rocks that have not been analyzed, unless most meteorites do not have large iridium abundances. (A comet, for example, would leave much less iridium for the same magnitude impact event because it is roughly half water ice—the iridium would be contained only in the rocky part—and because a typical comet impact would occur at much higher velocity than an asteroid impact. Comets originate from the outer solar system or beyond and often have orbits that are highly inclined to Earth's orbit, sometimes even in the opposite direction. A typical comet that hit Earth would do so at ~60 km/s, compared to ~20 km/s for a typical Earth-crossing asteroid. The kinetic energy of the impact is proportional to the square of the velocity: K.E. = 1/2 mv^2. Thus, for impacts of the same total kinetic energy, a comet would deliver only about 1/20th as much iridium as would an asteroid.)
5. *Plants as well as animals should have suffered as a result of the meteorite impact.* There is

FIGURE 5 The Shoemaker curve: the frequency of collisions of extraterrestrial material with Earth, as a function of the size of the material. (*Source:* Luis W. Alvarez, *Physics Today,* July 1987, pp. 24–33.)

now clear evidence of significant turnover in the types of vegetation inhabiting the land surface, as recorded particularly well by spores and pollen (Figure 6).

6. *The gross chemical composition of the boundary clays should be identical worldwide, given that they*

all originated from the same excavated material. The K–T boundary clays from Denmark and from the central Pacific are reported to be so similar in composition as to preclude diverse, local origins. The boundary clay is thought to contain debris from the impactor itself, along with a larger amount of

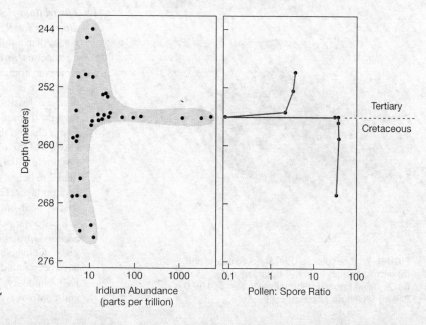

FIGURE 6 The Cretaceous–Tertiary iridium anomaly is coincident with a major change in the types of plants inhabiting the Raton Basin of New Mexico, as indicated by the fossil pollen-to-fern spore ratio. A diverse community of plants collapsed to one dominated by a few species of fern. Samples were drawn from a drill core at the depths indicated on the graph. (*Source:* Luis W. Alvarez, *Physics Today,* July 1987, pp. 24–33.)

material from Earth's crust and upper mantle that was excavated by the impact.

7. *The boundary clays should differ in composition from more typical clays deposited above and below the boundary clays at individual sites.* Compositional differences between the iridium-rich boundary clays and the surrounding sediments have been confirmed at a number of sites.

8. *Any chemical or isotopic signature in the boundary clay will have a significant extraterrestrial component.* The iridium anomaly is the best studied of these anomalies, although other geochemical and isotopic signatures are arguably extraterrestrial.

9. *The boundary clays should bear some evidence of the high temperatures generated during impact.* Small *spherules* of silicate minerals (Figure 7) have been found in the boundary clays. These

(a)

(b)

FIGURE 7 [See color section] Shocked quartz and (b) microspherules from K–T boundary clays. (*Source:* (a) Dr. David Kring/SPL/Photo Researchers and (b) David Parker/ SPL/Photo Reasearchers.)

spherules are thought to have formed when molten rock droplets, ejected into the atmosphere during the impact, cooled and solidified into glassy spheres before being redeposited at Earth's surface.

10. *The boundary clays should bear some evidence of the high pressures generated during impact.* Small, fractured grains of *shocked quartz* are commonly found in boundary clays (see Figure 7). These grains form only when quartz is subjected to very high pressures—the sort we would expect from a meteorite impact. Under these conditions, the crystal structure of quartz is deformed in a characteristic fashion, so geologists can easily differentiate shocked quartz from quartz that is gradually subjected to the high pressures deep within Earth. Shocked quartz has also been found near known meteorite craters and in rocks surrounding the sites of underground nuclear explosions.

11. *The K–T event should have generated wildfires that might have left a sedimentary record of charred material.* Charcoal is indeed commonly found in K–T boundary clays. Calculations by Jay Melosh of the University of Arizona and colleagues provide a natural explanation for the apparent worldwide occurrence of wildfires during the K–T event. The impact excavated a huge amount of material in forming the crater, and this material was blasted in all directions away from the point of impact. Some of it was injected high into the atmosphere. The heating associated with reentry of ejected material through the atmosphere, estimated to be 50–100 times the solar flux, created unbearably hot conditions in cloud-free regions all over the world. Thus, a mechanism for rapid drying and ignition of vegetation on all continents would have existed. In cloudy areas, or beneath the sea or lakes, this energy would instead have gone into evaporating liquid water in cloud droplets.

12. *The iridium-rich layer should be just above the last dinosaur fossil.* At Gubbio, Italy, the iridium layer is less than a millimeter above the last occurrence of Cretaceous *foraminifera* (microscopic plankton). However, foraminifera are not dinosaurs. Dinosaur fossils are rare, and we are unlikely to find the last dinosaur fossil directly below the iridium layer (although, theoretically, if we keep looking we might find a charred dinosaur fossil buried in iridium-rich clay). Paleontologists have found articulated dinosaur fossils (fossils with joints intact) no closer than 2 m below the K–T boundary, as defined by the iridium layer. The low probability of preservation of fossils near boundaries can make an abrupt mass extinction appear to be gradual; this is called the *Signor-Lipps effect* and is well known to paleontologists. Conversely, disarticulated dinosaur fossils have been found in sedimentary rocks well above the K–T boundary. This has generated some confusion and controversy, but these fossils likely have been

eroded from older rocks and redeposited in younger sediments. No complete dinosaur skeleton has ever been found above the boundary.

13. ***The pattern of extinction should show no evidence of preferential survival of species that were well adapted to the Cretaceous environment.*** As mentioned before, mass extinctions in general, and the K–T one in particular, have been notably nonspecific. However, it does appear that large land animals were particularly hard hit by the K–T mass extinction; virtually all species with average weights greater than 25 kg (55 lb) went extinct. In contrast, mammals, which at the time were lightweights, fared much better. Perhaps smaller animals fared better simply because their population sizes were larger: Statistically speaking, some would survive the event. Or perhaps they were better able to avoid the immediate effects of the meteorite impact. After the extinction, mammals evolved, filling many of the niches left vacant by the demise of the dinosaurs.

The confirmation of the Alvarez predictions supports the meteorite-impact theory for the K–T extinction, but it does not prove it. The volcanic theory of mass extinction shares many features of the meteorite-impact theory, and is a more plausible explanation for the end-Permian mass extinction. Large increases in volcanic activity could, in the short term, increase the amount of sulfuric acid aerosol in the stratosphere, cooling the climate. Indeed, several such volcanic cooling events have been identified in the climate record of the past few centuries. However, only explosive volcanoes like Mt. Pinatubo or El Chichón inject aerosols into the stratosphere. Large volcanic eruptions did occur during the Late Cretaceous; they formed great layers of basalt in India that are known as the Deccan Traps. If these flows resembled modern flood basalts, though, they were gentle outpourings of basalt that did not produce much aerosol. The settling ash from volcanic eruptions could create a worldwide clay layer similar to the K–T boundary clay and might also produce spherules and shocked quartz. In the long term, carbon dioxide released by volcanism would lead to global warming. These climatic fluctuations would present environmental stresses to which many groups of organisms could not adapt. However, according to Alvarez, the volcanic theory is inconsistent with three observations:

1. Sand-sized spherules, even if ejected by volcanoes, would not reach ballistic orbits (as do impact ejecta) or be distributed globally, as the K–T spherules are observed to be.
2. Shocked quartz of the sort found at the K–T boundary has never been found in deposits of volcanic origin but is common in deposits associated with known impact craters.
3. Volcanic ejecta tend to have very low iridium concentrations.

Who is right? The arguments are complicated, but the evidence strongly favors the impact hypothesis. Indeed, since the Alvarez team performed their study, additional evidence has emerged that provides further support for the impact hypothesis. One such new piece of evidence is the discovery of fullerenes or "buckyballs" in K–T boundary sediments. *Fullerenes* are large cagelike molecules containing 60 or more carbon atoms arranged in a sphere. (They derive their name from architect Buckminster Fuller, who designed the first geodesic dome. Fullerenes resemble a tiny version of his visionary creation.) Fullerenes are formed in all sorts of environments where carbon is burned, including ordinary candle flames. However, the fullerenes found at the K–T boundary contain helium with isotopic ratios that are clearly extraterrestrial. (Recall that most of Earth's helium, ^{4}He, is produced from decay of uranium and thorium. By contrast, the K–T fullerenes contain mostly ^{3}He. This suggests that they were formed in the expanding envelopes of dying, carbon-rich stars.)

This argument, like most of the original arguments presented by the Alvarez team, is somewhat technical. It is convincing to most experts in the field, but is hard to explain to a nonscientist. As we will see, however, the evidence for the impact hypothesis has become quite down-to-Earth.

The Smoking Gun: The Chicxulub Crater

Another prediction from the meteorite-impact theory is that somewhere on Earth a very large crater should exist, representing the site of impact of the 10-km meteorite. Until very recently, scientists had explained their inability to locate such a crater by pointing out that it was probably excavated in oceanic crust, given that three-quarters of Earth's surface is ocean-covered, and thus might have already been subducted into the mantle by plate tectonics. Even if the impact had occurred in continental crust, they argued, the crater is likely to have been eroded. Nevertheless, the search continued. Several putative K–T craters were discovered but found to be of a different age or of insufficient size to explain the observed iridium anomaly.

Then, in the early 1990s, geologists discovered convincing evidence that a structure buried 1 km below the surface, located near the town of Chicxulub (sheek'-soo-loob), Mexico (Figure 8), was indeed of K–T age. Previous investigators had suspected, on the basis of remotely sensed geophysical anomalies, that this structure was an impact crater. The only expression at the surface of this subsurface feature was a ring of sinkholes, known in Mexico as cenotes. Then, exploratory wells previously drilled into the Chicxulub structure by Pemex, the Mexican oil company, provided samples containing shocked quartz and glass microspherules that closely resembled samples from known K–T intervals elsewhere. Further analysis of the drilled core materials revealed very strong enrichments of iridium. Isotopic age dating and paleomagnetic evidence

FIGURE 8 (a) The location of the Chicxulub impact crater. (b) The shape of the crater as inferred from gravity anomalies. (*Source:* Courtesy V. L. Sharpton, Lunar and Planetary Institute.)

constrained the age of the materials to polarity chron C29R, the interval containing all K–T iridium anomalies. Current estimates of at least a 200-km diameter for the crater indicate that it is the largest on Earth and one of the largest in the solar system.

Environmental Consequences of the K–T Meteorite Impact

What was Earth like during the Late Cretaceous period when the meteorite hit? How did the global environment change after the impact? If we could transport ourselves back 65 million years to the day of the impact, we would find ourselves in a world quite different from that of today. Equator-to-pole gradients in temperature were less, and the

poles were essentially ice-free, most likely the result of high atmospheric CO_2 levels. Dinosaurs inhabited tropical to near-polar latitudes—not in the abundances of their peak some tens of millions of years before, but still in sufficient numbers to dominate higher levels of the food chain.

The impact would have been unexpected and sudden. The passage of the meteorite through the atmosphere would have converted nitrogen gas (N_2) to nitric oxide (NO), as does lightning on a smaller scale today. Produced in large quantities, the NO would have destroyed the stratospheric ozone layer by catalyzing reactions that consume ozone, allowing ultraviolet radiation to reach Earth's surface unimpeded for as long as several years. Organisms unfortunate enough to be on the Yucatan Peninsula would have instantly been annihilated as an explosion of unimaginable intensity sent shock waves across the landscape. A huge crater would have been carved out immediately. The excavated material would have been sent on ballistic trajectories, enveloping Earth in a blanket of dust and debris. As the impact ejecta passed back through the atmosphere, the material would have been heated to temperatures sufficient to ignite wildfires in the affected areas, and those organisms not protected beneath the water surface or underneath clouds would have been subjected to air temperatures likened to putting your head in the oven on "broil." Soot would have been introduced into the atmosphere, further reducing the amount of sunlight reaching Earth. Because the bedrock of the Chicxulub area (mostly limestone) contained a thick layer of the calcium sulfate mineral *anhydrite,* a huge quantity of sulfuric acid aerosol would have been injected into the stratosphere. The scattering of sunlight from this aerosol layer would have reduced the amount of incoming solar radiation even further. Presuming a coastal impact, huge *tsunamis* (tidal waves) would have been initiated, wreaking havoc on Caribbean coastal environments. Evidence of tsunamis has been found on the island of Haiti and elsewhere in the Caribbean area.

In the next weeks, an unrelenting series of environmental insults would have ensued that few organisms could survive. The amount of solar radiation reaching Earth's surface would have been drastically reduced because of the presence of dense debris clouds and aerosol layers. The resultant dramatic cooling at all latitudes and cessation of photosynthesis would have removed the source of food for most of the life on the planet, both on land and in the sea. Where precipitation fell, it would have been in the form of rain and snow of sulfuric and nitric acids, produced from the rainout of sulfate aerosols and oxidation of NO. The acid rain may have been the least of the dinosaurs' problems, though.

Over the next several months, these tremendously detrimental effects would have lessened. The dust, soot, and much of the sulfate aerosol would have rained out of the atmosphere, and the acidity of the precipitation would have been reduced. However, very little life would have remained. The organisms that had survived the direct effects of the impact would have been subjected to a scarcity of food and suitable habitat. Cool climates would have continued for more than a year because of the approximately 6-month residence time of sulfate aerosol in the stratosphere.

Environmental recovery would have continued over the next few years, as the ozone layer was restored and the climate warmed. However, the warming would have continued well beyond the initial state as the result of thousands of gigatons of carbon dioxide released from the vaporization of limestone at the impact site. Atmospheric

pCO_2 may have increased to a few thousand ppm, and global average temperatures could have risen 10–15°C. These warm conditions could have persisted for thousands to tens of thousands of years. Given that many organisms are intolerant of rapid temperature excursions, this warming (following the initial cooling) might have assisted in the mass extinction and been at least one of the factors delaying the reestablishment of an active oceanic *biological pump* for hundreds of thousands of years.

A CLOSER LOOK
The K–T Strangelove Ocean

Scientists studying the isotopic composition of carbon in skeletons of foraminifera deposited in sediments that span the K–T impact have found an intriguing perturbation of the marine ecosystem that persisted for hundreds of thousands of years after the K–T event. Normally, the operation of the oceanic biological pump causes an enrichment in the carbon isotope ^{13}C in surface waters and an enrichment in ^{12}C in deep waters. The ^{12}C is preferentially incorporated into algal tissue during photosynthesis. It is then added to deep waters as the organic carbon in that tissue settles to the deep ocean and is decomposed by aerobic processes to dissolved CO_2. As a result, the ^{13}C:^{12}C ratio is enhanced in surface waters and diminished in deep waters. Foraminifera and other calcareous organisms (those producing $CaCO_3$ skeletons) record the ratio of ^{13}C to ^{12}C in their skeletons. Planktonic foraminifera, which live near the surface, record surface-water ratios, whereas benthic foraminifera, which live on the seafloor, record deep-sea ratios. In the modern ocean and in sediments recovered from layers deposited prior to the K–T event, the measured difference in the ^{13}C:^{12}C ratio between planktonic and benthic foraminifera is about 2 per mil (parts per thousand). However, as shown in Box Figure 2, the K–T event is marked by a collapse of this gradient. The implication is that the biological pump ceased to exist and that the ocean was essentially lifeless. Scientists have dubbed this the Strangelove Ocean, an allusion to the classic 1964 movie about nuclear war, *Dr. Strangelove*.

Perhaps even more intriguing than the collapse of the biological pump itself is its persistence. According to the isotopic record, the export of organic carbon from the surface ocean persisted at very low levels for hundreds of thousands of years, despite rapid rates of origination of new species and reestablishment of ecosystems in other settings. Although it is conceivable that slow rates of evolution retarded the reestablishment of the biological pump, other explanations seem to be required. One possibility is that toxic levels of trace metals such as copper, cadmium, and zinc resulted from the dissolution of the impact ejecta. Only after hundreds of thousands of years were these metals reduced to sufficiently low concentrations that metal-intolerant organisms could become reestablished.

BOX FIGURE 2 Changes in the ratio of carbon isotopic composition between the surface ocean and deep ocean as a result of the Cretaceous–Tertiary mass extinction. The ocean's isotopic value is recorded in the skeletons of planktonic foraminifera, which represent surface waters, and benthic foraminifera, which represent deep waters. (*Source:* J. C. Zachos, M. A. Arthur, and W. E. Dean, *Nature* 337, 1989, pp. 61–64.)

Other factors that influence the recovery interval include persistently high levels of toxic metals brought to the ocean with the impactor and the inherent time it takes to reestablish ecosystems and biodiversity.

EXTRATERRESTRIAL INFLUENCES AND EXTINCTION

There are two varieties of impacts: those caused by comets and those caused by asteroids. **Comets** are essentially large, dirty snowballs. They are composed of dust (metallic and rocky material) and solidified compounds that exist on Earth as gases: water, ammonia, methane, and carbon dioxide. Comets exist in stable orbits around the Sun, well beyond Pluto, in a region known as the **Oort cloud** (Figure 9), and closer in, outside of Neptune in the *Kuiper Belt*. The Oort cloud is a spherical reservoir of comets that extends more than one light year from the Sun. Comets in the Oort cloud can be perturbed by passing stars into orbits that pass through the solar system. Because they are arranged in a sphere, they can come in from any direction. These comets include many that have been observed over historic time, such as Halley's comet and comet Hale–Bopp. Kuiper Belt comets, by contrast, orbit the Sun in the same direction as do the planets. They are essentially pieces of material that never accreted to form a planet

because they formed too far from the Sun and they did not collide frequently enough. Paradoxically, the Oort cloud comets are actually thought to have formed closer to the Sun, mostly in the Uranus/Neptune region, from which they were ejected early in solar system history by near-collisions with the giant planets.

Asteroids, by contrast, are composed of minerals and metallic elements characteristic of Earth and the other inner solar system planets (Mercury, Venus, and Mars). Most asteroids are in orbit around the Sun in a region known as the **asteroid belt,** between Mars and Jupiter (see Figure 9). The asteroid belt represents the remains of an inner planet that failed to form, probably because of the gravitational influence of nearby Jupiter. The largest asteroid, Ceres, is 1000 km in diameter, and two others, Vesta and Pallas, are both ~500 km in diameter. Were any of these three bodies to hit Earth, they would likely vaporize the entire ocean and might sterilize Earth completely. Fortunately, most asteroids are much smaller than this. Many thousands of kilometer-sized bodies exist, and collisions between these bodies create millions of small, dust-sized fragments.

As mentioned earlier, iridium is an indicator of an asteroid impact because it is associated with the mineral and metallic material in extraterrestrial materials. Earth has lots of iridium as well; however, nearly all of it is in the core because iridium is a **siderophile** element that

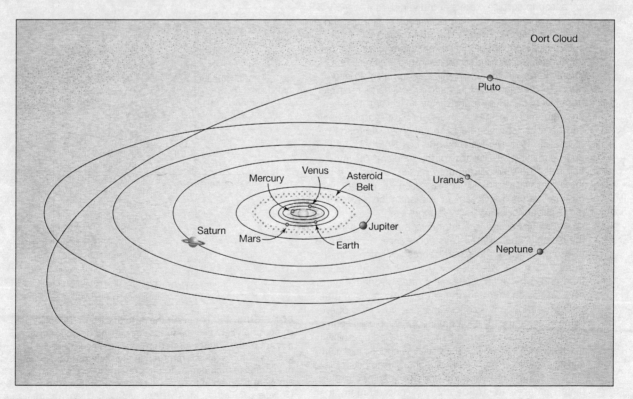

FIGURE 9 The solar system, showing the location of the Oort cloud (not drawn to scale) and the asteroid belt. (*Source:* From T. McKnight, *Physical Geography: A Landscape Appreciation*, 6/e, 1999. Reprinted by permission of Prentice Hall, Upper Saddle River, N.J.)

dissolves readily in molten iron. (The term *siderophile* means "iron-loving.") As we have seen, an asteroid impact should produce a significantly higher concentration of iridium than would a comet impact because of the differences in their composition and in their expected impact velocities. The large iridium spike in the K–T boundary clay thus indicates that the impactor was most likely an asteroid. Some of the other Phanerozoic mass extinctions for which no Ir layer exists—which, if you recall, is all the rest of them—could conceivably have been caused by comets.

Most asteroids in the asteroid belt and comets in the Oort Cloud or Kuiper Belt pose no immediate threat of impact. Their orbits can be disturbed, however, sending them on paths through the inner solar system. For example, collisions within the asteroid belt occasionally cause asteroids to be deflected into what's called a 3:1 *resonance* with Jupiter. At this distance the orbital period of the asteroid is precisely one-third that of Jupiter (3.95 Earth years, compared to 11.86 Earth years for Jupiter). This resonance occurs at an orbital distance of 2.50 astronomical units from the Sun, that is, 2.50 times the mean Earth–Sun distance. Asteroids that find themselves within the 3:1 resonance do funny things. Because they always pass by Jupiter on the same side of the Sun, their orbits become elongated by the tug of Jupiter's gravity. Eventually, the orbits become **chaotic**. To a mathematician or celestial mechanician, this means that small changes in their positions at some initial time can lead to large changes in their positions at some later time. In practice, some of these asteroids get shunted into orbits that pass through the inner solar system and directly across the path of planet Earth. Some of these bodies, like the K–T impactor, end up hitting Earth and causing mass extinctions.

Comets get deflected from their normally stable orbits by other means. Oort cloud comets can be perturbed by passing stars or by shifting tidal forces caused by the rotation of the galaxy. Comets on the inner edge of the Kuiper Belt get "nibbled" away by Neptune's gravity, causing some of them to begin orbiting within the normal boundaries of the solar system. Such comets eventually pass near to one of the giant planets. This provides a gravitational "slingshot" effect that ejects most of them right out of the solar system. However, a few get kicked into Earth-crossing orbits, and a few of those wind up eventually hitting Earth. Sometimes, of course, the giant planets get hit as well, as happened in July 1994 when the comet Shoemaker–Levy collided with Jupiter.

Periodicity of Impacts and Extinctions?

A quantitative analysis of the fossil record by Robert Rohde and Richard Muller of the University of California, Berkeley, using the older, pre-2008 biodiversity curve, has revealed a 62-million-year **periodicity**—a time interval of regular recurrence—in the fossil diversity curve. A separate, and earlier, analysis by Jack Sepkoski (see above) and his colleague David Raup revealed a 26-million-year

periodicity in the extinction rate curve. Any such long-term regularity in the fossil record that can be shown to be a robust feature (in other words, not simply some bias) suggests an extraterrestrial pacemaker for extinctions and/or originations, because no known Earthbound process has such regular periodicities at these long time scales. However, another theory is required to link these periods to higher likelihoods of asteroid or cometary impact if one wants to demonstrate that impacts have been the major driver of diversity trends over the Phanerozoic. The presence of another star or undetected large planet circling our star with elongated orbits and periodically disturbing the Oort cloud or asteroid belt is one such theory. Another is a regularity in the oscillation of our galaxy through the galactic plane and spiral arms of the Milky Way galaxy that would also create gravitational disturbances. Alternatively, mechanisms other than impacts might be responsible for these patterns. Moreover, the jury is still out on the issue of whether there are periodicities at all in these data, and if so, whether they require extraterrestrial explanations. Strong evidence for impact as the kill mechanism during mass extinctions exists only for the K–T event; for the others, extreme global warming brought on by massive volcanism or release of methane from the seafloor (for the end-Permian and Triassic–Jurassic extinctions), oceanic anoxia (for the end-Permian extinction and Late Devonian biodiversity loss) or glaciation and sea-level fall (for the Late Ordovician event) seem to be adequate explanations for the tremendous losses of biodiversity experienced.

Future Impacts

What are the odds that a large impactor will hit Earth in our lifetime? They are higher than you might think. The direct correlation between impactor size and diameter (see Figure 5) allows us to make this determination with some confidence. Let us assume that humans live about 100 years (admittedly, a bit optimistic). Because 100-m-diameter impactors (the size of the one that created Meteor Crater in Arizona) strike Earth about every 10,000 years, the likelihood of one striking Earth during your lifetime is about (100 years)/(10,000 years), or 1 in 100. The environmental consequences of such an impact are not tremendous, however, except close to the impact site. The impact frequency decreases by a factor of 100 for every factor of 10 increase in impactor diameter. Thus, the probability of a 1-km meteorite impact during your lifetime is about 1 in 10,000, and the probability of a K–T-sized impact during that time is 1 in 1 million. By comparison, your chances of being struck by lightning are about 1 in 3,000. Your chances of being killed by a lightning strike are quite high compared with your chances of being killed by the direct effects of a 1-km meteorite. But the likelihood that civilization will be destroyed by a meteorite impact is much larger than that of destruction by lightning strikes.

Chapter Summary

1. The diversity of life on Earth has varied in response to imbalances between the origination of new species and the extinction of existing species.
2. The fossil record of species-level diversity is biased by preservational artifacts associated with the likelihood of discovering fossils from a given interval of time.
3. The fossil record of genus-level diversity has been largely corrected for these biases and can thus be interpreted in terms of true trends in biodiversity through Earth history.
   a. Biodiversity of marine organisms increased dramatically during the Cambrian through Devonian.
   b. The largest extinction known occurred 252 million years ago when approximately 75% of all genera became extinct.
   c. Biodiversity recovered relatively rapidly after this event, and the general trend continues to the present. A significant disruption to this trend occurred 65 million years ago, at the end of the Cretaceous period, but it too was followed by a period of rapid origination of new species (and genera).

4. The Cretaceous–Tertiary mass extinction is the best studied of all major mass extinctions. Current scientific opinion favors the impact of a 10-km-diameter meteorite as the primary cause of this extinction.
   a. All available geological data are consistent with this hypothesis.
   b. A large crater dated as 65 million years old has been found in the subsurface at Chicxulub, Mexico.
   c. The meteorite impact would have destroyed the ozone layer, blocked out sunlight for days to weeks, ignited wildfires worldwide, baked organisms exposed to red-hot reentering ejecta, bathed the land surface in acid rain, and caused substantial global warming from elevated atmospheric CO_2.
   d. Although asteroid or cometary impact seems to be the best explanation for the K–T event, the other mass extinctions seem to have been the result of Earthbound causes: massive volcanism causing extreme global warming, or glaciation and sea-level fall.

Key Terms

adaptation
asteroid belt
asteroids
biodiversity
chaotic orbit
comets
evolution

extinction
iridium
mass extinction
meteorite
natural selection
niche
Oort cloud

origination
periodicity
Siberian Traps
siderophile
taxon
taxonomy

Review Questions

1. How do paleontologists deal with the incomplete nature of the fossil record to establish a geologic history of biodiversity changes?
2. What two processes cause the diversity of life on Earth to change through time?
3. How has fossil diversity changed over time? Why do these trends differ among taxonomic levels?

4. What explanations have been proposed for the mass extinction at the K–T boundary? Why is a meteorite impact the favored theory today?
5. What are the environmental consequences of the impact of a 10-km-diameter meteorite with Earth?
6. What are some other hypotheses for mass extinctions?

Critical-Thinking Problems

1. Changes in biodiversity over time are the result of imbalances between origination and extinction. Stability in diversity requires that either or both of these processes depend on the diversity at any particular time. In many ways, this situation is similar to the controls on the growth of populations. Here you will calculate the change in a population of organisms (N) as a result of births and deaths. A mathematical expression can be used to calculate next year's population (N_{t+1}) on the basis of this year's population (N_t), where t = years

$$N_{t+1} = N_t + rN_t\left(1 - \frac{N_t}{K}\right).$$

Let us dissect this equation. The potential growth rate—that is, the birth rate minus the death rate—is r, and the carrying capacity—the population size that can be supported (given constraints of food or other resource availability, competition, and so on)—is K. If the population is small relative to K, then the term in parentheses is essentially 1, and the potential growth rate is achieved. In other words, next year's population would simply be some multiple of this year's population (exponential growth). As N approaches K, the population will tend to slow its growth, finally reaching the carrying capacity. This behavior is called *logistic growth*. You will also witness something bizarre: behavior that has been labeled chaos.

PART 1 (Logistic growth): Fill in the following table, and then graph N_t versus t; assume that $r = 1.0$ and $K = 1,000$.

TABLE 1

Time (years)	N_t	$1 - \dfrac{N_t}{K}$	$rN_t \times$ $1 - \dfrac{N_t}{K}$	N_{t+1} (use as N_t next time)
1	20.0	0.98	19.6	39.6
2	39.6	0.96	38.0	77.6
3	77.6	0.92	71.6	149.2
4				
5				
6				
7				
8				
9				
10				

Describe the growth curve, and explain why it has the logistic growth shape (on the basis of the numbers you calculate).

PART 2 (Chaos): Now repeat your calculations (do 15 years' worth) for the following values of r:

$$r = 2.0$$
$$r = 2.8$$

Graph your results, either on separate graphs or using different symbols or colors on the same graph (be sure the graph[s] is [are] legible). If the population goes negative, call it quits on that series of calculations; the population has gone extinct.

Describe how the behavior changes as the growth rate increases from 1.0 to 2.0 to 2.8. When $r = 2.8$, the system is described as being chaotic. A scientist who observed this population might conclude that purely random factors are controlling the size of this population. What is wrong with this conclusion?

2. Perform the calculation that Luis Alvarez used to establish the size of the K–T impactor. Use the following information:
   a. Assume that the clay layer with iridium was uniformly distributed around Earth by the impact.
   b. On average, the layer had a concentration of iridium of 10 parts per billion (ppb) by weight.
   c. On average, the layer was 4 cm thick.
   d. The density of the layer was 2.5 g/cm^3.
   e. Assume the meteor was spherical, with a density of 6.0 g/cm^3, and an iridium content of 0.5 parts per million (ppm) by weight.
   f. The radius of Earth is 6378 km.
      What is the diameter of the meteorite? The answer isn't exactly 10 km, as stated. By how much would you have to change the assumed thickness of the iridium layer to arrive at an asteroid diameter of exactly 10 km?
3. Determine the probability that an asteroid of the following diameters will hit Earth during your (optimistic) 100-year lifetime: 1 m, 100 m, 10 km.

Further Reading

General

Erwin, D. H. 2006. *Extinction: How life on Earth nearly ended 250 million years ago* (p. 296). Princeton, NJ: Princeton University Press.

Fastovsky, D. E., D. B. Weishampel, and J. Sibbick. 2005. *The evolution and extinction of dinosaurs* (p. 485). Cambridge: Cambridge University Press.

Hallam, A. 2004. *Catastrophes and lesser calamites* (p. 274). Oxford: Oxford University Press.

Ward, P. D. 2008. *Under a green sky: Global warming, the mass extinctions of the past, and what they can tell us about our future* (p. 242). New York: HarperCollins.

Advanced

Alroy, J. et al. 2008. Phanerozoic trends in the global diversity of marine organisms. Science 321:97–100.

Alvarez, L. W. 1987. Mass extinctions caused by large bolide impacts. *Physics Today*, July 1987, pp. 24–33.

Bambach, R. K. 2006. Phanerozoic biodiversity and mass extinctions. In *Annual Reviews of Earth and Planetary Sciences* 34, ed. R. Jeanloz, A. L. Albee, K. C. Burke, and K. H. Freeman, 127–55.

(a)   (b)

FIGURE 7 Shocked quartz and (b) microspherules from K–T boundary clays. (*Source:* (a) Dr. David Kring/SPL/Photo Researchers and (b) David Parker/SPL/Photo Reasearchers.)

Pleistocene Glaciations

Pleistocene Glaciations

Key Questions

- What has caused Earth to oscillate in and out of glacial states over the past 2 million years?
- What geologic evidence substantiates theories about the causes of glaciation?
- How are glacial-to-interglacial cycles related to changes in Earth's orbit?

- Have components of the Earth system amplified the glacial climate response?
- What caused the abrupt and brief return to the glacial state after the latest deglaciation?

Chapter Overview

When viewed on multimillion-year time scales, Earth is presently in a glacial interval. Thick continental ice sheets cover Antarctica and Greenland, and only 20,000 years ago vast portions of northern North America and Scandinavia and other parts of northern Europe and Asia were covered with accumulations of ice that were many kilometers thick. Although polar ice has existed on Antarctica for tens of millions of years, only during the past 2.5 million years have ice sheets extended from the Arctic into the northern midlatitudes. Thus, there is something peculiar about the operation of Earth's climate system during the past 2.5 million years that distinguishes it from the rest of the past 300 million years of Earth history.

In addition, there is now convincing evidence that this glacial interval, known as the **Pleistocene epoch** (1.8 million years ago to about 12,000 years ago), was characterized by regular cycles of growth and decay of Northern Hemisphere continental ice sheets. The oscillations are likely to continue. The warmer interval we are enjoying now, known as the **Holocene epoch**, would under natural conditions end several thousand years from now as the Northern Hemisphere ice sheets return. Continued burning of fossil fuels may, however, forestall or even prevent this transition to the glacial state. What causes this cyclicity of glaciation?

As we will see, changes both in the distribution of sunlight across Earth's surface (insolation) and in atmospheric CO_2 seem to be involved. These changes in insolation are a predictable feature of Earth's orbit about the Sun—during warm as well as cold intervals of Earth history. The magnitude of the forcing is small compared with that of the changes brought about by solar evolution on 100-million-year time scales. Yet as we narrow our focus to shorter time scales of climate change, these more subtle forcings increase in importance. During the Mesozoic, orbital changes caused cyclical variations in sedimentation that likely reflect climate change. But the Pleistocene climate system seems to have been especially attuned to these forcings, as indicated by the large oscillations of continental ice sheets.

GEOLOGIC EVIDENCE OF PLEISTOCENE GLACIATION

The scenic beauty of Canada and the northern portions of the United States, Asia, and Europe is to a great extent the result of the action of tremendously large sheets of ice that covered these regions during the Pleistocene epoch (Figure 1). Buried under more than a kilometer of ice, the land surface was plucked, ground up, and excavated. With the melting of the ice, the depressions formed in this way were filled with water and became the thousands of lakes that pepper the North country. In this section we will see that the modification of the landscape by glaciers, together with their effect on the isotopic composition of seawater, provide convincing evidence that continental ice sheets expanded and decayed several times during the Pleistocene with almost clockwork regularity.

Glacial Deposits Document Major Glaciations

Several types of geological features are characteristic of glaciation. As glaciers advance, rocks frozen to their base gouge the bedrock below. These gouges, called **glacial striations** (Figure 2a), indicate the direction of past glacial movement. The advance of continental ice sheets modifies the landscape in other ways as well. Ridges of sediment, known as **moraines** (Figure 2b), are deposited at the front and sides of the ice sheets. When the ice melts, these ridges are left behind, marking the farthest advance of the ice sheet. The indiscriminate nature of glacial erosion and deposition is reflected in the sediment contained in moraines and other glacial deposits. This sediment, called **till** (Figure 2c), contains a mixture of material of various sizes, from mud to boulder-sized rocks, and various composition, reflecting rocks eroded from a variety of places and transported to the point of deposition by the advancing ice sheet. Some of the material produced by glacial abrasion is silt-sized (about hundredths of a millimeter in diameter). When deposited in the typically arid region that surrounds continental ice sheets, this material is picked up by the wind and carried great distances. Such windblown deposits, known as **loess** (Figure 2d), form the rich soils of the midwestern U.S. grain belt.

Geologists of the 19th century used glacial deposits, including the geographical distribution of moraines, to define four main intervals of glaciation in Europe, from oldest to youngest: the Gunz, the Mindel, the Riss, and the Würm. In the early part of the 20th century, four glaciations were also identified in North America, from oldest to youngest: the Nebraskan, the Kansan, the Illinoian, and the Wisconsinan. These glaciations on separate continents are now known to have been coincident with each other, and they represent the largest of the glacial episodes. Ice sheets in the Northern Hemisphere were advancing and retreating in unison. But the number four greatly underestimates how often this process has occurred. The problem is that each successive advance obliterates much of the geological record of earlier advances.

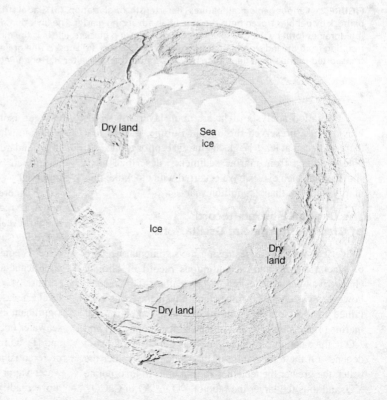

FIGURE 1 The Pleistocene ice sheet at maximum extent. (*Source:* From W. K. Hamblin and E. H. Christiansen, *Earth's Dynamic Systems*, 8/e, 1998. Reprinted by permission of Prentice Hall, Upper Saddle River, N.J.)

FIGURE 2 Various geological features characteristic of glaciation. (a) Glacial striations are formed by the gouging out of bedrock by pebbles frozen onto the base of an advancing glacier. The lineations indicate the direction of glacial movement. (b) Moraines form by the bulldozing action of advancing glaciers. (c) Till is the mix of sediments of various types and sizes resulting from the indiscriminate transportation by glaciers. (d) Loess is fine-grained sediment produced by glacial abrasion and transported to the site of deposition by wind.   (*Sources:* (a) Walter H. Hodge/Peter Arnold and (b), (c), (d) TLM Photo.)

Detailed analysis of layers upon layers of wind-blown loess, preserved throughout Europe, proved that there had been at least 17 glacial intervals prior to the last. And evidence from marine sediments, described next, showed that such cycles have occurred with clocklike regularity for more than 2.5 million years.

The Oxygen Isotope Record of Glacial–Interglacial Oscillations

While ice sheets were destroying the sedimentary record of glaciation on land, a continuous record of climate change was being deposited on the seafloor. This record, however, was chemical rather than physical; it was contained in the isotopic composition of the skeletons of marine organisms. The ratio of the stable isotopes ^{18}O and ^{16}O in the calcium carbonate skeletons of marine plankton depends on the temperature of that water. The colder the water, the greater the tendency for minerals to incorporate ^{18}O, and thus the larger the ratio of ^{18}O to ^{16}O in $CaCO_3$.

Oxygen isotope ratios are typically reported in "delta" notation, where (^{18}O is the ratio of ^{18}O to ^{16}O normalized to a standard (either seawater or a standard limestone) and multiplied by 1000 to accentuate the small differences observed.

Theoretically, then, the isotopic analysis of skeletal material recovered from cores of deep-sea sediments should reveal the history of temperature fluctuations in the overlying surface waters. However, an additional isotopic effect is equally important. As continental ice sheets grow, significant quantities of water are removed from the oceans (Figure 3). Aside from causing considerable drops in sea level (the last glaciation dropped sea level by about 120 m), significant changes in the oxygen isotopic composition of seawater occur as well. Evaporation transfers both $H_2^{16}O$ and $H_2^{18}O$ from the ocean to the atmosphere, but there is a preferential release of $H_2^{16}O$ to the vapor phase. Moreover, water-vapor molecules containing ^{18}O tend to condense more readily than do those containing ^{16}O, the lighter

Evaporation

Ice sheet

Ocean

Land

FIGURE 3 Changes in the oxygen isotopic composition of seawater during the growth of continental ice sheets.

○ H_2O containing ^{16}O
● H_2O containing ^{18}O

isotope. Thus, rain falling from the atmosphere preferentially removes ^{18}O, leaving the residual water vapor further enriched in ^{16}O. Snow falling onto the ice caps has traveled considerable distances and has had its ^{16}O content considerably enriched. The net preferential removal of ^{16}O from the oceans to ice sheets increases the $\delta^{18}O$ of the oceans. This effect adds to the direct temperature effect: Calcium carbonate precipitated from a glacial-age ocean has a larger $\delta^{18}O$, both because the water is cold and because the seawater is enriched in the heavier isotope.

In the 1950s the first deep-sea sediment cores were recovered, and isotopic analyses were performed on them. Instead of the four glaciations originally indicated by the continental record, the marine record indicated that dozens of climate swings have occurred over the course of the Pleistocene (Figure 4). The major intervals of Northern Hemisphere glaciation—**glacials**—of the past 700,000 years appear to have occurred every 100,000 years or so. During glacials, the globally averaged surface temperature was about

9–10°C (about 5–6°C cooler than today) and atmospheric CO_2 concentrations were about 200 ppm. These cold intervals are separated by warmer, shorter intervals known as **interglacials**. During interglacials, continental glaciation is limited to Greenland and Antarctica; globally averaged surface temperatures are about 15°C and atmospheric CO_2 concentrations are about 280 ppm. The Holocene epoch (the past 10,000 years) represents one such interglacial.

The regularity of glacial–interglacial variation is remarkable. The **period** of a cyclical phenomenon is the time it takes to complete one cycle. Curiously, the dominant periodicity (cyclical nature) of glacial–interglacial variation seems to have been different prior to 700,000 years ago. Before that time, glacial–interglacial swings were smaller and occurred on approximately a 40,000-year time scale. Something fundamental to the climate system changed 700,000 years ago, and scientists are actively working to resolve what that fundamental change was. The pre-Pleistocene cooling and the onset of significant continental glaciation in the Northern Hemisphere

FIGURE 4 Deep-sea record of the $\delta^{18}O$ of seawater during the Pleistocene epoch. The analyses were performed on two genera of bottom-dwelling foraminifera deposited in the sediments of the midlatitude North Atlantic. Interglacials appear as peaks, with smaller values of $\delta^{18}O$; glaciations appear as valleys. Note that time proceeds forward to the left. (*Source:* M. E. Raymo, *Annual Review of Earth and Planetary Sciences* 22, 1994, pp. 353–383.)

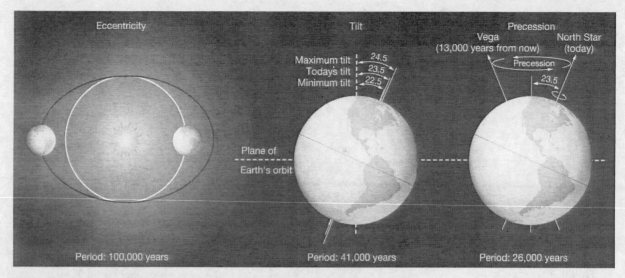

FIGURE 5 Aspects of Earth's orbit around the Sun that have implications for climate change. (a) The elliptical nature of the orbit (eccentricity) changes on 100,000- and 400,000-year time scales. (b) The tilt of the spin axis with respect to the plane of Earth's orbit around the Sun (obliquity) changes on a 41,000-year time scale. (c) The orientation of the spin axis in space wobbles (precesses) with a 26,000-year period.   (*Source:* From J. P. Davidson, W. E. Reed, and P. M. Davis, *Exploring Earth: An Introduction to Physical Geology*, 1997. Reprinted by permission of Prentice Hall, Upper Saddle River, N.J.)

(from 3.0 to 2.5 million years ago) are also apparent in the oxygen isotope record (see Figure 4).

Why has Earth's climate system been oscillating between these two states—glacial and interglacial—with apparent periods of 100,000 and 40,000 years? The answer seems to involve small changes in the way Earth orbits the Sun, changes that repeat in a predictable fashion over tens of thousands of years. Three sorts of changes are involved (Figure 5):

1. changes in the degree to which Earth's orbit around the Sun is elliptical (eccentricity);
2. changes in the tilt of Earth's spin axis with respect to the plane of its orbit around the Sun (obliquity); and
3. changes in the orientation of the spin axis with respect to Earth's orbit (precession).

The pacemaker that determines the variability of climate requires amplification, especially for the 100,000-year climate cycles, because only small changes in annual-average insolation result from eccentricity variations. We will first explore these orbital variations and will compare their predictions to the isotopic record from deep-sea sediment cores. We then discuss feedback mechanisms (including those affecting atmospheric CO_2) that may have provided the amplification necessary to create the large climate swings of the Pleistocene.

MILANKOVITCH CYCLES

What causes these remarkably regular shifts in Earth's climate? Long before the oxygen isotope evidence was obtained, scientists of the 19th century had suspected that the

Pleistocene glacial–interglacial cycles were caused by variations in Earth's orbit around the Sun. In the early part of the 20th century, this hypothesis was put on a quantitative footing by the Serbian mathematician Milutin Milankovitch. He not only elaborated the mathematical theory of how orbital variations affect climate, but also calculated the changes in orbital parameters over the past several thousand years and demonstrated the connection between this theory and the rather scant geological record that existed during his time. The regular variations in Earth's orbit are often referred to as *Milankovitch cycles* in honor of this achievement. Milankovitch suggested that the critical factor for Northern Hemisphere continental glaciation was the amount of summertime insolation at high northern latitudes. High insolation leads to warmer summers, and the winter snowpack melts (as we see today). However, under low insolation the snowpack would survive over the summer, allowing snow and ice to accumulate and an ice sheet to form. Subsequent summers would allow further growth of the ice sheet toward lower latitudes.

Despite the elegance of Milankovitch's "astronomical theory of the Ice Age," it was strongly criticized by the scientific community in the 1920s and 1930s, in part because the available geologic record did not support the hypothesis of many Pleistocene glaciations. His response to these criticisms is perhaps best reflected in this excerpt from his 1941 book: "I do not consider it my duty to give an elementary education to the ignorant, and I have also never tried to force others to apply my theory, with which no one could find fault." Given the rather limited amount of tact with which Milankovitch presented his theory of the Ice Ages, it is not surprising that his brilliance was not widely acknowledged until well after his death.

Orbital Theory

Orbital theory itself predates Milankovitch; the fundamentals of this theory were developed in the 17th century by Johannes Kepler and Isaac Newton. The results are summarized by three rules that are known as *Kepler's laws* (see the Box "Thinking Quantitatively: Kepler's Laws"). The most important of these laws for our purposes is the first: The planets travel around the Sun in *elliptical* orbits with the Sun at one *focus.*

An ellipse is defined mathematically as the collection of points whose combined distance to two fixed points (the *foci*) is equal to a constant. The constant is equal to the length of the long, or *major,* axis of the ellipse (see Box Figure 1). This may be easily verified by adding up line segments along the major axis, remembering that the figure is symmetric about both the major and minor (vertical) axes. The degree to which the orbit of a planet (or other rotating object) is elliptical is called its **eccentricity**. For Earth, the distance from the center of the elliptical orbit to either focus is only 1.7% of the distance from the center to the edge of the ellipse along the major axis. In other words, the foci and the center are nearly indistinguishable, and Earth's orbit is very nearly circular. The eccentricity (often designated as *e*) is expressed numerically as this percentage in decimal form ($e = 0.017$).

Because planetary orbits are eccentric, Earth is closer to the Sun at some times of the year than at others. The point of closest approach is called **perihelion**, and the point of maximum Earth–Sun distance is called **aphelion** (see Box Figure 1). The amount of sunlight hitting Earth is slightly greater at perihelion than at aphelion (as we will see in "Critical-Thinking" Problem 2). Perihelion occurs on January 3, 13 days after the Northern Hemisphere winter solstice, so Northern Hemisphere winters are somewhat milder than Southern Hemisphere winters. They are also somewhat shorter, as the planet moves faster at perihelion than at aphelion, according to Kepler's second law. Conversely, Northern Hemisphere summers tend to be longer and milder than Southern Hemisphere summers.

Another factor that affects Earth's climate is the planet's **obliquity**, the fact that its spin axis is tilted 23.5 degrees from the perpendicular to the plane of its orbit. Obliquity creates the contrast between the seasons; with no obliquity, the annual variation in the amount of solar insolation (resulting from the eccentricity of the orbit) would be very small. Winter and summer would basically not exist. Earth's relatively high obliquity means that there is a large **seasonal temperature contrast** between summer and winter. The eccentricity of Earth's orbit causes this seasonal temperature contrast to be slightly greater in the Southern Hemisphere than in the Northern Hemisphere.

THINKING QUANTITATIVELY
Kepler's Laws

First law: The orbit of each planet is an ellipse with the Sun at one focus.

Half of the major axis of an ellipse is called the *semimajor axis.* This is also the average planet–Sun distance. The semimajor axis is usually represented by the letter *a.* The distance from the center of the ellipse to one focus is equal to the length of the semimajor axis (*a*) multiplied by the eccentricity (*e*) (see Box Figure 1). In other words, the eccentricity of the ellipse can be determined by dividing *ae* by *a.* An ellipse with zero eccentricity is a circle (the two foci coincide with the center of the circle). Earth's current eccentricity is 0.017; Earth's orbit is nearly circular, but not quite.

Second law: A line joining a planet to the Sun sweeps out equal areas in equal times.

Box Figure 1 shows that to sweep out an equal area (each shaded region) in the same amount of time (Δt), Earth must travel farther around the perimeter of the ellipse when it is close to the Sun than when it is far from it. From a practical standpoint, then, this law means that the planet moves faster when it is closer to the Sun and slower when it is farther away.

Third law: The square of a planet's orbital period is proportional to the cube of its semimajor axis.

A planet's orbital *period* is the time that it takes the planet to go around the Sun. If we express the period *P* in Earth years and the planet's semimajor axis *a* in astronomical units (AU, the average Earth–Sun distance), we can replace the word *proportional* with *equal* and write Kepler's third law as: $P^2 = a^3$.

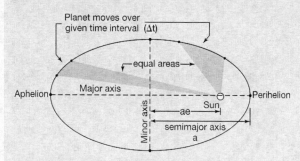

BOX FIGURE 1   Earth's elliptical orbit, showing the Sun at one focus.   (*Source:* From T. McKnight, *Physical Geography: A Landscape Appreciation,* 6/e, 1999. Reprinted by permission of Prentice Hall, Upper Saddle River, N.J.)

Changes in Earth's Orbit through Time

Milankovitch's theory predicts that the gravitational influences of the Moon and the other planets, combined with Earth's slightly nonspherical shape, induce small but important variations in Earth's orbital parameters. These variations affect the amount of summertime insolation at high northern latitudes, triggering the onset and end of glacial intervals.

Precession of the Spin Axis

The most noticeable change in Earth's orbit has to do with the direction of its spin axis. The spin axis moves around in space because of the pull of the Sun and the Moon on Earth's equatorial bulge. (See the Box "Thinking Quantitatively: Effect of the Sun and Moon on Earth's Obliquity and Precession.") Currently, the spin axis is oriented such that the North Pole points almost directly at the bright star *Polaris,* otherwise known as the North Star. The direction of the spin axis remains constant as Earth orbits around the Sun, so the North Star remains at geographic north during both summer and winter.

The spin axis has not always pointed in that direction, however. Egyptian pyramids built in 3000 B.C. were designed to observe the north star of the time, *Alpha Draconis,* not *Polaris.* Thirteen thousand years ago, the bright star *Vega* was approximately at geographic north. Over time, the North Pole describes a circle in space as the spin axis points to different parts of the sky. The period of **precession** (i.e., the time it takes for the spin axis to *precess* one complete circle) is 25,700 years. However, the direction of the major axis of Earth's elliptical orbit is also precessing, but in the opposite direction, a phenomenon referred to as the *precession of perihelion.* Because perihelion is precessing in the opposite direction from the spin axis precession, the amount of time required to go through a complete precessional Milankovitch cycle is shorter than 25,700 years. The orbital precession is affected most strongly by two other planets, Venus (because it is close) and Jupiter (because it is big). Thus, two main periods result, at 23,000 and 19,000 years.

Precession modifies the relationship between the seasons and the distance from the Sun shown in Box Figure 1. Every half precession cycle, the hemisphere with the greatest degree of seasonal contrast switches between the north and the south. When the Southern Hemisphere has mild summers and winters, the Northern Hemisphere has hot summers and cold winters, and vice versa. Northern Hemisphere glaciation is promoted by a precessional state, as today, with northern summer at aphelion and thus low seasonal contrast. The maximum interglacial condition was achieved 9,000 years ago, with hot summers in the north.

Obliquity Variations

The same phenomenon that causes Earth's spin axis to precess also causes the obliquity to vary from 22 to 24.5 degrees, with a dominant cycle length of about 41,000 years. If you observe a spinning top carefully, you will notice that it, too, undergoes periodic changes in its tilt as its spin axis precesses. This effect becomes more pronounced as the spin rate of the top decreases: The top begins to wobble. Like precession of the spin axis, a change in obliquity does not alter the total amount of sunlight striking Earth. Rather, it determines the extent of seasonal contrasts: The warmth of summers and the coldness of winters is increased by higher obliquities (Figure 6). (See also the Box "Thinking Quantitatively: Effect of the Sun and Moon on Earth's Obliquity and Precession.")

Eccentricity Variations

Earth's eccentricity also undergoes oscillations that can affect climate. The combined gravitational effect of all the planets causes Earth's eccentricity to vary periodically between 0 and 0.06. (Recall that the current value is 0.017.) As was true of the precessional cycle, two main periods are predicted. They are much longer in this case, however: about 100,000 years and about 400,000 years.

The eccentricity variations differ from the precessional and obliquity variations in one other significant respect: Eccentricity variations cause changes in the annually averaged amount of sunlight hitting Earth, whereas precessional and obliquity variations do not. (The direction and steepness of tilt of a planet's spin axis have no direct effect on the total amount of sunlight the planet receives.) One can show mathematically that Earth receives about 0.2% more sunlight at maximum eccentricity than at minimum eccentricity. This difference is thought to be too small to cause major climate shifts by itself, but it might have some effect if it is amplified by a feedback mechanism (discussed later in this chapter).

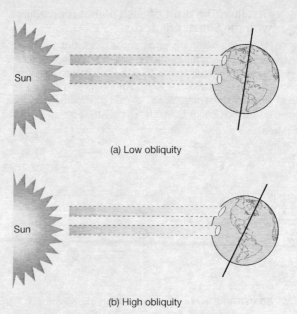

(a) Low obliquity

(b) High obliquity

FIGURE 6   (a) At low obliquity, Earth has less contrast in insolation between the seasons. (b) At high obliquity, the seasonal contrast is greater.

THINKING QUANTITATIVELY

Effect of the Sun and Moon on Earth's Obliquity and Precession

The fundamental reason why Earth's spin axis precesses, and one reason why its obliquity varies, is because Earth is not perfectly round. Because it is spinning rapidly, it bulges slightly at the equator. The diameter through the equator is 12,756 km, while the polar diameter is about 43 km less. The Sun and the Moon pull on this bulge gravitationally (Box Figure 2a), thereby causing Earth's spin axis to precess in a circle and also to bob up and down slightly, giving rise to periodic variations in Earth's obliquity.

The same phenomena can be observed in a simple home experiment with a spinning top (Box Figure 2b). Earth's gravity is pulling the top toward the floor. If the top is standing straight up, the gravitational pull is along the

top's spin axis, and the top spins smoothly, without precessing. If the top is tilted sideways, however, then the gravitational pull is partly perpendicular to the spin axis, and the top precesses around in a circle. As its rotation rate slows down (due to friction with the surface), the top will also begin to bob up and down, or *nutate*. This nutation is analogous to changes in Earth's obliquity.

What would happen to this system if one took away the Moon? (This is not just a hypothetical question; there may be Earthlike planets around other stars that lack large moons.) The Moon accounts for roughly two-thirds of the gravitational force acting on Earth's equatorial bulge. The Sun accounts for the other one-third. If the Moon were not present, the net force would be smaller, and Earth's spin axis would precess more slowly. Jacques Laskar and his colleagues at the University of Paris have shown that under these circumstances, Earth's obliquity would vary chaotically from 0° to as much as 60° on a time scale of tens of millions of years. (The reason is that the period of the spin axis precession would now match up with periods observed in the orbits of the other planets, such as the precession of their perihelia.) This would wreak havoc with Earth's climate. Continents located at high latitudes, like much of North America and Europe, would be subject to extreme seasonal variations. This has led some astronomers to suggest that a large moon may be necessary in order for a planet to have a stable obliquity and climate. In reality, the situation is more complicated than this because a more rapidly spinning Earth would *not* experience this problem, but it is still true that the Moon exerts a major influence on Earth's climate.

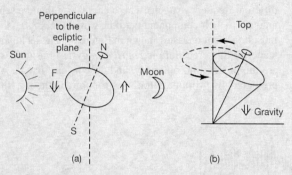

(a) (b)

BOX FIGURE 2 The effects of the Sun and Moon on Earth's obliquity. (a) Both the Sun and Moon exert a torque on Earth, causing it to precess and bob up and down. (b) Analogous motion of a top spinning on its side.

Probably more important is the fact that eccentricity influences the climatic effect of the precession cycle. When Earth's eccentricity is nearly zero, there is no difference between the perihelion distance and the aphelion distance from the Sun, so it does not matter when summer or winter occurs. When the eccentricity is large, Northern Hemisphere glaciation is especially favored when precession causes Northern Hemisphere summer to occur at aphelion. Of course, within a half precession cycle the situation reverses, with Northern Hemisphere summer at perihelion. Nevertheless, analysis of past glaciations indicates that ice sheets survive this effect of high eccentricity. At present we are at low eccentricity, and according to the calculations of Belgian astrophysicist André Berger, the eccentricity will be decreasing to a minimum near zero in about 30,000 years from now. With eccentricity so low, the unusually cold winters needed to initiate Northern Hemisphere ice-sheet growth don't occur. Thus, climatologists predict that the present interglacial will be long-lived (at least 1.5–2.5 precession cycles). The buildup of carbon

dioxide in the atmosphere from fossil-fuel burning only serves to strengthen that prediction.

Comparing Orbital Forcing and Climatic Response by Means of Oxygen Isotopes

The combination of these various orbital forcings causes Earth's climate system to oscillate between two states. The situation can be displayed in a diagram. The glacial and interglacial states are represented as valleys separated by a ridge (Figure 7). Presumably the glacial state is situated in a deeper valley than the interglacial state, because a greater fraction of Pleistocene time was spent in glaciation. Orbital forcings continually rock the system back and forth. Since 700,000 years ago, the amplitude of this rocking has exhibited a strong 100,000-year periodicity. When these variations exceed a threshold, the system moves over the ridge into the other state. High eccentricity increases the amplitude of the variations on precessional

FIGURE 7 Stability of the glacial and interglacial states, relative to the changes in high-latitude Northern Hemisphere insolation that rock the state of the system back and forth.

cycles and thus is more likely to be associated with transitions from interglacial to glacial states (or vice versa).

We can now piece together the various parts of the astronomical theory of the Ice Ages described previously and test the theory against the oxygen isotopic record of temperature and sea-level changes during the Pleistocene. The precession, obliquity, and eccentricity variations can all be described mathematically, and the resulting

equations can be solved for the amount of insolation received on a monthly or annual basis for any particular latitude. This is nothing new, of course; Milankovitch made these calculations many decades ago. However, some improvements have been made on the original calculations by Milankovitch. The particular result shown at the top of Figure 8 is the average monthly insolation (Q) for June, at 65° N latitude.

Shown at the bottom of Figure 8 is the past 400,000 years of the oxygen isotope record from Figure 4. Is the observed climate response ($\delta^{18}O$) the expected response to the climate forcing (Q)? Such a comparison is difficult; indeed, we might conclude from a visual inspection that the two curves are unrelated. However, the wiggles of these curves can be considered as the combination of a number of waves of different frequency (the mathematical inverse of period) and amplitudes, much as a musical chord is the combination of a number of notes, each of a different frequency (pitch). These curves can then be separated into their component periodic waves (or *bands*); the most important ones are shown in Figure 8. (The technical name for this procedure is *Fourier analysis*.) For Q these are the precession, obliquity, and eccentricity bands. As predicted by Milankovitch's astronomical theory, the

FIGURE 8 Northern Hemisphere June insolation (Q, the climate forcing) and marine oxygen isotopic composition ($\delta^{18}O$, the climate response) and their dominant periodic components. (*Source:* Imbrie et al., *Paleoceanography* 7, 1992, pp. 701–738.)

dominant periodicities of the $\delta^{18}O$ record occur at these same bands (19,000 years and 23,000 years, 41,000 years, and 100,000 years, respectively). Thus, there is compelling evidence that the pacemaker for the ice ages is the "Milankovitch" signal.

Moreover, the amplitude of the response to the precession and obliquity changes seems to be roughly proportional to the amplitude of the forcing. These observations suggest that a simple link exists between fluctuations in the amount of radiation received at high latitudes and the extent of glaciation.

A closer inspection of Figure 8, however, reveals an important departure from a straightforward link between climate forcing and climate response: The direct forcing, that is, the average annual insolation change, in the eccentricity band is very small (some 10% of that in the other bands), yet the climate response is the largest of the three bands. The importance of eccentricity is evidently more indirect. Eccentricity modulates the insolation changes associated with the precessional band, as can be seen in the envelope of variation for precession in Figure 8. Nevertheless, climate amplification of the 100,000-year forcing is considered necessary to create the climatic response from eccentricity forcing. Do positive feedback loops in the climate system amplify the weak eccentricity forcing into the major climatic response to orbital fluctuations?

GLACIAL CLIMATE FEEDBACKS

The timekeepers for the glacial–interglacial climate fluctuations during the Pleistocene were subtle, periodic changes in Earth's orbital parameters. However, these changes have been small. Moreover, the dominant periodicity of glacial–interglacial fluctuations has been 100,000 years; if this phenomenon is the result of eccentricity changes, an amplifier is needed. The important climate variables that we need to consider are albedo and the greenhouse effect. Clearly, the growth of continental ice sheets influences the albedo of the planet, so this effect must be incorporated into any model that attempts to explain Pleistocene climates. Clouds exert a major control on planetary albedo, and we may wonder whether the cloud albedo varies in concert with the Milankovitch cycles. Finally, we have seen how changes in the greenhouse effect of atmospheric

CO_2 have affected climate on long time scales; perhaps the Pleistocene climate system has responded to more rapid fluctuations in atmospheric CO_2.

Ice–Albedo Feedbacks

Any change in the seasonal distribution of solar luminosity that affects the growth of ice during the winter or the melt-back during the summer has the potential to affect the planetary albedo. As ice sheets begin to grow, they convert a region that previously had reduced albedo during the summer, as snow melted, to one that maintains high albedo throughout the year. The average annual albedo thus increases, which will lead to both a regional and a global cooling. This cooling will accelerate the growth of the continental ice and will allow it to spread to lower latitudes.

The positive ice–albedo feedback involves global temperature, ice-sheet growth, and albedo (Figure 9). In Figure 9 the forcing is also indicated; note that a small change in the intensity of summer insolation at high northern latitudes could potentially lead to large changes in ice-sheet coverage and global temperature. Researchers have shown that the growth and destruction of the Northern Hemisphere ice sheet has a characteristic response time of about 100,000 years. Thus, the dynamics of glaciation are especially tuned to a frequency of one cycle per 100,000 years and should respond quite sensitively to eccentricity-induced changes. Numerical models show that instabilities develop as an ice sheet becomes very large, such that fairly subtle changes in high-latitude insolation can lead to its catastrophic destruction.

The ice–albedo feedback has significant effects on Northern Hemisphere climates, but can't explain why Southern Hemisphere climate changes are both large and in step with those in the Northern Hemisphere. Studies of polar ice cores indicate that carbon dioxide levels have also varied substantially. The greenhouse effect associated with these changes is not negligible, and may be the explanation for the link between northern and southern climate change. Ice cores also reveal that the number of cloud condensation nuclei in the atmosphere has changed with the Milankovitch cyclicity. We now explore some of the proposed mechanisms for large and rapid changes in atmospheric CO_2 levels and cloud condensation nuclei on glacial time scales.

FIGURE 9 Feedback diagram showing the effect of changes in glacial growth on global temperature.

Evidence from the Vostok (and Dome C) Ice Cores

During the Southern Hemisphere summer of 1982–1983, French and Soviet scientists met in Vostok, on the high plateau of Antarctica, to take samples from the longest, most continuous ice core ever recovered from the Antarctic Ice Sheet. With each length of ice removed from this 2-km-deep hole, our knowledge of Earth's climate history was extended millennia into the past. By the time the last, deepest section was recovered and sampled, 200,000 years of ice accumulation were revealed. The samples were taken to France, where the oxygen isotopic composition of the ice was analyzed. This analysis revealed a history that matched well what we would expect from the marine record of isotopic changes during the Pleistocene. Since then, the coring has been extended to 3.3-km depth at a nearby site, Dome C, revealing ice deposited some 800,000 years ago.

However, one of the most important discoveries made by the scientists studying the Vostok ice core was the realization that the ice contained air bubbles frozen into the glacier as it grew. Using extreme care, the scientists were able to measure the concentration of carbon dioxide in the bubbles. Air bubbles in ice cores have also been used to estimate atmospheric CO_2 concentrations on much shorter time scales (the past 1,000 years). The Vostok core gives us long time scales because the rate of snow accumulation at Vostok is very small, a few centimeters per year. By contrast, snowfall at Siple Station is many meters per year.

The results of the Vostok scientists' analyses provide a firm link between global climate change and variations in the quantity of greenhouse gases in the atmosphere. What they found is that the CO_2 concentration falls and rises in concert with variations in local temperatures (recorded in the hydrogen isotopic composition of the ice, and both records are well correlated with global changes in temperature and ice-sheet size determined from $\delta^{18}O$ variations.

The rapidity of some of the changes is truly remarkable. The increase from glacial-stage levels (about 190 ppm) to nearly contemporary CO_2 levels (240 ppm) occurred over only 4,000 years, between 16,000 years and 12,000 years ago. Analyses of bubbles from ice created during the next-to-last deglaciation, approximately 145,000 years ago, display a similarly rapid rise in CO_2. The drop in CO_2 levels from the previous interglacial (about 130,000 years ago) to the height of the last glacial (about 20,000 years ago) was more subdued—about 1 ppm per millennium. The sawtooth nature of these changes is nearly identical to the oxygen isotope record, suggesting a close link between CO_2 changes, ice volume, and global temperature.

Feedbacks Affecting Atmospheric CO_2 on Glacial Time Scales

On long time scales (millions of years) the carbonate–silicate geochemical cycle, together with the weathering and deposition of organic carbon-rich sedimentary rocks, determines the steady-state atmospheric CO_2 level. When studying glacial–interglacial fluctuations, however, other processes must be included because the assumption of steady state with respect to these processes may not be valid on shorter time scales (thousands to hundreds of thousands of years). The partitioning of carbon between the atmosphere and terrestrial biomass, and between the atmosphere and ocean, as affected by the oceanic biological pump, are potentially of great importance to the CO_2 balance during glacial cycles. So, too, are the processes of limestone weathering and limestone deposition. On glacial–interglacial time scales, limestone weathering need not be balanced by limestone deposition, and any imbalance will affect atmospheric and oceanic concentrations of CO_2. Let us explore these feedbacks in greater detail.

ROLE OF THE BIOLOGICAL PUMP   The photosynthetic conversion of dissolved carbon dioxide to organic matter in the surface ocean, the settling of this material through the water column, and its decomposition at depth (that is, the *biological pump*) dominates the distribution of carbon throughout the world's ocean. Because the atmosphere equilibrates with the surface ocean, that photosynthetic conversion dominates the atmospheric CO_2 content as well. An atmospheric CO_2 pressure of 280 ppm (the preindustrial level) represents a biological pump that operates at intermediate efficiency, because regions of the ocean exist today (and presumably in preindustrial times as well) where nutrient concentrations are not completely depleted by biological uptake. If nutrients were completely utilized—that is, if the biological pump were 100% efficient in removing nutrients and CO_2 from surface waters—the atmospheric CO_2 pressure would be reduced to about 165 ppm. At the other extreme, if the biological pump ceased completely, the atmospheric CO_2 level would rise to about 720 ppm as the CO_2-charged deep waters mixed with the surface waters and homogenized the chemical composition of the ocean. Thus, the low CO_2 concentrations of glacial intervals might be the result of a more efficient biological pump.

Why might the glacial ocean support greater biological productivity? Most of the answers proposed in the scientific literature involve increased nutrient supply through upwelling or riverine delivery. The hypotheses described next are intended to explain why nutrients might have been more available to the oceanic biota during glacial times.

SHELF NUTRIENT HYPOTHESIS   The CO_2 concentration at the height of the last glaciation (20,000 years ago) was about 190 ppm. Might the biological pump have been more effective during the glaciation than it is today, perhaps as a

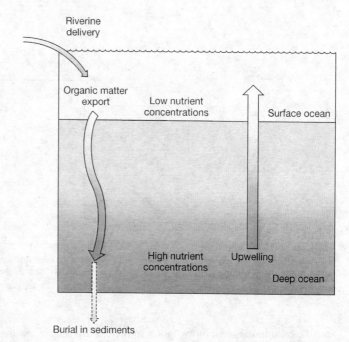

FIGURE 10 Simplified view of the nutrient throughput of the oceans.

result of a higher concentration of nutrients in the ocean as a whole? The nutrient concentration of the ocean represents a balance between supply by rivers (and, for nitrogen, by bacterial processes that convert nitrogen gas from the atmosphere to nutrient nitrate) and removal, primarily by sedimentation of organic matter (Figure 10). Thus, if the biological pump was intensified by higher nutrient concentrations during glacial intervals, either riverine fluxes were greater or sedimentation rates were lower.

As the glaciers grew, sea level fell, exposing the vast, low-relief margins of the continents (the **continental shelves**). Sediments of the continental shelves are rich in organic matter and nutrients, as the result of the highly productive nature of the overlying waters. When these sediments became exposed, weathering reactions released the nutrients (especially phosphate) to the rivers draining the shelves (Figure 11). This nutrient release enhanced the global delivery of phosphate to the oceans, causing an

increase in oceanic phosphate concentrations, marine productivity, and carbon export from the surface ocean and a drop in atmospheric CO_2. The resulting effect on global temperature and ice volume created a positive feedback loop, as shown in Figure 12. An attractive aspect of this hypothesis is that the residence (response) time of phosphate in the ocean is about 40,000 to 100,000 years, which essentially matches the major periodicity of glacial–interglacial cycles. The oceanic phosphate cycle is thus "tuned" to a major Milankovitch frequency and should be able to provide at least part of the required amplification of the Milankovitch forcing.

However, there are problems with this *shelf nutrient hypothesis*. The distribution of the trace element cadmium throughout the ocean follows that of phosphate very closely. Cadmium is incorporated into $CaCO_3$ skeletons of bottom-dwelling organisms in proportion to its oceanic concentration, whereas phosphate is not. Thus, paleoceanographers

FIGURE 11 The exposure of nutrient-rich shelf sediments as a result of a drop in sea level, part of the shelf nutrient hypothesis for the cause of changes in biological productivity on glacial time scales.

FIGURE 12 Systems diagram of the shelf nutrient hypothesis for the reduction of atmospheric CO_2 during glaciation.

use the cadmium content of the fossils of bottom-dwelling foraminifera as a proxy indicator of changes in the phosphate content of the oceans in the past. What these researchers find is that the cadmium content of these fossils does not indicate higher phosphate concentrations during glacial intervals. This inconsistency has led scientists to shift the focus of their search for productivity changes to other nutrients, particularly iron.

THE IRON FERTILIZATION HYPOTHESIS   Iron plays an important role in limiting primary productivity in certain regions of the ocean (Figure 13). In these regions the major nutrients are not depleted as they are in the rest of the surface ocean, and productivity appears to be limited by trace nutrients such as iron. Moreover, nitrogen-fixing cyanobacteria have large demands for iron, which is an essential metal for the synthesis of the enzyme that catalyzes nitrogen fixation. Much of the iron supplied to the oceans today comes from windblown dust particles, which typically have a coating of iron that dissolves in seawater. The Saharan and Gobi deserts today provide considerable quantitities of dust to the Atlantic and Pacific oceans, respectively. Aridity appears to have increased during glacial times. Further-

more, the east–west winds should have intensified in response to the greater equator-to-pole temperature gradient. Both of these factors would have increased the flux of dust to the oceans during glacial times. The record of wind-blown dust accumulation in marine sediments supports this *iron fertilization hypothesis;* rates increase severalfold during glacial intervals.

Recognition that primary productivity in large regions of the world's oceans is iron-limited today has led to the suggestion that fossil-fuel emission of carbon dioxide might be countered by iron-induced stimulation of biological uptake of CO_2 and its transfer to the deep sea (via the biological pump). Small-scale ocean experiments have indicated that iron fertilization is feasible, but also reveals that there may be detrimental and unexpected consequences of this environmental manipulation, including depletion of dissolved oxygen in the deep ocean.

THE CORAL REEF HYPOTHESIS   The continental shelves between 30° N and 30° S latitude provide a habitat that is ideal for the growth of corals and other calcium carbonate-secreting organisms (Figure 14). As these organisms

FIGURE 13 The iron fertilization hypothesis for the intensification of the biological pump during glaciations.

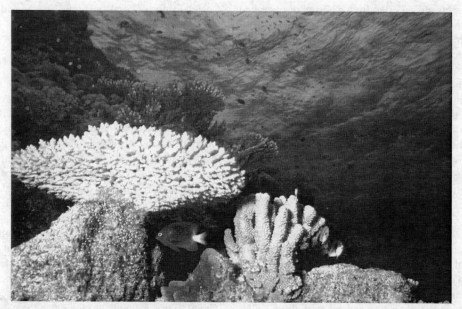

FIGURE 14 [See color section] Coral reefs may be responsible for the changes in atmospheric carbon dioxide concentrations that occur between glacials and interglacials. (*Source:* Photos.com/Jupiter Images Unlimited.)

grow, they add incrementally to the rock framework of the reef, building laterally as well as vertically, until the water surface is reached.

The production of $CaCO_3$ can be written as follows:

$$Ca^{2+} + 2HCO_3^- \rightarrow CaCO_3 + CO_2 + H_2O.$$

Thus, the growth of coral reefs serves as an additional source of carbon dioxide to the atmosphere. (The effect is only temporary, however; after tens of thousands of years, this excess carbon dioxide becomes converted to bicarbonate, as the result of mineral weathering, and is redeposited as $CaCO_3$.) In contrast, when ancient reefs are exposed by a drop in sea level, chemical weathering leads to their dissolution. This process is the reverse of reef growth: Atmospheric CO_2 is converted into bicarbonate, which is carried by rivers to the ocean. Thus, the growth and destruction of coral reefs can affect atmospheric CO_2 on glacial–interglacial time scales.

The link to glacial–interglacial CO_2 fluctuations is once again through sea-level changes. As the glacial interval ends and the ice sheets begin to melt, sea level rises, flooding the continental shelves. In the tropics, reef growth resumes and CO_2 is released to the atmosphere. The increase in atmospheric CO_2 causes an increased greenhouse effect, thereby amplifying the original climate warming (Figure 15). Conversely, as sea level begins to fall at the end of the interglacial, reefs become exposed to the atmosphere, and rain, soil, and groundwaters begin the process of reef dissolution. Again, the feedback loop is positive.

The importance of this feedback depends on the rates of these processes and on how responsive the rates are to sea-level changes. Studies of rates of calcium carbonate formation by reef-building organisms indicate that the reef ecosystem can easily keep pace with sea-level rise. The rate of limestone dissolution, however, is relatively slow. Thus, it is possible that, in this *coral reef hypothesis,* there is an unbalanced response to sea-level rise and fall in terms of reef growth and dissolution.

FIGURE 15 Systems diagram of the coral reef hypothesis.

Coral reefs are suffering from a host of diseases and other influences today. These are probably the result of multiple stresses, including warmer sea temperatures, increased human perturbation (ship groundings, pollution, destructive collection of reef rock and reef organisms), and perhaps even an increase in the flux of dust from distant lands carrying pathogens and iron, which fertilizes the algal competitors of corals. Perhaps the most pervasive anthropogenic stress is the direct response of the ocean's carbon chemistry to increasing atmospheric CO_2. Recall that as atmospheric CO_2 increases, the pH of the surface ocean decreases and the carbonate ion concentration falls. Carbonate, together with calcium ion, is essential for corals to precipitate their skeletons. The historical rise of atmospheric CO_2 over the last century has reduced the carbonate ion concentration of ocean surface waters by a measurable amount and may already be causing significant stress to corals. Projections for the future are not encouraging: corals may lose their ability to precipitate skeletons by early in the next (22nd) century. Scuba divers, or rather those who hope that their descendants will enjoy scuba diving, along with those who recognize the intrinsic and societal value of coral reefs thus have an additional reason to be concerned about future CO_2 increases.

Changes in Terrestrial Biomass: A Negative Feedback

In living tissue, the terrestrial biomass today contains about the same amount of carbon (600 Gton[C]) as does the atmosphere; about twice that much is contained in dead and decaying organic material in soils. On the basis of studies of plant fossils and other climatic indicators, it appears that the amount of forest coverage, and thus terrestrial biomass, was drastically reduced during the last glacial interval (Figure 16). Much of the northern forests were covered with ice, and tropical regions experienced greater aridity and thus the replacement of tropical rainforests with grasslands. Estimates have been made of the total amount of carbon that was transferred from the oceans to the terrestrial biomass at the end of the last glaciation. These numbers have large uncertainties, but it is clear that the change (around 700 Gton[C]) was many times larger than the net change in the amount of CO_2 in the atmosphere (around 160 Gton[C]).

FIGURE 16 The difference in South American vegetation between (a) the last glacial maximum and (b) today. Note the large increase in forest cover at the expense of grassland and savannah. The present-day map shows the "potential" vegetation cover; deforestation and other human activities have reduced the forest cover from its potential coverage shown here. (*Source:* Courtesy J. Adams, Oak Ridge National Laboratory.)

FIGURE 17 Systems diagram showing negative feedback between the size of the terrestrial biomass and climate change on glacial–interglacial time scales.

The growth of the terrestrial biomass during deglaciation and its destruction during the initiation of a glacial interval represent the only negative feedbacks that we have been able to identify to changes in atmospheric CO_2 on glacial time scales (Figure 17). That the CO_2 level rose and fell in concert with global temperature during the past 220,000 years indicates that positive feedback mechanisms have predominated. Note that this is just the opposite of what would be expected if organisms were modulating the climate system in such a way as to increase ecosystem stability. Gaia, if she exists, is destabilizing on glacial-to-interglacial time scales.

Cloud–Albedo Feedbacks

Recall that the process of cloud formation is critically dependent on the presence of small droplets (aerosols) known as *cloud condensation nuclei*. Besides dust (and pollution) over land and tiny sea-salt droplets over the ocean, two compounds are particularly important in the formation of cloud condensation nuclei: **methane sulfonic acid (MSA)** and sulfuric acid. The record of variation in the abundance of these cloud seeds can be read in the sulfur content of glacial ice in Greenland and Antarctica. Analysis of the composition of the Vostok ice revealed that the amount of MSA in the atmosphere of the Southern Hemisphere has varied with temperature over the past 150,000 years (Figure 18). During glaciations, the MSA content of the atmosphere over the Southern Ocean apparently was substantially greater than during interglacials. Might this have had a climatic consequence?

Both MSA and sulfur dioxide have an important biological source on the unpolluted Earth. Marine algae produce the gas *dimethyl sulfide* (DMS) as a byproduct

FIGURE 18 MSA content of Antarctic ice, compared with the relative local temperature (as indicated by the hydrogen isotopic composition of the ice), over the past 150,000 years. (*Source:* Legrand et al., *Nature* 350, 1991, p. 144.)

of the regulation of the salt content of their cells. DMS escapes to the atmosphere, where it undergoes chemical transformation to either MSA or sulfur dioxide. *Aerosols* (suspended atmospheric particles—in this case, tiny droplets) are formed that can serve as nuclei for the condensation of water vapor in the formation of clouds. It is likely that the rates of production of DMS, MSA, and sulfur dioxide increase as marine algal productivity increases. This increase in aerosol production would increase the aerosol concentration in the atmosphere. As a result, there should be an increase in the number of cloud water droplets in clouds, with a reduction in their size. In turn, cloud albedo would increase and thereby reduce Earth's average surface temperature.

The high content of MSA in ice formed during glacial intervals suggests that the productivity of the glacial ocean was greater than that of the interglacial ocean. Why? Should not marine algae be more productive when water temperatures are warmer? Some of the most productive waters of the world are at high latitudes. The detrimental effects of the lack of sunlight and of cold water temperatures on marine algae seem to be more than compensated for in these regions by a high supply of nutrients. Today, a strong thermocline at low latitudes stabilizes the water column and tends to prevent upwelling. In contrast, high-latitude surface waters lack a thermocline. Wind mixing penetrates to great depths and mixes nutrient-enriched deeper waters to the surface. Thus, cooling of higher-latitude temperate waters during glacial intervals should have reduced the thermocline, fostered water-column overturn, and brought a greater nutrient supply to surface waters, supporting higher rates of primary production.

If marine algal productivity tended to increase during glaciations, the feedback loop would be positive: This set of processes would tend to amplify the climate systems response to the Milankovitch forcing (Figure 19). The fact that the MSA content of Antarctic glacial ice rises as global temperature falls suggests that this feedback loop is important in Earth's climate system during at least the recent geologic past.

The Younger Dryas

In very broad terms, Earth began to warm about 15,000 years ago. The ice sheets that covered large areas of North America and northwest Europe began to retreat. Global sea levels rose as the glaciers melted, and the erosion from large volumes of meltwater reshaped the landscape around the edges of the former ice margins. Vegetation began to colonize the previously glaciated regions, and new vegetation patterns developed as soils formed and temperature and rainfall patterns changed. This spread of milder, more benign conditions came to an abrupt if temporary end 12,900 years ago in a 1,300-year climatic reversal known as the **Younger Dryas** event. The Dryas flower was widespread at that time—giving its name to the climatic event— but is currently found only in arctic and alpine tundra.

Some of the best evidence of climate and vegetation changes during the Younger Dryas comes from pollen and geologic analyses in northern Europe. As the climate warmed after the glacial retreat, there was a general increase in the density of vegetation, particularly grasses and sedges. This increase was followed by an increase in shrubs such as juniper and in willow; in some areas, the shrubs were later replaced by birch woodland. Pollen analysis shows a similar sequence of events in the British Isles, Ireland, and Scandinavia. Geologic evidence indicates that most of Scotland was probably deglaciated by 13,000 years ago. At this point a major climatic reversal occurred. By about 12,300 years ago, there was a new ice sheet several hundred meters thick over western Scotland, and there was renewed advance of valley glaciers in the upland regions of northern Europe. (*Valley glaciers* are individual glaciers that form at the head of a valley in mountainous regions and flow down the valley.) The pollen evidence shows a synchronous change in vegetation. The northern woodland diminished in area and was restricted to a few sites. The vegetation became more open, and the pollen data show a predominance of cold-tolerant vegetation types.

These changes represent a significant climate shift in northern Europe. However, the global impacts of this shift are more subtle. There is evidence of a similar climate shift in New England and along the east coast of Canada. There is little other evidence from North America except in the Gulf of Mexico and the Gulf of California, and there is only limited evidence from the Mediterranean. However, climatic reversals also appear to have occurred in the Andes and in Africa. The strongest evidence from Africa comes from lake levels, which increased after the northern deglaciation. But, while the Younger Dryas event was taking place in northern Europe, much of Eastern Europe and tropical and subtropical

FIGURE 19 Cloud–albedo climate feedbacks involving the algal production of cloud condensation nuclei.

Africa experienced increased aridity. Humid conditions returned to this region at the end of the Younger Dryas, and during the early Holocene, what we know today as the Sahara Desert was primarily grassland (savannah). Furthermore, data obtained from ocean cores taken in the western tropical Pacific Ocean and off the coast of Japan show some indication of a climate change at that time. Glaciers in the Southern Alps of New Zealand also re-advanced during this interval.

The Younger Dryas thus appears to be centered primarily on the North Atlantic region, but nearly synchronous climate changes occurred in many other parts of the Northern Hemisphere, if not globally. What process might explain a shift in climate that has a strong regional, rather than global, focus yet is able to influence widely scattered regions across Earth's surface?

NORTH ATLANTIC DEEP-WATER FORMATION A prime candidate for explaining the strong regional focus of the Younger Dryas climate change is the ocean circulation of the North Atlantic. The relatively high sea-surface temperatures in the northeast North Atlantic, which bring mild conditions to northern Europe today, result from the northward movement of the warm surface waters of the Gulf Stream and North Atlantic Drift. This movement is controlled in part by the atmospheric circulation and in part by the thermohaline circulation. Recall that the North Atlantic thermohaline circulation involves deep-water formation in the Norwegian and Greenland seas: As the cold and highly saline water subsides and moves southward, it is replaced by warm, northward-moving water at the surface. Geochemist Wallace Broecker has suggested that some of the climate changes that accompanied deglaciation resulted from events that cut off or reduced this deep-water formation. One hypothesis is that meltwater from the North American ice sheet, perhaps collected in glacial Lake Agassiz, catastrophically drained eastward through the Gulf of St. Lawrence. The result would have been a large infusion of cold freshwater to the northern North Atlantic. Because freshwater is less dense than saltwater, this infusion would have produced a stable surface layer that would freeze very easily, pushing the sea-ice margin southward and cutting off the formation of the North Atlantic deep water. Both the change in the thermohaline circulation and the southward expansion of the sea ice would have cut off the flow of warm surface water in the North Atlantic Drift, which would have resulted in a significant climate change in the region. Such a process could account for the climate reversal experienced during the Younger Dryas and would also explain the apparent focus on the North Atlantic region.

AN ON–OFF SWITCH IN THE NORTH ATLANTIC Although we have known about the Younger Dryas event for years and we have known that the event took place fairly rapidly

(in geological terms), using ice-core data obtained from the Greenland ice cap in the early 1990s, a team led by Richard Alley (a glaciologist at Pennsylvania State University) revealed the startling information that these changes might have taken place in less than a decade. The snow accumulation record (Figure 20) shows increased accumulation in the warmer intervals; it also shows that the switch from cold to warm intervals occurred over a very short time span. Atmospheric dust deposited on the ice and recorded in the ice cores reveals similar rapid changes in deposition rates. More dust is deposited during glacials than during interglacials, because the increased north–south temperature gradient results in a stronger atmospheric circulation; that stronger circulation carries more dust. Both the snow accumulation and the dusty deposition, therefore, indicate a shift in the atmospheric circulation. The rapidity with which these changes occur suggests that the system switches almost instantly between two modes of circulation.

The exact mechanism for explaining the shift in circulation is the subject of much speculation and discussion. One suggestion is that attributing the cause to any single process may be a mistake. An alternative approach is to view the system as chaotic. *Chaos theory* represents a rapidly emerging branch of science dealing with dynamic systems. Chaotic systems are iterative: The state of the system at one point in time is dependent on the state at the previous point. However, a characteristic of these systems is that very slight changes in the starting point are amplified through positive feedbacks, so the possible results diverge rapidly after only a short interval. Almost identical starting points can result in very different outcomes, and different starting points can produce outcomes that are very similar. The consequence is that, after a certain interval, the system becomes essentially unpredictable.

In 1960, Edward Lorenz, a meteorologist at the Massachusetts Institute of Technology, was the first to recognize that the atmosphere is a chaotic system. Since then we have known why accurate long-range weather forecasting is impossible and why accurate daily weather forecasts can be effective only on time scales of days to a couple of weeks. One important attribute of chaotic systems, however, is that they exist in quasi-equilibrium states; in the case of the atmosphere, for example, we know in general what it will be like next year, even though we cannot predict exactly what it will be like on any given day. In the terminology of chaos theory, these quasi-equilibrium states are called *strange attractors:* The system is never precisely at that point, but it is always somewhere close to it. Another characteristic of chaotic systems is that they may switch rapidly between two or more of these quasi-equilibrium states. The point at which this switch occurs is called a *bifurcation point.*

FIGURE 20 The snow accumulation record from a Greenland ice core. (*Source:* R. Alley et al. "Abrupt Increase in Greenland Snow Accumulation at the end of the Younger Dryas Event" *Nature* 362, 1993, pp. 527–529.)

We can view the climate system as having two (or more) stable steady states: glacial and interglacial, with the transition between the two representing the bifurcation point (see Figure 8). When the climate system is near the bifurcation point (e.g., at the end of the last glaciation), the system is unstable and any number of small perturbations could be amplified through positive feedbacks to push the system rapidly toward one stable state or the other. This possibility leads us to the second reason why the Greenland ice-core data have generated considerable interest. If these data do indicate that climate can switch rapidly between two very different stable states after a relatively small perturbation, a new wrinkle is added to the greenhouse warming question: If increased greenhouse gases should lead to a rapid shift in the climate system (possibly to a third, much warmer, quasi-equilibrium state), then our expectations of global warming may significantly underestimate the strength and the speed of the climate response to greenhouse forcing (see the Box "A Closer Look: Stochastic Resonance and Rapid Climate Change").

As our discussion turns to the issues of short-term climate change, both natural and anthropogenic, we must not forget that we are living in a time of unparalleled sensitivity of the climate system. The rapid climate shifts that Earth has experienced in its most recent geologic past caution us that tampering with the climate system might result in unexpectedly large climate responses. Furthermore, a prediction of future climate based solely on the Milankovitch forcing indicates that Earth should soon (geologically speaking) slip into the next glaciation. But, as a result of fossil-fuel burning and its effect on atmospheric CO_2 levels, it is not at all clear that this will be the case. We will draw on our knowledge of paleoclimates in subsequent chapters to make a more informed prediction of the future climates of Earth.

A CLOSER LOOK

Stochastic Resonance and Rapid Climate Change

In the text we describe the rapid climate shift back into the Younger Dryas that occurred as the climate was warming from the last glacial maximum. We also explained how this could come about through shutting down the thermohaline circulation in the North Atlantic, followed by feedback processes that reduce atmospheric CO_2 concentrations. If we look in a little more detail at the climate record, however, we see that rapid climate changes such as these are actually very common (Box Figure 3). The temperature record from central Greenland (ice-core data) reveals large swings in climate during the last glaciation. Warm episodes punctuate the generally cold conditions and, as we move out of the glaciation, we see the system gradually warming then suddenly dropping back into cold conditions, warming, and dropping back again. Some of these rapid cooling events are accompanied by the flooding of the North Atlantic with glacial meltwater as described in the text, but many of them are not. Some appear to be random, while others appear to be periodic. Nothing we have discussed in the text really accounts for the behavior that we see here. One explanation that is gaining in popularity is the concept of stochastic resonance. Looking at the temperature record up until the start of the Holocene we see the characteristics of what is referred to by physicists as an "excitable system"—a system that has a stable and an unstable

mode. It appears that there is a preferred "cold" mode and an unstable warm mode that the system cannot occupy for long.

Imagine a very weak but periodic forcing. This could, for example, be a very small change in solar output that occurs on a regular cycle, but is too weak to promote a significant change in climate. Superimposed on this are random variations that are inherent in the climate system. Taken together, these push the system across a threshold, and then what we need is a mechanism that can amplify the signal (Box Figure 4). The most likely mechanism that we can come up with at present is a change in the thermohaline circulation. It doesn't have to be anything as dramatic as shutting it down—maybe just a change in the location of the bottom water formation. What we then have is a situation with a stable cold mode (during the glaciation) with random perturbations (the "stochastic" part of stochastic resonance). At periodic intervals some other forcing gives a very weak push to the system, which "resonates" with the random variations and pushes the forcing beyond a critical threshold. At that point the change is amplified by the amplification mechanism (maybe ocean circulation) and pushes the climate into an unstable warm mode. The climate stays in this mode for a short interval before dropping back into the stable cold mode again. Analysis of the ice-core data by Richard Alley

Temperature history in central Greenland

BOX FIGURE 3 Temperature reconstruction for central Greenland based on ice-core data. Very large fluctuations have been common except recently. (*Source:* Courtesy Richard Alley, Pennsylvania State University.)

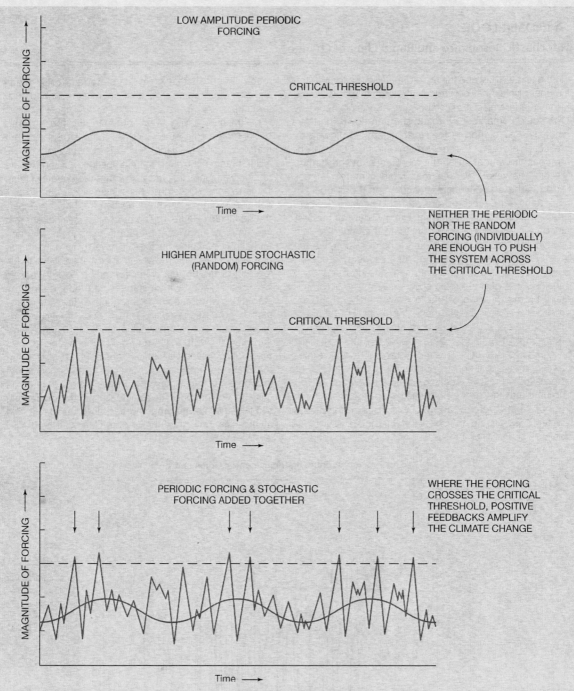

BOX FIGURE 4   Schematic representation of stochastic resonance.

and colleagues (see text) indicates that there is indeed a periodic forcing that occurs at an interval of about 1,500 years that accounts for much of the variation in the temperature record.

    As we move out of the glacial episode, the reverse seems to happen. Now the system is warming up but we

have sudden events like the meltwater release to the North Atlantic that temporarily pushes the climate back into a cold mode again. Where does this leave us? Climate scientists are looking at these ideas and asking, if these are correct, where does the periodic forcing come from? What is the amplification mechanism—is there more than one? Can the same thing happen during interglacials, when the planet seems to be in a more stable warm mode? Is there some other altogether different process waiting to be discovered that would explain what we see in the record? All of these are interesting questions, but why this is truly worth a closer look in the context of this text is because the climate record clearly shows that rapid and large changes do occur that are essentially unpredictable. It also shows that as the system is transitioning between states (i.e., as Earth was warming coming out of the last glaciation) it is common for it to be pushed back in the other direction very rapidly. Neither of these possibilities is taken into account in any of the projections currently put forward for global warming. At the back of your mind you should keep note of the fact that processes such as those described here have the potential to surprise us—and completely change the magnitude (and maybe even direction) of the changes we predict for the future.

Chapter Summary

1. Earth's climate has varied on a number of time scales, from decadal to millennial changes we can directly observe to the billion-year evolution drive by solar evolution.
2. The best documented of these changes are those that occurred on intermediate time scales during the glacial cycles of the Pleistocene.
3. Substantial, periodic swings in climate over the past 2 million years are indicated by the geologic record of glacial deposits and by the oxygen isotopic record of global temperature and of continental ice-sheet volume.
4. Orbital (Milankovitch) theory provides the answer to the question of causation of glacial–interglacial cycles.
   a. Small changes in the configuration of Earth's orbit around the Sun, varying in a predictable fashion, have provided the slight changes in seasonal insolation necessary to initiate these climate swings. These include changes in orbital eccentricity, obliquity, and the precession of the spin axis.
   b. The climate response matches the relative magnitude of the forcing at the frequencies of the precessional and obliquity changes.
   c. However, the dominant periodicity of glacial–interglacial fluctuation is 100,000 years. The forcings from eccentricity changes at this periodicity are too small.

5. The climate system seems to have amplified the 100,000-year signal preferentially, through feedbacks involving the dynamics of continental ice sheets, the albedo of ice and clouds, and the controls on marine productivity and the growth of coral reefs and thus also on the cloud albedo and greenhouse effect.
6. As Earth warmed up from the effects of the last glaciation, a sudden and very rapid climate reversal occurred (the Younger Dryas event), resulting in the readvance of ice sheets and glaciers over much of northern Europe and other parts of the globe.
   a. Several hypotheses have been proposed to explain the Younger Dryas, the most likely of which involves the switching on and off of the thermohaline circulation in the North Atlantic Ocean.
   b. Regardless of the exact cause of this shift in climate, the Younger Dryas is of particular interest because recent ice-core data show that the change occurred very rapidly, over years to decades; the apparent ability of the climate system to shift rapidly between two very different states poses some interesting questions about how the climate may respond to future greenhouse warming.

Key Terms

aphelion
continental shelves
eccentricity
glacial
glacial striations
Holocene epoch
interglacial

loess
methane sulfonic acid (MSA)
moraine
obliquity
perihelion
period
Pleistocene epoch

precession
seasonal temperature contrast
stochastic resonance
till
Younger Dryas

Review Questions

1. What types of geologic evidence are diagnostic of glaciation?
2. What causes changes in the oxygen isotopic composition of seawater?
3. Which three characteristics of Earth's orbit around the Sun vary on the time scale of Pleistocene glaciations? How does each of these affect the amount of energy received from the Sun?
4. What orbital configuration favors glaciation? Why?
5. How is the oxygen isotopic record of marine limestones used to test Milankovitch's theory of the ice ages?

6. What role do biologically produced sulfur gases play in glacial climate fluctuations?
7. What factors might have caused atmospheric CO_2 variations that kept pace with glacial climate fluctuations?
8. Explain why the formation of North Atlantic Deep Water might have played a role in causing the Younger Dryas event.

Critical-Thinking Problems

1. Construct a Daisyworld-like model of the MSA-climate feedback loop shown in Figure 19. First sketch a graph of how DMS production by algae would affect global temperature. Then sketch another graph of your view of how changes in global temperature might affect algal DMS production. Defend both graphs in writing. Then combine these graphs and discuss the stability of the equilibrium states indicated.
2. An ellipse is defined as the locus of all points such that the sum of the distances to two fixed points, called the foci, is a constant. We can easily show that this constant is equal to $2a$, where a is the semimajor axis of the ellipse. (See Box Figure 1 and the accompanying discussion.) The eccentricity e of the ellipse is defined such that the distance from one focus to the midpoint of the figure is ae. An ellipse with $e = 0$ is a circle.
   a. Kepler's first law states that the planets move around the Sun in elliptical orbits with the Sun at one focus. Earth's present orbit has a semimajor axis of 1 AU and an eccentricity of 0.017. The point of closest approach to the Sun is the perihelion; the point farthest away is the aphelion. How much closer is Earth to the Sun at

perihelion than at aphelion? Express your answer in astronomical units.
   b. The Milankovitch theory of the ice ages holds that the most important forcing factor is the difference in solar heating at high latitudes when Northern Hemisphere summer occurs at perihelion as opposed to aphelion. Using the inverse square law, find the solar flux at perihelion and at aphelion. Recall that the solar flux at 1 AU is 1370 Watts/m^2. How much higher is the solar flux at perihelion than at aphelion today? Express your answer as a percentage. How much warmer is the effective radiating temperature of Earth?
   c. The eccentricity of Earth's orbit varies with time as a consequence of gravitational perturbations caused by the other planets. Repeat Problem 2b for e at its maximum value of 0.06.
   d. Kepler's third law states that the square of a planet's period P is proportional to the cube of its semimajor axis a. When P is expressed in Earth years and a is in AU, the relationship is simply $P^2 = a^3$. Venus and Mars have semimajor axes of 0.72 and 1.52 AU, respectively. How many Earth years does it take for them to go around the Sun?

Further Reading

General

Alley, R. B. 2000. *The two-mile time machine: Ice cores, abrupt climate change, and our future* (p. 229). Princeton, NJ: Princeton University Press.
Broecker, W. S. 1995. Chaotic climate. *Scientific American*, November 1995, pp. 62–68.
Broecker, W. S., and G. H. Denton. 1990. What drives glacial cycles? *Scientific American*, January 1990, pp. 48–56.

Advanced

Berger, A. 1995. Modeling the response of the climate system to astronomical forcing. In *Future climates of the world*, ed. A. Henderson-Sellers, World Survey of Climatology. Amsterdam: Elsevier Science.
Imbrie, J. et al. 1992, 1993. On the structure and origin of major glaciation cycles, Parts 1 and 2. *Paleoceanography* 7:701–38, and 8:699–735.
Kump, L., and J. Lovelock. 1995. The geophysiology of climate. In *Future climates of the world*, ed. A. Henderson-Sellers, World Survey of Climatology. Amsterdam: Elsevier Science.
Liu, H.-S. 1995. A new view on the driving mechanism of Milankovitch glaciation cycles. *Earth and Planetary Science Letters* 131:17–26.

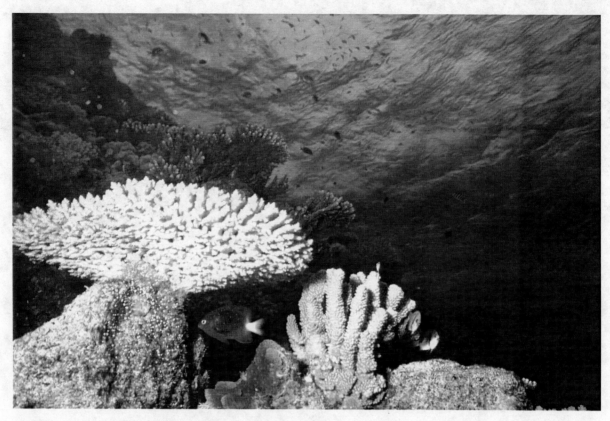

FIGURE 14   Coral reefs may be responsible for the changes in atmospheric carbon dioxide concentrations that occur between glacials and interglacials.   (*Source:* Photos.com/Jupiter Images Unlimited.)

Global Warming, Part 1
Recent and Future Climate

Key Questions

- What causes climate change on short time scales?
- How has climate varied over the past 10,000 years?
- Are the observed changes in climate over the past century natural or human-induced?
- How do anthropogenic carbon fluxes compare with natural fluxes?

- How much are atmospheric CO_2 and other greenhouse gases expected to rise over the next few decades to centuries, and how will this rise affect Earth's climate?

Chapter Overview

Earth's climate has remained remarkably stable over the past 10,000 years, although it was slightly warmer 5,000 to 6,000 years ago (the Holocene Climatic Optimum) and slightly cooler from about A.D. 1600 until 1850 (the Little Ice Age). Since 1850, the global average surface temperature has increased by about 0.8°C. The largest part of this change has occurred over the past 40 years and has likely been caused by human activities: release of CO_2 by fossil-fuel burning and deforestation and release of CH_4 and N_2O from agriculture. If no actions are taken to reduce emissions, CO_2 levels are expected to more than double over the next century and could increase by a factor of 6 to 8 over the next few centuries. Temperature increases within the next century are predicted to be only a few degrees Celsius, but long-term climate changes could be substantially larger than this. The oceanic thermohaline circulation might also slow down as a consequence of increased rainfall in the North Atlantic and resulting decreases in salinity of surface water in that region.

INTRODUCTION

Earth's climate has varied on a number of different time scales. Over the past few billion years, the Sun has brightened considerably and Earth's climate has gone through a series of warm and cold periods. Earth has even experienced brief periods where the surface seems to have been completely frozen. But the system has recovered from these catastrophes and has remained within a range conducive to the continued presence of life. Over the past few million years, the climate has oscillated between glacial and interglacial intervals triggered by variations in Earth's orbit and amplified by internal feedbacks within the climate system.

Humans are now altering Earth's climate by adding greenhouse gases to its atmosphere. We see evidence for this in the plots of atmospheric CO_2 concentration and global mean surface temperature. But how can we know if the observed temperature changes have been caused by humans, or if they simply represent natural fluctuations in the climate system? And how can we tell if the recent increase in atmospheric CO_2, which itself is not disputed, will continue into the future? To answer these questions, we need to do several things: First, we must examine climate change over the past 10,000 years, termed the **Holocene epoch**, so that we can place modern climate change in perspective. Then, we must look more carefully at the modern CO_2 cycle to see how humans are perturbing it. And, finally, we need to look at climate modeling results to understand how high-powered computer models are being used to make projections of future climate change. It is a daunting task.

HOLOCENE CLIMATE CHANGE

Proxy Climate Data

We have a vast quantity of data with which to describe and analyze the present-day climate system. In particular, an array of measuring stations with accurate thermometers covers much of Earth's land surface, and ships and floating buoys provide measurements for much of the world's oceans. These data extend back to about A.D. 1850. Where there are gaps in the coverage, we can fill them in today with satellite data. In fact, in terms of quantity, satellites now provide the bulk of the observational climate data set. Consistent and reliable satellite data, however, have been available only since the early 1970s. The data prior to the satellite era have huge gaps over the oceans, and over the land the climate record is highly variable—some regions have several hundred years of observations, others less than 30. With such a short record of observational data, how do we determine climate variability and climate change of the past?

The data problem gets much worse prior to 1850. Accurate, mercury-based thermometers had been invented over 100 years before this time by the German physicist Daniel Gabriel Fahrenheit, but their use was restricted primarily to Europe and North America. To obtain estimates of global temperatures prior to this time, we have to resort to the use of **proxy data**. We have already seen some examples of proxy climate data. The geological evidence of the advance and retreat of continental glaciers, such as glacial till deposits and moraines, as well as atmospheric and climate reconstructions derived from ice cores. As we move to time scales covering the past 10,000 years, we make use of other types of evidence in addition to ice cores. Two of the most useful techniques for reconstructing past climates are based on *palynology* and *dendrochronology*.

Palynology is the study of pollen and organic microfossils. Pollen grains are preserved in many different environments (for example, lake sediments and peat bogs). If we drill a core into sediments from a lake or from a peat bog, divide the core into segments going back through time, and then extract the pollen from each layer, we can reconstruct the plant assemblages that lived in the area of

that core at each time interval in the past. We then use the present-day distribution of those assemblages to place constraints on what the environment was like in the past. Pollen data from peat bogs have been used to reconstruct climate over the past 30,000 to 35,000 years in the British Isles. Radiocarbon dating can be used to date different levels of the core to associate environmental changes with particular time periods.

Dendrochronology is a method of dating trees by counting their annual growth rings. This method uses the growth characteristics of certain tree species. The cross section of a tree trunk consists of a series of rings, each ring representing growth over one year. By counting the annual rings, we know the age of the tree. The width of each ring indicates the amount of growth that occurred during the growing season. In certain circumstances, that amount can be related to the temperature during the growing season or to water availability, both of which can tell us something about the climate while the tree was alive. For example, a climate record that extends back almost 5,500 years has been reconstructed from tree rings of bristlecone pines in the White Mountains of California.

Holocene Warm and Cold Periods

By combining ice-core data with data from these other techniques, we can make estimates of how global surface temperatures have varied over the past few tens of thousands of years. Figure 1b, for example, shows how climate has varied over the past 20,000 years. If we zoom in a little closer (Figure 1c), we can look at the variations in surface temperature over the past 1,000 years. These changes are compared to the Pleistocene glacial–interglacial changes in Figure 1a. As mentioned already, the really big temperature changes occurred prior to about 10,000 years ago. But significant fluctuations, of the order of 1–2°C, have occurred all the way up to the present time. If one looks at the data in more detail, one finds that the pattern of change is not uniform across the globe. It is difficult to generalize, but there appears to be a dominance of temperature changes in the midlatitudes and high latitudes, whereas the tropics and subtropics appear to have experienced greater changes in moisture availability. These changes result partly from orbital effects that enhance seasonality and continentality (which directly affect the temperature regime) and partly from the resulting circulation changes (such as changes in the monsoon circulation) that affect precipitation patterns. Other factors may also have played a role in regional climate changes, as we will see later in this chapter.

Another point to note is that relatively small changes in the mean global temperature are associated with relatively large changes in the physical environment. Mean global temperatures at the height of the last glaciation were probably only 5 to 7°C lower than the 20th-century mean. Eight

FIGURE 1 Mean global temperature change since the last glacial maximum. (a) Generalized oxygen isotope curve from deep-sea sediments. (b) General estimates from pollen data and alpine glaciers (emphasis on midlatitudes from eastern North America and Europe). (c) General estimates from historical documents (emphasis on the North Atlantic region). (*Source:* Adapted from U.S. Committee for GARP, *Understanding Climate Change: A Program for Action,* National Academy of Sciences, Washington, DC, 1975.)

or relatively slow warming over the next several thousand years—the **Holocene Climatic Optimum**. Evidence suggests that summer temperatures were slightly higher in the Mid-Holocene (5,000 to 6,000 years ago) than are recorded in the recent (20th-century) record. This interval was long thought of as a time of persistent mild conditions with very little climate change. This view originates from early studies in Europe, where the pollen record shows little evidence of major climatic shifts. Elsewhere in the world the picture is less straightforward.

Ancient lake levels in East Africa and the Sahara Desert show evidence of much wetter conditions than exist today. These high lake levels occurred when temperatures were higher—presumably, evaporation would have been greater then. This means that the amount of rainfall in the region must also have been greater than it is today. The evidence suggests a northward shift of the intertropical convergence zone in the Northern Hemisphere summer, bringing higher rainfall to the Sahara and East Africa and an enhanced monsoonal circulation (increased summer rain) in Arabia and northwest India. There is also evidence that the Mediterranean Sea experienced increased summer rainfall during this same interval. Turkey and western Iran, however, appear to have been more arid than at present.

That the Mid-Holocene climate was very different from today's climate is also indicated by archeological evidence. The Tarim Basin, the site of the ancient silk route from China to Europe, is currently a desert, but between 5,000 and 6,000 years ago it was forested and populated with numerous settlements. Nomads grazed cattle in the central Sahara, and the Harappan culture flourished in the Indus River valley. This agricultural society, located in what is now the Rajasthan Desert, may have been the first to cultivate cotton. At first glance, changes in climate would appear to be a likely explanation for the decline of these earlier civilizations. Undoubtedly, the Sahara, for example, is now much drier than it was then. In several cases, however, it is possible that human land-use practices, rather than a change in climate, led to land degradation. In fact, it is likely that the collapse of some of these cultures resulted from the interaction of both factors—where land degradation due to human land use was amplified by changing climate conditions. It would seem reasonable to look back at this, and other warm periods, and suggest that they might be an indicator of what our future climate may be like as global warming progresses. Unfortunately, analogs from the past are of limited use for predicting the future as the forcing factors are different. The climate response, therefore, is also likely to be different.

THE MEDIEVAL WARM PERIOD Temperatures fell after the Holocene Climatic Optimum, reaching a minimum about 3000 years ago, but rose to a new maximum during the European **Medieval Warm Period**. Temperatures in Greenland appear to have increased after A.D. 600 to 650, with the temperatures in the North Atlantic (Greenland and

hundred years ago, when the Vikings were able to colonize parts of Greenland and grow sufficient crops to maintain a continuous settlement, mean global temperatures were only 0.5°C or so warmer than they are today. The significance of these numbers is highlighted by the fact that global temperature changes predicted for a doubling of atmospheric CO_2 are on the order of 1.5 to 4°C. In other words, the changes we predict for potential global warming in the 21st century are much greater than anything that has occurred in the past 10,000 years, and those changes are of comparable magnitude to the warming that took place between the last glacial maximum and the present day.

THE HOLOCENE CLIMATIC OPTIMUM The short cold interval of the Younger Dryas event ended with a rapid shift to warmer conditions, followed by a constant climate

Iceland) reaching a maximum around A.D. 1100. At this time the Vikings established a self-supporting colony on the southwest coast of Greenland. The colony lasted more than 400 years and, at its largest extent, had 280 farms and a population of 3,000. By the end of the 12th century, however, because of the decreasing temperatures, the sea ice east of Greenland grew more extensive. By the middle of the 14th century, ships had to take a more southerly route to avoid the ice. By A.D. 1410, communication with the Greenland colonies was lost completely.

Farther south, in northern, western, and central Europe, the Medieval Warm Period reached a maximum between A.D. 1150 and A.D. 1300. During this period, wheat was grown in Norway at about 64° N, oats and barley were grown in Iceland, vineyards were cultivated in England, and farm settlements spread to higher elevations in Norway, northern England, and Scotland—all evidence of milder climates than those areas have today. The average temperature of central England during this interval is estimated to have been 0.5 to 0.8°C above the mean for the first half of the 20th century.

From the beginning of the 14th century, the climate became more variable. Wetter (and probably colder) summers in Europe from A.D. 1313 to 1317 led to a succession of failed harvests and widespread famine, and the expansion of farms into the upland regions of northern Europe and Scandinavia came to an abrupt end. The interval from A.D. 1250 to A.D. 1350 was one of numerous large storms and floods. It has been suggested that the storminess was caused by a cooling at high latitudes that caused the sea ice to expand southward, resulting in an increased temperature gradient in the North Atlantic. Flooding along the North Sea coasts of Denmark and Germany was extensive, and 100,000 to 400,000 people were reported to have drowned in the floods that occurred at that time. The impact of these large environmental changes on human societies was then compounded by the arrival in Europe of the bubonic plague in 1346. The plague lasted until 1361, killing an estimated 25 million people (one-quarter of Europe's population).

THE LITTLE ICE AGE   The extreme climatic fluctuations that marked the end of the Medieval Warm Period led to an interval of cooling until the early 1500s, after which the climate stayed relatively stable or even began to recover in some areas. The North Atlantic climate, however, entered a renewed episode of rapid cooling in the late 1500s, a period now known as the **Little Ice Age**. Although the cooling was originally thought of as a regional climate fluctuation centered on western Europe and the North Atlantic, a growing body of evidence from the European Alps, Asia and the Himalayas, South America, New Zealand, and Antarctica suggests that changes might have occurred over much of the globe. However, not all parts of the world show evidence of a climate change at this time. Where they do, it is not clear that the changes were synchronous or that they lasted the same length of time everywhere. The Little Ice Age continued through the middle of the 19th century, but the reduced temperatures were not continuous. The Little Ice Age is characterized by considerable variability, with episodic cold spells that varied in timing and duration from place to place.

The evidence of the Little Ice Age takes numerous forms, among them the readvance of mountain glaciers, the lowering of tree lines, increased erosion and flooding, sea-ice expansion, and the freezing of canals and rivers. The canals of Holland have long been used for transportation, and there are reliable records of freeze-up since 1633. The canals seldom freeze over in today's climate, but in the 15th and 17th centuries it was common for them to be frozen for 3 months at a time. There is also documented evidence of glaciers in the Swiss Alps advancing and covering houses on the outskirts of several villages (Figure 2). A climate change is also suggested by indicators of population

(a)   (b)

FIGURE 2   The Argentiere glacier in the French Alps. (a) An etching made about 1850, showing the extent of the glacier during the waning phase of the Little Ice Age. (b) The same view, photographed in 1966.   (*Source:* (a) National Academy Press and (b) National Academy Press.)

decline: the abandonment of settlements and decreasing agricultural productivity. However, the societal evidence is not straightforward; population changes and declining productivity were almost certainly influenced by societal and political factors and by disease.

As with the Younger Dryas event described earlier, the Little Ice Age appears to have had a strong regional focus, yet evidence is mounting that many other parts of the world also experienced a similar cooling. In this case, however, there was no retreating continental ice sheet to help force large changes in the oceanic circulation. Are there any other likely explanations for this particular shift in the climate system?

Volcanoes and Climate

One possibility is that the Little Ice Age was caused by increases in volcanic activity. We saw in earlier chapters that volcanism releases CO_2, which helps warm Earth by contributing to the greenhouse effect. But volcanoes can also cause short-term cooling by injecting sulfur dioxide (SO_2) into the atmosphere. This SO_2 is eventually oxidized to form sulfate aerosols, in much the same way as SO_2 released from coal-burning forms aerosols today. Some volcanoes, however, are highly explosive and can inject SO_2 high into the stratosphere. Because clouds and rain, which normally remove sulfate aerosols, are not present in the stratosphere, these aerosols can remain aloft for many months and can have a significant cooling effect on Earth's climate. As early as 1784, Benjamin Franklin hypothesized that the abnormally cold winter of 1783–1784 might have been due to the 1783 eruption of Hekla, a volcano on Iceland. Actually, any climate anomaly in that year was more likely due to the 1783 eruption of Laki, another Icelandic volcano. Laki is, in fact, the largest effusive eruption in the historic record, producing about 12 km^3 of basalt lava flows.

The degree to which a volcanic eruption affects climate depends in part on the location of the eruption and on the way the atmospheric circulation distributes the stratospheric aerosols globally. Mt. Pinatubo in the Philippines experienced a major eruption in June 1991, when the equivalent of 3 to 5 km^3 of dense rock was ejected into the atmosphere (Figure 3). The ejecta also included approximately 20 Mton of SO_2 gas, which was subsequently converted to sulfuric acid aerosol particles, with the largest concentration occurring in the lower stratosphere at an altitude between 15 and 20 km. The aerosol cloud was distributed very rapidly around the globe by the stratospheric circulation, circling the entire globe in only 22 days. The cooling from this event lasted approximately 1–2 years. The maximum temperature drop in late 1992 was about 0.5°C.

The 1815 Tambora eruption is probably the most renowned eruption in terms of its effect on climate. Large acidity peaks for that time in ice cores from both Greenland and Antarctica show a global distribution of

FIGURE 3 The eruption of Mt. Pinatubo in the Philippines, June 1991. (*Source:* USGS.)

the aerosol cloud, which is estimated to have been about 10^{11} kg (about five times larger than the cloud from the Pinatubo eruption). The following year, 1816, has been referred to as the "year without a summer" in Europe and northeast North America. Hudson Bay remained ice-covered that summer, and estimated average daily temperatures in this region were 5 to 6°C below the long-term average. Although these conditions were maintained only for 2 years, the cold weather from the winter of 1815–1816 through the summer of 1817 produced crop failures in China and bad harvests in India. The failure of the Indian harvest resulted in famine, which was followed by an outbreak of cholera that, over the next two decades, spread through Asia and Europe. However, the cold weather in the eastern Hudson Bay began with a series of anomalously cold years from the winter of 1811–1812, suggesting that not all the cold weather in 1816 was due to the eruption. Nevertheless, several other large eruptions occurred between 1811 and 1814, including the eruption of Vesuvius in 1813. The resulting cold temperatures could have been the cumulative result of the combined volcanic activity.

From the analysis of Greenland ice cores, we know that the interval from A.D. 1250 to 1500 and A.D. 1550 to

FIGURE 4 The butterfly diagram, showing the distribution of sunspots over the Sun's surface.   (*Source:* From E. Chaisson and S. McMillan, *Astronomy: A Beginner's Guide to the Universe,* 2/e, 1998. Reprinted by permission of Prentice Hall, Upper Saddle River, N.J.)

1700 were times of high volcanic activity, whereas A.D. 1100 to 1250 had far fewer volcanic events. The first two intervals coincide with the Little Ice Age; A.D. 1100 to 1250 lies in the Medieval Warm Period. Again, the evidence suggests a link between volcanic activity and climate, but that link is still not conclusive.

Solar Variability

Another possible source of Holocene climate fluctuations is changes in solar output. We have already seen that the output of the Sun has changed considerably over the long period of Earth's history. At the short time scales we are considering here, however, we tend to regard the solar output as constant. In fact, the output from the Sun probably varies slightly at *all* time scales—but is the solar variability sufficient to explain the observed climate changes?

The greatest changes in solar output at the decade-to-century time scale accompany variations in the number of sunspots. **Sunspots** are dark areas of lower-than-normal temperatures on the surface of the Sun. Imagine that magnetic field lines wind around the Sun like elastic bands. Where these bands are twisted together, the "knot" at the surface inhibits convection from below, resulting in an area of lower temperatures (sunspots). Telescopes were first used by Galileo to observe sunspots in about 1610, but reliable sunspot data exist only for about the past 150 years. The historic record shows an 11-year cycle in sunspot

activity (11 years between the peaks in sunspot abundance) superimposed on a 22-year cycle of magnetic reversals. Just like the magnetic field on Earth, the Sun's magnetic field also experiences periodic reversals, but the Sun's magnetic reversals are more frequent and regular.

The pattern of sunspot activity is illustrated by the *butterfly diagram* in Figure 4, which plots the location of sunspots on the Sun's surface through time. In late 1933, there were very few sunspots, but the number increased into 1937. Sunspots appeared first at higher solar latitudes, but, as they increased in abundance, the concentration shifted toward the solar equator. Sunspots then decreased in number until the next minimum in 1944, when, again, the activity switched to the higher latitudes. Plotted in this fashion, the cloud of points in Figure 4 resembles a butterfly wing. Note that the period of cycle is not always exactly 11 years. Even when the period is exactly 11 years from minimum to minimum, the curve is not symmetric: Less time passes between a minimum and a maximum than between the maximum and the next minimum.

Somewhat surprisingly, an increase in the abundance of sunspots, which are darker (cooler) areas on the Sun's surface, corresponds to an *increase* in the amount of solar radiation Earth receives. The Stefan–Boltzmann law suggests that the opposite should occur: An increase in sunspot abundance should result in decreased luminosity and a drop in solar radiation. The reason for this behavior is that the sunspots are surrounded by bright areas of higher-than-normal temperature called **plages**, and the area of plages is larger than the area of spots. The net result is that the Sun is actually slightly brighter during periods when sunspots increase; hence, the amount of solar radiation emitted also increases. In reality, the dark areas of the sunspots and the bright areas of the plages almost cancel each other out.

How does this variation in sunspot activity relate to Earth's climate? Studies have discovered an 11-year or a 22-year cycle in numerous climate records (records of regional floods, droughts, temperatures, and so on). However, the change in total solar output over the 11-year cycle is very small. Satellite measurements for the 1980s show that the incoming solar radiation decreased by only about 0.1% from the maximum to the minimum in sunspot activity. The direct climatic consequences of such a change are so small that they would be undetectable. At present, there are no commonly accepted mechanisms for explaining how such a small change in insolation could have a measurable impact on climate. That said, it should be pointed out that the amount of ultraviolet radiation, especially at wavelengths of 200 nm and below, changes by as much as a factor of 3 from solar maximum to solar minimum. This radiation is absorbed high up in Earth's atmosphere, and relatively little energy is involved, so it is hard to see how it could affect Earth's surface temperature. But this has not prevented researchers from proposing correlations between sunspot activity and climate.

Systematic records of sunspot activity were initiated in 1848 by Rudolf Wolf, director of the Bern Observatory, after an amateur astronomer, Heinrich Schwabe, published sunspot observations from 1826 to 1843. Wolf also compiled all of the pre-1826 data that were available, extending the record of sunspot abundance back to 1700. He also published the years of sunspot minima and maxima from 1700 back to the invention of the telescope by Galileo in 1610. The pre-1826 data are far from reliable, but they do indicate an interval between 1645 and 1715 when very few sunspots were recorded. The low sunspot abundance during this interval was noted by astronomers at the time and was discussed in detail by two solar astronomers in the late 19th century, Gustav Spörer and E. W. Maunder. This period of low sunspot activity is now referred to as the **Maunder Minimum**.

Large groups of sunspots, which occur during periods of maximum solar activity, can be seen by the naked eye (note that looking at the sun directly can damage your eyes—don't attempt to do this without the correct viewing equipment). Most of the earliest recorded sunspot observations, dating back to 28 B.C., were made in Japan, Korea, and China. More-reliable data come from another form of proxy data: the ^{14}C content of tree rings. The variations in solar output over the sunspot cycle cause changes in the magnetic properties of the solar wind (the output of energetic particles from the Sun), which is thought to affect the production of ^{14}C in Earth's upper atmosphere. High

sunspot activity increases the magnetic field strength of the solar wind, causing a greater deflection of galactic cosmic rays away from Earth. The reduction in number of cosmic rays entering Earth's atmosphere results in low ^{14}C production. Conversely, low sunspot numbers result in high ^{14}C production. The ^{14}C content recorded in annual tree rings is thought to be related to the amount of ^{14}C produced in the atmosphere.

The naked-eye observations and the proxy data indicate two other intervals when few sunspots occurred: The **Spörer Minimum** (1450–1534) and the **Wolf Minimum** (1282–1342). The fact that the Maunder and Spörer minima coincide with one of the major climate changes in the Holocene, the Little Ice Age, has led some researchers to speculate that the two may be related. Furthermore, the 12th and 13th centuries (the Medieval Warm Period) were the interval with the greatest sunspot activity in the record. Detailed studies of ^{14}C tree-ring records have also shown that midlatitude glaciers advanced and temperatures fell when sunspot numbers were low and that temperatures increased and glaciers retreated when sunspot numbers were high. Unfortunately, not all of the changes in the ^{14}C record match suspected global climate changes. So, it may be that the apparent correlations between sunspot activity and climate are simply coincidental. In any case, it is difficult to argue (as some global warming skeptics have done) that changes in solar activity have confused the climate record to such an extent that man's recent influence is obscured. Such opinions are based more on wishful thinking than on sound scientific evidence.

The Last 150 Years

It is against this backdrop of naturally occurring, short-term climate variability that we must view the surface temperature changes that have occurred more recently. Recall that the "real" surface temperature record—that is, temperatures measured with thermometers—goes back only as far as about 1850. Surface temperatures have increased by about 0.8°C since that time. We also saw that the surface temperature increase has not been uniform in time; rather, temperatures increased gradually from 1850 until 1940, then leveled out or decreased slightly from 1940 to 1970, and finally began to increase more rapidly from 1970 until the present. The slowing, or even reversal, of surface warming between 1940 and 1970 was attributed, tentatively, to cooling caused by sulfate aerosols emitted by the combustion of coal.

A question that has occurred to almost everyone who has studied this temperature record is: How much of the observed surface temperature increase over the past 150 years has been caused by humans, and how much of it might have occurred anyway? After all, if Earth was experiencing a "Little Ice Age" from 1600 until 1850, might it not simply be recovering from that unusually cold period?

To answer this question, one needs to make use of the tools of modern climatology, some of which we have mentioned in this text. In particular, modern climatologists depend extensively on complex computer models of the climate system called general circulation models (GCMs), which were mentioned earlier in the book and are discussed further in the box titled "A Closer Look: Three-Dimensional General Circulation Models (GCMs)." In recent years, much of this computer modeling work has been coordinated by the Intergovernmental Panel on Climate Change, or IPCC. The IPCC's answer to this question is shown in Figure 5. Figure 5a shows the observed surface temperature record (black curve), along with the average of an ensemble of different model calculations (dotted blue curve). The predictions of individual climate models are shown as thin blue curves. These climate models have been executed with a combination of natural and anthropogenic forcings. The natural component includes both solar and volcanic forcings. Major volcanic eruptions (Santa Maria, Agung, El Chichón, Pinatubo) are marked with thin, gray vertical lines. After each one of these, global temperatures decrease briefly by a few tenths of a degree in both the models and the observations, before recovering. As one can see from the figure, the climate models, taken together, agree well with the observations.

What happens, though, if the anthropogenic forcing—most of which consists of increased greenhouse gas concentrations—is removed? The answer is shown in the bottom panel of Figure 5b. When the human influence is removed, the models all predict that the climate should have cooled slightly since 1965, whereas the data indicate that it has instead warmed by nearly 0.7°C. Although the models are admittedly not perfect, this is still strong evidence that humans are indeed perturbing the climate. The agreement among the various models and the data also demonstrates that the science of climate modeling has progressed significantly

FIGURE 5 Global mean surface temperatures derived from observations compared to those predicted by climate models. (a) and (b) The solid black curve shows the observations. The thin curves show the range of model calculations, and the dotted blue curves show the average of those calculations. Vertical gray lines show the timing of major volcanic events. (a) The models are driven by both natural and anthropogenic forcings; that is, greenhouse gases are assumed to be increasing. (b) The models are driven by natural forcings only, and greenhouse gases are held constant. Only in (a) do the models agree with the observations.

within the past 6 years since the previous IPCC report was issued. This gives us confidence that we can predict the temperature changes that may occur in the near future.

CARBON RESERVOIRS AND FLUXES

Let us now examine in more detail how humans are perturbing the climate system. Atmospheric CO_2 concentrations have increased by about 25% since the beginning of the 19th century. This change is larger than any natural fluctuation that has occurred since the retreat of the glaciers 11,000 years ago and is almost certainly attributable to human-induced causes, principally the burning of fossil fuels and deforestation. To understand why the human influence is so noticeable, it is useful to compare the sizes of the various carbon reservoirs and the rates at which carbon cycles in both the natural and perturbed systems.

Natural Reservoirs and Fluxes

The carbon cycle is diagrammed in Figure 6. This diagram combines the essential features of the organic and inorganic carbon cycles. It also includes a box labeled "fossil

fuels," which includes several types of compounds—most importantly coal, oil, and natural gas. Fossil fuels are, in many respects, a natural part of the carbon cycle. (It is the rate at which they are being oxidized that is unnatural.) They were created over many millions of years by the accumulation of dead organic matter in soils and sediments. Table 1 lists the relative amounts of different types of fossil fuel. Most of it is coal, which is stored in vast quantities in many parts of the world.

The total amount of fossil fuels is uncertain, because new reservoirs are continually being discovered and because whether a given reservoir is counted depends on the price of fuel. Estimates of the amount of fossil fuel that is economically recoverable at 2008 market prices range from 4000 to 6000 Gton(C), 7 to 10 times the amount of carbon that was present in the preindustrial atmosphere as CO_2, 590 Gton(C). The value quoted in Table 1, 5050 Gton(C), is in the middle of this range. These numbers, it should be noted, represent the estimated total resources, not just the proven reserves. (The proven reserves are smaller by about a factor of 3.) This gives us our first indication of why the burning of fossil fuel is a potential problem: Simply, a lot of it is available. In Critical-Thinking

FIGURE 6   The major reservoirs and fluxes in the global carbon cycle. Units are Gton(C) for reservoir sizes and Gton(C)/yr for the fluxes.   (*Source: Modified from Climate Change 1994: Radiative Forcing of Climate Change*, Cambridge: Cambridge University Press, p. 21.)

TABLE 1 Fossil-Fuel Reservoir Sizes and Burning Rates

Reservoir	Size,[*] Gton(C)	Burning rate, Gton(C)/yr	Projected lifetime[**] (yrs)
Coal	3800	2.8	1360
Oil	680	3.3	200
Natural gas	570	1.5	380
Cement production		0.3	
Total	5050	7.9	

[*]Reservoirs have been converted from gtoe (gigatons of oil equivalent) to Gton(C). The following conversion factors were applied: Coal: 1gtoe = 1.12 Gton(C); oil: 1 gtoe = 0.83 Gton(C); gas: 1 gtoe = 0.65 Gton(C).

[**]Projected lifetime = reservoir size ÷ burning rate.

Sources: Reservoir sizes from Table 9 of H.-H. Rogner, *Annual Review of Energy and the Environment* 22, November 1997, pp. 217–262, doi:10.1146/annurev.energy.22.1.217.; 2004 burning rates from U.S. Carbon Dioxide Information Analysis Center (CDIAC) website, http://cdiac.ornl.gov/trends/emis/tre_glob.htm.

Problem 1, we shall compute what would happen to atmospheric CO_2 concentrations if all the fossil fuel were to be burned instantaneously.

Two additional points should be noted about the fossil-fuel reservoirs listed in Table 1. First, the value given for oil reserves, 680 Gton(C), includes both conventional and unconventional reserves. Conventional oil reserves, that is, oil that can be pumped directly out of the ground, make up only 240 Gton(C) of this amount. The rest of the oil is in the form of oil shales, tar sands, and heavy crude oil that is more difficult to access and process. Second, the natural gas values include both conventional (easy to access) and unconventional reserves also, but they do not include methane hydrates. Over the past decade, oceanographers have discovered vast quantities of methane-rich ice on the seafloor just off the continental shelves. Technically, this material is termed **methane clathrate hydrate**. It is a solid in which CH_4 molecules are encased in a lattice of 5 to 6 H_2O molecules. Such methane hydrates form when organic matter decomposes anaerobically at great depths. The overlying water must be at least 300 m deep and must be cold as well in order for methane hydrates to be stable. The total amount of methane hydrate on the seafloor is uncertain but some estimates are as high as 18,000 Gton(C), or more than 3 times higher than the rest of the fossil-fuel reserves! We do not list this in Table 1 because it is not recoverable at current market prices, but if someone discovers how to extract it economically the problem of global warming will become even more difficult.

Of equal importance to the carbon reservoirs themselves are the fluxes that connect them. These fluxes are in many cases wholly disproportionate to the size of the reservoirs involved. For example, the huge carbonate rock reservoir is connected to the rest of the system by only a tiny flux, about 0.06 Gton(C)/yr. Shown in Figure 6, this volcanic CO_2 flux must, on average, equal the rate at which carbonate sediments are preserved. Despite its large size, this reservoir exerts little influence on the rest of the carbon cycle on any time scale shorter than hundreds of thousands of years. So, processes such as silicate weathering and volcanism, which were extremely important on geologic time scales, should have little effect on atmospheric CO_2 levels over the next few centuries.

The largest fluxes in the natural carbon cycle are the exchange of carbon between the atmosphere and the terrestrial biosphere, about 60 Gton(C)/yr, and between the atmosphere and surface ocean, about 60 Gton(C)/yr. The terrestrial biosphere, largely composed of terrestrial vegetation and soils and detritus, exchanges CO_2 with the atmosphere by way of the short-term organic carbon cycle. In that cycle, the photosynthetic uptake of CO_2 by forests is balanced by the respiration and decay of plant material. This cycle is responsible for the seasonal fluctuations in atmospheric CO_2 (the Keeling curve). The ocean exchanges CO_2 with the atmosphere by diffusion through the surface interface. Once in the surface ocean, CO_2 is taken up by marine photosynthesizers. The net rate of photosynthesis in the oceans, about 60 Gton(C)/yr, is comparable to that on land, but it does not affect the atmosphere in the same way, because the amount of living biomass is very small: The marine biota contain only about 3 Gton of carbon, as compared with approximately 610 Gton of carbon in forests. Free-floating marine organisms and seaweed do not need the massive amounts of structural carbon required by trees. As a result, the marine organic carbon cycle is more closely balanced than the terrestrial cycle and does not contribute appreciably to the seasonal fluctuations of CO_2 in the atmosphere.

Rates of Fossil-Fuel Burning and Deforestation

The currently observed increase in atmospheric CO_2 concentrations is attributable, at least in part, to the combustion of fossil fuels. For natural gas (which is mostly methane), the combustion reaction can be written as

$$CH_4 + 2\,O_2 \rightarrow CO_2 + 2\,H_2O.$$

The combustion reactions of coal and oil are more complicated, as these fuels consist of mixtures of more-complex hydrocarbons, but the main reaction products are the same, CO_2 and H_2O. The rate of fossil-fuel consumption is known fairly accurately (to within 10% or better) because records are kept by companies that produce fossil fuels and by the countries in which these companies operate. The 2004 value was about 7.9 Gton(C)/yr (Table 1). (2004 is the last year for which complete information concerning emissions is available from the U.S. Carbon Dioxide

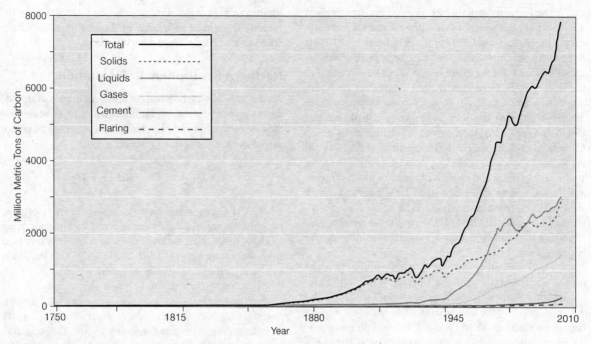

FIGURE 7 Coal, oil, and natural gas consumption rates, 1750–present. (*Source:* Carbon Dioxide Information Analysis Center, Oak Ridge National Labs, available online at http://cdiac.ornl.gov/trends/emis/glo.htm.)

Information Analysis Center. We will cite some more recent figures below.) World population is currently about 6 billion, so this consumption rate amounts to 1.3 metric tons of carbon per person per year. The rate of fossil-fuel burning is about 10 times less than the rate of CO_2 exchange with the terrestrial biosphere but 100 times larger than the rate of CO_2 release by volcanos. Its effect on the atmosphere is disproportionately large, however, because this part of the global carbon cycle is not in balance.

All three of the major fossil fuels are being consumed at appreciable rates, but oil leads the way at 3.3 Gton(C)/yr, followed by coal at 2.8 Gton(C)/yr and natural gas at 1.5 Gton(C)/yr (Table 1 and Figure 7). This implies that the different forms of fossil fuel have vastly different projected lifetimes. Recall that the residence time of a reservoir is just the reservoir size divided by the outgoing flux. As fossil fuels are not forming at appreciable rates, their residence times indicate how long they will last at current burning rates. From Table 1, we see that oil has the shortest projected lifetime, ~200 years, while coal has the longest, ~1,360 years. These values can be misleading, though. Conventional oil will be exhausted in less than 75 years at current burning rates and could be gone much sooner than that if world oil consumption increases. Global warming is not the only potential problem on the horizon. Depletion of oil reserves is also something that must be considered.

Fossil-fuel consumption is distributed unequally among the various nations of the world. As shown in Table 2, most of the fossil fuel is burned in the Northern

TABLE 2 Fossil-Fuel Consumption by Geographic Region

Region	Consumption rate, Gton(C)/yr
North America	1.8
Central and South America	0.4
Western Europe	0.9
Eastern Europe (incl. Russia)	0.8
Middle East	0.4
Africa	0.3
Oceania (Australia and Japan)	0.4
China and Vietnam	1.4

Source: 2004 burning rates from U.S. Carbon Dioxide Information Analysis Center (CDIAC) website, http://cdiac.ornl.gov/trends/emis/tre_glob.htm.

Hemisphere, with North America and the Far East essentially tied for the lead at nearly 1.8 Gton(C)/yr apiece. The United States, with only about 5% of the world's population, accounts for some 1.65 Gton(C)/yr, or 21% of global CO_2 emissions. Thus, our *per capita* emissions (emissions per person) are about 4 times the world average. The large amount of CO_2 emitted reflects our high standard of living and energy-intensive lifestyle. Other countries are catching up, however. China, in particular, has a rapidly growing economy and an increasing appetite for fossil fuels to go with it. With its large population, extensive coal reserves, and newfound thirst for oil as well, China became the world's largest CO_2 emitter in 2006–2007.

The increase in global CO_2 emissions over the past 15 years has been so rapid that it deserves additional comment. In 1990, global CO_2 emissions from fossil fuels were about 6.2 Gton(C)/yr. That was the year for which the emission limits for the Kyoto Protocol, to be discussed in the next chapter, were standardized. (Actually, the Kyoto agreement asks developed countries to reduce emissions to 5% less than 1990 values by 2020—but we shall save that discussion for later.) According to a 2007 paper by Josep Canadell and colleagues in the Proceedings of the National Academy of Sciences (PNAS), global CO_2 emissions from fossil-fuel burning and cement production for 2006 were 8.4 Gton(C)/yr, or 35% higher than 1990 values! Such an increase in emissions exceeds the most pessimistic projections of the previous (2001) IPCC report. We are proceeding along the climate change highway faster than anyone had imagined.

The Canadell study provides an estimate for the global carbon budget for the time period 2000–2006. During this interval, an average of about 7.6 Gton(C)/yr was produced by the combustion of fossil fuels and by cement production. An additional 1.5 Gton(C)/yr was produced by deforestation, primarily in the tropics. The clearing of forests and the utilization of land for agricultural purposes generally results in a substantial release of carbon into the atmosphere, both from the trees themselves and from the soil beneath them. Thus, the total anthropogenic CO_2 source during this interval was about 9.1 Gton(C)/yr. Of this, about 4.1 Gton(C)/yr accumulated in the atmosphere. This number can be calculated directly from the observed 1.9 ppm/yr rate of atmospheric CO_2 increase. (We shall do so in Critical-Thinking Problem 2.) Another 2.2 Gton(C)/yr is estimated to have been absorbed by the oceans, as the imbalance in fluxes between the atmosphere and the surface ocean (Figure 6) indicates. The remainder, about 2.8 Gton(C)/yr, is thought to be accumulating in forests and soils. So, surprisingly, despite the deforestation that is occurring in the tropics, the biosphere as a whole is currently acting as a net sink for carbon! The reasons are discussed below.

CO_2 REMOVAL PROCESSES AND TIME SCALES

How fast the CO_2 released from fossil-fuel burning will disappear and where it will ultimately go are perhaps the most confusing aspects of the whole global warming issue. The confusion arises because the carbon cycle is complex and involves processes that operate on a variety of time scales. Scientists have developed computer models of the carbon cycle that are capable of simulating many of these processes and that can be used to make projections of future atmospheric CO_2 concentrations. Some of these model predictions will be described in the following section. To understand these predictions, however, and to gain some idea of how reliable they might be, we must consider the physical processes involved. Next, we describe the major CO_2-uptake processes in decreasing order of the speed at which they are expected to occur.

Northern Hemisphere Reforestation

As the previous carbon budget numbers demonstrate, the fastest uptake process for anthropogenic CO_2 is photosynthesis by the terrestrial biosphere. We can represent photosynthesis by the simplified reaction

$$CO_2 + H_2O \rightarrow CH_2O + O_2,$$

where CH_2O represents more-complex forms of organic matter. This organic matter can accumulate either in living biomass or in soils. When it does so, carbon is removed from the atmosphere, at least temporarily. This carbon is eventually returned to the atmosphere when trees are cut down and burned or when soil organic matter decays.

Whether photosynthesis will act as a sink for anthropogenic CO_2 over the next few centuries depends largely on whether forests expand or shrink in size. Deforestation causes them to shrink, so the terrestrial biosphere acts as a CO_2 source. Reforestation causes them to expand, so the biosphere acts as a CO_2 sink. Studies suggest that a significant amount of reforestation, about 0.5 Gton(C)/yr, is occurring in temperate parts of the Northern Hemisphere. Recall that deforestation of North America during the 19th century, the *pioneer effect,* was responsible for most of the rise in atmospheric CO_2 between 1800 and 1850. Much of the deforested land was converted to farms and remains farmland today, so that land cannot be where the carbon is going. But the mountain ridges in Pennsylvania were stripped of trees to provide fuel for making steel and for powering trains. The demand for wood is now lower, and many areas are protected from logging by the state and federal governments. Consequently, the forests are regrowing and are probably contributing to the Northern Hemisphere CO_2 sink. Most of these forests will not reach maturity for another century or more, so this sink should remain active for some time into the future.

Northern Hemisphere forest regrowth, however, cannot be the only place where CO_2 is disappearing. According to the carbon budget numbers presented, the total biospheric uptake of CO_2 is approximately 2.8 Gton(C)/yr. Northern Hemisphere reforestation is only about 20% of that figure. Where is the rest of the CO_2 going?

CO_2 and Nitrogen Fertilization

A substantial part of the missing carbon may be going into existing forests as a consequence of higher atmospheric CO_2 concentrations. Most plants raised under greenhouse conditions, where plenty of water and other nutrients are available, grow faster when exposed to higher CO_2 levels. (But about 5% of plants, termed C_4 plants, do *not*) This process is termed **CO_2 fertilization**. The increased growth rate is caused, in part, by the fact that CO_2 is a limiting nutrient under these conditions. But there is an indirect stimulation effect as well. Plants tend to use water more efficiently under elevated CO_2 conditions. Plants have small openings, called *stomata,* on the undersides of leaves that allow air to pass in and out of them; these stomata need not open as wide as normal when CO_2 levels are high. As CO_2 from the atmosphere enters the leaf, water vapor from inside can escape. Not opening their stomata as wide allows plants to survive under drier conditions, allowing the plants to grow faster under high CO_2 levels. The number of stomata per leaf also tends to decrease in plants grown under elevated CO_2 concentrations. Whether forests and other natural ecosystems should respond similarly to CO_2 fertilization is a question that has aroused considerable debate. Ecologists have noted that many natural ecosystems are limited by other factors, such as nutrient availability and competition for sunlight. In such cases, higher atmospheric CO_2 concentrations should have little effect on plant growth. Even if CO_2 fertilization is occurring, other factors might come into play in the future as the climate warms. One concern is that soil carbon might decay more rapidly under such conditions. Tropical soils, for example, are deficient in carbon as a result of rapid rates of decomposition. Because most of the carbon in temperate forests resides in the soil rather than in the trees themselves, the total amount of carbon stored in forest ecosystems could actually decrease in the future even if the trees themselves grow faster. In any case, most computer model simulations now suggest that the terrestrial biosphere will become less efficient at absorbing CO_2 as the climate warms. This could lead to a faster rate of CO_2 accumulation in the atmosphere.

A related phenomenon that might be encouraging CO_2 uptake by the terrestrial biosphere is **nitrogen fertilization**. Nitrogen is an essential nutrient for all organisms, and it is often in short supply because it is difficult to convert atmospheric N_2 into fixed nitrogen that organisms can use. Humans have been helping out in this regard by adding nitrogen fertilizer to agricultural fields and by emitting large amounts of nitrogen oxides from combustion. Agricultural activity does not normally lead to net uptake of CO_2, because the crops that are grown are harvested and eaten and the remaining organic matter is burned or decays. But the nitrogen oxides released into the atmosphere are oxidized to nitric acid, HNO_3, and are removed by precipitation. If the concentration of nitric acid in rainwater becomes too high, the resulting acid rain is harmful to plants and to other organisms, especially fish (although nitric acid generally contributes less to acid rain than does the sulfuric acid generated from SO_2 released by coal burning). At more modest concentrations, the nitric acid becomes a source of fixed nitrogen, which can stimulate plant growth. So, some of the increased forest growth currently taking place may be a response to anthropogenic nitrogen emissions.

Dissolution in the Oceans

The next-fastest mechanism for removing anthropogenic CO_2 from the atmosphere is dissolution in the oceans. This process, too, is complex, because CO_2 reacts chemically when it dissolves, unlike N_2 or O_2. The chemical process by which the oceans dissolve CO_2 is described in the Box "A Closer Look: The Chemistry of CO_2 Uptake." According to Figure 6, the flux of CO_2 between the atmosphere and oceans is on the order of 60 Gton(C)/yr, so the residence time for atmospheric CO_2 with respect to this process, t_{OA}, is on the order of 12 years.

This time scale, however, is somewhat misleading. Recall that the ocean can be thought of as consisting of two layers: a well-mixed surface layer approximately 75 m thick and a poorly mixed deep-ocean layer nearly 4 km thick. These layers can be represented schematically by separate boxes, as shown in Box Figure 1. Only the shallow surface layer is capable of rapid CO_2 exchange with the atmosphere. Because of its small volume, its CO_2 uptake capacity is relatively low. The uptake capacity is determined largely by the abundance of carbonate ion (see the Box "A Closer Look: The Chemistry of CO_2 Uptake"). The deep ocean has a much larger volume and, hence, a much larger CO_2 uptake capacity, but its turnover time, t_{SD}, is on the order of 1,000 years. So, CO_2 exchange between the atmosphere and the oceans occurs on a variety of time scales, ranging from 8 years to more than 1,000 years. Because the uptake of CO_2 by the oceans is a chemical process, the lifetime of anthropogenic CO_2 depends on how much of it we produce. The first puffs of CO_2 released at the dawn of the industrial age were taken up almost immediately by the surface ocean. But the more CO_2 we release, the deeper it must penetrate into the ocean in order to be buffered by reaction with carbonate ion. The lifetime of CO_2 released today is estimated to be only about 60 years, but the lifetime of CO_2 released in the future is predicted to be much longer. Computer models that take this chemistry into account are required to calculate how fast the ocean will actually take up anthropogenic CO_2.

The limited CO_2 uptake capacity of the surface ocean can be viewed in another way—one that makes clear its importance for marine ecosystems. In reality, one can continue to pump CO_2 into seawater, even after its natural carbonate ion content is depleted. But doing so causes the pH of the water to decrease substantially, that is, it makes the water more acidic. And this, in turn, can be destructive to organisms such as foraminifera or corals which form shells or other habitats out of calcium carbonate, because it causes them to dissolve. Model simulations suggest that the pH of the surface ocean has already dropped by about 0.1 unit since the beginning of the industrial revolution in 1850. Because pH is evaluated on a log scale ($pH = -\log[H^+]$), this corresponds to a 30% increase in the H^+ concentration. One simulation discussed in the 2007 IPCC report (Vol. 1, p. 529) suggests that

A CLOSER LOOK

The Chemistry of CO_2 Uptake

The rate at which CO_2 can be taken up by the oceans depends on ocean chemistry as well as ocean mixing. The reason is that CO_2 does not simply dissolve in seawater as would a gas such as N_2 or O_2. When CO_2 dissolves in water, it forms carbonic acid, H_2CO_3, which then dissociates into bicarbonate ions, HCO_3^-, and carbonate ions, CO_3^{2-}. Long before humans began perturbing the Earth system, the ocean contained substantial quantities of carbonate and bicarbonate ions as part of the natural inorganic carbon cycle. The presence of these ions in solution makes it possible for seawater to absorb more anthropogenic CO_2 than would otherwise be possible. The reason is that these ions, carbonate ion in particular, moderate the change in the ocean's acidity as CO_2 is added. A chemist would say that they serve as a pH **buffer**, a dissolved substance that helps maintain a stable pH. At pH values that are typical of the surface ocean (pH of about 8), the chemical reaction that occurs can be written as

$$CO_2 + CO_3^{2-} + H_2O \rightarrow 2\,HCO_3^-$$

Each anthropogenic CO_2 molecule that enters the ocean combines with one carbonate ion and one water molecule, yielding two bicarbonate ions. A similar reaction converts borate ion ($H_2BO_3^-$) into boric acid (H_3BO_3). The presence of borate increases the ocean's buffering capacity by an additional 25%. The fact that such chemical reactions occur implies that the ocean's capacity to absorb CO_2 is limited. If the amount of anthropogenic CO_2 added to the ocean exceeds the amounts of carbonate ion and borate ion that were initially present, the ocean's buffering capacity will be exhausted and its ability to absorb CO_2 will be greatly diminished. We can estimate the CO_2 uptake capacity of the ocean by measuring the dissolved carbonate ion concentration in the surface and deep ocean and multiplying by the volumes of the respective reservoirs. (We shall do so in "Critical-Thinking" Problem 3.) The results are shown in Box Figure 1. The surface ocean has only a small buffering capacity compared with the amount of CO_2 that could be produced from the burning of fossil fuels. The deep ocean contains enough carbonate and borate ion to react with approximately 30% of the fossil-fuel reservoir.

The oceans can also absorb anthropogenic CO_2 by dissolving carbonate sediment on the seafloor. The chemical reaction involved is

$$CO_2 + CaCO_3 + H_2O \rightarrow Ca^{++} + 2\,HCO_3^-$$

This reaction is similar to that by which seawater itself absorbs CO_2, except that the required carbonate ion is initially attached to a calcium ion. Neither of these two processes is a permanent sink for CO_2 because, even after the reactions have occurred, the CO_2 is still present in the oceans as bicarbonate. This bicarbonate will eventually be removed when enough calcium ions have been provided by silicate weathering to reprecipitate it as carbonate sediments. Only then will the anthropogenic CO_2 truly be gone.

BOX FIGURE 1 Two-box ocean model illustrating the capacity of the ocean for CO_2 uptake. The numbers in the ocean boxes represent the amount of carbonate ion that can react with CO_2.

surface ocean pH could drop by more than 0.7 unit—corresponding to a fivefold increase in $[H^+]$—over the next few centuries if CO_2 emissions continue unabated. This would likely wreak havoc with marine ecosystems by making it extremely difficult for carbonate-secreting organisms to survive.

Dissolution of Seafloor Carbonates

Carbon dioxide can also be taken up by the dissolution of carbonate sediments on the seafloor, spurred by the higher H^+ content of CO_2-enriched seawater. This may at first seem surprising, as we learned previously that the precipitation of carbonate sediments, in conjunction with silicate weathering, removes CO_2 from the atmosphere–ocean system. Carbonate sediments are the long-term sink for CO_2. On shorter time scales, however, just the opposite occurs: Atmospheric CO_2 is taken up when carbonate sediments dissolve, because both compounds are converted to bicarbonate.

Carbonate sediments dissolve when CO_2-enriched seawater comes in contact with the sediments. For this to occur, the CO_2-rich water needs to be carried down into the deep ocean. As discussed earlier, this is a slow process, requiring many hundreds of years. Furthermore, the sediments on the seafloor need to be stirred to expose fresh surface area for the reaction. This stirring, or **bioturbation**, is accomplished by burrowing organisms, such as worms, that make their homes in the sediments. Bioturbation occurs primarily in the uppermost 10 cm of sediments, but repeated episodes of carbonate dissolution followed by renewed burrowing can eventually cause the uppermost 40 to 50 cm of marine sediments to dissolve. As Wallace Broecker of Lamont-Doherty Earth Observatory has observed, "even the worms will do their part in [taking up fossil-fuel CO_2]!" Thus, seafloor carbonate dissolution may eventually play an important role in CO_2 removal, but it is not likely to prevent atmospheric CO_2 from rising over the next few decades to centuries.

Weathering of Continental Rocks

The slowest, but most permanent, sink for anthropogenic CO_2 involves the weathering of silicate rocks on the continents, followed by the precipitation of carbonate sediments on the seafloor. The combination of these two processes can be represented by the chemical reaction

$$CaSiO_3 + CO_2 \rightarrow CaCO_3 + SiO_2,$$

where $CaSiO_3$ represents a variety of more-complicated silicate minerals. This process is much slower than the carbonate dissolution process discussed because it requires that Ca^{2+} ions produced by weathering accumulate in the ocean. The time required to precipitate anthropogenic CO_2 as carbonate can be estimated by dividing the total amount of carbon in the combined atmosphere–ocean system, about 38,000 Gton, by the rate at which CO_2 is consumed by silicate weathering, 0.06 Gton(C)/yr. This time scale, which is in excess of half a million years, is the characteristic response time of the carbonate–silicate cycle. Our human-induced perturbation to the natural carbon cycle is likely to last at least that long.

Carbonate rocks on the continents can also be weathered and dissolved. This process is analogous to seafloor carbonate dissolution and provides another "temporary" sink for CO_2. The CO_2 is not really gone, because it is stored in the oceans as bicarbonate. Carbonate rocks dissolve more rapidly than do silicate rocks, so this loss

process could become important on time scales of only a few thousands of years.

PROJECTIONS OF FUTURE ATMOSPHERIC CO_2 CONCENTRATIONS AND CLIMATE

Once we have understood the present-day sources and sinks for CO_2, the really difficult task begins: We need to project this information into the future to try to estimate future atmospheric CO_2 levels. Doing so involves making various assumptions about how much fossil fuel people will consume and how much deforestation/reforestation will take place. If we input this information into a computer model of the global carbon cycle that includes the various CO_2 removal processes just described, we can attempt to predict how atmospheric CO_2 concentrations will change. Then, this information can be used in global climate models to predict how future climate may be affected. However, we must consider other greenhouse gases as well because CO_2 is not the only greenhouse gas that is increasing.

Atmospheric CO_2 Levels for Different Emission Scenarios

Rather than try to make our own estimates for how much fossil fuel will be burned over the next few decades, we will rely on projections made, or adopted, by the IPCC. Although many different scenarios have been analyzed, the 2007 report focused on three in particular, labeled A2, A1B, and B1. These correspond, respectively, to high, medium, and low rates of future CO_2 emissions. The projected emission rates and corresponding predicted atmospheric CO_2 concentrations are shown in Figure 8.

Let us begin with the most optimistic scenario. In the "low" emissions case, CO_2 emissions rise from their current level of about 8 Gton(C)/yr to a peak of about 12 Gton(C)/yr in 2040, then gradually decrease to under 5 Gton(C)/yr by the end of the century (Figure 8b). Atmospheric CO_2 for this case rises gradually to about 550 ppm by the end of the century. This is very close to double the preindustrial CO_2 concentration of 280 ppm. Atmospheric CO_2 looks as if it has nearly stabilized by this time; however, as we will see later, that would happen only if emissions were cut to approximately 2 Gton(C)/yr over the next two centuries.

In the "medium" scenario, CO_2 emissions rise to considerably higher values, about 17 Gton(C)/yr (or twice the current value) by 2050, then decline to about 14 Gton(C)/yr by 2100. Atmospheric CO_2 climbs more rapidly in this case, reaching just over 700 ppm by the end of the century. CO_2 concentrations are clearly still growing at this time, so further increases and associated climate warming would be expected. CO_2 doubling from preindustrial levels occurs by the year 2050.

In the "high" scenario, CO_2 emissions track the medium case up through 2050, but then continue to climb

FIGURE 8   Estimated CO_2 emissions (b) and atmospheric CO_2 concentrations (a) for the next century for different assumptions about population and economic growth. (*Source:* http://www.globalwarmingart.com/wiki/ Image:Carbon_Dioxide_Emissions_Scenarios_png.)

throughout the latter half of the century, reaching nearly 30 Gton(C)/yr by 2100. The cumulative CO_2 emissions over the next century in this case are roughly 2000 Gton(C), or almost half the recoverable fossil-fuel reserves. (By comparison, about 500 Gton[C] had already been emitted prior to 2006.) Atmospheric CO_2 concentrations increase steeply as well, climbing to almost 850 ppm by this time. Although this scenario may seem extreme, it was not the most pessimistic case considered by the IPCC. The A1F1 scenario (not shown) pushed atmospheric CO_2 concentrations to nearly 1000 ppm by the end of the century. Considering that we have already exceeded the IPCC's highest emissions estimate over the past 5 or 6 years, such a scenario is not out of the question.

By how much would we expect climate to change in these various cases? We can derive a preliminary answer from the one-dimensional, radiative–convective climate models, and then return to the question with more sophisticated models later once we've assessed the projected trends in other greenhouse gases. Doubling the atmospheric CO_2 concentration in such a model produces about a 2.5°C increase in global mean surface temperature when the water vapor feedback is included. This temperature increase could occur by the year 2050 in the IPCC's

high- and medium-emissions cases or by 2100 in the low-emissions case. Doubling CO_2 a second time would produce approximately the same amount of warming, yielding 5°C total. The high scenario does not quite reach quadrupled CO_2 by the year 2100, so we should reduce this number slightly. Hence, we estimate that global temperatures could increase by as much as 4°C (7°F) over the next century in the worst-case scenario. In the most favorable case, the warming would be about 2°C. Both of these numbers should be compared with the warming of 0.8°C that has taken place over the past 100 years. Evidently, climate change during the next century is likely to be considerably more rapid than it was in the last century. A prediction of this nature, however, is not considered good enough for making policy decisions because it overlooks several factors that should affect Earth's climate over the next few decades. These factors include radiative forcing by trace gases other than CO_2, the oversimplification of one-dimensional models, and the thermal properties of the ocean.

Increases in Other Trace Gases

Carbon dioxide is not the only atmospheric greenhouse gas that is currently increasing in concentration. Methane and nitrous oxide have also been increasing in concentration over the past 200 years, as evidenced by measurements of their concentrations in air bubbles trapped in polar ice cores. Methane has strong anthropogenic sources, mostly cattle raising and rice cultivation, that account for 60 to 70% of its total emissions. Consequently, methane has more than doubled from its preindustrial concentration of 750 ppb to a modern value of nearly 1800 ppb (1.8 ppm). About 30% of nitrous oxide emissions come from bacterial denitrification in fertilized soils; the remaining 70% is natural. Hence, the increase in N_2O concentrations has been more modest—only about 50 ppb, or roughly 20% since preindustrial times. Chlorofluorocarbon compounds (CFCs) have also been increasing over the past several decades, but here the future projections are quite different. Most conventional CFCs, such as freon-11 and freon-12, have now been banned in order to protect the ozone layer. Thus, they are not expected to contribute to future global warming. Freon replacement gases are beginning to accumulate, and these gases could eventually contribute to global warming, but so far this is not a big problem.

Interestingly, the increase in atmospheric methane concentrations appears to have slowed, or even stopped, over the past few years. Figure 9a shows the measured, global average CH_4 concentration from 1983 until 2006. Figure 9b shows the rate of change in CH_4 (technically, the derivative, for those who are familiar with calculus). Evidently, the rate of change in CH_4 concentrations has oscillated around zero since about the year 2000. This may reflect the fact that most arable land, especially that suitable for growing rice, is already being cultivated. This

(a)

(b)

FIGURE 9 (a) Globally averaged atmospheric CH_4 measurements since 1983. (b) The rate of change of the measurements shown in (a). Figure 9 shows that the increase in CH_4 has virtually stopped since the year 2000.

suggests that while CH_4 may have contributed to global warming over the past century, its additional effect over the next century may be minimal.

By contrast, nitrous oxide concentrations have continued to rise over this same time period (Figure 10). Because N_2O production is enhanced by use of nitrogen-based fertilizers, its production rate can continue to increase even if the total area of cultivated land remains constant. Fortunately, because of its relatively low abundance, N_2O is less of a greenhouse threat than either CO_2 or CH_4, as we shall see below.

The Concept of Radiative Forcing

The contributions of each of these different gases to the atmospheric greenhouse effect can be measured in terms of

FIGURE 10 Measurements of atmospheric N_2O made since 1978. Slightly different values are reported for the Northern Hemisphere (NH) and Southern Hemisphere (SH).

a quantity termed **radiative forcing**. Radiative forcing refers to the change in the outgoing infrared flux caused by a change in the concentration of a particular greenhouse gas. A doubling of atmospheric CO_2 levels produces a radiative forcing of about 4.4 W/m^2. We have already seen that such a forcing produces a surface temperature increase of about 2.5°C in radiative-convective climate models. In three-dimension climate models (discussed below), the predicted change is 2–4.5°C.

The top panel in Figure 11a shows the radiative forcing produced by the increases in different greenhouse gases between 1750 and 2005. As one can see,

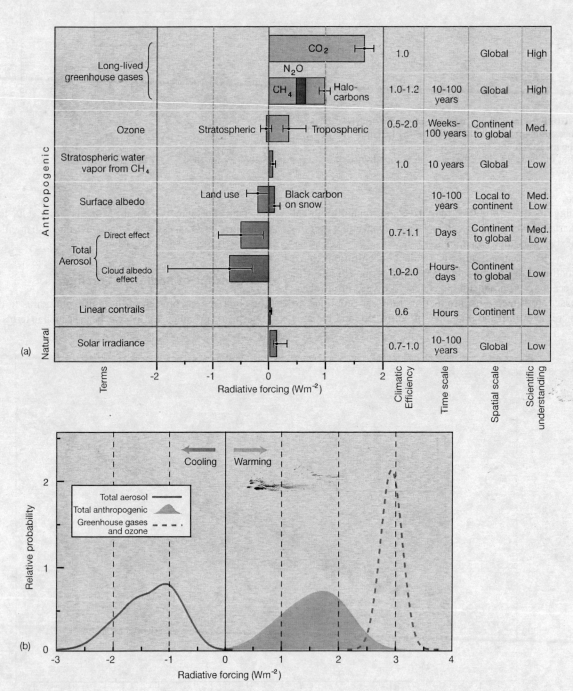

FIGURE 11   (a) Net radiative forcing by different atmospheric trace gases and other factors. The confidence in these estimates decreases from top to bottom. (b) Net radiative warming from greenhouse gases (right-hand dashed curve), net cooling from aerosols (left-hand dashed curve), and combined radiative effect (filled curve).   (*Source:* IPCC 2007, Chapter 2, Figure 2.20.)

the increases in radiative forcing are about 1.7 W/m^2 for CO_2, 0.5 W/m^2 for CH_4, 0.15 W/m^2 for N_2O, and about 0.4 W/m^2 for halocarbons (CFCs). Other factors contribute to radiative forcing as well (Figure 11a). The forcings from greenhouse gases such as CO_2, CH_4, and N_2O are positive. Other forcings, however, are negative. Increases in sulfur dioxide (SO_2) gas emissions, largely from coal-fired power plants, for example, lead to increased concentrations of sulfate aerosols. Such particles cool the surface by increasing Earth's albedo. Sulfate aerosols may also cool the surface by acting as **cloud condensation nuclei (CCN)**, thereby increasing the reflectivity of clouds (see bar labeled "cloud albedo effect" in Figure 11a). The different radiative forcing factors are listed in order of how well we understand them. Those near the top of the diagram (which includes the greenhouse gases) are relatively well understood whereas those near the bottom are poorly understood.

The combined effects of these different radiative forcings can be estimated by adding them together, as has been done in Figure 11b. The dashed curve on the right shows the radiative forcing caused by increases in greenhouse gases, including ozone. The width of the curve indicates the uncertainty in the estimate. The greenhouse gas curve is narrow because the forcing is well understood. The solid curve on the left part of the diagram represents the radiative forcing from sulfate aerosols (both direct and via clouds). This curve is broad because the uncertainties are much greater. The filled curve in between the two dashed curves shows the combined radiative forcing of greenhouse gases plus aerosols. Although the uncertainties are large, the most likely value is about +1.8 W/m^2, indicating that the net forcing is positive and should therefore cause warming.

One can better appreciate the climatic effects of aerosols by comparing the net radiative forcing, +1.8 W/m^2, with that from greenhouse gases alone, +2.9 W/m^2. Evidently, about one-third of the forcing caused by greenhouse gases has been offset by increases in aerosols. The most visible manifestation of this effect was the slowing of surface temperature increases between 1940 and 1970 (Figure 5). Unfortunately, this offsetting influence on climate is likely to be less important in the future, for two reasons. First, the aerosols have short lifetimes, typically a week or two, whereas some greenhouse gases—CO_2 in particular—have very long lifetimes. And, second, other nations are likely to want to reduce their SO_2 and hydrocarbon emissions in the future, just as the United States and Europe have done over the past 40 years. The motivation for this change was to reduce air pollution and acid rain. We should be encouraging developing countries to follow this same path. But, by doing so, we may unavoidably exacerbate the problem of global warming.

AOGCM Predictions of Global Warming

The IPCC has made estimates for how much atmospheric CH_4 and N_2O will change over the next century and for how future production of SO_2 will affect sulfate aerosol concentrations. These estimates (which are not shown here) are generally in accord with the assumptions made regarding emissions of CO_2. In the most pessimistic case (the high-emissions case in Figure 8), CH_4 increases by a factor of about 2 over the next century (from 1.7 to ~3.4 ppm), while N_2O increases by about 50% (from 310 to 450 ppb). As we have already seen (Figure 9), that assumption may be overly pessimistic. Similarly, although nitrous oxide concentrations are still going up (Figure 10), they can only increase by a modest amount because a significant fraction of the present N_2O sources are nonanthropogenic. These factors are taken into account in the IPCC estimates. Various assumptions are made regarding SO_2 emissions as well. In the low-emissions model, SO_2 emissions remain roughly constant for the next 40 years, then decline gradually until the end of the century, whereas in the other two models, SO_2 emissions increase at first and then slowly decline. In the two higher-emission cases, the growth in SO_2 emissions significantly reduces the climate warming expected by the middle of the next century.

To convert these estimates for future trace gas emissions into predicted temperature changes, it is necessary to use numerical climate models. However, as mentioned earlier, the most reliable climate model predictions do not come from simple, one-dimensional climate models, but rather from three-dimensional general circulation models, or GCMs. (See the Box "A Closer Look: Three-Dimensional General Circulation Models [GCMs].") GCMs can predict the geographical distribution of future climate change, along with changes in other important variables such as precipitation. Furthermore, GCMs that include the ocean as well as the atmosphere, so-called AOGCMs (atmosphere–ocean general circulation models) can simulate another important effect as well. As the global climate warms, the ocean is expected to heat up more slowly than the atmosphere. It then acts as a brake on how fast the atmosphere itself can warm. Technically, it exerts a **thermal drag** on the system. Thus, the *transient* (time-dependent) response of the atmosphere to greenhouse gas increases is smaller than the *equilibrium* response.

The various climate-modeling groups within the IPCC have taken the greenhouse gas scenarios described previously and used them as input for time-dependent climate models. Some of these models are true AOGCMs. AOGCMs are very time-consuming to run, however, so not all of the scenarios have been modeled by multiple AOGCMs. Some climate predictions have been generated with simpler climate models that are "tuned" to reproduce the behavior of a true AOGCM. All such models include the thermal drag of the ocean, which reduces the rate at

A CLOSER LOOK
Three-Dimensional General Circulation Models (GCMs)

The most accurate and detailed predictions of future climate are made with three-dimensional general circulation models, or GCMs. These models were originally developed for weather forecasting. They can, however, be used for longer-term projections of climate. Fortuitously, the acronym GCM also stands for "global climate model," so we shall use these terms interchangeably.

In a GCM, the surface of the globe is divided into a two-dimensional array of longitude–latitude cells, as shown in Box Figure 2. The atmosphere above each cell is also divided into discrete layers, so that the model itself is comprised of a three-dimensional grid of boxes. Using these models we can now do the same sorts of calculations, but each box can also exchange energy with the boxes above and below, and on all four sides (east–west and north–south). Not only can we include the effects of different latitudes, but we can also take geography into account. Whether, for example, we are over land or water, mountains or plains, deserts or tropical forests has an effect on the local climate. Putting all of these together allows for a much more realistic simulation of the global climate and how it is distributed.

To understand how such a model works, imagine that solar radiation enters a grid box at the top of the atmosphere. The model calculates how much radiation is reflected back to space by air molecules, how much is absorbed within the cell, and how much is transmitted down to the next level. The same calculations are made as the radiation is transmitted downward through each level until it reaches the surface. There, radiation is either reflected back upward or absorbed. The absorbed radiation heats the surface, which then emits longer wavelength infrared radiation upward as a function of its temperature. This is an application of the Stefan–Boltzmann law. Some of this emitted radiation is absorbed by clouds, water vapor, and other greenhouse gases, thereby raising the temperature of the atmospheric grid boxes. Each box, in turn, emits infrared radiation both upward and back down toward the surface. The downward radiation, of course, is what we term the "greenhouse effect."

The radiation absorbed at the surface also results in evaporation and the transfer of sensible and latent heat upward into the atmosphere. As the model develops differences in temperature, vertically or horizontally, this causes changes in air density that result in the movement of air between adjacent boxes on each side (horizontal winds) or vertically (uplift or convection, and subsidence). As the air moves between these boxes it carries with it

BOX FIGURE 2   Schematic diagram of a three-dimensional general circulation model (GCM). These models are also called global climate models.   (*Source:* http:/ /en. wikipedia. org/ wiki/ Global_climate_model.)

energy, mass (including water vapor and aerosols), and momentum. Depending on the temperature and humidity of the box, the water may stay as a gas or it may condense to form clouds. The clouds produce rain that falls through the atmosphere. It may evaporate as it falls, or it may reach the surface as precipitation, which can occur as rain or snow, depending on the temperature. The changing characteristics of the box (in terms of water vapor, aerosols, temperature, clouds) all change the radiative properties of the box, which further changes the transmission, absorption, and reflection of the solar and terrestrial radiation fluxes and the transfer of sensible and latent heat.

All of this sounds complicated enough, but present-day global climate models include many other details, as well. The variables seem endless. The surface cells can be land or water. If they are land cells they have an elevation, so the model takes into consideration the surface topography, as well as soil and vegetation cover. When rain falls on the surface, some evaporates, some infiltrates the soil, and some runs off over the surface. How much depends on the soil characteristics, the surface temperature, how much water is already present, and the surface slope. The soil is divided into layers, allowing for water and heat to be transferred up and down in the soil and for water to flow laterally between adjacent boxes below the surface. Each model grid cell has a characteristic surface cover that includes a predominant vegetation type.

The vegetation type determines how deeply roots penetrate the soil (which influences water infiltration rates and evapotranspiration), and each vegetation type has a characteristic stem and leaf structure (which also affects evapotranspiration). In addition, the type of vegetation helps determine the surface albedo and also the surface roughness. How "rough" the surface is affects the friction between the low-level wind and the surface, which influences air movement (turbulence) and affects the rate at which heat is exchanged between the surface and the atmosphere. If precipitation falls as snow, this not only changes the albedo, but may also smooth out the surface as the vegetation becomes covered by snow (thus changing heat fluxes). Each of these processes and interactions is described by an equation or series of equations that can be solved by the model.

Some 3-D models, termed atmosphere–ocean general circulation models, or AOGCMs, include ocean circulation models that are as detailed as the atmospheric component. The ocean is divided into layers. Energy, mass, and momentum are exchanged at the ocean surface. The wind drives ocean currents and mixes the surface layers, and the model tracks temperature and salinity changes that determine water density and drive the deep–ocean (thermohaline) circulation. Convergence and divergence result in downwelling and upwelling water that connects the deep ocean and the surface layers. Sea ice forms where the surface ocean temperature is at or below the freezing point. Again, within each cell, the ice is divided into layers, heat is transferred through the ice, and the ice thickens and thins through the seasons as the water and air temperatures change.

This still does not give a full description of all the processes and calculations that are included in a global climate model. Hopefully, however, this description does illustrate the point that these are very sophisticated models.

There is one somewhat more technical wrinkle that deserves to be discussed here. In the past, these models were constructed essentially the way we described—by dividing the globe into boxes and calculating all of the transfers across the adjacent cell boundaries. All of the model equations were expressed as finite difference equations; that is, the transfers of energy, mass, and momentum between boxes were calculated as some function of the difference in various quantities (e.g., temperature) between the boxes. These models are, therefore, referred to as finite difference models. Because the atmosphere is unbounded at the sides (i.e., it is continuous around the globe), however, it is possible to express all of these equations very differently, as wave functions. In a model that uses wave functions, the number of waves resolved determines the spatial resolution of the model—the equivalent to the grid size in the finite difference models. These models are referred to as spectral models. Such models have certain numerical, or computational, advantages, compared to finite difference models; hence, most current GCMs are spectral models. Their output, however, is still usually presented as a gridded product.

which the global climate can warm. The results of these simulations for the three cases described earlier are shown in Figure 12. Somewhat surprisingly, the results are remarkably similar to the estimates given earlier, which were based on simple one-dimensional climate model calculations. For the optimistic, low-emissions case, the climate warms by about 2°C relative to the year 2000, or about 2.7°C overall. (Remember that the surface temperature in 2000 was already 0.7°C warmer than its 1850 value.) For the pessimistic high-emissions case, the predicted warming from 2000 to 2100 is about 3.8°C. Also shown is a case in which both greenhouse gases and aerosols were held constant at 2000 levels. The climate

still warms by about 0.6°C over the next century because of the thermal inertia of the oceans, which are still catching up with the atmosphere. The various curves represent the average surface temperatures calculated by a number of different climate models. Not all of the models agree with each other. The range of uncertainty for the amount of warming produced by the year 2100 is shown by the error bars in Figure 12. The total range of uncertainty for all climate models and all greenhouse gas scenarios is shown by the shaded region of the figure. When all the uncertainties are taken into account, the predicted range of climate warming by the year 2100 (relative to 2000) is 1.4–4.0°C.

FIGURE 12 Predicted trends in global surface temperature over the next century for the three cases shown in Figure 8. The shaded area shows the total range of temperatures predicted by different climate models for the various scenarios. The bottommost curve shows the temperature change predicted when greenhouse gases and other forcings are held constant at 2000 values. (*Source:* IPCC 2007, Summary for Policy Makers, Fig. SPM.5.)

Long-Term Climate Warming

The climate calculations discussed so far extend only to the year 2100. But, as described in the Box "A Closer Look: Long-Term CO_2 Projections," atmospheric CO_2 could continue to rise for several centuries beyond that time and its concentration might eventually reach 2100 ppm—almost eight times its preindustrial value. What effect would this extended rise have on Earth's climate?

The greenhouse effect of CO_2 is roughly logarithmic, which means that each factor-of-2 increase in CO_2 produces roughly the same amount of warming. An eightfold increase in CO_2 should therefore cause about three times as much warming as would a twofold increase (because $8 = 2^3$.) Thus, a GCM that predicted 3°C of warming for doubled-CO_2 conditions should produce about 9°C of warming for an eightfold CO_2 increase.

The actual range of GCM responses to doubled atmospheric CO_2 is between 2.0 and 4.5°C of warming. The corresponding range for an eightfold CO_2 increase is 6.0 to 13.5°C of warming. It is instructive to compare these numbers to estimated surface temperature changes during the past 100 million years of Earth history. The warmest part of the Mesozoic is thought to have been about 6 to 10°C warmer than today on a global average. The coldest part of the Pleistocene was probably about 10°C cooler than today. Thus, regardless of whether we believe the low climate model estimates or the high ones, the warming from an eightfold CO_2 increase could make Earth warmer than it has been for tens of millions of years.

Possible Changes in the Thermohaline Circulation

Finally, we should note that future changes in climate could also cause changes in ocean circulation. One particular aspect of ocean circulation that has been studied extensively with regard to global warming is the Atlantic Conveyor Belt. This is the thermohaline circulation pattern in which deep water forms in the North Atlantic, spreads out globally at depth, then is upwelled and returns to the North Atlantic as a warm surface current. Recall that this circulation pattern is responsible for keeping western Europe warm in the wintertime. Without it, winters there would be much colder. This circulation pattern probably did cease for almost a thousand years during the Younger Dryas event at the end of the last Ice Age. The cause of that shutdown is thought to have been a pulse of freshwater from the melting of the Laurentide ice sheet that flowed down the

A CLOSER LOOK

Long-Term CO₂ Projections

What will happen to atmospheric CO_2 levels in the distant future if we continue to burn fossil fuels? This question can be studied by using specially designed computer models that are able to take large time steps. For illustrative purposes, let us assume that most of the fossil-fuel reserve listed in Table 1, 4200 Gton(C), is consumed during the next 400 years. Let us further assume that current deforestation trends continue until only 30% of the world's forests remain.

This particular scenario has been investigated with a computer model that includes a six-box ocean, along with separate boxes to represent the atmosphere, forests, and carbonate sediments on the seafloor. The results of the simulation are shown in Box Figure 3. Box Figure 3a shows

BOX FIGURE 3 Long-term projections for atmospheric CO_2 for (a) the next 3,000 years and (b) the next several million years. The total amount of fossil fuel consumed is equivalent to 4200 Gton(C). (*Source*: Walker and Kasting, *Global and Planetary Change* 97, 1992, p. 151.)

calculated atmospheric CO_2 concentrations over the next 3,000 years. The computer model predicts that atmospheric CO_2 levels will increase to a peak of about 2100 ppm by the year A.D. 2300. At that time, the fossil-fuel reserves will be exhausted and atmospheric CO_2 will begin to decline.

If we extend this calculation further into the future, the atmospheric CO_2 concentration must eventually return to its preindustrial value of 280 ppm, because the model assumes that the carbon cycle was balanced at that time. The amount of time required to return to that steady-state level is shown in Box Figure 3b. There, the date is displayed on a logarithmic scale extending millions of years into the future. The processes that are responsible for CO_2 uptake on different time scales are indicated. Most of the CO_2 is removed over the next few thousand years by dissolution in the deep ocean and by the dissolution of carbonate sediments and rocks. The last vestiges of the CO_2 pulse are removed by silicate weathering over a period of more than 1 million years.

Although the calculations shown here are speculative, they suggest an intriguing possibility. If the climate record of the past few million years were extended into the future, we would expect that Earth should experience at least 10 major glacial–interglacial cycles over the next 1 million years. But atmospheric CO_2 levels were relatively low, 200 to 280 ppm, during the previous glacial cycle, whereas they are predicted to exceed 350 ppm during most of the next 1 million years. Could the addition of this much anthropogenic CO_2 break the glacial–interglacial cycle? If it did, the results would be at least partly beneficial; after all, no one looks forward to the beginning of the next Ice Age. Yet, the accompanying increase in sea level over this time could cause shorelines to move substantially inland and force massive relocations of people. The possible long-term effects of the burning of fossil fuels on the Earth system are evidently quite large and will eventually need to be considered.

In 2005, David Archer of the University of Chicago published similar long-term simulations of the effects of fossil-fuel burning. The results of his simulations for total burns of 1000 Gton(C) and 5000 Gton(C) can be found in the 2007 IPCC report. The peak CO_2 concentration reached in the 5000 Gton(C) simulation is 1750 ppm, about 10% lower than shown here, probably because of a more realistic treatment of seafloor carbonate dissolution. The time scale for recovery, however, is quite similar to that in the Walker and Kasting model shown here, and so the basic conclusions are the same: We probably *do not* want to do this!

St. Lawrence River and into the North Atlantic. This created a *freshwater cap* that was too buoyant to sink easily. Recall that Europe grew much colder again during this time, leading to the reappearance of alpine flowers like the dryas.

In at least some AOGCMs, a similar phenomenon is predicted to occur in the future, although to a lesser extent and for a somewhat different reason. Melting of the Greenland ice cap could, of course, supply freshwater that might duplicate the effect of the meltwater from the Laurentide ice sheet. That effect, if it occurred, would likely be several centuries in the future. In some AOGCMs, however, another similar phenomenon takes place much earlier, within the next 100–200 years. Global warming causes increased evaporation in the low-latitude to midlatitude Atlantic Ocean, putting more moisture into the air. This moisture is transported northward by winds and falls out as rain in the North Atlantic. The increased rainfall freshens the surface layer, reducing its density, and making it less likely to sink. In at least some models this causes the thermohaline circulation to slow appreciably within the next century. This is not a robust prediction at this time, as this type of couple ocean–atmosphere calculation is still considered to be difficult. If this were to occur, however, something really paradoxical might happen: Europe might cool temporarily as the rest of the world warmed! It is unlikely that Europe would experience a new Ice Age, as the global climate by this time would be significantly warmer than it was 11,000 years ago, but the predicted temperature drops could still be severe. This is yet one more example of why we must consider the entire Earth as a system. It takes a tightly coupled systems model, an AOGCM in this case, to predict this type of counterintuitive behavior.

Chapter Summary

1. Climate has remained remarkably stable over the last 10,000 years (the Holocene), although small changes have occurred. Temperatures were slightly higher during the Holocene Climatic Optimum, 5,000–6,000 years B.P., and again during the Medieval Warm Period, A.D. 1150–1300. They then decreased until the early 1500s. The Little Ice Age, A.D. 1600–1850, was unusually cold. Since then, surface temperatures have been increasing.
   a. One of the contributing causes of the colder temperatures during the Little Ice Age may be the effect of a higher frequency of volcanic eruptions.
   b. Decreased solar activity (as evidenced by decreases in sunspots) has also been linked to the Little Ice Age.
2. Volcanoes cause short-term climatic cooling.
   a. The sulfur dioxide injected into the stratosphere by an eruption hydrolyzes, forming sulfuric acid droplets, which both reflect solar radiation and absorb some of the long-wave radiation emitted from the troposphere.
   b. The result is lower-than-normal surface air temperatures for 1 to 2 years after a major eruption.
3. The observed rise in atmospheric CO_2 concentrations is caused chiefly by the burning of fossil fuels and, to a lesser extent, by tropical deforestation. The anthropogenic CO_2 source is much smaller than the rate at which CO_2 is released by respiration and decay but much larger than the rate at which CO_2 is emitted by volcanos. It therefore represents a substantial perturbation to the global carbon cycle.
4. The CO_2 generated by human activities can be removed from the atmosphere by several mechanisms.
   a. The fastest of these mechanisms is photosynthesis, but this sink will be effective only if forests are replanted or if CO_2 fertilization of plant growth continues to cause additional carbon to be stored in forests and soils.
   b. Much of the fossil-fuel CO_2 will dissolve in the oceans. The rate of CO_2 uptake is limited by the mixing rate of the deep ocean and by the chemical buffering capacity of seawater. Only about 30 to 40% of the available carbon in fossil fuels can be absorbed in this manner.
   c. Additional CO_2 can be removed by the dissolution of carbonate sediments on the seafloor and of carbonate rocks on land, but these processes occur over hundreds to thousands of years.
   d. The fossil-fuel CO_2 pulse would be completely removed by silicate weathering on a time scale of about 1 million years.
5. Computer models of the global carbon cycle predict that atmospheric CO_2 levels will double within the next 50 to 100 years and that CO_2 concentrations could exceed 2000 ppm within a few centuries if nothing is done to limit emissions. Radiative forcing of climate could be accelerated by increases in other trace greenhouse gases, although the increase in CH_4 appears to have slowed or stopped over the past few years. Earth's climate could warm by several degrees Celsius over the next century and by as much as 10 to 15°C in the long term. The warming will be unevenly distributed, with the polar regions warming the most and the tropics warming the least. Potentially damaging consequences of such warming include the drying out of continental interiors, the spread of insect pests and tropical diseases, and substantial increases in sea level.
6. Oceanic circulation could also change as the climate warms. Freshening of the North Atlantic from increased rainfall and melting of Greenland ice may tend to slow down the thermohaline circulation, causing Europe to cool transiently even as the rest of the world warms. Detailed understanding of the coupling between the atmosphere and oceans is needed to know whether such predictions are robust.

Key Terms

bioturbation	Little Ice Age	proxy data
buffer	Maunder Minimum	radiative forcing
cloud condensation nuclei (CCN)	Medieval Warm Period	Spörer Minimum
CO_2 fertilization	methane clathrate hydrate	sunspots
dendrochronology	nitrogen fertilization	thermal drag
Holocene epoch	palynology	Wolf Minimum
Holocene Climatic Optimum	plages	

Review Questions

1. What is the Holocene epoch?
2. What are proxy data? Describe several examples of proxy climate data.
3. Briefly describe the Younger Dryas, the Holocene Climatic Optimum, the European Medieval Warm Period, and the Little Ice Age.
4. How do volcanoes affect climate?
5. What are sunspots? Why are they thought to have a possible effect on climate?
6. How does the amount of CO_2 produced by fossil-fuel consumption compare to the natural flux of CO_2 in the carbon cycle?

7. What are the major processes that can remove CO_2 from the atmosphere? What are the approximate time scales for these processes to be effective?
8. What is the size of the fossil-fuel reservoir compared with the atmospheric CO_2 reservoir?
9. Why does the ocean have a limited capacity for CO_2 uptake?
10. By how much is global temperature predicted to rise over the next century?
11. Why do some climate models predict that the thermohaline circulation might shut down?

Critical-Thinking Problems

1. a. The present atmosphere contains approximately 700 Gton(C) in the form of CO_2. Earth's total recoverable fossil-fuel reserves contain at least 4200 Gton(C), mostly in the form of coal. (We shall use the value 4200 Gton[C] to be specific.) At present, about half the CO_2 produced by the burning of fossil fuels stays in the atmosphere. The other half dissolves in the oceans or is taken up by the terrestrial biosphere. If this ratio remained constant and we burned up all of our fossil fuels instantaneously, by how much would atmospheric CO_2 concentrations rise? (Express your answer in terms of the new CO_2 level divided by the old one.)

   b. Climate models predict that each doubling of the atmospheric CO_2 concentration will cause the mean global temperature to increase by 1.5 to 4.5°C. (The range is due largely to uncertainties about how clouds will respond.) By how much would the mean temperature increase for the scenario described in part a? Express your answer as a temperature range in degrees Celsius and in degrees Fahrenheit.

   c. The actual problem of global warming could be more severe than we have just calculated. Forests and soils together contain an additional 2100 Gton of carbon that

might go into the atmosphere if deforestation is not prevented. The ocean becomes more acidic as it absorbs CO_2, so it might not be able to continue taking up as much CO_2 as it has been until now. If we burned up all our fossil fuels and deforested one-third of the globe without losing any CO_2 to the ocean (or to CO_2 fertilization), by how much would atmospheric CO_2 and temperature increase?

2. The atmospheric CO_2 concentration is currently increasing by about 1.9 ppm/yr. How many gigatons of carbon are being added to the atmosphere each year? (*Hint:* The total mass of the atmosphere is 5×10^{18} kg, and its mean molecular weight is about 29. You will need to do the calculation in moles and then convert back to mass units.)

3. The surface ocean contains about 2.6×10^{16} liters of water with a carbonate ion content of about 2×10^{-4} mol/L. The deep ocean contains about 1.4×10^{21} L of water with a carbonate ion content of roughly 9×10^{-5} mol/L. If each mole of carbonate reacts with 1 mol of CO_2 according to the reaction

$$CO_2 + CO_3^= + H_2O \rightarrow 2\,HCO_3^-,$$

what percentage of the fossil-fuel reservoir, 4200 Gton(C), can be neutralized by the surface ocean? By the deep ocean?

Further Reading

General

Archer, D. 2009. *The long thaw: How humans are changing the next 100,000 years of Earth's climate.* Princeton, NJ: Princeton University Press.

Mann, M. E., and L. R. Kump. 2008. *Dire predictions: Understanding global warming.* Upper Saddle River, NJ: Pearson Education.

Philander, S. G. 1998. *Is the temperature rising: The uncertain science of global warming*. Princeton, NJ: Princeton University Press.

Advanced

Archer, D. 2005. Fate of fossil fuel CO_2 in geologic time. *Journal of Geophysical Research Oceans* 110 (C9), C09505, doi: 10.1029/2004JC002625.

Lemke, P., J. Ren, R. B. Alley, I. Allison, J. Carrasco, G. Flato, Y. Fujii, G. Kaser, P. Mote, R. H. Thomas, and T. Zhang, 2007: Observations: Changes in Snow, Ice and Frozen Ground. In: *Climate Change 2007: The Physical Science Basis. Contribution of Working Group I to the Fourth Assessment Report of the Intergovernmental Panel on Climate Change* [Solomon, S., D. Qin, M. Manning, Z. Chen, M. Marquis, K. B. Averyt, M. Tignor, and H. L. Miller (eds.)]. Cambridge University Press, Cambridge, United Kingdom and New York, NY, USA)

Global Warming, Part 2
Impacts, Adaptation, and Mitigation

Key Questions

- How is sea level projected to change over the next century?

- How will forests and other ecosystems respond to atmospheric CO_2 increases?

- How will global warming affect humans, and how will the effects vary in different parts of the world?

- How can one estimate the economic damages from global warming, along with the costs necessary to combat it? Should we start doing so now, or should we postpone action until the future?

- What specific policies might be adopted to reduce future CO_2 emissions?

Chapter Overview

The effects of climate change are likely to affect both abiotic and biological parts of the Earth system. Sea level is predicted to rise by 0.1–0.3 m over the next century from thermal expansion of seawater as the ocean warms. Much larger increases in sea level—from several meters to several tens of meters—could occur in the more distant future if sustained warm surface temperatures lead to melting of the Greenland and West Antarctic ice sheets. Future increases in atmospheric CO_2 concentrations and changes in climate are also likely to affect both natural and human ecosystems. Some of these changes may be difficult or impossible to counter, whereas humans may be able to simply adapt to other changes. Slowing or halting global warming will require widespread changes in modes of energy production and perhaps (although not necessarily) in lifestyles, as well. Specific policies that might be implemented to make this happen include taxes on carbon emissions and tax incentives for renewable energy resources and for fuel-efficient vehicles. The long-term nature of the global warming problem means that policy decisions made today will affect the lives and welfare of future generations in the United States and elsewhere. Hence, issues of international and intergenerational equity must be considered.

INTRODUCTION

Both atmospheric CO_2 concentrations and global surface temperatures are predicted to rise over the next few centuries if fossil fuels continue to be burned in large quantities. These changes may be accompanied by changes in the distribution and intensity of rainfall and in ocean circulation. But the climate system itself is not the only thing that concerns us. Rather, it is the predicted changes in sea level and effects on ecosystems, both natural and human, that are of primary importance. What are the most significant impacts expected to be, and how might we adapt to them? Even more importantly, if we decide that these impacts are unacceptable, how might we go about slowing or halting global warming? Here, we explore some of these questions, along with specific policies that might be adopted, both nationally and globally, to solve this problem.

CHANGES IN SEA LEVEL

How concerned should we be about the prospect of future global warming? The answer depends not only on the magnitude and rate of the climate change itself, but also on the effects of that change on other parts of the Earth system. One factor that we must consider in any discussion of long-term global warming is sea level. But before we consider how sea level might change in the future, we must backtrack momentarily and see what we understand about sea-level changes in the recent past.

Sea-Level Change during the 20th Century

Researchers have estimated that sea level has increased by approximately 20 cm since 1880 (Figure 1). The data come from tide gauges on various shorelines around the world and, more recently (since 1992), from satellite altimetry. The satellite data are the most accurate, but the record is short, only about 17 years. Interpreting the tide gauge measurements is complicated, because the solid Earth itself is moving up or down in some locations. Parts of Canada and Europe, for instance, are moving upward at a rate of a few centimeters per century, because they are still rebounding from the weight of the great ice sheets that covered these regions as recently as 11,000 years ago. In contrast, the Nile River delta is subsiding, because silt from the Nile has increased the loading in this region. These localized trends in land surface elevation must be subtracted from the tide gauge data before we can draw any inferences about sea-level change.

The increase in global sea level during the 20th century parallels the rise in global mean surface temperature. Indeed, approximately half of the rise in sea level can be at-tributed to simple **thermal expansion** of surface-ocean water. Water, like most other materials, normally expands as it warms. (More correctly, pure water expands when it warms except when its temperature is between 0 and 4°C, when warming causes it to contract. Seawater, however, does not exhibit this unusual behavior.) Because the lateral boundaries of the ocean are largely fixed, any expansion of ocean volume must result in a rise in sea level. The 0.8°C atmospheric temperature rise during the 20th century is expected to have warmed the surface ocean by this same amount, which should have increased sea level by about 8 cm. An increase of 0.8°C in the temperature of the deep ocean would cause a much larger increase in sea level, but such a change would take many centuries to occur, because the thermohaline circulation is very slow. Changes in deep-ocean temperatures caused by Milankovitch cycles may be responsible for periodic sea-level fluctuations of about 5 m that are recorded in carbonate platforms formed during the Mesozoic and Paleozoic eras.

Most of the remaining increase in sea level during the 20th century is thought to have been caused by melting of **mountain glaciers**, ice fields formed on the cold, upper reaches of mountains (Figure 2). Several glaciers in the Alps are known to have retreated during the past two centuries as Earth emerged from the Little Ice Age. Glaciers in the high Andes Mountains in Peru are also known to be receding rapidly at present. If this trend were to continue, sea level might eventually rise by another 40 cm from this source alone.

Sea-Level Rise in the Future

A serious concern for the future is that the polar ice caps will begin to melt. Only the ice that is now on land is important in this respect. The melting of sea ice does not

FIGURE 1 Global sea-level rise since 1880 (relative to the interval 1961–1990). Most of the data come from tide gauges. The last 15 years are from satellite altimetry. (*Source:* IPCC 2007, Chapter 5, Fig. 5.13.)

FIGURE 2 A mountain glacier. (*Source:* Gilbert S. Grant/ Photo Researchers.)

increase sea level, because floating ice displaces an amount of seawater that is precisely equal to its mass. This may be thought of as an application of Archimedes' principle.

Today, large continental ice sheets are found on Greenland and Antarctica. The Greenland ice sheet contains enough water to raise sea level by approximately 7 m, were it to melt entirely. The Antarctic ice sheet contains much more water—some 60 to 70 m of equivalent sea-level rise. However, these two ice sheets are expected to behave quite differently as the climate warms. The island of Greenland extends to lower latitudes than does the continent of Antarctica, so the climate in southern Greenland is considerably warmer than the Antarctic climate. The Greenland ice sheet is therefore much more likely to experience increased melting as the climate warms than is the Antarctic ice sheet. Over most of Antarctica increased snowfall (resulting from warmer ocean temperatures and increased evaporation rates) is expected to cause the ice sheet to thicken over the next 50 to 100 years. This phenomenon could, paradoxically, cause global sea level to decrease as atmospheric CO_2 levels increase. However, it is likely to be outweighed in importance by melting that occurs in other regions.

The West Antarctic Ice Sheet

The actual situation in Antarctica is even more complicated than we have indicated. The Antarctic ice sheet can be divided geographically into an eastern and a western part. The East Antarctic ice sheet contains most of the water (about 60 m of equivalent sea level) and is the part that might thicken as the climate warms. The West Antarctic ice sheet contains less water (about 5 to 6 m of equivalent sea level), but its response to greenhouse warming is expected to be quite different. This ice sheet flows primarily into the Ross and Weddell seas, where it forms **ice shelves**, large expanses of floating sea ice formed at the margins of continents. That in the Ross Sea is called the Ross Ice Shelf,

and that in the Weddell Sea is called the Filchner-Ronne. Both ice shelves are grounded at several points on offshore islands.

Glaciologists have speculated that an increase in water temperature of just a few degrees in the Ross and Weddell seas could melt enough ice off the bottom of these ice shelves to cause them to become completely free-floating. As a result of this melting, those parts of the West Antarctic ice sheet that feed these shelves might flow much more rapidly, because the contact with the offshore islands currently inhibits the glaciers' flow. Such a sudden, rapid increase in a glacier's flow rate is called a **glacial surge**. Glacial surges are occasionally observed in mountain glaciers, and there is indirect evidence (from ice-rafted debris in North Atlantic sediments) that they occur in continental-scale glaciers as well. Once started, a glacial surge tends to perpetuate itself, because the increased flow rate causes frictional heating at the base of the glacier. This heating, in turn, produces a thin layer of water that allows the glacier to slide more smoothly over the surface. If such a positive feedback process were to be triggered by global warming, the West Antarctic ice sheet might thin relatively rapidly and could contribute significantly to sea-level rise over the next few centuries.

Projections of Future Sea-Level Rise

Given all these possible effects, what can we say about sea-level change in the near future? Will the observed upward trend of the 20th century continue?

The IPCC's projections of possible sea-level increase during the 21st century are shown in Figure 3. The curve shown is for the A1B or medium-emissions scenario. These calculations take into account thermal expansion of the oceans and melting of mountain glaciers, along with a minimal contribution from polar ice-sheet melting. The projected increases in sea-level range from 20 to 50 cm for this medium-emissions scenario. These rates of increase are two to three times faster than the rate of increase that occurred in the 20th century. Sea-level increases of this magnitude could pose problems for low-lying areas such as the Gulf coast of North America, Bangladesh, and numerous islands in the South Pacific and Indian oceans.

A potentially more serious problem is the change that might occur in the more distant future. (Indeed, some glaciologists believe that such changes might begin to occur within the next century as a consequence of nonlinear ice-sheet dynamics that are not included in the IPCC projections.) The amount of water now tied up in polar ice is so large, and the projected time scale for global warming is so long, that sea level could ultimately increase by many meters. As one concrete example, Chapter 10 of the 2007 IPCC report discussed one particular simulation in which an AOGCM was coupled to a model of the Greenland ice sheet. The atmospheric CO_2 concentration was held constant at four times the preindustrial value, and the two models were run together for a total time of 1,760 years. The resulting behavior

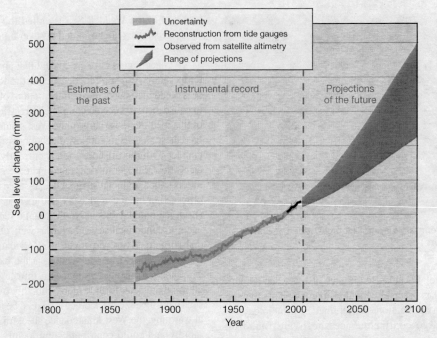

FIGURE 3 Predicted changes in sea level over the next century for the medium-emissions case shown in Figures 15-8 and 15-12. (*Source:* IPCC 2007, FAQ5.1, Fig. 1.)

of the ice sheet is shown in Figure 4. By the end of the first 270 years, the ice sheet has lost 20% of its volume. This would correspond to a sea-level rise of a little over 1 m. The next 20% of the ice sheet disappears by year 710. By the end of the simulation, only 20% of the ice-sheet remains, so sea level should be higher by about 4–5 m.

Although these projected future changes in Greenland ice-sheet volume are highly speculative, there is reason to believe that such behavior is not impossible. Sea level during the previous interglacial period (termed the Eemian), about 125,000 years ago, is thought to have been about 6 m

higher than today. Evidence from ice cores in south Greenland suggests that ice may not have been present in this region and that as much as half of the 6-m sea-level increase may have been caused by melting of the Greenland ice cap. This interpretation is disputed by some glaciologists, and so it should not be blindly accepted. Global surface temperatures during the Eemian, however, were only about 1°C warmer than today, based on oxygen isotopes. Could the Greenland (and West Antarctic) ice sheets be less stable than we think? This is a research question that clearly deserves further study.

FIGURE 4 Predictions of Greenland ice-sheet mass for a climate simulation in which the atmospheric CO_2 concentration was held constant at four times its preindustrial value. (*Source:* IPCC 2007, Chapter 10, Fig. 10.38.)

How serious would such a change be if it were to happen today? A sea-level increase of this magnitude would wreak havoc with Earth's present geography. A 6-m rise in sea level, like the one that occurred during the Eemian, would submerge the southernmost one-third of Florida. In the very long term (thousands of years in the future), it is conceivable that the polar caps could melt entirely if we were to consume all of the available fossil fuels. This melting would increase sea level by 70 to 80 m and would submerge roughly 20% of the present continents. So, our decisions about fossil-fuel usage over the next few centuries could have major repercussions for our descendants.

EFFECTS ON ECOSYSTEMS

We have already mentioned several effects of increased CO_2 on terrestrial and marine ecosystems. Higher atmospheric CO_2 concentrations are expected to cause increased rates of plant growth. Plants are also expected to use water more efficiently at high CO_2 levels, because they do not need to open their stomata as wide to obtain CO_2 for photosynthesis and because stomatal density also decreases in plants grown under elevated CO_2. This increased efficiency might be offset in some regions by decreased soil moisture during the summertime growing season.

If we examine ecosystems in more detail, the possible changes induced by higher CO_2 levels and higher temperatures become more and more complex. This should not come as too much of a surprise, as biological systems are incredibly complicated by comparison with most physical systems. Here, we mention only a few of the many changes that are expected to take place.

C$_3$ and C$_4$ Plants

Different types of plants have different mechanisms of **carbon fixation**, the biochemical process that occurs during photosynthesis by which atmospheric CO_2 is converted to organic carbon. Most photosynthetic organisms alive today (about 95% of all terrestrial plants) fix carbon by a biochemical pathway called the **Calvin cycle**. The first step of this cycle involves the production of a stable, intermediate compound (3-phosphoglyceric acid) that contains three carbon atoms. Hence, this process is called *C$_3$ photosynthesis*, and plants that metabolize in this way are termed **C$_3$ plants**.

Some plants, however, including corn, sugarcane, and many tropical grasses, begin the photosynthetic process by producing a four-carbon compound. (Actually, corn and sugarcane are themselves species of grasses, although we do not usually think of them as such.) Plants of this type are termed **C$_4$ plants**. As a consequence of biochemical modifications, C$_4$ plants are able to photosynthesize at much lower CO_2 concentrations than are C$_3$ plants. Indeed, C$_4$ plants became widespread only about 7 or 8 million years ago, possibly in response to decreased atmospheric CO_2 levels caused by the uplift and weathering of the Himalayan Mountains. Also, C$_4$ plants are much less responsive to CO_2 increases than are C$_3$ plants. Thus, whereas CO_2 fertilization might have an important effect on the growth rate of C$_3$ plants, it is not expected to have a large effect on C$_4$ plants. Certain agricultural crops, such as corn, could be at a disadvantage compared with C$_3$ weeds in a high-CO_2 world.

Changes in Speciation within Forests

Even within the C$_3$ world, different types of plants are expected to exhibit different responses to changes in temperature and moisture availability that might accompany CO_2 increases. Figure 5 shows the predicted response of various tree species in Minnesota to estimated climate

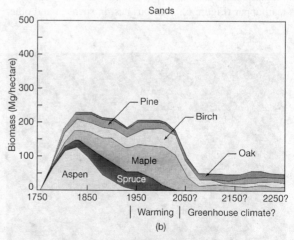

FIGURE 5 Predictions of species composition, in terms of (aboveground) biomass in Minnesota forests under doubled-CO_2 conditions, (a) for a clay soil, with a high water-holding capacity, and (b) for a sandy soil, with a low water-holding capacity. (*Source:* IPCC, *Climate Change: The IPCC Scientific Assessment,* Cambridge: Cambridge University Press, 1990.)

changes since 1750 and projected to A.D. 2250. The results depend strongly on whether the local soil has a high water-holding capacity (Figure 5a) or a low one (Figure 5b). In the first case, some species (maple and birch) thrive at high CO_2 levels, whereas others (aspen and spruce) decline when the temperature becomes too warm. In the second, all species do poorly after A.D. 2050 because the soil becomes too dry to support them. A general conclusion that we can reach, irrespective of the details of the calculation, is that species distributions within ecosystems are likely to change as the global climate warms.

A particular concern related to this change in species distribution is whether midlatitude forests will be able to keep pace with the anticipated rate of climate change. Climatic warmings have occurred many times in the past, most recently at the end of the last glaciation around 12,000 years ago. However, the modern world is different from the postglacial world in several respects. Perhaps most importantly, forests in regions such as North America and Europe have been dissected by farms and highways, which tend to inhibit the migration of species. Thus, the poleward spread of species adapted to warmer climates might not occur fast enough to keep pace with the rate at which the climate warms. The extinction of many species of trees and animals could result unless humans intervene actively to facilitate the migration process.

Other Concerns

Accompanying the poleward migration of temperate and subtropical vegetation would be a migration of animal and insect species that live in warm climates. Insects, in particular, pose a significant problem for agriculture. If midlatitude winters become less severe, insect pests that are confined to the tropics today could expand their ranges to midlatitudes. For example, in the United States the potato leafhopper (Figure 6), a serious pest in soybean and other

FIGURE 6 A potato leafhopper. This insect, along with other agricultural pests, could expand its range poleward if the climate warms. (*Source:* Donald Specker/Animals Animals/Earth Scenes.)

crops, is currently confined to a narrow band bordering the Gulf of Mexico. Warmer winters might allow this pest to double or triple its range. The expansion of insect ranges might well be one of the most economically damaging consequences of climate change.

Various human diseases, such as malaria, that are currently confined to the tropics might become a problem at midlatitudes as well. Malaria is spread by the *Anopheles* mosquito, whose life cycle does not allow it to survive cold winters. If wintertime temperatures remained above freezing in the continental United States, as might happen 100 to 200 years from now if atmospheric CO_2 levels continue to increase, malaria-bearing mosquitoes might be able to live there, presenting a whole new set of potential health problems.

Increased atmospheric CO_2 levels and associated global warming could also affect marine ecosystems. Aquatic photosynthesizers, which include both phytoplankton and larger, multicellular organisms such as kelp, are not expected to have increased growth rates from CO_2 fertilization because their growth rates are generally limited by other nutrients, especially phosphorus, nitrogen, and iron. Corals are likely to be directly affected by the acidification of the ocean that accompanies the buildup of atmospheric CO_2. This stress on their ability to grow their calcium carbonate skeletons is in addition to the stress from elevated sea-surface temperatures that are already causing "bleaching events"—the loss of the corals' symbiotic algae. Warmer temperatures could also affect ocean currents and upwelling zones, for example, by stabilizing the water column against mixing and wind-driven upwelling. Upwelling of nutrient-rich deep water is the key factor that accounts for regions of high productivity in the modern oceans, such as the Grand Banks off the coast of Labrador or the fisheries off the coast of Peru. If the intensity or location of upwelling were to change as the climate warms, it could have major effects on both the high-productivity ecosystems themselves and on the fishing industry that takes advantage of them.

HUMAN IMPACTS OF GLOBAL WARMING

Floods, Droughts, and Freshwater

A likely consequence of increasing atmospheric carbon dioxide levels is an intensification of the hydrological cycle, that is, the global average rates of evaporation and precipitation. Climate models project that this will translate into a more complex geographical pattern of more frequent droughts and floods in areas already subject to these extreme climate events.

A reliable and clean drinking water supply is perhaps the most fundamental requirement of a healthy world population. Much of the current increase in population is occurring in regions that have marginal or unreliable water supplies. As a result, these supplies are already being taxed. Specific examples include:

- More frequent droughts in regions such as the southwestern United States are likely to exacerbate water-supply problems in the future.
- Nearly 15% of the world's population depends on seasonal melting of mountain glaciers for their drinking water supply, and these glaciers are disappearing at an alarming rate as a consequence of climate change.
- Sea-level rise causes saltwater intrusion into coastal aquifers, rendering them unusable to a growing coastal population.

Global Conflict

The risks from global warming extend well beyond the issues of ecosystem damage, sea-level rise, and food and water shortages. One key area of concern is national security. Our ongoing dependence on foreign oil is obviously of great concern to countries such as the United States that import most of their fossil fuel, and is one of the more immediate drivers for the development of alternative energy sources. A more subtle, but growing, concern is the opening of the Arctic Ocean, which has been becoming increasingly ice-free during the latter part of Northern Hemisphere summer. Nations now see opportunities for shipping through the Arctic Ocean during the summer and fall months, but they also recognize that they have new coastlines to protect. The Arctic seafloor is also thought to be rich in petroleum, and several countries are now jockeying for control of the mineral rights of this newly accessible real estate. In other parts of the world, climate change is already creating "environmental refugees" who are fleeing their drought-afflicted homelands. Such influxes of refugees across national boundaries can lead to unrest and discontent. Rainfall distributions, river courses, and groundwater resources know no political boundaries (except to the extent that they have already been modified by engineering activities designed to capture water). As water supplies diminish and populations grow, the potential for conflict continues to escalate.

Food Shortages

Amidst these dire predictions for the future is one positive consequence of the buildup of carbon dioxide: an increase in crop productivity for large regions of North America and Europe. Climate models predict that these regions should experience generally favorable shifts in precipitation, coupled with longer growing seasons. Furthermore, C_3 crops, which include most common food sources, will be "fertilized" by elevated carbon dioxide, a plant nutrient. However, other regions are likely to suffer reduced crop yields because of decreased rainfall. Moreover, the benefits in North America and Europe are projected to be only short

term. Eventually, as CO_2 levels continue to increase and the global climate continues to warm, most of the agricultural regions of the world are expected to suffer reduced agricultural productivity. Moreover, marine fisheries are likely to be impacted by warming sea temperatures, resulting in reduced biological productivity and fish populations.

ADAPTING TO GLOBAL WARMING

According to the latest IPCC report, even if we were to stop burning fossil fuels and cutting down old-growth forests today, global temperature would increase by another 0.6°C by the end of the century because certain components of the climate system (*e.g.*, the oceans and glaciers/ice sheets) respond sluggishly to climate forcing. Moreover, as this chapter is being written, there is no sign that we will significantly reduce, let alone eliminate, anthropogenic greenhouse-gas emissions in the near future. Thus, some amount of adaptation to climate change will be necessary. Vulnerability to the detrimental effects of climate change differs among nations, and as it turns out, those regions most vulnerable (e.g., Africa) are often not the major contributors to the problem. Below we discuss two environmental changes to which society will need to adapt in the coming decades: sea-level rise and challenges to water supply and agriculture. In the next section we discuss the alternative to adaptation, namely, *mitigation*. Clearly, a measure of each of these approaches will be key to creating a sustainable human future.

Adapting to Sea-Level Rise

A significant problem facing society is that a large fraction of the world's population lives close to sea level. Researchers at Columbia University, who define low-elevation coastal zones (LECZs) as those with an elevation of less than 10 m above sea level, place this number at 10%. Of particular concern are the developing countries of Bangladesh and Vietnam, both of which have large numbers of people living in LECZs.

The developed world is also at risk. Consider the United States: many of its major urban centers, including parts of New York City, Miami, and Boston, where more than 20 million people live, are in LECZs (Figure 7). The Netherlands already has 60% of its population living in LECZs. Based on their experiences and on others we have learned quite a bit about which measures to protect LECZs work and which don't. With varying levels of success, inundated land has been reclaimed, and dikes and dams have been installed. These measures have their limits, though, and ultimately people living in LECZs will have to find ways to accommodate inundation. These include building flood-proof structures and using floating agricultural systems. Eventually, retreat to areas further inland may be the only adaptation available. The low slope

FIGURE 7 Map showing the low-elevation coastal zone (LECZ) along the east coast of the United States. An LECZ is defined as a region that is within 10 m of sea level. (*Source:* http://sedac.ciesin.columbia.edu/gpw/maps/lecz/USA_10m_LECZ_and_population_density.jpg.)

of coastal zones means that 1 m of sea-level rise could translate into a kilometer or more of required retreat.

Water Management

How do we ensure adequate and clean water for the burgeoning world population in a time when human-induced climate change is reducing the quantity and dependability of existing water supplies? A number of steps can be taken to both provide more water and to reduce demand. On the supply side, more effort can be placed on prospecting for groundwater, collecting rainwater, and building larger reservoirs for water storage. Seawater desalinization plants can be built in coastal areas, and more efficient water transport networks can be constructed. Demand can be reduced by recycling water and wastewater after treatment (so-called beneficial reuse). Cropping calendars, crop mixes, irrigation methods, and areas planted can all be adjusted to minimize irrigation demands on water. In urban areas, economic incentives including metering and higher pricing can be used to reduce water demand.

POLICIES TO SLOW GLOBAL WARMING

Should we take action now to slow or halt global warming? Whether immediate action is warranted is one of the most hotly debated political issues of our time. The theoretical argument that warming will eventually occur is rock solid. The evidence that CO_2-induced global warming has already started is also very strong. Because of the high cost of addressing the problem, however, there is an understandable reluctance in most societies to act hastily. The attitude of many citizens and some governments is to wait and see how bad the problem is before we commit any substantial resources to addressing it.

The Kyoto Protocol

In 1997, an international conference was convened in the city of Kyoto, Japan, for the purpose of creating an international treaty, or protocol, to regulate CO_2 emissions. The treaty called for economically developed countries, like the United States, Europe, and Japan, to roll back CO_2 emissions to 5% below 1990 levels. Since that time, 182 countries have ratified the **Kyoto Protocol**, including all members of the European Union, Russia, and Japan. Many developing countries, such as India, Brazil, and China, also ratified the treaty. This was easy for them to do, however, because the treaty did not require any emissions reductions from developing nations. The United States, notably, has *not* signed the Kyoto Protocol. There are several reasons for this—one of them being skepticism about climate science on the part of the Bush administration. To be fair, however, the Kyoto treaty was first proposed under the preceding Clinton administration, which also failed to take any action on it. Indeed, in 1997 the U.S. Senate (which must approve all international treaties) voted 95–0 against supporting any CO_2 treaty that did not include limits on emissions from developing nations. So, there has been bipartisan opposition to this treaty within the United States, even though many U.S. climate scientists (and former vice president Al Gore) strongly supported it.

Energy Conservation and Other "Soft" Measures

Whether or not the Kyoto treaty was worth signing, many U.S. citizens are convinced that actions should be taken to reduce emissions of CO_2 and other greenhouse gases and to at least make a start in slowing the process of global warming. To begin, there are a number of "soft" measures that might be taken that would be relatively inexpensive and that would require little or no change in people's lifestyles. One step on which virtually everyone agrees is to encourage energy conservation. Every kilowatt-hour of electricity or gallon of gasoline saved is one less that contributes to CO_2 buildup in the atmosphere. Indeed, many conservation measures have already been implemented. Homes built in the United States today are typically much better insulated than were homes built a generation ago. New cars get significantly better fuel mileage than did cars built in the 1960s, although the trend toward larger cars and SUVs during the past two decades has rolled back some of the gains in fuel efficiency that had occurred during the 1970s and early 1980s. Gasoline prices near $4 per gallon are now starting to push back car sales to smaller, more fuel-efficient vehicles. (Note added in proof: As a result of the 2008 recession, gas prices *fell* to below $2 per gallon! However, they are creeping up again in early 2009, and we suspect that they will top $4 per gallon again within the next year or two.)

Planting trees is another step that can be taken with which few people would disagree. Trees take up CO_2 during the time that they are growing to maturity. This typically takes on the order of 50 to 100 years. Once a forest has reached steady state, however, then further CO_2 uptake is generally balanced by CO_2 released from the death and decomposition of older trees. Furthermore, living forests contain only about the same amount of carbon as does the atmosphere, whereas the amount of carbon potentially available from fossil fuels is much larger. So, this policy could potentially buy us some time, but it is not a long-term solution to the problem of global warming.

Energy-conservation and tree-planting measures are to be lauded, but those who have thought seriously about the global warming problem realize that these measures by themselves are not likely to solve it. One way of demonstrating this is by performing "inverse" calculations with carbon cycle models. In an inverse calculation, one *assumes* a specified stabilization level for atmospheric CO_2 and then calculates what level of CO_2 emissions would be required to produce it. For example, suppose we wanted to stabilize atmospheric CO_2 at 450 ppm. According to Figure 8, this stabilization would require a decrease in net CO_2 production from 6 Gton(C)/yr to just over 1 Gton(C)/yr by the year 2300. Cutting global fossil-fuel usage by this amount would be a daunting task. The task might be made somewhat easier if the terrestrial biosphere were still absorbing CO_2 at that time, but such absorption may or may not occur. Thus, we can conclude that large reductions in fossil-fuel consumption would be necessary to stabilize atmospheric CO_2 anywhere near its present value. With world population increasing, and with developing countries eager to raise their standard of living to levels comparable to those in the West, the demand for energy is likely to increase despite our best efforts to conserve. If we wish to fulfill this demand and still reduce CO_2 emissions, we will either have to develop nonfossil energy sources or figure out ways to capture and sequester CO_2.

FIGURE 8 (a) Various prescribed levels of atmospheric CO_2. Stabilization at these levels requires (b) these new CO_2 emission rates. (*Source: Climate Change 1994: Radiative Forcing of Climate Change*, Cambridge: Cambridge University Press, 1994.)

Alternative Energy Sources

What alternative, nonfossil energy sources might we turn to? For the production of electricity, nuclear energy is one option that is currently available. Conventional nuclear power plants (Figure 9) produce energy from the **nuclear fission** of uranium atoms, the splitting of an atomic nucleus into two fragments, accompanied by the release of energy. This process, which is the basis for the atomic bomb, produces no CO_2 (although some CO_2 is produced in mining the uranium fuel by means of conventional, gasoline-powered machinery). Many environmentalists, however, feel that nuclear power poses its own threat to the global environment. A large part of their concern stems from the problem of disposal of long-lived radioactive wastes. Although several methods have been proposed for handling wastes, none of them is totally without risk. Nuclear waste disposal sites are vigorously opposed by citizens in areas where the potential sites are to be located. Local opposition has so far prevented the United States from opening its planned nuclear waste storage facility

at Yucca Mountain in Nevada. Although many Nevadans see such a delay as positive, it is not without negative consequences. From a practical standpoint, most of the waste produced by existing nuclear reactors is still stored on-site in large underground "swimming pools" rather than in a long-term facility designed for that purpose.

Acceptance of nuclear power varies widely from one country to another. The United States produces about 20% of its energy from nuclear power, but no new nuclear plants have been ordered by utilities for more than 25 years, partly as a result of pressure from vocal antinuclear lobbying groups. Germany and Sweden have also almost abandoned this energy option. Conversely, both France and Japan have active nuclear programs, and both produce the majority of their electricity from nuclear power. One reason for their different outlook may lie in the fact that neither country has appreciable domestic reserves of coal or oil.

A second type of nuclear power that shows some hope for the future is **nuclear fusion**, the combining of

FIGURE 9   A nuclear power plant.   (*Source:* Petr
Student/iStockphoto.)

lightweight atomic nuclei into a heavier nucleus, with an
accompanying release of energy. The fusion of hydrogen
atoms into helium is the energy source that powers the
Sun. Prototype fusion reactors on Earth use the hydrogen
isotopes deuterium (^{2}H) and tritium (^{3}H) as fuel, because
these atoms can fuse at lower temperatures than can the
normal (^{1}H) isotope. Deuterium is fairly abundant on
Earth; 16 of every 100,000 atoms of hydrogen in seawater
consist of this isotope. Unfortunately, designing a success-
ful fusion reactor is a technologically daunting task. As
one wag put it, "nuclear fusion has been 30 years over the
horizon for the last 50 years." If ongoing efforts to design
fusion reactors succeed, this process could eventually be
an important source of energy.

Other non-CO_2-producing energy sources include
wind power, tidal power, geothermal power, and biomass-
based fuels. **Wind power** generates electricity by means of
windmills, which utilize Earth's solar-energy-driven winds.
Wind power is "clean and green," but it is not a consistent
source of energy because the wind does not blow all the
time. Hence, it generally must be backed up with more reliable sources of power. **Tidal power** produces electricity by

using long, floating booms to harness the energy of ocean
tides. Its potential disadvantage is that it encroaches on
coastal areas that often have many other uses, such as recre-
ation. **Geothermal power** utilizes temperature gradients
within the solid Earth as an energy source for generating
electricity. It works best in places like Iceland, where hot
magma is only a few kilometers beneath the surface.

Biomass-based fuels are liquid fuels, such as methanol
(CH_3OH) or ethanol (C_2H_5OH), that are produced from
fast-growing plants. **Ethanol** is produced from corn in the
United States and from sugarcane in Brazil. **Biodiesel** is
another biomass fuel that is produced from fats or oils
(soybean oil, in particular) and that is widely available in
Europe. These fuels deserve special attention because they
can be (and are being) used to power vehicles, thereby sup-
plementing or replacing conventional oil-based gasoline.
Biomass fuels release CO_2 when they are burned, but the
plants from which they are made absorb CO_2 while they
are growing, so the net effect on the atmospheric CO_2
budget is zero. It would seem at first glance that these fuels
are an unadulterated "plus" from an environmental standpoint. In reality, though, the story is more complicated.
Corn-based ethanol actually reduces CO_2 emissions by
only a small amount because of the large amount of energy
needed to grow and harvest it. **Cellulosic ethanol** (ethanol
produced from the woody cellulose part of plants) would
be more efficient, but economical ways of producing it are
still under development.

All biomass fuels suffer from another problem that is
even more serious. Devoting land (and fertilizer) to growing them reduces the amount of land that is available to
cultivate food crops. Production of corn-based ethanol in
the United States has already driven up the price of corn by
more than a factor of 2 over the past few years. The effects
of this price increase have been felt not just in the United
States, but also in countries such as Mexico that import
U.S.-grown corn. Hence, the environmental benefits from
the use of biomass fuels must be weighed against the negative impacts on food production and food prices. This
does not mean that we should abandon biomass fuels, but
it does indicate that we must carefully consider their overall impact on the global economy and on global welfare in
general.

Perhaps the most promising energy source in the
long term is solar energy. Sunlight is a clean and virtually
inexhaustible energy source that is on the verge of becoming economically competitive. In some favorably situated
areas, such as southern California, solar power is already
competitive and contributes a substantial amount of electrical energy to local power grids. In sunny areas, **solar
thermal power** is an efficient method for producing electricity (Figure 10). In this method, sunlight is used to heat
a fluid that, in turn, drives a turbine. In more northern regions, the production of electricity from **photovoltaic
cells**, specially designed panels that can directly convert
sunlight into electricity, may be the most practical solution.

FIGURE 10 A solar thermal power plant. (*Source:* Hank Morgan/Photo Researchers.)

Photovoltaic cells, similar to those flown on satellites, are currently more expensive than conventional energy sources, however. Ultimately, huge orbiting **solar-power satellites** may collect the Sun's energy in space and beam it to Earth's surface as laser or microwave radiation. Another idea is to build solar-power collectors on the Moon and beam the energy back from there. (Surprisingly, this appears to be technologically feasible!) Such systems could be built by the more industrially developed nations to provide power across the entire globe. Much work would need to be done to determine whether space-based solar-power systems could be designed to be both economical and safe. They appear to be exorbitantly expensive today, but they might be more cost-effective in the future as space technology advances.

Carbon Capture and Storage

Another approach to CO_2-free electrical power generation is to continue to burn coal, but to trap the CO_2 that is produced and bury it underground, either in deep, land-based geological formations, the deep ocean, or the upper parts of the oceanic crust. This approach is termed **carbon capture and storage (CCS)** or, equivalently, **carbon sequestration**. There are several approaches to doing this. One is to burn the coal in pure O_2 rather than air. The exhaust is then composed of nearly pure CO_2 plus H_2O. The two gases can be easily separated by cooling because H_2O condenses at a higher temperature. The CO_2 can then be liquified and transported to the storage site by pipelines. A second approach is to run hot steam through the coal before it is burned. The coal is partially oxidized during this process and it releases **syngas**, which is a mixture of CO (carbon monoxide) and H_2. The CO is then oxidized to CO_2 by the **water–gas shift reaction**:

$$CO + H_2O \rightarrow CO_2 + H_2$$

The net result of this process is the production of molecular hydrogen, H_2, which can be cleanly burned to produce H_2O as the only byproduct. CO_2 is generated in both steps of this process; however, it is in a nearly pure-CO_2 airstream and can be captured and sequestered, as before.

CCS technology is promising and is being further developed by a number of different countries. If it proves to be commercially feasible, it would allow us to continue to use our abundant coal reserves as a source of energy without exacerbating the problem of global warming. There are downsides to this process, however. For one, the technology is relatively expensive. It has been estimated that implementing CCS would increase the cost of electrical power generation by at least 50% for new coal-fired plants and by as much as a factor of 2 for existing plants that would need to be retrofitted. Although painful, these additional costs might well be worth bearing if they allowed us to protect the environment. A more serious issue with CCS is that the long-term effects of CO_2 sequestration are largely unknown. Injection of CO_2 into the deep ocean could contribute to ocean acidification, which is a hazard to marine life. CO_2 storage on land could result in highly acidic groundwater, which might then leach out of confinement and create problems with groundwater supplies in nearby areas. Neither of these problems appears insurmountable; however, the environmental effects of CO_2 sequestration clearly require further study. If CCS can be done in an environmentally friendly way, then perhaps this technology will play an important role in satisfying our long-term energy requirements.

Geoengineering of Global Climate

Even more exotic approaches have been discussed to combat global warming. Perhaps the most extreme idea is to allow greenhouse gases, including CO_2, to accumulate, but then to counteract their effects by artificially cooling the climate. This class of solutions is referred to as **geoengineering**. This sounds difficult, and indeed it would be, but there may be ways to do this using current technology. The idea that has received the most attention so far is to purposely seed the stratosphere with sulfate aerosol particles. This could be done, for example, by building large guns at many different locations around the globe and using them to shoot sulfate-filled explosive capsules up into the stratosphere. Sulfate aerosols cool the climate by reflecting some of the incident solar energy back to space, that is, by increasing Earth's albedo. Aerosol particles remain in the stratosphere for only a few months; hence, they would need to be continually injected in order for this mechanism to work.

While this class of solutions deserves careful study, there are reasons to think that this approach is of questionable value. Stratospheric aerosol particles would be unlikely to remain evenly distributed from one location to another; hence, they might alter global weather patterns in ways that are difficult to predict. Aerosol particles can also serve as surfaces that liberate chlorine from unreactive compounds and convert it into forms that can destroy ozone. Paul Crutzen, a famous atmospheric chemist who received the Nobel Prize for his work on ozone depletion, has pointed out that this should not necessarily pose a problem, because stratospheric chlorine levels should be significantly lower by the end of this century as a result of ozone protection policies that have already been enacted. Still, one wonders whether there might be other such reactions that might become important should the stratosphere become loaded with aerosol particles.

An additional objection that applies to other geoengineering approaches as well is that, while they address the problem of global warming, they do not address the related problem of ocean acidification. As we saw in the previous chapter, atmospheric CO_2 concentrations could approach 2000 ppm if we burn an appreciable fraction of the available fossil fuels. This could cause an appreciable drop in surface-ocean pH, and that in turn could result in the dissolution of many species of calcareous plankton and corals. So, even if a geoengineered climate was deemed acceptable by humans, the effects on marine ecosystems might be so severe that this option would be rejected for other reasons.

Specific Policies That Might Be Adopted

How could a shift to nonfossil energy sources be promoted if such action is deemed necessary? More generally, what types of policies might be adopted that would reduce greenhouse gas emissions by whatever mechanism?

One way of reducing carbon dioxide emissions is by the imposition of direct governmental regulations. An example that is already in effect in the United States is the **CAFÉ** (Combined Automobile Fleet Emissions) **standard** that governs cars sold. Each manufacturer's fleet must meet an average fuel economy rating specified by the federal government. These standards may well be raised in the near future if Congress decides that more fuel-efficient cars should be available. There is a downside to this, though. In the past, auto manufacturers have circumvented the rules by helping to get SUVs classified as "light trucks," for which the fuel-efficiency standards are less strict. And, although the CAFÉ standards undoubtedly increase the number of small, fuel-efficient cars that are sold, they do little to encourage people to drive less or to live closer to their workplace. If one drives 75 minutes each way to work—which is the average commute in both Los Angeles and Atlanta—then even if one is driving a Prius, the amount of CO_2 released will still be relatively large.

A more efficient mechanism for reducing CO_2 emissions would be to impose a tax on any energy source that produces CO_2. Such a **carbon tax** would make other forms of energy more economically competitive and, hence, more likely to be exploited. It would, for example, favor nuclear- or wind-based production of electricity as opposed to coal-fired power plants. It would also encourage people to drive cars that are fuel efficient and to commute shorter distances to work. The carbon tax could be augmented by a "gas-guzzler" tax on fuel-inefficient automobiles. Such taxes need not represent an additional burden on the average citizen, because

all or part of the revenue that they generate could be returned to the public in the form of income tax breaks. Some of the proceeds might also be used to construct better rail systems so that more people and goods could be moved by trains (which could be designed to be entirely electric). A carbon tax would be costly to some industries and localities, however, particularly those involved in mining coal or in producing oil. In the United States, the energy-rich western states, along with some eastern coal-producing states, including Pennsylvania and West Virginia, might lose jobs if such a policy were implemented. Thus, measures such as this are not likely to be accepted unless the population at large becomes alarmed about global warming.

ECONOMIC CONSEQUENCES OF GLOBAL WARMING

How can we decide which policy would best deal with global warming? Should we take strong steps now, or should we wait and see for a while longer and see how things develop? One approach that is certain to be used to address this question is to analyze the problem from an economic standpoint. Each of the physical effects that we have talked about will have some effect on the future economy of the United States and of the world as a whole. Agricultural output, for example, is almost certain to be affected. Some of the changes, such as decreased soil moisture in continental interiors, will be detrimental to agricultural output while other changes, CO_2 fertilization of plant growth for example, are expected to be beneficial. By now, many economists have developed forecast models that attempt to calculate how the projected changes in CO_2 and climate will affect the global economy.

Cost–Benefit Analysis

The way that such calculations are typically done is by what is often termed **cost–benefit analysis**. At least some of the changes anticipated from global warming are likely to cost money to deal with. Relocating cities away from continental coastlines is one obvious example. On the other hand, reducing CO_2 emissions is likely to cost money, too. As discussed further below, alternative means of producing energy are available, but none of these is currently as convenient or inexpensive as fossil fuels. Thus, if society chooses to reap the economic benefits of limiting climate change, certain costs will be incurred. The goal of economic models of global warming is to determine how these projected costs and benefits balance out. From an economic standpoint, the optimum solution is one in which the benefits less the costs is at a maximum.

A detailed analysis of such economic models is beyond the scope of the present discussion. It may nonetheless be useful to make a few comments about them because of their importance to climate policy. The first comment is that all of the economic models are highly uncertain—more so, even, than the physical models of global warming. This should come as no surprise. Predicting the behavior of humans is inherently more difficult than predicting the behavior of physical systems. This does not mean that economic models are of no use, however. As with physical models that contain large inherent uncertainties (clouds in climate models, for example), we can still use these models to help guide our choices.

Economic models, however, often contain value judgments in addition to other uncertainties. As an example, consider the ongoing debate about how much money to put into (or pay out of) the Social Security system. Social Security is predicted to go bankrupt sometime before the middle of this century unless Social Security taxes are raised or benefits are reduced. The government could fix this problem by taking one or both of these actions now, or it could postpone dealing with the problem until 10 or 20 years from now. In the first case, the present generation of taxpayers and beneficiaries would be affected. In the second case, the future beneficiaries of the system would bear the costs. Which course should government take? The answer involves a value judgment. One has to decide how much economic hardship is worth putting up with now in order to avoid economic hardship for a somewhat different group of people several decades in the future.

The Stern Review on the Economics of Global Warming

Within the last few years, the debate about the economic effects of global warming has heated up (just as Earth itself has done!). In late 2006 the British government released a report from a committee led by the economist Nicholas Stern; hence, it is referred to as the *Stern Review on the Economics of Global Warming.* In it, Stern and his colleagues used a collection of different models to estimate the economic impact of global warming. They concluded that by the end of the next century (i.e., by the year 2200) the potential damages could be enormous—as much as 30% of the world per capita GDP (see Figure 11). **Gross domestic product (GDP)** is the total amount of money generated by all of the world's people. The term **per capita** simply means "per person." Not all of their predictions were this dire. In a more conservative case, the damages were only about 5% of world GDP. Even this, though, is an enormous amount of money. Stern's group went on to recommend a variety of strict measures to reduce greenhouse gas buildup, including high taxes on carbon emissions to discourage the use of fossil fuels. Such a carbon tax is a policy favored by many economists as an efficient tool to combat global warming.

Not all economists agreed with Stern's analysis, however. Indeed, many of them, including the influential Yale economist William Nordhaus, thought that Stern's economic assumptions were flawed and that his policy recommendations were therefore invalid. Nordhaus advocates carbon taxes as well; however, he thinks that Stern's proposed tax would be far too high.

Why would two different, well-educated economists disagree so strongly on global warming economic policy? The reason is primarily due to their different approaches to **economic discounting**. Because this concept is critical to making decisions about climate policy, or any other long-term environmental problem, we discuss it further below.

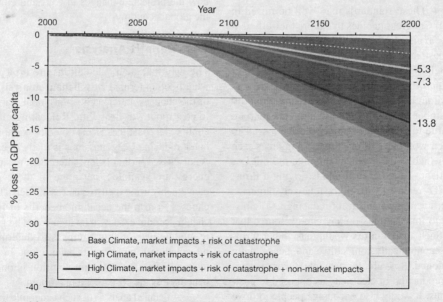

FIGURE 11 Projected future decreases in per capita GDP (gross domestic product) for three different global warming scenarios. The shaded regions show the uncertainty in the calculations. (*Source:* N. H. Stern, *The Economics of Climate Change: The Stern Review,* Cambridge: Cambridge University Press, available online at http://www.hm-treasury.gov.uk/independent_reviews/stern_review_economics_climate_change/sternreview_index.cfm.)

Economic Discounting

In economic models of global warming, the key question is: How much should we pay now in order to avoid damages that may be incurred in the distant future? Global warming is a slow process. As we have already seen earlier in this chapter, the biggest changes in climate, and hence the largest economic damages, are not likely to occur until more than 100 years from now. In a typical cost–benefit analysis, such as one to decide whether or not to build a dam or a powerplant, future damages or benefits are *discounted* at a rate of as much as 10% a year. That is, a benefit of $100 that is realized 1 year from now is valued at only $90.91 [= $100/(1 + 0.1)]. The same benefit reaped 2 years from now is valued at $82.64 [= $100/(1 + 0.1)^2], and so forth. This **discount rate** takes into account two factors: (1) If one saves money now by not building the dam, one could invest this money somewhere else and make a profit. This is called *growth discounting*. (2) Most people would rather have a dollar today than a dollar 10 years from now (after adjustment for inflation). This is called *time preference discounting*.

In models of global warming, growth discounting is generally accounted for in one way or another. This makes a certain amount of sense: If society is richer 100 years from now than it is today, then people at that time can afford to pay more than they can at present. (On the other hand, if the change one is considering is essentially irreversible, like sea-level rise, then no amount of economic growth may compensate for it.) Economic models of global warming usually include time preference discounting as well. According to analyses of past economic behavior, societies as a whole exhibit a preference for having money right now, as opposed to receiving it sometime in the future. The Yale economist William Nordhaus, mentioned earlier, has studied investment behavior in U.S. society over the past 40 years and has determined that the *pure rate of social time preference*, as it is formally termed, is about 3% per year. Thus, a benefit (or cost) that was worth $100 today would be valued at $97.08 one year from now, $94.26 two years from now, and so on.

A discount rate of 3% per year may not sound like much, and indeed significantly larger discount rates (7–10%/yr) are often used in short-term cost–benefit analyses. Consider what happens over long time spans, however. In 50 years, the assigned value of a $100 benefit (or damage) would be $100/(1 + 0.03)^{50} = $22.81. In 100 years, the value drops to $5.20. In 200 years, it is $0.27. Thus, even if some truly catastrophic change were predicted to occur 200 years from now, its influence on a typical cost–benefit analysis would be minimal. The damages could be real and could be large in real economic terms, but time preference discounting ensures that they would be essentially neglected.

Cost–Benefit Calculations with Different Discount Rates: Nordhaus versus Stern

As a concrete example of the importance of discounting, let us examine some calculations performed by Nordhaus using his Dynamic Integrated Climate-Economy (DICE) model. The DICE model is typically run over a time span that extends 400 years into the future. It attempts to predict global economic growth, taking into account such factors as increases in population, new developments in technology, and climate change. Then, by performing a cost–benefit analysis, the model generates numbers that can be used to calculate the optimal amount of money that should be devoted to reducing greenhouse gases. Or, alternatively, it can be used to estimate the optimal carbon tax that would produce this result and, at the same time, do minimal damage to the world economy.

Figure 12 shows the results of two such calculations over the next century. Figure 12a shows the optimal carbon tax for Nordhaus's standard DICE model (bottom curve) and for Stern's more aggressive approach to combating global warming. Figure 12b shows the global CO_2 emissions that would result from these two different policies. Also shown in (b) are three other scenarios: (1) a "business as usual" scenario in which fossil-fuel emissions are not reduced at all; (2) a curve showing what would have happened if the 1997 Kyoto Protocol had been signed and implemented by all nations that attended the conference (which did *not* happen in reality); and (3) another ambitious strategy for CO_2 emissions reductions suggested by former U.S. vice president Al Gore. Figure 13 shows what would happen to atmospheric CO_2 levels and to global temperatures over the next two centuries, were any of these particular policy recommendations to be followed.

Let us start by looking at Figure 13. In the "business as usual" scenario, atmospheric CO_2 levels would increase to over 1100 ppm before the year 2200, while global temperatures would rise by approximately 5°C (9°F). The Kyoto Protocol, had it been fully implemented, would have done little to alter this outlook, largely because developing nations such as India and China were exempted from its regulations. By contrast, Nordhaus's prescription would keep atmospheric CO_2 concentrations below 700 ppm and would limit the temperature increase to about 3.5°C. Both Stern's and Gore's proposals would keep CO_2 levels below 450 ppm and would allow a surface temperature increase of only about 1.5°C.

Look next at the CO_2 emissions required to achieve each of these scenarios. In the business-as-usual scenario, CO_2 emissions increase from about 8 Gton(C)/yr today to almost 20 Gton(C)/yr in 2100. Nordhaus's prescription would hold CO_2 emissions to less than 10 Gton(C)/yr, declining back to 6 Gton(C)/yr in 2100. The latter number is approximately equal to 1990 consumption levels. By contrast, Gore's proposal would reduce emissions to less than 1 Gton(C)/yr by 2050 and hold them there indefinitely. Stern's proposal would

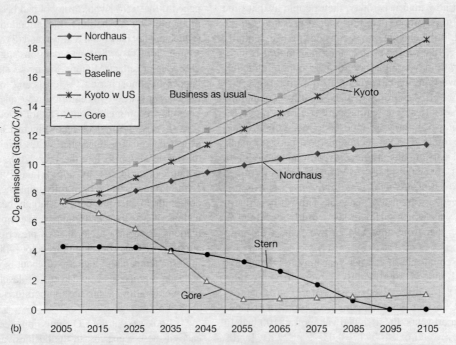

FIGURE 12 (a) Optimal carbon tax (in $US/ton) predicted by the economic models of Stern and Nordhaus. (b) The projected CO_2 emissions corresponding to these two models. Also shown in (b) are the projected emissions for a "business as usual" scenario, a scenario based on enactment of the 1990 Kyoto Protocol, and a scenario based on a proposal by former U.S. vice president Al Gore.   (*Source:* William Nordhaus, *The Challenge of Global Warming: Economic Models and Environmental Policy,* New Haven, CT: Yale University Press, July 24, 2007.)

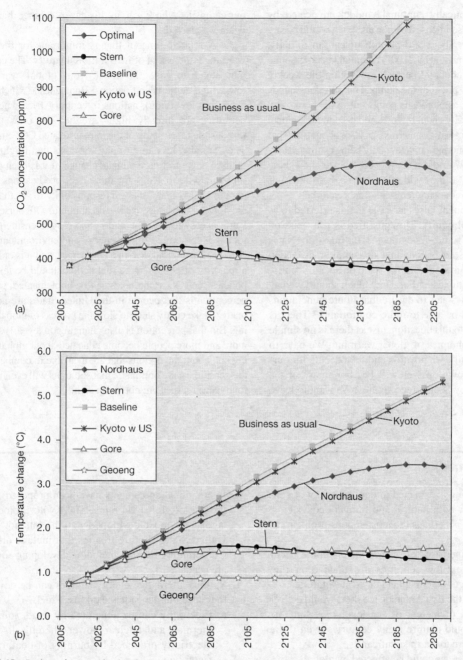

FIGURE 13 Projected atmospheric CO_2 concentrations (a) and surface temperature increases (b) for the emissions scenarios shown in Figure 8b. The bottom curve shows a geoengineered climate solution. (*Source:* William Nordhaus, *The Challenge of Global Warming: Economic Models and Environmental Policy,* New Haven, CT: Yale University Press, July 24, 2007.)

reduce emissions somewhat more slowly, but would eventually achieve even lower emission levels.

Many environmentalists think that we will ultimately need to reduce CO_2 emissions by large amounts, as suggested by Stern and Gore. But what type of economic policy would be required to do that? The carbon tax necessary to encourage this kind of behavior is shown in Figure 12a. It starts at about $100 per ton of carbon initially and rises to about $950 per ton within 100 years. In terms of commodities that people buy,

the initial $100/ton tax would be equivalent to about a $0.30 per gallon tax on gasoline, or about a 3¢/kilowatt-hour tax on electricity (about 30% of its current market price). The proposed gasoline tax is less than 10% of the current market price, which is just under $4/gallon as this chapter is being drafted. But this would rise to about $3/gallon by 2100, effectively doubling the price of gas for citizens of the United States. Most Europeans already pay prices this high or higher because of gas tax policies enacted for other reasons.

The economically "optimal" model advocated by Nordhaus would also impose a carbon tax, but it would be significantly smaller: about $30 per ton of carbon initially, increasing to $200 per ton by 2100. The initial tax on gasoline would amount to about 9¢ per gallon—within the weekly fluctuations of gas prices at the pump. This solution sounds relatively painless, as Nordhaus points out in his books and papers. But is it really enough? In Nordhaus's model, global temperatures increase by as much as 3.5°C, or about 6°F. That is a lot! Are the economic damages really being estimated correctly in this model? And is it really acceptable to allow these damages to occur, as they will affect not us, but rather our children, or perhaps our children's children's children?

This last thought raises an issue that is referred to as **intergenerational equity**. How justified is it to pass on economic costs to future generations? This question relates directly to the question of economic discounting, discussed previously. And it is similar to the issue of Social Security benefits, also mentioned earlier. How much should we pay now in the United States to ensure that future generations of Americans will be able to retire comfortably? There is no simple answer to this question, just as there is no simple answer to the economics of global warming. We have to debate the merits of each position and then decide for ourselves what our own answer will be. For many of us, though, the old Boy Scout creed applies: We want to leave our campsite—the Earth, in this case—cleaner than it was when we arrived.

A related concept that is important for the global warming issue is that of **international equity**. The countries that stand to lose the most from global warming—low-lying Pacific island nations, Bangladesh (which is also extremely low-lying), nations in central Africa where temperatures are already high—are not the ones that are responsible for the bulk of the human-related CO_2 emissions. They are also less able to pay for costs that might enable them to adapt to future climate change, if it is even possible for them to do so. Don't the more developed nations, including the United States, have a responsibility to see that others are not hurt by things that we do at home? Of course we do. But it is easy to say that, and not so easy to ensure that this idea is incorporated in our energy and environmental policies. We do, after all, live in a democracy, and it is only when a majority of people agree that action should be taken that policies such as carbon taxes can be implemented. Our own perception is that people in the United States are not quite ready to take costly steps to slow the process of global warming. But that perception is also changing on a yearly basis as more and more people become educated about global warming and about the options that are available to combat it. For this reason, we are optimistic that solutions will eventually be found, even if they are not yet in sight.

Chapter Summary

1. Global warming is expected to have a variety of consequences for both natural and human ecosystems. Sea-level rise is perhaps the most serious problem for humans.
   a. Sea-level increases of several meters could occur over the next few centuries if extensive melting were to occur on Greenland or West Antarctica.
   b. Melting of the East Antarctic ice sheet would deliver many tens of meters of sea-level rise, but this change would require many centuries even if the climate were to warm significantly.
2. Natural ecosystems could be affected by global warming in many ways.
   a. Higher CO_2 levels will favor C_3 plants over C_4 plants. This could affect agriculture, as well, because corn and sugarcane are C_4 plants, whereas most weeds are C_3 plants.
   b. The speciation of trees in forests is expected to change as deciduous forests expand their range poleward.
   c. Insect pests, including mosquitos that carry diseases such as malaria, may expand their range from tropical regions to midlatitudes.
   d. In the oceans, coral growth could be inhibited by warming seawater and ocean acidification.
3. International agreements have been proposed to slow the rate of global warming. The Kyoto Protocol was signed by most developed nations but not by the United States. Future treaties that include all major CO_2-emitting nations, including developing countries, are needed.
4. Various alternative energy sources can be developed to reduce our dependence on fossil fuels.
   a. Electricity can be generated by wind, solar, geothermal, and nuclear power, thereby displacing electricity produced by burning of coal, oil, and natural gas.
   b. Biomass fuels, including (but not restricted to) ethanol, can be used to replace gasoline and diesel fuel.
   c. A tax on carbon would be an efficient method of encouraging the development of alternative energy sources.
5. There are ways to continue to burn fossil fuels and yet to reduce or eliminate their effects on climate.
   a. Carbon capture and storage (CCS) can be employed to sequester CO_2 in underground reservoirs.
   b. Earth's climate can be deliberately "geoengineered" by methods such as stratospheric aerosol injection.

6. Economic cost–benefit analyses of global warming reach different conclusions because of different assumptions in the models.

    a. Most models predict that at least a modest carbon tax should be imposed in the near future to help reduce the economic costs of future global warming.

    b. Models in which the discount rate is set to a low value suggest that higher carbon taxes are needed. The discount rate determines how much costs or benefits in the future matter compared to the same costs or benefits today.

Key Terms

biodiesel	discount rate	nuclear fission
biomass-based fuels	economic discounting	nuclear fusion
C_3 plants	ethanol	per capita
C_4 plants	geoengineering	photovoltaic cells
CAFÉ standard	geothermal power	solar-power satellites
Calvin cycle	glacial surge	solar thermal power
carbon capture and storage (CCS)	gross domestic product (GDP)	syngas
carbon fixation	ice shelves	thermal expansion
carbon sequestration	intergenerational equity	tidal power
carbon tax	international equity	water–gas shift reaction
cellulosic ethanol	Kyoto Protocol	wind power
cost–benefit analysis	mountain glaciers	

Review Questions

1. What processes contribute to increases in global sea level, and by how much has it gone up in the recent past?

2. Why is predicting future sea-level change such a tricky task?

3. How are changes in climate predicted to affect natural ecosystems, including forests and insects?

4. What are some of the predicted effects of global warming on human populations?

5. What provisions did the Kyoto Protocol make to slow global warming, and why did the United States decline to sign it?

6. What role can energy conservation play in combating global warming?

7. What are some alternative energy sources that might be used to replace fossil fuels?

8. How can carbon capture and storage be used to burn coal in an environmentally safe way?

9. What are some ways in which Earth's climate might be "geo-engineered"?

10. What do economists mean by the term "cost–benefit analysis"?

11. What role does economic discounting play in cost–benefit analyses of global warming?

12. What specific differences in global warming policy are advocated by William Nordhaus and Nicholas Stern?

Critical-Thinking Problems

1. Write a two- or three-page typewritten, double-spaced essay on the following topic: Should the world collectively take immediate action to limit CO_2 emissions? If so, what steps should be taken in the United States and abroad to deal with this issue? Is nuclear power an acceptable option for producing electricity, or should we rely on renewable energy resources such as wind and solar power? Should we impose a carbon tax in the United States? Should developing nations such as China and India be required to cut emissions as well? If so, how might they be induced to do so? If immediate action is not warranted, what might be the best ways to deal with the anticipated effects of global warming? Do any of the proposed *geoengineering* solutions appear viable? In short, what would *you* do about global warming if you were president of the United States?

Further Reading

Nordhaus, W. D. 2008. *A question of balance: Weighing the options on global warming policies* (p. 234). New Haven, CT: Yale University Press.

Stern, N. H. 2007. *The economics of climate change: The Stern review* (p. 692). Cambridge: Cambridge University Press.

Ozone Depletion

Ozone Depletion

Key Questions

- How is ultraviolet radiation categorized, and what are its biological effects?

- How is the thickness of the ozone layer measured, and how does this layer vary from place to place?

- How do trace chemicals catalyze the destruction of ozone?

- What is the cause of the Antarctic ozone hole?

- What is being done to prevent ozone depletion in the future?

Chapter Overview

Solar ultraviolet radiation between 200 and 320 nm poses significant health hazards if not effectively blocked by stratospheric ozone. Ozone is formed by reactions initiated by the splitting of O_2 and can be destroyed by various catalytic cycles involving the elements nitrogen, chlorine, and bromine. The latter two elements have large anthropogenic sources and therefore have generated concern. Chlorine, in particular, has been directly implicated in the formation of the Antarctic ozone hole and may be responsible for a slow, long-term decrease in midlatitude ozone levels. International agreements that are already in place are expected to halt the depletion of ozone and to restore the stratosphere to its natural state.

INTRODUCTION

We have discussed in detail the evolution of Earth's climate on different time scales. Our reason for dwelling on climate is twofold: First, the prospect of global warming over the next few decades to centuries is probably the most intractable environmental problem that we currently face. Second, the many different aspects of climate serve as an excellent case study for illustrating the interactions among the various elements of the Earth system, along with the system's capacity for self-regulation.

No book on global change, however, would be complete without a discussion of Earth's ozone layer and the possibility that it could be depleted. The development of a protective ozone screen to shield out harmful solar ultraviolet radiation was an important step in the evolution of advanced forms of life. The ozone layer arose naturally as a by-product of the evolution of photosynthesis and the rise of atmospheric oxygen. It is a relatively fragile feature, however, that is now threatened by chemicals released into the atmosphere by industrial activities. Unlike global warming, ozone depletion is widely recognized as a serious problem, and significant steps have already been taken to reduce its impact. It is important to understand why the ozone layer is so essential and why we must remain committed to protecting it.

ULTRAVIOLET RADIATION AND ITS BIOLOGICAL EFFECTS

Ozone absorbs ultraviolet (UV) radiation in the 200- to 400-nm region, where few other atmospheric gases absorb. Here, we look at this spectral region in greater detail.

TABLE 1 Classification of UV Radiation Wavelength

Range (nm)	Name	Biological Effect
320–400	UVA	Relatively harmless; causes tanning but not burning
290–320	UVB	Harmful; causes sunburn, skin cancer, and other disorders
200–290	UVC	Extremely harmful but almost completely absorbed by ozone

UVA and UVC Radiation

Ultraviolet radiation between 200 and 400 nm is usually subdivided into three distinct spectral ranges, as shown in Table 1. The longer wavelengths are termed *UVA*, the middle wavelengths are termed *UVB*, and the shortest wavelengths are termed *UVC*. The solar flux increases with increasing wavelength throughout this spectral region, as shown in Figure 1a. Thus, more UVA photons are available at the top of the atmosphere than are UVB or UVC photons. The ozone *absorption coefficient* is also low in the UVA region. The **absorption coefficient** is a measure of how strongly a molecule absorbs electromagnetic radiation of a given wavelength. Because the ozone absorption coefficient is low at UVA wavelengths, most of the incident photons make it down to the ground.

Fortunately, UVA radiation appears to be relatively harmless to humans and other forms of life. Many tanning parlors use UVA radiation to tan their patrons "safely." However, whether UVA radiation is really safe for humans is not fully understood. Overexposure to UVA radiation may lead to premature aging of the skin, and there is some evidence that it can damage the immune system. We are certain, though, that UVA radiation is much less dangerous than shorter-wavelength UV radiation.

(a)

(b)

FIGURE 1 (a) Diagram showing the three different categories of solar UV radiation. The curve labeled O_3 is the ozone absorption coefficient. (b) Graph illustrating the significance of UVB radiation. The shaded area represents the dose rate of the UV radiation that causes sunburn. (*Source:* R. Turco, *Air Pollution*, New York: Oxford University Press, 1997.)

At shorter, UVC wavelengths, the solar flux is lower and the ozone absorption coefficient is high. Thus, relatively few UVC photons hit the top of the atmosphere, and even fewer make it to Earth's surface. This is a good thing for humans and other organisms, because UVC radiation is extremely dangerous to most forms of life. Indeed, the absorption peak for DNA, the molecule that contains the genetic information for all organisms, is right in the middle of the UVC region. Some single-celled, prokaryotic microorganisms have developed highly efficient DNA-repair mechanisms and can tolerate substantial doses of UVC radiation. However, more advanced, eukaryotic organisms, including all multicellular life-forms, are extremely sensitive to radiation at these wavelengths.

UVB Radiation and Its Biological Effects

The wavelengths between about 290 and 320 nm, UVB radiation, are the ones of current concern to us. At these wavelengths, the solar flux is relatively high and the ozone absorption coefficient is relatively low. Thus, a substantial radiation flux reaches Earth's surface. The biological effect of this radiation is determined by the **dose rate**, which is the number of UV photons per unit time that lead to a specific biological response, such as sunburn or skin cancer. The dose rate is the product of the surface UV flux and the action spectrum for the particular response being studied. The **action spectrum** of a biological response is the relative efficiency with which UV photons at different wavelengths contribute to that response in a specific organism. For example, the **erythemal action spectrum** shown in Figure 1b describes the appearance of sunburn in humans. The dose rate (in relative units) leading to sunburn is indicated by the shaded area in the figure. Clearly, most of the UV rays that cause sunburn are in the UVB spectral region.

Although UVB radiation is not quite as harmful to organisms as is UVC radiation, it is still capable of causing substantial damage. In addition to sunburn, overexposure to UVB radiation can lead to skin cancer in humans. This radiation is also harmful to the eye, where it can cause cataracts and damage the retina. Many animals other than humans, such as hippopotami, are susceptible to sunburn, and at least half of the terrestrial plants that have been studied exhibit slower growth and smaller leaves when exposed to enhanced UVB fluxes. Increases in UVB radiation could be detrimental to aquatic life, including phytoplankton, zooplankton, larval crabs and shrimp, juvenile fish, and corals. Thus, almost all inhabitants of the Earth system have an interest in ensuring that the UVB flux does not increase above its present value.

Relationship between UVB Flux and Stratospheric Ozone

How do we know that decreasing stratospheric ozone increases the UVB flux at the ground? In general, this inference is derived theoretically. (We shall do so in "Critical-Thinking" Problem 2.) In a few cases, however, scientists have been able to measure both quantities directly and to show that these quantities behave as expected. Figure 2 shows simultaneous measurements of atmospheric ozone content and ground-level UVB flux at Melbourne, Australia, both before and after the intrusion of ozone-poor air from Antarctica in mid-December 1987. (The units in which ozone is measured are Dobson units, and are explained further below.) By January 1, ozone levels had dropped by about 16% and the UVB flux had increased by about 25%. A similar inverse relationship between ozone and UVB radiation has been observed more recently in Antarctica. The strong negative correlation between the two quantities gives atmospheric scientists great confidence that UVB fluxes will go up if ozone levels go down.

FIGURE 2 Comparison of solar UVB radiation flux at ground level and ozone column depth observed over Melbourne, Australia, from December 1987 to January 1988, during an intrusion of ozone-poor air. (*Source:* World Meteorological Organization, *Scientific Assessment of Ozone Depletion,* 1991.)

OZONE VERTICAL DISTRIBUTION AND COLUMN DEPTH

Most of Earth's ozone (O_3) is confined to the stratosphere. Indeed, the reason the stratosphere exists is because the absorption of solar UV radiation by ozone heats the air and causes the temperature to increase with altitude. The ozone layer is not as uniform, though. Rather, it varies with both latitude and time of year.

Measurements of Ozone Column Depth

Several methods exist for measuring the vertical distribution of ozone. Two of the most common methods are remote sensing from satellites and in-situ measurements from **ozonesondes**, balloon-borne instruments that measure the concentration of stratospheric ozone. A comparison of the results of these two methods is shown in Figure 3. Ozone concentrations are given in units of **number density**, or number of molecules per cubic centimeter. At its peak in the stratosphere, near 20- to 25-km altitude, the ozone number density is typically about 5×10^{12} molecules/cm^3. In terms of relative concentration, this amounts to a few parts per million. In the example shown here, the two methods for measuring ozone agree to within a few percent at all altitudes above about 16 km, which is where most of the ozone resides. The satellite does not produce accurate results at low altitudes, because it is looking down through the bulk of the ozone layer.

The flux of solar UV radiation that reaches Earth's surface depends on the **solar zenith angle**—that is, the angle of the Sun from the vertical (Figure 4)—and on the vertical column depth of ozone. The **column depth** is the total amount of ozone per unit area above a certain location at the surface. It is measured in several ways. The simplest unit is molecules of O_3 per square centimeter. In this unit, the sum of the ozone number densities at all altitudes multiplied by the height of the atmosphere is equal to the ozone column depth. A typical, midlatitude ozone column depth is about 8×10^{18} O_3 molecules/cm^2, meaning that there are 8×10^{18} molecules over 1 cm^2 of Earth's surface.

A second way of measuring column depth is to express it as the thickness that a layer of pure ozone would have at 1 atm pressure. One *atmosphere-centimeter* (1 atm-

FIGURE 3 Ozone vertical profile measured in number density (molecules per cubic centimeter) by ozonesonde (solid curve; data from World Ozone Data Center) and by satellite instrument at sunset over Wallops Island, Virginia.

cm) is equal to 2.687×10^{19} molecules/cm^2. Thus, a typical midlatitude ozone profile would have a column depth of about 0.3 atm-cm. Physically, this means that the ozone in Earth's atmosphere is equivalent to a 0.3-cm-thick layer of pure ozone at the surface. The small magnitude of this number gives a preliminary indication of why the ozone layer is so fragile.

The unit atmospheric chemists use to measure ozone column depth is called the **Dobson unit** (DU). One Dobson unit is equivalent to a layer of pure ozone 0.001 cm thick at 1 atm pressure. Because 1 atm-cm is equal to 1000 DU, a typical midlatitude ozone column depth is about 300 DU. The Dobson unit is named after Gordon Dobson, an English physicist who in 1925 became the first person to measure ozone column depth accurately. The ground-based device that he developed has become known as a *Dobson spectrophotometer.* The instrument compares the different amounts of ozone absorption at two wavelengths of sunlight. By measuring the solar UV flux at both wavelengths and at two or more solar zenith angles, it is possible to calculate the ozone column depth directly.

FIGURE 4 The pathlength through the ozone layer depends on the solar zenith angle, θ (theta).

Spatial Distribution of Ozone

Satellite measurements represent a tremendous advance over ground-based measurements because satellites make it possible to determine ozone column depth at all points over the globe during all seasons of the year. The results from satellite measurements made during Northern Hemisphere summer and winter of 1999 are shown in Figure 5. Ozone column depths are typically highest at mid-to-high latitudes and lowest over the equator. But a low in ozone over Antarctica in December represents the remainder of the ozone hole that had formed earlier during Southern Hemisphere springtime.

The reason ozone is distributed in this manner is complex. As we shall soon see, the greatest production of ozone occurs in the tropics, where the solar UV flux is the highest. Both the mid-to-high latitude peak and the equatorial minimum in column depth are caused by stratospheric circulation: Ozone-rich air from the tropical upper stratosphere is transported poleward by north–south winds. The details of this stratospheric circulation are beyond the scope of our discussion. Figure 5 does explain, however, why it is easier to get sunburned in Florida (25–30° N) than in New York (about 43° N). Not only is the Sun higher in the sky at low latitudes than it is farther north, but the ozone column depth is also smaller than at higher latitudes. The combination of these two effects allows a much higher percentage of the incident UV photons to make it to the surface at low latitudes.

June 22, 1999

December 22, 1999

200   250   300   350   400   450   500
Total ozone (dobson units)

FIGURE 5 [See color section] Global ozone column depths measured by satellite during in June and December 1999. (*Source:* World Meteorological Organization, *Scientific Assessment of Ozone Depletion: 2006*, Geneva, Switzerland, 2006.)

Tropospheric Ozone

Not all of Earth's ozone is confined to the stratosphere. Roughly 10% is in the troposphere, where it plays a key role in tropospheric chemistry. Its most important function is to provide a source of oxidizing radicals (highly reactive molecules) that help cleanse the lower atmosphere of pollutants such as carbon monoxide (CO) and sulfur dioxide (SO_2). The radicals are produced when the ozone molecule is split by short-wavelength UV radiation. So, a certain amount of ozone in the troposphere helps keep our air fit to breathe.

Too much ozone at ground level, conversely, is a bad thing. Ozone in high concentrations is toxic to plants and irritates both our eyes and lungs. Indeed, ozone is a key component of the photochemical smog that forms over Los Angeles, Denver, and many other large cities. As with many other things in life, ozone has both a good side and a bad side. Ozone that is found in the stratosphere, however, is always good from our human perspective.

THE CHAPMAN MECHANISM

To understand why the ozone layer is susceptible to alteration by anthropogenic processes, we must examine the chemistry by which ozone is formed and destroyed. The first person to describe these processes was Sydney Chapman, an atmospheric chemist who published a ground-breaking paper on ozone photochemistry in 1930. The four chemical reactions that he proposed for a simplified (pure oxygen-nitrogen) atmosphere have become known as the **Chapman mechanism** (Table 2).

Production of Ozone

The first step in the Chapman mechanism is the splitting apart of molecular oxygen, O_2, by an ultraviolet photon to form two atomic oxygen (O) atoms. The splitting of a molecule by the absorption of light or by UV radiation is called **photolysis**, or **photodissociation**. UV radiation at wavelengths shorter than 240 nm is required to photolyze O_2. One UV photon in this wavelength range will split apart one O_2 molecule. Here is where the particulate behavior of light, becomes evident. Two visible-light photons with the same combined energy as one UV photon will not be able to split O_2, because photolysis reactions are discrete events.

Once it has formed in the atmosphere, an atomic oxygen atom reacts quickly with another O_2 molecule to form ozone (reaction 2 of the Chapman mechanism). This process cannot occur in isolation, however, because the colliding molecules have too much energy to stick together unless some third molecule, represented by M, is available to carry it away. Molecule M can be N_2, O_2, ^{40}Ar, or any of the other molecules in Earth's atmosphere.

The situation is analogous to a billiards shot (Figure 6). If you shoot at a single, isolated ball (Figure 6a), chances are that the cue ball and target ball will roll away in different directions. At best, if you hit the target ball

TABLE 2 The Chapman Mechanism of Ozone Production and Destruction

Reaction*

1) $O_2 + UV\ photon \rightarrow O + O$ ⎫
2) $O + O_2 + M \rightarrow O_3 + M$ ⎬ production

3) $O_3 + photon \rightarrow O_2 + O$ ⎫ destruction
4) $O + O_3 \rightarrow 2\ O_2$ ⎭

Overall reaction: $3\ O_2 \xrightarrow{\text{sunlight}} 2\ O_3$

*The symbol M represents a third molecule necessary to carry off the excess energy of the collision between an O atom and an O_2 molecule.

straight on with the proper amount of backspin, the cue ball will remain motionless after contact, while the target ball will roll in the forward direction. If you place a third ball in contact with the target ball, however, and hit the pair dead on, the third ball will roll away and the cue ball and the target ball will remain together (Figure 6b). This, essentially, is what happens in the atmosphere when an ozone molecule is formed by the collision of an O atom with an O_2 molecule.

Destruction of Ozone

Once formed, an ozone molecule can be photolyzed by the absorption of another photon (reaction 3 of the Chapman mechanism). Photolysis reverses the process that occurred in reaction 2. Unlike O_2, O_3 can be split by radiation in the visible-light range. Because many more visible photons than UV photons are available, O_3 is photolyzed much

(a)

(b)

FIGURE 6 The ozone formation reaction (Chapman reaction 2) is analogous to hitting a billiards shot. (a) Hitting a target ball with the cue ball will result in the movement of both in different directions. (b) A third ball is required to allow the cue ball and the target ball to stick together.

faster than O_2. Furthermore, O_3 can be photolyzed all the way down to Earth's surface, whereas O_2 can be photolyzed only above about 20 km. All of the short-wavelength UV radiation required to split O_2 is absorbed above this height. That is why the ozone layer is located in the stratosphere and not near Earth's surface.

The fourth reaction in the Chapman mechanism is the reaction of an O atom and an O_3 molecule to yield two O_2 molecules. This is a slow reaction, as measured in the laboratory, but as we will see, it is the key to understanding ozone photochemistry. The reason is that when ozone reacts with atomic oxygen (reaction 4), the ozone is destroyed permanently, whereas when ozone is photolyzed (reaction 3), the resulting O atom is free to combine with another O_2 molecule, reforming O_3.

Odd Oxygen

We can express the difference in reactions 3 and 4 of the Chapman mechanism more precisely by defining a quantity called **odd oxygen,** or O_x. As its name implies, odd oxygen includes all pure, oxygen-containing atoms or molecules that have an odd number of oxygen atoms. Thus, the concentration of odd oxygen, denoted by $[O_x]$, is equal to the sum of the concentrations of atomic oxygen and ozone: $[O_x] = [O] + [O_3]$. Ordinary molecular oxygen, O_2, contains an even number of oxygen atoms; it is not counted as O_x.

With the concept of odd oxygen, we can analyze the Chapman mechanism at a deeper level. Table 3 shows the change in odd oxygen for each of the four reactions. Reaction 1 produces two O atoms from one O_2 molecule, so the change in O_x is +2. Reactions 2 and 3 merely interconvert two forms of odd oxygen, O and O_3, so the change in O_x is 0 for each reaction. Reaction 4 destroys both an O atom and an O_3 molecule, so the change in O_x is -2.

The significance is the following: The two slow reactions, 1 and 4, are the most important, because they control the abundance of odd oxygen. The two fast reactions, 2 and 3, determine the ratio of the O abundance to the O_3 abundance, but they have no direct effect on the concentration of odd oxygen. As we will see in the next section, it is the destruction of odd oxygen that really matters in ozone photochemistry.

TABLE 3 The Chapman Mechanism and Odd Oxygen

Reaction*		Rate	ΔO_x
1) O_2 + UV photon $\rightarrow$ O + O	} production	Slow	+2
2) $O + O_2 + M \rightarrow O_3 + M$		Fast	0
3) O_3 + photon $\rightarrow O_2 + O$	} destruction	Fast	0
4) $O + O_3 \rightarrow 2 O_2$		Slow	-2

*The symbol *M* represents a third molecule necessary to carry off the excess energy of the collision between an O atom and an O_2 molecule.

CATALYTIC CYCLES OF NITROGEN, CHLORINE, AND BROMINE

The Chapman mechanism provides the basis for understanding ozone chemistry, but it does not by itself provide an accurate description of Earth's stratosphere. When the Chapman mechanism is included in a computer model of the stratosphere, the model predicts about 30% more ozone than is actually present. Other processes must be destroying ozone as well or, equivalently, destroying odd oxygen.

The shortcoming of the Chapman mechanism is that it ignores the effects of atmospheric trace constituents such as nitrous oxide (N_2O), water vapor, and freons. These trace gases can be photolyzed, producing highly reactive radicals that keep ozone abundances lower than they would otherwise be.

The Nitrogen Catalytic Cycle

One such radical is nitric oxide, NO. NO produced by lightning discharges constitutes a natural source of fixed nitrogen in the oceans. Lightning does not occur in the stratosphere, but NO can be produced from nitrous oxide, N_2O (as we will see in the next section). Nitric oxide is one of several radicals that can facilitate the destruction of ozone. The destruction process consists of the following two reactions:

$NO + O_3 \frown NO_2 + O_2$		**fast**
$NO_2 + O \frown NO + O_2$		**fast**
Net: $\quad O_3 + O \frown 2 O_2$		**fast**

In the first reaction, nitric oxide reacts with ozone, forming nitrogen dioxide (NO_2) and molecular oxygen. Nitrogen dioxide is a brownish gas that is a major component of photochemical smog. It is visible in the "brown cloud" that hangs over Denver and many other large cities on weekdays. In the second reaction, nitrogen dioxide reacts with atomic oxygen, reforming nitric oxide and producing a second O_2 molecule.

We can determine the net effect of the two reactions by adding the reactions together and cancelling out atoms or molecules that occur on both sides of the reaction arrows. When we do this, we find that the net reaction is exactly the same as step 4 in the Chapman mechanism. Thus, this reaction results in the destruction not just of ozone but of odd oxygen as well.

This destruction process is an example of a **catalytic cycle**, a set of chemical reactions facilitated by the presence of a catalyst. A **catalyst** is a substance that increases the rate of a chemical reaction but is itself unchanged by the reaction. In the nitrogen catalytic cycle, the catalyst is the NO molecule. The NO molecule is destroyed in the first step of the cycle, but it is reformed in the second step and, hence, is free to react again. In the lower stratosphere, one NO molecule can destroy hundreds or thousands of O_3 molecules. Furthermore, both steps in the cycle are fast reactions, as measured by laboratory experiments. As a catalyzed reaction should be, the net reaction is therefore also fast in comparison with the direct reaction between O_3 and O.

The Chlorine Catalytic Cycle

Similar ozone-destroying catalytic cycles can be created by other radicals. One very important cycle involves atomic chlorine, Cl:

$$Cl + O_3 \curvearrowright ClO + O_2 \qquad \textbf{very fast}$$
$$ClO + O \curvearrowright Cl + O_2 \qquad \textbf{very fast}$$

Net: $\quad O_3 + O \curvearrowright 2\,O_2 \qquad \textbf{very fast}$

In the first step of this cycle, atomic chlorine reacts with ozone, forming chlorine monoxide (ClO) and O_2. The chlorine monoxide then reacts with atomic oxygen, forming Cl and another O_2. This cycle is analogous to the nitrogen catalytic cycle, with NO replaced by Cl and NO_2 by ClO. The individual reactions in the chlorine catalytic cycle are faster than those in the nitrogen cycle. Hence, this cycle is even more effective at destroying ozone. Or, to look at it in another way, less chlorine is needed than nitric oxide before the loss rate of ozone becomes significant.

Other Important Catalytic Cycles

Nitrogen and chlorine compounds are not the only compounds that affect stratospheric ozone. Ozone can also be destroyed by catalytic cycles involving *bromine (Br) radicals* and **hydroxyl (OH) radicals**. Bromine radicals have both natural and anthropogenic sources (as we will see next), but hydroxyl radicals are entirely natural. Thus, the photochemistry of even the unperturbed stratosphere is, in reality, quite complex. Elaborate computer models are needed to simulate all of the possible catalytic cycles that affect the ozone concentration.

SOURCES AND SINKS OF OZONE-DEPLETING COMPOUNDS

The Odd Nitrogen Cycle

The NO and NO_2 that participate in the nitrogen catalytic cycle are referred to as **odd nitrogen** (NO_x) compounds, which contain an odd number of nitrogen atoms to distinguish them from N_2. Odd nitrogen is similar in concept to the *fixed nitrogen*. The first term is used by atmospheric chemists, the second by biologists. In both cases, the important characteristic of the molecules is that the strong bond between the two nitrogen atoms in N_2 has been split. Hence, odd nitrogen molecules are much more reactive than is N_2.

Stratospheric odd nitrogen derives primarily from nitrous oxide, N_2O. The reaction that produces NO is

$$N_2O + O^* \rightarrow 2\,NO$$

Here, O^* is an electronically excited atomic oxygen atom produced by the UV photolysis of ozone. It is much more reactive than normal, ground-state, atomic oxygen. (Normal O atoms are incapable of reacting with N_2O.) The N_2O itself comes from Earth's surface, where it is produced by microbial

FIGURE 7 The atmospheric odd nitrogen cycle.

activity in soils and in the ocean (Figure 7). This activity is enhanced in places by the addition of nitrate fertilizers to the soil. Much of the nitrate in such fertilizers is taken up by growing plants. However, a substantial fraction undergoes bacterial denitrification and is subsequently released as either N_2 or N_2O.

The nitrous oxide makes its way to the stratosphere, where some of it reacts to form NO. The rest is photolyzed back to N_2 and O. The NO so produced participates in the ozone-destroying nitrogen catalytic cycle, forming NO_2 in the process. Every once in awhile, however, the resulting NO_2 molecule, instead of reacting with atomic oxygen, encounters a hydroxyl radical instead. The hydroxyl radical combines with the NO_2 molecule, producing nitric acid, HNO_3:

$$NO_2 + OH + M \rightarrow HNO_3 + M$$

The *M* in this reaction is a third molecule that carries off the excess energy of the collision. Nitric acid then diffuses down into the troposphere, where it dissolves in cloud droplets and is removed by precipitation. The nitric acid makes the rain slightly more acidic, but the amount of acid formed is so small that it poses no environmental problem. Acid rain itself is a problem in some areas, but it is caused by nitric and sulfuric acids formed within the troposphere.

Although N_2O is currently the largest source of stratospheric odd nitrogen, most of the concern about these compounds stems from potential increases in their abundance caused by high-flying, *supersonic transport* airplanes, or SSTs. Jet airplanes produce nitric oxide during the process of combustion. The reaction is similar to the production of NO by lightning. In each case, the high temperatures that are generated cause N_2 and O_2 to react with each other to form two NO molecules. Conventional jets fly in the upper troposphere and, hence, are not a threat to the ozone layer. The SSTs, however, inject nitric oxide and other exhaust products directly into the stratosphere. The French and British had been flying an SST called the *Concorde* since 1977, mostly on trans-Atlantic flights. In the face of declining revenues and one fatal accident, the Concorde was taken out of service in late 2003. Other governments, however, including the United States, may consider developing this type of aircraft. Because of the possible impact on ozone, careful environmental impact studies should be performed before large fleets of SSTs are built and flown.

The Chlorine Cycle

The attention of most stratospheric chemists is currently on chlorine. Chlorine is introduced into the stratosphere by several different gases produced at Earth's surface. The chlorine-containing gases that occur naturally are methyl chloride (CH_3Cl) and hydrogen chloride (HCl). Methyl chloride is produced in large quantities by marine plankton. Most of the methyl chloride released at the surface reacts in the troposphere, however. The amount that makes its way up to the stratosphere is enough to produce a stratospheric chlorine concentration of only about 0.6 ppb. By comparison, the current stratospheric chlorine concentration is approximately 3.3 ppb. So, most of this chlorine must derive from other sources.

Hydrogen chloride has received a great deal of attention because it is released in large quantities during volcanic eruptions. Particularly violent eruptions inject gases directly into the stratosphere. This fact has led some skeptics to suggest that most stratospheric chlorine derives from volcanoes and that we need not worry about anthropogenic sources. However, detailed studies of the El Chichón eruption in Mexico in 1982 and of the Mt. Pinatubo eruption in the Philippines in 1991 have led to the conclusion that very little of the HCl released in such events reaches the stratosphere. Most of the emitted HCl dissolves in water droplets that condense out of the volcanic plume. It is removed when these droplets fall out as rain.

Hydrogen chloride is also emitted by less violent volcanic eruptions and by the evaporation of sea spray. Seawater contains chloride ion, Cl^-, which forms HCl when the water evaporates. However, the HCl from these sources typically does not reach the stratosphere, because it, too, is removed by precipitation before it can leave the troposphere. The same is true of the chlorine released from swimming pools. This chlorine comes off the water surface as molecular chlorine, Cl_2, but is quickly converted to HCl by photochemical reactions in the lower troposphere. Hence, despite what you may hear on "talk radio," nearly all of it is removed from the atmosphere before it can damage the ozone layer.

The largest sources of stratospheric chlorine today are *chlorofluorocarbons* (CFCs), or *freons,* which are anthropogenic compounds. The two most common of these are freon-11 (CCl_3F) and freon-12 (CCl_2F_2). These compounds are also known as F-11 and F-12, respectively. Their atmospheric concentrations have increased by about a factor of 2 since first measured in 1977 (Figures 8a and 8b). We mentioned these gases because they contribute to Earth's greenhouse effect. Freon-11 has been used as a propellant in spray cans and as a blowing agent for producing foams (e.g., Styrofoam). It is also used to clean semiconductor chips for computers and other electronic devices. Freon-12 is used as a refrigerant and until 1990 was the working fluid in most car air conditioners. However, the uses of freons are changing rapidly. Freon-11 has been banned from use in spray cans in the United States since 1978. Freon-12 has already been replaced by more ozone-friendly compounds in all new cars. This decrease in freon usage caused the atmospheric growth rates of these compounds to decrease substantially in the 1990s. Indeed, freon-11 concentrations peaked in 1993 and have begun a slow decline (see Figure 8b). Freon-12 concentrations appear to have leveled off by 2005 and may actually be starting to decline.

Also shown in Figures 8d and 8e are the abundances of two chlorocarbons, carbon tetrachloride (CCl_4) and methyl chloroform (CH_3CCl_3). Carbon tetrachloride is used in dry cleaning and methyl chloroform is used as a solvent in various manufacturing processes. These gases are also regulated under the Montreal Protocol (discussed later in the chapter) and, as one can see, their concentrations have decreased dramatically since about 1991. These chlorocarbons have shorter atmospheric lifetimes than their cousins, the chlorofluorocarbons; consequently, they have responded more quickly to decreases in their emission rates.

When freons were first introduced in the 1930s, they were considered to be wonder chemicals. Not only did they have useful thermodynamic properties, but also they were inert and nontoxic to humans. In contrast, early refrigerants such as ammonia and sulfur dioxide could be quite dangerous if they leaked. It is this very property of being inert, however, that makes freons dangerous to the ozone layer (Figure 9). Freons do not react in either the troposphere or the lower stratosphere. Hence, freon gases released at the surface diffuse all the way to the upper stratosphere (above 40-km altitude). Once there, they are photolyzed by short-wavelength UV radiation, which breaks the molecules apart and releases their chlorine as atomic Cl. The Cl then proceeds to destroy ozone by way of the chlorine catalytic cycle.

Skeptics of the prospect that ozone depletion is anthropogenic occasionally suggest that freon gases, being heavier than air, should tend to stay in the lower atmosphere rather than diffusing upward to the stratosphere. (The molecular weight of freon-11, for example, is 136, whereas that of air is only about 29.) This idea, however, is based on a misconception about how the atmosphere mixes. In actuality, winds and eddies cause the atmosphere to be well mixed up to an altitude of about 100 km. Only above that height do heavier gases begin to separate from lighter ones. So, freons are able to deliver ozone-destroying chlorine atoms to the stratosphere despite their high molecular weights.

As in the case of the odd nitrogen cycle, the chlorine cycle in the stratosphere is eventually broken. In this case, Cl reacts with methane (or with H_2), forming hydrogen chloride:

$$Cl + CH_4 \rightarrow HCl + CH_3$$

Hydrogen chloride, like nitric acid, is relatively unreactive and diffuses downward into the troposphere, where it is

FIGURE 8 Atmospheric concentrations of (a) freon-12, (b) freon-11, (c) CFC-113, (d) carbon tetrachloride, and (e) methyl chloroform since 1977. (*Source:* World Meteorological Organization, *Scientific Assessment of Ozone Depletion: 2006*, Geneva, Switzerland, 2006.)

FIGURE 9 The atmospheric chlorine cycle.

removed by precipitation. Dissolved in water, HCl is the very strong acid hydrochloric acid. However, the actual amount of hydrochloric acid formed is relatively small, so it has little effect on the acidity of rainwater.

The Bromine Cycle

Atmospheric bromine, like chlorine, has several different sources. Methyl bromide (CH_3Br) like methyl chloride, is produced naturally as a by-product of biological activity in the oceans. However, it is also used as a fumigating agent for soil pests, including termites. Some 15% of manufactured methyl bromide is used in California for agricultural fumigation. The other major source of atmospheric bromine involves artificial chemical compounds known as **halons**, which are used in certain types of fire extinguishers. The two most common of these are halon-1211 (CF_2ClBr) and halon-1301 (CF_3Br).

Some types of fire extinguishers use CO_2 instead of halons. Both gases are nonflammable and heavier than air, so they are relatively efficient at keeping oxygen away from a flame. Being heavier than air does make a difference in this case, because the gas released from a fire extinguisher does not have time to disperse before it reaches the flame.

The atmospheric bromine cycle is analogous to the chlorine cycle: Most of the methyl bromide reacts in the troposphere, whereas the halons diffuse up into the stratosphere. There, they are photolyzed by short-wavelength UV radiation, and bromine atoms are released. Bromine is removed by the formation and eventual rainout of hydrogen bromide, HBr.

THE ANTARCTIC OZONE HOLE

Science, like life, is full of surprises. Perhaps the biggest surprise for most atmospheric chemists was the discovery of the Antarctic ozone hole in 1985. Recall that the ozone hole was overlooked for 6 years in the *Nimbus-7* satellite measure-

ments because the observed column depths were considered too low to be real. Computer models also failed to predict its occurrence until long after it was observed. By taking a closer look at what causes the ozone hole, we can see why it caught atmospheric scientists off guard.

To begin, recall that the ozone hole occurs only during the month of October; it apparently did not occur at all prior to about 1976; and it is found primarily over Antarctica. A corresponding Arctic ozone hole has been seen in March of some years, but it is not nearly as pronounced as the Antarctic hole and is not seen at all in other years. So, perhaps we should not be surprised that the explanation of the ozone hole turns out to be rather complicated.

Homogeneous and Heterogeneous Reactions

The chemistry that we have touched on in the last few sections is reasonably well understood. The chemical reactions that we have discussed are all **homogeneous reactions**, that is, reactions between molecules that are in the gas phase. We can study gas-phase reactions in the laboratory if we keep the reacting molecules away from the walls of their container. In contrast, the chemistry that causes the ozone hole involves **heterogeneous reactions**, which are reactions that occur on solid surfaces, such as particles. These reactions are more difficult to study experimentally; consequently, much less is known about them.

The particles involved in the formation of the Antarctic ozone hole are collections of droplets called **polar stratospheric clouds (PSCs)**. They form over Antarctica and, occasionally, in the Arctic, as well (see Figure 10.) These clouds were first discovered by high-flying spy planes. Over most of the globe, clouds form only in the troposphere; the stratosphere is too dry for condensation to occur. However, in winter the polar stratosphere is so cold, especially over Antarctica (Figure 11), that certain trace atmospheric constituents can condense. The particles that form typically consist of a mixture of water and nitric acid. Although they are very tenuous by comparison with normal, tropospheric clouds, these PSCs alter the chemistry of the lower stratosphere in two fundamental ways: (1) by coupling between the odd nitrogen and chlorine cycles and (2) by providing surfaces on which heterogeneous reactions can occur, as we will see next.

Coupling between the Odd Nitrogen and Chlorine Cycles

Throughout most of the lower stratosphere, the nitrogen and chlorine cycles are coupled by way of the reaction

$$ClO + NO_2 + M \rightarrow ClONO_2 + M$$

The product formed in this reaction, chlorine nitrate ($ClONO_2$), does not react directly with either ozone or atomic oxygen and can be converted back to ClO only with difficulty. Thus, it serves as a relatively inert storage reservoir for chlorine, keeping it out of the more reactive

A CLOSER LOOK

How the Link between Freons and Ozone Depletion was Discovered

The first step in establishing the link between freons and ozone depletion was made by James Lovelock, the same Lovelock who formulated the Gaia hypothesis. Long before he became known as a theorist, Lovelock established his scientific reputation by inventing a device called the *electron capture detector*. When mounted on an instrument called a gas chromatograph, this device can be used to measure the concentrations of extremely dilute atmospheric gases. Lovelock used his detector to measure the concentration of freon-11 and other chlorine-containing gases. He published his measurements in 1970.

By comparing his measured concentrations with estimates of freon emission rates, Lovelock was able to show that most of the freon-11 that had been produced up until that time was still present in the atmosphere. This meant that freon-11 must have a very long atmospheric lifetime. The lifetimes of freon-11 and freon-12 have since been determined to be about 60 years and 130 years, respectively. Ironically, Lovelock was not the least bit concerned about this finding, because freon gases were at that time considered to be totally harmless. Indeed, he wrote that "The presence of these compounds [CFCs] in the atmosphere constitutes no conceivable hazard." This sentence was added to ward off environmentalists, who were at that time quick to warn about the health effects of newly discovered chemicals.

Lovelock, though, was wrong on this last count for reasons that were entirely different from what he had in mind. Chemists had known since the 1930s that Cl and ClO were capable of destroying ozone. It did not take long after Lovelock's discovery for atmospheric scientists to put two and two together. The critical paper was published in 1974 by Sherwood Rowland and Mario Molina, two atmospheric chemists at the University of California at Irvine. Rowland and Molina pointed out that the long lifetimes of freon gases would allow them to diffuse up into the stratosphere, where the chlorine released by their decomposition could wreak havoc on the ozone layer. This idea, obvious in retrospect but quite novel at the time, caught on quickly in the scientific community and earned them a share of the Nobel Prize in Chemistry in 1995. (The prize was shared with Paul Crutzen, who developed the theoretical foundation for understanding ozone-destroying catalytic cycles.) More than 10 years passed and many pitched battles were fought, however, before it was finally accepted by the chemical industry. These battles have been referred to as the "ozone wars." We owe a debt of gratitude to all the scientists who participated in those wars and helped bring us to the understanding that we have today.

FIGURE 10 Photograph of an arctic polar stratospheric cloud.   (*Source:* NASA/Lamont Poole.)

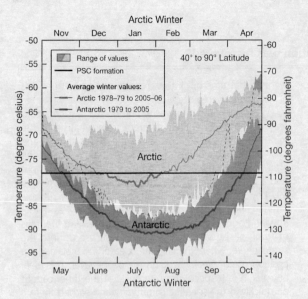

FIGURE 11 Minimum air temperatures in the polar lower stratosphere over the Arctic (top curve) and Antarctic (bottom curve). The solid line at −78°C shows the temperature at which polar stratospheric cloud particles can condense. (*Source:* World Meteorological Organization, *Scientific Assessment of Ozone Depletion: 2006*, Geneva, Switzerland, 2006.)

FIGURE 12 Schematic diagram of the Antarctic circumpolar vortex. (*Source:* Climate Prediction Center/NOAA.)

forms, Cl and ClO. Because they can directly catalyze ozone destruction, Cl and ClO, along with compounds that can be easily converted into them by photolysis, are collectively termed **reactive chlorine**.

Under normal conditions in the polar stratosphere, NO_2 is always sufficiently abundant to tie up a significant fraction of the available chlorine in the form of chlorine nitrate. In the wintertime Antarctic stratosphere, however, NO_2 concentrations become very low, because most of the odd nitrogen has been converted into HNO_3 and subsequently incorporated into cloud droplets as PSCs. This removal allows reactive chlorine concentrations to increase, because less chlorine is bound up as chlorine nitrate.

The PSC particles also help convert unreactive forms of chlorine into reactive chlorine by providing surfaces on which heterogeneous reactions can occur. For example, one reaction that is thought to be important is

$$ClONO_2 + HCl \rightarrow Cl_2 + HNO_3$$

Molecular chlorine, Cl_2, does not react directly with ozone itself but is readily photolyzed to atomic chlorine:

$$Cl_2 + photon \rightarrow Cl + Cl$$

Once formed, atomic chlorine can execute its destructive effect on ozone.

The Polar Vortex

We now have the chemistry we need to understand how the ozone hole forms. Some knowledge of stratospheric circulation is required, however, to complete the story.

The prevailing surface winds at polar latitudes blow from east to west. The opposite is true, however, in the wintertime stratosphere: the winds blow from west to east. When viewed from above the South Pole, this wintertime circulation pattern appears as a gigantic whirlpool called the **polar vortex** (Figure 12). The cold, dense air in the middle of the vortex is subsiding in much the same way as water going down a drain. The sinking air carries cloud particles along with it, permanently removing odd nitrogen from the stratosphere. The polar vortex also effectively isolates the Antarctic stratosphere from the rest of the globe. The air inside the vortex is rotating much faster than the air outside, making it difficult for air to pass through the vortex boundary. Some air does get through and replaces the air that is sinking in the center of the vortex, but the amount is small compared with normal rates of latitudinal mixing. Thus, the odd nitrogen removed from the polar stratosphere during winter is not replaced by odd nitrogen from lower latitudes. The same phenomenon also ensures that very little new ozone can be brought in once the ozone hole forms.

The full story of the ozone hole involves an intricate coupling of chemistry, atmospheric circulation, and the availability of sunlight. During the long Antarctic winter (May through September), the stratosphere becomes cold enough to allow PSCs to form. These PSCs deplete the polar stratosphere of odd nitrogen and help convert unreactive forms of chlorine ($ClONO_2$ and HCl) into more reactive forms, such as Cl_2. The reactive chlorine, however, remains bound to the surfaces of cloud particles until late September, when the Sun first peeks over the Antarctic horizon. The sunlight releases reactive chlorine from the particle surfaces, and the chlorine wreaks havoc with the ozone layer during October. The result is a massive hole in the ozone layer, as

October 4, 2001

100   200   300   400   500

Total ozone (dobson units)

FIGURE 13 [See color section] Satellite measurements showing the Antarctic "ozone hole." Minimum values of total ozone inside the ozone hole are close to 100 Dobson units compared with normal springtime values of about 200 DU. (*Source:* World Meteorological Organization, *Scientific Assessment of Ozone Depletion: 2006*, Geneva, Switzerland, 2006.)

shown vividly in Figure 13. Near the end of the month, the polar vortex breaks down, allowing fresh ozone and odd nitrogen to be brought in from lower latitudes; the ozone hole then disappears until the following October.

Why does this process not occur to the same extent over the Arctic during Northern Hemisphere spring? The answer seems to lie in the stratospheric circulation. As a result of geography, the Arctic polar vortex is less fully developed than the Antarctic vortex and breaks up earlier in the spring. The Southern Hemisphere contains a roughly symmetric continent (Antarctica) surrounded by a large ocean. The Northern Hemisphere contains a mixture of land and ocean, and it also has large, north–south mountain ranges, such as the Rocky Mountains in North America. The mountains disrupt the east–west tropospheric circulation and create atmospheric waves that propagate up to the stratosphere and deposit energy there. This energy warms the stratosphere and disrupts the

smooth, circumpolar flow. If an Arctic ozone hole were to occur, it would form during April. By this time of year, however, the Arctic polar vortex has typically already disappeared. Thus, the unique combination of conditions that occur in the Southern Hemisphere is not duplicated in the north.

Is the ozone hole starting to go away now that we have started to reduce freon emissions? Not yet! These days, the size and the intensity of the ozone depletion in the hole are monitored carefully each year from satellites (Figure 14). The ozone hole areas are contrasted to the area of various continents in the upper panel of the figure. The lower panel shows the minimum ozone column depth versus time. The minimum ozone column depth gradually increased from 1980 until about 1994. It remained roughly constant during the late 1990s, but has been quite variable since then. In 2002, and to a lesser extent in 2004, the hole was unusually small and the amount of ozone depletion

FIGURE 14 Change in size (a) and minimum ozone amount (b) of the Antarctic ozone hole since 1980. Values in (a) are for the area enclosed by the 220-DU total ozone contour. (*Source:* World Meteorological Organization, *Scientific Assessment of Ozone Depletion: 2006*, Geneva, Switzerland, 2006.)

was much lower. The 2007 ozone hole was also somewhat smaller than usual, but not as small as the 2004 hole. But it is not clear that this is a positive trend, because the 2005 hole was big and deep, and the 2006 hole was one of the biggest ever at 27 million square kilometers. Most of the year-to-year variability is thought to be a consequence of changes in atmospheric circulation, rather than of changes in atmospheric chlorine concentrations. Predictions are that the ozone hole will indeed eventually recover. However, the recovery is not expected to be complete until sometime in the latter half of this century.

EVIDENCE OF MIDLATITUDE OZONE DEPLETION

The fact that we do not observe an ozone hole over the Arctic does not mean that residents of the Northern Hemisphere should be complacent about ozone depletion. Indeed, there is considerable evidence that ozone decreased slowly at midlatitudes in both hemispheres throughout much of the 1990s. However, the good news is that this decline appears to have slowed or stopped entirely in recent years. Average midlatitude ozone column depths for the 2002–2005 period were approximately 3% below 1980 values in the Northern Hemisphere and 6% below those values in the Southern Hemisphere, essentially the same as in the 1998–2001 time period.

Sources of Natural Variability in Ozone

Detecting trends in ozone column depths at low- and midlatitudes is difficult because the rates of change are not nearly as large as those seen over Antarctica. Furthermore, before we can identify any long-term trends, we must first correct for natural variability. Figure 15, which shows satellite measurements of ozone column depth over Hohenpeissenberg, Germany, illustrates the problem. The first signal that we see in the data is a strong annual cycle of ±75 Dobson units. For reasons that are related to stratospheric circulation patterns, ozone is most abundant during the spring and least abundant during the fall. But there are other, more subtle oscillations in the data as well. These oscillations include the solar cycle—the 11-year cycle in sunspot number—and the *quasi-biennial oscillation,* or QBO, which is a 27-month cycle in the direction of winds in the equatorial lower stratosphere.

The sunspot cycle affects ozone because the amount of ultraviolet radiation emitted by the Sun varies with sunspot activity. When sunspots are abundant (termed **solar maximum**), as they were in 2002, the Sun gives off more UV energy. The added UV radiation comes not from the spots themselves but from bright areas called *plages* surrounding the spots.

FIGURE 15 Weekly averaged satellite data on ozone column depth over Hohenpeissenberg, Germany. A strong annual cycle is observed in the data. (*Source:* World Meteorological Organization, 1994.)

Higher UV fluxes cause more O_2 to be photolyzed, resulting in increased production of ozone. At times of low sunspot activity (**solar minimum**), as in 1986 and 1997, the solar UV flux is low and ozone production decreases.

The effect of the solar cycle on stratospheric ozone is illustrated in Figure 16. The solid curve shows the flux of 10.7-cm radio emission from the Sun, which happens to be well correlated with the solar UV flux. The dashed curve shows the percentage change in average ozone column depth (40° N to 40° S) after the seasonal cycle, QBO, and longer-term trend have been removed. Ozone column depth is about 2–3% higher during solar maximum than during solar minimum. As this variation is of the same magnitude as the trend in the satellite data, it, too, must be removed before the trend can be determined.

Long-Term Trends in Ozone

By removing all the known sources of natural variability from the satellite data, it is possible to identify long-term trends in ozone column depths over the entire globe. The data, which are shown in the top panel of Figure 17, indicate that global average ozone column depths decreased steadily from 1975 until about 1994. The decrease worsened during the last three of these years when volcanic aerosols from the Mt. Pinatubo eruption in 1991 were present in the stratosphere. Since 1994, however, ozone has recovered slightly. At present, global ozone is about 4% below the 1964–1980 average.

The bottom panel in Figure 17 compares ozone changes between 1980 and 2004 for different latitudes. The largest decreases have occurred at the highest latitudes in both hemispheres because of the large winter–spring depletion in the polar regions. The losses in the Southern Hemisphere are greater than those in the Northern Hemisphere because of the Antarctic ozone hole. Long-term changes in the tropics are much smaller because reactive halogen gases are less abundant in the tropical lower stratosphere.

We conclude that the long-term prognosis for the ozone layer looks promising. However, this does not mean that we should be complacent! Below, we describe why progress is being made on this environmental problem and

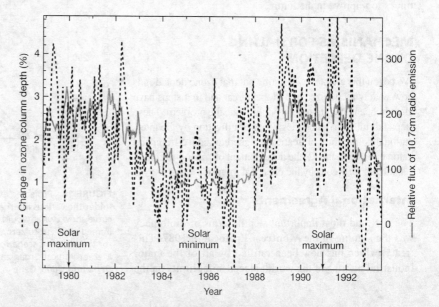

FIGURE 16 Response of average ozone column depth (40° N to 40° S) to the solar cycle after the seasonal cycle, quasi-biennial oscillation, and long-term trend have been removed. (*Source:* World Meteorological Organization, *Scientific Assessment of Ozone Depletion: 1994.*)

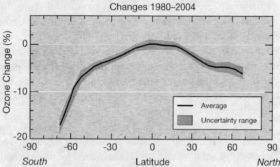

FIGURE 17 Change in ozone column depth over the past few decades, as measured from satellites. (a) The change in global average column depth relative to the 1964–1980 average. (b) The difference between the 2004 and 1980 values as a function of latitude. (*Source:* World Meteorological Organization, *Scientific Assessment of Ozone Depletion: 2006*, Geneva, Switzerland, 2006.)

what steps are being taken to ensure that the situation continues to improve in the future.

MECHANISMS FOR HALTING OZONE DEPLETION

We began this chapter by pointing out that ozone depletion is now widely recognized as a global threat and that steps have already been taken to reduce or eliminate the problem. These steps fall into two categories: (1) the ratification by the international community of treaties designed to reduce freon and halon emissions and (2) the development of "ozone-friendly" substitutes for freons by the chemical industry.

International Agreements

The first and most important step in terms of diplomacy was the signing of the **Montreal Protocol** in 1987. This treaty, which has now been ratified by all of the major industrial nations of the world, placed strict limits on the

amount of freons and halons that could be released into the atmosphere by any country. The original treaty was agreed on prior to the crucial measurement that linked the Antarctic ozone hole to anthropogenic chlorine. That discovery, however, solidified international opinion on the issue and has led to several subsequent revisions of the treaty, which ultimately placed even stricter limits on freon emissions. The expected effect of these treaties up to A.D. 2075 is shown in Figure 18. Figure 18a shows that in the absence of any kind of international agreement ("No protocol"), stratospheric chlorine levels would have been expected to have risen quite rapidly over the next few decades. Under such

FIGURE 18 Projected atmospheric chlorine concentrations under the various international agreements. (a) The dashed curve shows what would happen if chlorine emissions were immediately cut to zero. (b) Estimated increase in skin cancer for the different scenarios shown above. (*Source:* World Meteorological Organization, *Scientific Assessment of Ozone Depletion: 2006*, Geneva, Switzerland, 2006.)

circumstances, computer models predict that ozone column depths could decrease precipitously, and skin cancer cases could increase correspondingly (Figure 18b). The Montreal Protocol alone would have slowed this process, but stratospheric chlorine concentrations would still have continued to rise. With the most recent international treaty (the Beijing 1999 Accord) in place, the outlook is much improved. As shown earlier (Figure 8), tropospheric concentrations of most anthropogenic chlorine-containing gases peaked in 1994 or earlier and are beginning a slow decline. Gas concentrations in the stratosphere lag those in the troposphere by 3 to 5 years, so stratospheric chlorine and bromine abundances will probably continue to increase until about the turn of the century. By A.D. 2060, stratospheric chlorine should be back down to about 2 ppb, its value in the late 1970s when the Antarctic ozone hole first appeared. Hopefully, the hole will disappear at that time. Within the following century, stratospheric chlorine should reach the background level of 0.6 ppb that results from naturally produced methyl chloride.

Freon Substitutes

Can the world make do without conventional freon gases? The answer appears to be yes. Substitutes for freons are already being developed by major chemical companies. At least two different strategies are being employed. One of these is to replace one of the chlorine or fluorine atoms with a hydrogen atom to make compounds referred to as *HCFCs*. An example is the compound HCFC-22 ($CHFCl_2$), which can be used as a substitute for freon-12. Attaching a hydrogen atom to a CFC makes the CFC susceptible to chemical attack by the hydroxyl radical, OH (Figure 19). Recall from earlier in the chapter that radicals play an important role in removing pollutants from the atmosphere. Because of its increased reactivity, an HCFC-22 molecule released at the surface has only a 5% probability of reaching the stratosphere, compared with a virtually 100% probability for freon-11 or freon-12. The other 95% of the HCFC-22 is destroyed in the troposphere, where it can do no harm to ozone. So, this compound is 20 times more ozone-friendly than normal freon gases.

A potential downside of this strategy is that the more reactive HCFCs may pose direct health threats. Hence, thorough testing of the biological effects of these

compounds is required. On the bright side, HCFC-22 has a short lifetime (about 15 years), which means that it contributes far less greenhouse-enhanced warming than does a long-lived gas such as freon-12. Thus, replacing CFCs with HCFCs can help slow global warming while it reduces the destruction rate of stratospheric ozone.

A second strategy is to eliminate chlorine from the CFC molecule, creating an HFC compound. An example of this type is the compound HFC-134a (CF_3CH_2F), which has replaced freon-12 as a refrigerant in most new cars. Because HFCs contain no chlorine, they pose no significant threat to ozone. (The reason is somewhat paradoxical: Fluorine radicals are *more* reactive than Cl radicals. Indeed, they are so reactive that they combine directly with water vapor to form hydrofluoric acid, HF. Like HCl, HF is a tightly bound molecule that drifts down to the troposphere, where it is removed by rainout. So, fluorine radicals are removed from the stratosphere before they do much damage to ozone.) Also, HFC-134a is relatively short-lived (about a 16-year lifetime), so it is a good choice in terms of climate as well. That said, the abundances of this gas and other freon substitutes are currently increasing at a rapid rate (Figure 20), and the European Union plans to ban its use beginning in 2011. (HFO-1234yf ($CF_3CF{=}CH_2$) is the suggested replacement.) Clearly, it would be wise to monitor the concentrations of these gases carefully to make sure that we do not create a new environmental problem while eliminating an old one.

Lessons Learned from the Ozone Experience

The manner in which the international community and the chemical industry have responded to the threat of ozone depletion shows that we *can* deal successfully with global environmental problems. This success, however, did not come without a fight. In the 1970s, when the danger posed by freons had just been discovered, the chemical industry vigorously opposed the idea that their products might be harmful. A concerted effort by atmospheric scientists associated with universities and national laboratories caused the industry to look more closely at the problem. Eventually, companies such as DuPont hired their own atmospheric chemists and confirmed for themselves that action needed to be taken. Now, DuPont is leading the chemical industry in the design and marketing of freon substitutes.

It remains to be seen whether energy companies and consumers will follow a similar path with regard to global warming. That problem, unfortunately, is much more difficult to correct. Fossil fuels are a much bigger part of the global economy than are freons, and adequate substitutes might be harder to develop or be prohibitively expensive. Hopefully, though, the precedent that has been set on ozone depletion will eventually help guide us to a solution to the global warming problem.

FIGURE 19 Hydroxyl (OH) radicals can react with hydrogen atoms in HCFCs to form unstable radicals plus water.

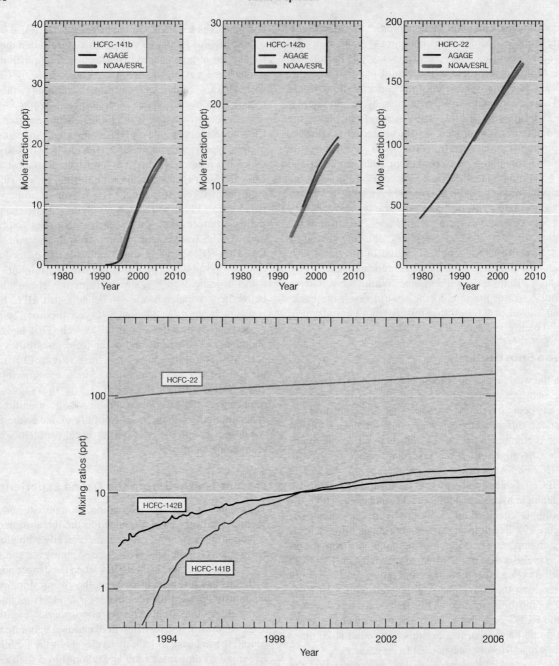

FIGURE 20   Abundances of various freon replacements: (a) HCFC-141b, (b) HCFC-142b, (c) HCFC-22.   (*Source:* World Meteorological Organization, *Scientific Assessment of Ozone Depletion: 2006*, Geneva, Switzerland, 2006.)

Chapter Summary

1. Solar ultraviolet radiation between 200 and 320 nm poses significant dangers to humans and other organisms if not effectively blocked by stratospheric ozone. The wavelength region of greatest concern is the UVB region, between 290 and 320 nm, where the solar flux is relatively high and the ozone absorption coefficient is relatively low.

2. The flux of solar UV radiation that reaches Earth's surface depends on the ozone column depth, which is a measure of the total amount of ozone overhead. The column depth varies regionally; it is generally highest near the poles and lowest near the equator. This distribution, combined with the fact that the Sun is generally higher in the sky near the equator, produces much

higher ground-level UV fluxes in the tropics than at high latitudes.

3. Ozone chemistry in a pure oxygen–nitrogen atmosphere can be described by a set of four reactions known as the Chapman mechanism.

   a. The first and last of the Chapman reactions affect the abundance of odd oxygen (O_3 and O); the middle two reactions cause the different forms of odd oxygen to interconvert.

   b. In the real atmosphere, catalytic cycles involving nitrogen, chlorine, and bromine provide alternative, faster ways of destroying odd oxygen. Both chlorine and bromine have large anthropogenic sources (freons and halons, respectively) that are considered to be a threat to the ozone layer today.

4. The most striking evidence of ozone depletion comes from Antarctica, where an ozone hole forms each year during October.

   a. The ozone hole is apparently caused by a complex series of reactions that occur on the surfaces of polar stratospheric cloud particles. These same particles remove odd nitrogen from the polar stratosphere, breaking the coupling between the odd nitrogen and chlorine cycles and allowing free chlorine to wreak havoc on the ozone layer.

   b. The Arctic stratosphere behaves differently than the Antarctic stratosphere, because the wintertime polar vortex is not as well developed or long-lasting in the Arctic.

   c. Ozone has also been decreasing at a lesser rate at midlatitudes in both hemispheres. However, that decrease appears to have slowed or stopped within the last few years.

5. International agreements, namely the Montreal Protocol and various follow-on accords, have placed strict limits on future freon and halon emissions. If these accords are enforced and obeyed, stratospheric chlorine concentrations should decline to their natural levels during the course of the next century, and the ozone hole should disappear. It is important that we continue to recognize the wisdom of these agreements and the reasons why they were established.

Key Terms

absorption coefficient	halons	photodissociation
action spectrum	heterogeneous reaction	photolysis
catalyst	homogeneous reaction	polar stratospheric clouds (PSCs)
catalytic cycle	hydroxyl (OH) radical	polar vortex
Chapman mechanism	Montreal Protocol	reactive chlorine
column depth	number density	solar maximum
Dobson unit (DU)	odd nitrogen	solar minimum
dose rate	odd oxygen	solar zenith angle
erythemal action spectrum	ozonesondes	

Review Questions

1. What are the three categories of UV radiation? Which of these are considered to be biologically harmful?

2. What is ozone column depth? In what units is it measured?

3. What are the four chemical reactions that comprise the Chapman mechanism? Which ones affect odd oxygen?

4. What is a catalyst?

5. How do nitrogen and chlorine catalyze the destruction of ozone?

6. What role do polar stratospheric clouds play in the formation of the Antarctic ozone hole?

7. Why is a springtime ozone hole observed over the Antarctic but usually not over the Arctic?

8. What is the long-term trend in midlatitude ozone column depths? Can it be explained by the observed increase in stratospheric chlorine and bromine?

9. What strategies have been adopted for reducing or eliminating the use of freons?

Critical-Thinking Problems

1. a. According to Figure 5, the maximum ozone column depth occurs at high northern latitudes during late winter. The column depth there is 460 DU. How many molecules of ozone per square centimeter does this correspond to?

   b. The minimum ozone column depth, which occurs in the tropics, is 240 DU. How many ozone molecules are in a 1-cm^2 vertical column there?

   c. What was the approximate ozone column depth (in Dobson units) over Wallops Island, Virginia, at the time of the measurements shown in Figure 3? (*Hint:* Ozone column depth is ozone concentration [in molecules/cubic centimeter] multiplied by the height of the column. You may want to use a different average ozone concentration for the troposphere and the stratosphere.)

2. The absorption of solar ultraviolet radiation of a given wavelength l by atmospheric ozone follows Beer's Law:

$$\frac{F}{F_0} = \exp\left[-\frac{kN}{\cos\theta}\right],$$

where F = the UV flux at altitude z; F_0 = the UV flux at the top of the atmosphere; k = the absorption coefficient at wavelength l; N = the ozone column depth above height z; and θ = the solar zenith angle. (See Figure 4.)

The function $\exp(x)$ (or e^x on some calculators) is the exponential function, which also describes radioactive decay, population growth, and other interesting phenomena.

a. The wavelength region where changes in the solar UV flux have the most potential to do harm is around 290 nm, in the UVB range. The absorption coefficient of ozone at this wavelength is about 10 atm^{-1}-cm^{-1}. The average column depth of ozone from the ground up to the top of the atmosphere is about 0.3 atm-cm. By what factor is the incident solar UV flux at 290 nm attenuated today—that is, what is the current value of F/F$_0$ at ground level? Evaluate your answer for a solar zenith angle of 45°.

b. If the ozone column depth were to be reduced by 1% as a consequence of increasing concentrations of chlorofluorocarbons, what would be the resulting percentage of increase in the ground-level UV flux at 290 nm? What about for an ozone decrease of 10%? 50%? Assume a solar zenith angle of 45° in each case.

c. Suppose that we decided that we could tolerate a 10% increase in the UV flux at 290 nm for $\theta = 45°$, but no more. What would be the maximum percentage decrease in ozone that we could allow? (*Hint:* The inverse of the exponential function is called the natural logarithm, abbreviated as ln. If $y = \exp[x]$, then $x = \ln[y]$.)

3. New York City is at 43° N. Miami, Florida, is at 25° N. In March, when most colleges have their spring break and students go to Florida, the ozone column depth is about 280 DU over Miami and 350 DU over New York. Using the data from the previous problem, calculate the ground-level solar UV flux at 290 nm in Miami compared to that in New York at noon on March 21. Note that March 21 is the vernal equinox, so the Sun is directly over the equator. (*Hint:* It may help to draw a picture to help you visualize the geometry.)

Further Reading

General

Dotto, L., and H. Schiff. 1978. *The ozone war.* Garden City, NY: Doubleday.

Turco, R. P. 1997. *Earth under siege* (Ch. 13). New York: Oxford University Press.

Advanced

World Meteorological Organization. 2006. *Scientific assessment of ozone depletion: 2006.* Geneva, Switzerland. Available at http://www.wmo.ch/pages/prog/arep/gaw/ozone_2006/ozone_asst_report.html.

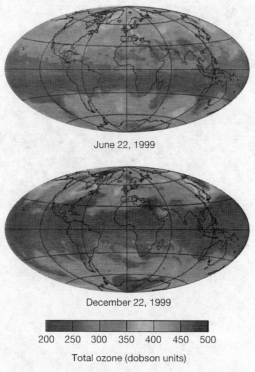

June 22, 1999

December 22, 1999

200   250   300   350   400   450   500

Total ozone (dobson units)

FIGURE 5   Global ozone column depths measured by satellite during in June and December 1999.   (*Source:* World Meteorological Organization, *Scientific Assessment of Ozone Depletion: 2006*, Geneva, Switzerland, 2006.)

October 4, 2001

100   200   300   400   500

Total ozone (dobson units)

FIGURE 13   Satellite measurements showing the Antarctic "ozone hole." Minimum values of total ozone inside the ozone hole are close to 100 Dobson units compared with normal springtime values of about 200 DU.   (*Source:* World Meteorological Organization, *Scientific Assessment of Ozone Depletion: 2006*, Geneva, Switzerland, 2006.)

Climate Stability on Earth and Earthlike Planets

Key Questions

- How will Earth's climate evolve in the distant future as the Sun continues to brighten?
- Is there anything we can do to change it?
- Why are Venus and Mars so different from Earth?

- What determines the width of the habitable zone around our Sun and other stars?
- What are the chances that life exists elsewhere in the universe, and can we detect it if it is there?

Chapter Overview

The Sun will continue to brighten in the future, as it has done throughout Earth's past. As Earth's climate warms, atmospheric CO_2 concentrations should decline in response to the negative feedback provided by the carbonate–silicate cycle. Eventually, this decline may pose a problem for life, because there will not be enough CO_2 in the atmosphere to support photosynthesis; thus, the life span of Earth's biota is limited, unless we manage to geoengineer a solution to our problems.

Although the CO_2–climate feedback may have stabilized Earth's climate over billions of years, it evidently did not operate on our neighboring planets, Venus and Mars. Venus is clearly outside the habitable zone around the Sun—that is, the region in which a planet can support liquid water at its surface. Mars appears to be outside the habitable zone as well, though perhaps as a result of the planet's small size, which prevents it from recycling CO_2 back into its atmosphere rather than its distance from the Sun. Habitable, Earthlike planets may exist around other nearby stars. Some of these planets may harbor life; of those, a few may harbor intelligent beings like ourselves. Space-based visible or infrared telescopes and ground-based radio telescopes may eventually tell us whether extraterrestrial life does indeed exist.

INTRODUCTION

A recurrent theme of ours has been the interaction between atmospheric CO_2 levels and climate. On long time scales, we have argued that these variables are connected by way of a strong negative feedback loop. A warmer climate increases the amount of precipitation, which, in turn, increases the rates at which silicate rocks are weathered and carbonate sediments are formed. As a result, the atmospheric CO_2 concentration drops, thereby decreasing the magnitude of the greenhouse effect and causing the climate to cool. The negative feedback produced by this mechanism was probably a major reason why Earth's climate has remained relatively stable for most of the past 3.5 billion years (the time during which we know that life has existed).

Climate, of course, is not absolutely stable. On shorter time scales, Earth's climate exhibits substantial fluctuations associated with glacial–interglacial cycles, and there do seem to have been relatively brief Snowball Earth episodes when climate stabilization has temporarily failed. But Earth has recovered from these episodes by way of the CO_2–climate feedback, and life has made it through essentially unscathed. The reason is that liquid water has always been present either at, or within a few meters of, the planet's surface. The presence of liquid water is the fundamental criterion for a habitable planet, because all known organisms require liquid water during at least part of their life cycle. And most advanced organisms, such as humans, require liquid water on a day-to-day basis.

Could life exist elsewhere in the universe? To answer this question, we need to determine the width of the liquid water *habitable zone* around the Sun and other stars. We know that within our own solar system only one planet, Earth, has liquid water at its surface. Venus is much too hot to have liquid water, and Mars is currently much too cold. Liquid water could be present on Mars several kilometers beneath its surface, where heat from Mars's interior could help keep temperatures above the freezing point. Jupiter's moon Europa may also have liquid water beneath its icy crust. In this case, the heat source is thought to be *tidal flexing* as Europa follows its slightly eccentric orbit around Jupiter. (Jupiter's gravity raises tides on Europa, just as the Moon raises tides on Earth. The same side of Europa always faces Jupiter, so these tides do not move across the surface as they do on Earth. However, because Europa's orbit is noncircular, it wobbles back and forth a little; this wobble causes heat to be released within Europa's crust.) But both of these environments are highly specialized. If life does exist in either place, it will only be detected by going there and drilling down beneath the planet's (or moon's) surface. Furthermore, the chances for finding anything larger than microbes on either Mars or Europa are extremely small. If we hope to find advanced life, we need to look for a planet not too different from Earth. There are no such other planets in our own solar system, but there may be around other stars. If we want to examine such planets remotely, which is all that seems feasible at the current time, we need to look for planets that have liquid water, and life, present at their surfaces.

What went wrong with Venus and Mars in our own solar system? Why were their climates not stabilized by the same silicate-weathering feedback that appears to have operated on Earth? In this chapter, we attempt to answer that question and to determine its implications for the possibility of life on planets around other stars. But first let us consider what the silicate–weathering feedback may mean to Earth's own climatic future.

CLIMATE EVOLUTION IN THE DISTANT FUTURE

The Sun has gotten brighter throughout its history as a result of the gradual conversion of hydrogen to helium. This process is ongoing, so the Sun is expected to continue to get brighter in the future. The Sun's luminosity is currently increasing by about 1% every 100 million years.

How long will Earth continue to be habitable? We know that the CO_2–weathering feedback must break down at some point. The Sun is currently a **main-sequence star**—that is, a normal, middle-aged star that shines by "burning" hydrogen. About 5 billion years from now, the Sun will reach the end of its main-sequence lifetime. Over the next few hundreds of millions of years, it will expand into a **red giant**, a large, reddish star that is intermediate in the post-main-sequence phase of its evolution. Its luminosity will increase by a factor of more than 1000, and its outer envelope will extend to somewhere between the orbits of Mercury and Venus. All life on Earth will, of course, have been fried to a crisp long before this point is reached. After that event, the Sun will contract and become a **white dwarf**, a small (Earth-sized), hot star that is at the final stage of evolution of a star such as our Sun. Earth itself will then become very cold, but this change will not matter to anyone because all life will have been extinguished during the prior, red-giant phase of the Sun's evolution.

In actuality, Earth's climate regulation system could begin to fail long before the Sun's red-giant stage is reached. Figure 1 shows the result of a computer simulation of Earth's climate over the next 1.6 billion years. During

(a)

(b)

FIGURE 1 Long-term projections of (a) solar luminosity and (b) surface temperature (T_s) and CO_2. Here S_0 is the present solar flux and P_{atm} and P_{soil} represent the CO_2 concentrations in the atmosphere and in the soil, respectively. (*Source:* Reprinted with permission from K. Caldeira and J. F. Kasting, *Nature* 300:721–723, 1992. Copyright 1992 Macmillan Magazines, Ltd.)

this time, solar luminosity should increase by about 16% (Figure 1a). Earth's surface temperature, T_S, is predicted to increase slowly at first, then more rapidly starting about 1 billion years away (Figure 1b). By 1.6 billion years from now, T_S could exceed 100°C (212°F), and Earth's surface could become uninhabitable for all but the most thermophilic (heat-loving) of microbes. Furthermore, the computer models indicate that another, irreversible change will take place, starting in about 1 billion years when solar luminosity has increased by about 10%: The stratosphere will become wet, and water will be lost rapidly by photodissociation followed by the escape of hydrogen to space. Eventually, Earth should evolve into a planet similar to Venus.

The CO₂ Compensation Point

Earth's biota could run into trouble long before the temperature becomes high and the oceans disappear. The reason that T_S remains low for the next billion years in this simulation is that atmospheric CO_2 is predicted to decrease rather rapidly (Figure 1b). (The current fossil-fuel CO_2 pulse, which will last for only a million years or so, is neglected in this calculation.) The calculation assumes that the silicate weathering rate is controlled by the partial pressure of CO_2 in the soil, P_{soil}, which is higher than that in the atmosphere, P_{atm}, as a result of the microbial decomposition of organic matter in soils.

This pumping is assumed to be provided by C_4 plants, which are capable of photosynthesizing down to CO_2 levels of about 10 ppm. The critical concentration of CO_2 required for photosynthesis to occur is called the **CO₂ compensation point**. Below this level, the rate of photosynthesis is slower than the rate of **photorespiration** (respiration induced by the absorption of sunlight), so the plants cannot grow. In the simulation shown in Figure 1b, C_4 plants are predicted to become extinct about 900 million years from now, when the atmospheric CO_2 concentration falls below the CO_2 compensation point. At this time, P_{soil} becomes equal to P_{atm} because the biological pumping action disappears.

The C_3 plants, which fix carbon by means of the Calvin cycle and constitute about 95% of the current terrestrial vegetation, could go extinct even earlier. Their CO_2 compensation point is about 150 ppm, approximately half of today's atmospheric concentration. A similar simulation (not shown) in which C_3 plants control the CO_2 partial pressure in soils indicates that C_3 plants should survive for only about another 500 million years. As their CO_2 compensation point is approached, they should gradually be replaced by C_4 plants (which photosynthesize at much lower CO_2 concentrations than do C_3 plants) or by new species of plants that evolve mechanisms for photosynthesizing at low atmospheric CO_2 concentrations.

Although all of these predicted effects of future solar luminosity increase are a long time away, they have implications both for the total amount of time that Earth

may remain habitable and for the possibility of finding life elsewhere in the galaxy. We will return to the latter question later in the chapter. We should note, though, that because humans are intelligent—by some definitions, at least—and because our technological capabilities have been expanding at a rapid rate, it may be possible to geoengineer a solution to this problem. (See the Box titled "A Closer Look: A Geoengineering Solution to Earth's Future Climate Problems.") The concept of geoengineering is controversial when applied to the problem of modern global warming: Some people think it is a good idea, and others do not. But as the Sun brightens and threatens to fry the Earth, trying to solve this problem technologically is essentially a "no-brainer." The good news is it doesn't look that hard to do.

CLIMATE EVOLUTION ON VENUS AND MARS

Why are the climates of Venus and Mars so different from that of Earth? Both these planets probably started out with the necessary ingredients (water, carbon, and silicate rocks) to allow the carbonate–silicate cycle to operate. Thus, the CO_2–climate feedback mechanism could in principle have operated on these planets as well. But this mechanism was clearly incapable of keeping their surface temperatures within the liquid-water regime.

The Runaway Greenhouse on Venus

The answer to our question about the climates of Venus and Mars is that even systems containing negative feedback loops commonly have limits beyond which they become unstable. In the case of Venus, the negative feedback loop between the surface temperature and the outgoing infrared flux breaks down when the solar heating is too strong. Venus orbits the Sun at about 0.72 AU, so the inverse-square law shows that the solar flux at the surface of Venus is about $1.9 (=1/0.72)^2$ times that at Earth's surface. Even early in the solar system's history when the Sun was 25–30% dimmer, the solar flux at Venus's orbit would still have been some 40% higher than the present flux at Earth's orbit.

Under these circumstances, climate models predict that the positive coupling between surface temperature and the outgoing IR flux disappears (Figure 2). Recall

FIGURE 2 Systems diagram illustrating the runaway greenhouse on Venus.

A CLOSER LOOK

A Geoengineering Solution to Earth's Future Climate Problems

Although the predicted demise of the biota is not exactly imminent, the results of this simulation are in some sense disturbing. It took almost 4 billion years to evolve multicellular life and another half billion years to produce humans. After all of this evolutionary hard work, it is troubling to think that less than 1 billion years may remain before the planet becomes uninhabitable. Fortunately, however, this does not have to happen. We are now, or soon will be, technologically capable of altering Earth's climate on a global scale. Of course, we are doing this at the moment by increasing the atmospheric CO_2 concentration, and thereby making Earth warmer. But, it may be possible to cool the planet as well by a variety of geoengineering techniques. Most of the ideas that have been suggested—injecting sulfate aerosols into the stratosphere, for example—are themselves quite risky. We do not think that any of them offers an acceptable way of dealing with the global warming problem. But if we are thinking of a problem like solar luminosity change, which occurs over

hundreds of millions of years, we can afford to think of truly "high-tech" geoengineering projects.

A high-tech proposal for cooling Earth has been outlined recently by Roger Angel, an astronomer at the University of Arizona. Angel made this proposal in response to the modern global warming problem, but it may actually make more sense as a solution to long-term global warming. His idea is to build a large solar shield in between Earth and the Sun. The shield would not be a single, solid object—that would be extremely massive and difficult to construct. Rather, it would be a collection of small lenses, each just under a meter in diameter. The lenses would be concave, rather than convex, and so they would tend to disperse sunlight rather than to focus it. Hence, the shield could not, even in principle, be turned into some kind of gigantic weapon. The total area covered by the lenses would have to be large enough to prevent an appreciable fraction of the Sun's rays from reaching Earth. Recall that Earth's projected surface area, as seen from the Sun, is πR_{Earth}^2, or roughly 1.3×10^{14} m^2. If each

BOX FIGURE 1   Lagrange points in the Earth–Sun system. These are points of neutral gravitational stability where an object could remain stationary either with no input of energy (L4 and L5) or with minimal energy input (L1–L3). The drawing is not to scale. The distance from L1 to Earth is about 1.5 million km, or about 1% of the mean Earth–Sun distance.   (*Source:* Image from Wikipedia.)

lens was exactly 1 m in diameter, it would take about 830 billion (8.3×10^{11}) of these lenses to compensate for a 1% increase in solar luminosity. (The answer is a factor of 2 smaller than one would expect because the lenses deflect sunlight over twice their surface area as a consequence of the properties of diffraction.) This sounds like a large number, and indeed it is! However, Angel estimates that such a shield could be constructed in 50 years or less by manufacturing the lenses either on Earth or on the Moon and launching big stacks of them into space using an electromagnetic rail gun.

How, one might ask, would the lenses stay in place, given that they must orbit the Sun at less than Earth's orbital distance? We know from Kepler's third law that orbital periods decrease as one moves inward toward the Sun; hence, one might expect that the shield would quickly become misaligned. The proposal takes advantage of an interesting piece of physics, however. In the late 18th century, the Italian-French mathematician Joseph-Louis Lagrange discovered that there are five points of neutral gravitational stability in the Earth–Sun system (Box Figure 1). These points, now called **Lagrange points** in his honor, are places where the gravitational potential energy of the Earth-Sun system is at a minimum. The first point, L_1, is between Earth and the Sun, and that of course is where one would want to build our solar shield. Technically, L_1 (like L_2 and L_3) is an unstable equilibrium point; hence, an object placed at L_1 would tend to drift away, just as a ball placed at the top of a hill will tend to roll down one side or the other. However, it is possible to orbit around such a point in a stable manner, and Angel's lenses would be able to maintain such an orbit by using some of the intercepted solar energy to keep themselves on the right path.

As an aside, the last two Lagrange points, L_4 and L_5, are stable equilibrium points, which means that an object placed there would remain there indefinitely. This fact came to the attention of Princeton physicist Gerard K. O'Neill back in the 1970s. O'Neill was aware that Earth would eventually be facing the problem of overpopulation. His proposed solution was to build large space colonies at the L_4 and L_5 Lagrange points and offload some of Earth's population there. Unlikely as it may seem, this idea attracted a following, and it spawned the formation of a group called the L_5 Society which was dedicated to making this happen. At some point, however, wiser heads prevailed and the scheme was abandoned. Babies are currently being born at the rate of about 10 per second globally. If each space colony could hold 20,000 people, as envisioned by O'Neill, one would need to build thousands of them each year in order to begin to make a dent in population growth. As with modern global warming, we probably need to look inward, rather than out to space, to solve this problem.

that this coupling is part of the fundamental feedback loop that keeps Earth's climate stable. On Venus, the atmosphere became so warm and so full of water vapor that virtually no infrared radiation from the surface was able to escape to space. Only the radiation from the cold upper troposphere and stratosphere was able to escape, and the flux of this radiation did not change as the surface became warmer and warmer. The resulting out-of-control climate system is called a **runaway greenhouse**. With the stabilizing feedback loop gone, the surface temperature "ran away" to values as high as 1500 K, the oceans evaporated, and all the water on the planet's surface turned to vapor. Even the stratosphere became filled with water vapor.

Once the stratosphere of Venus became wet, water would have been lost by photodissociation, followed by the escape of hydrogen to space. The oxygen left behind would have reacted with reduced materials, such as ferrous iron-bearing minerals, present at the planet's surface and with any reduced gases remaining in its atmosphere. With no liquid water remaining to facilitate silicate weathering, volcanic CO_2 would have accumulated, forming the dense atmosphere that exists today. The loss of water would also have removed the sink for sulfur-containing volcanic gases. These gases would likewise have accumulated in the atmosphere, giving rise to the dense sulfuric acid clouds that presently obscure the Venusian surface. The end result of this process is the hot, dry planet that we see today (Figure 3).

FIGURE 3 [See color section] The surface of Venus, as observed by *radar* from the Magellan spacecraft. (*Source:* Jet Propulsion Laboratory, NASA Headquarters.)

How do we know that this is actually what happened on Venus? Could Venus have simply started out with less water than Earth did as a consequence of being closer to the Sun? We cannot be sure because we cannot look back in time and because Venus is so hot that it would be extremely difficult to go there and look for the oxygen left behind from the loss of water. An important clue has been left behind in the Venusian atmosphere, however: The ratio of deuterium to hydrogen in the little water vapor that remains is more than 150 times higher than that ratio in Earth's oceans. Recall that deuterium, D, is an isotope of hydrogen that has an extra neutron in its nucleus. If Venus initially had a significant amount of water and if this water was lost by photodissociation followed by escape of hydrogen to space, we would expect that the lighter hydrogen isotope, H, would escape more quickly and that the heavier one, D, would become enriched in the water vapor that was left behind. The fact that this is exactly what we observe supports the idea that Venus was once a water-rich planet and that the runaway greenhouse hypothesis is correct.

Martian Climate Evolution

Mars, in contrast, faced just the opposite of Venus' climate problem. The solar flux reaching Mars is only 43% of that reaching Earth and would have been even lower early in the solar system's history. The solar heating was so low that CO_2 itself should have condensed, forming clouds and polar ice caps. We know CO_2 ice by the name *dry ice,* and it has many familiar uses, such as keeping ice cream cold. The present Martian polar caps contain a mixture of CO_2 ice and water ice.

The fact that CO_2 can condense on Mars makes that planet's climate evolution very different from that of Earth. On Mars, volcanic CO_2 would necessarily not have accumulated in the atmosphere if the surface temperature fell below freezing. Thus, the stabilizing feedback provided by the carbonate–silicate cycle would not have operated in the same way as on Earth.

The surprising thing about Mars is that, despite this problem of CO_2 condensation, the Martian surface was once warm enough to allow liquid water to flow on its surface (Figure 4). Most of the Martian channels, or *valleys,*

appear to have formed prior to about 3.8 b.y ago. (On Earth, a valley is the relatively wide region carved by a stream and a channel is the narrow stream that runs through it.) We infer this because the terrain on which most of the valleys are located is covered with lots of impact craters. By analogy with the cratering record of the Moon, this cratering occurred during the first 700 million years of the solar system's history. This inference remains valid regardless of whether the bombardment history of the inner solar system was continuous or whether it was a pulse at 3.8–3.9 Ga, as suggested by the Nice model. Evidently, Mars had a denser atmosphere at that time with enough greenhouse effect to keep its surface warm despite the low solar luminosity. Climate modelers are still not sure how to explain this warm climate, although greenhouse warming by CO_2 was almost certainly involved. High-altitude CO_2 clouds, which act somewhat like cirrus clouds on Earth, may also have played a role. (Recall that high-altitude clouds warm a planet's surface whereas low-altitude clouds tend to cool it.)

Why, then, did Mars become so cold? The answer may lie in the planet's small size. Mars has about half Earth's diameter and only about one-tenth its mass. A planet that size should have cooled off relatively quickly after its formation and would have a smaller radioactive heat source. (A planet's internal heat energy is proportional to its volume, which decreases more rapidly with radius than does the planet's surface area.) With less geothermal energy available to drive plate tectonics, the Martian crust might have solidified into a single unit early in the planet's history. This solidification would have shut down the carbonate–silicate cycle, because carbonate rocks would no longer have undergone metamorphism. With most of the planet's CO_2 trapped in carbonates or stored as dry ice in the Martian soil, the greenhouse effect would have diminished and Mars would have approached its present, frozen state.

HABITABLE PLANETS AROUND OTHER STARS

The question of what happened to Venus and Mars bears on another, even more interesting question: What is the chance that habitable planets exist elsewhere in our galaxy? We could broaden this to include the rest of the universe, but the question would then become entirely philosophical because we would have no way of verifying our predictions. As we will soon see, within the next 20 to 30 years we may be able to determine whether habitable (or even inhabited) planets exist within at least part of our own galaxy. Thus, it is not too soon to start thinking about whether they should be expected.

We know now that planets exist around other stars. As this chapter is being copyedited (late April 2009), some 346 planets have been found around stars other than the Sun. (This is up from 100 planets at the time of the previous edition of this book, 6 years ago.) Most of these

FIGURE 4   A Martian valley (Nanedi Vallis), seen from the *Mars Global Surveyor* spacecraft.   (*Source:* NASA Headquarters.)

planets are large, gas-giant planets like Jupiter and Saturn. (At least we assume they are gas giants because they are so massive.) Large planets are easier to detect than small ones, because their gravitational pull on their parent star is strong; it is the motion of the stars themselves that has been observed. But gas-giant planets are not likely abodes for life. They have no solid surface, and their atmospheres are highly convective. Thus, even though organisms could theoretically exist at some level in their atmospheres where liquid water is stable, the organisms would periodically be lofted to great heights, where the temperature is very cold, or carried to great depths, where they would be incinerated. Life *as we know it* requires a much more stable environment that is best provided by small, rocky planets like our own.

Formation of Earthlike Planets

A few of the **extrasolar planets** that have been found are too small to be gas giants. Planets with masses less than about 10 Earth masses are thought to be too small to capture significant amounts of gas from the stellar nebula in which they form. Approximately 10 of the known extrasolar planets appear to be below this limit. The lowest mass planet found so far is a 1.9-Earth-mass planet orbiting the star Gliese 581. This mass is actually only a lower limit, as the planet was found by looking at the back-and-forth motion it induces in its parent star—the so-called **radial velocity method** of planet hunting—and the orientation of the planet's orbit relative to the line of sight to the star is unknown. Still, this planet is in all likelihood a **super-Earth**, that is, a planet that is several times more massive than Earth, but which is still rocky, rather than gaseous. This particular planet is also getting thoroughly baked, as it orbits its parent star at a distance of only about 0.03 AU. (Mercury, by comparison, orbits the Sun at a distance of ~0.4 AU.) So, we have not yet found a true Earth analog, but we are coming very close to doing so.

What are the chances that we will find Earthlike planets around other stars? The answer to this question depends partly on how planets form and partly on what their climates are like later on. How a planet's climate evolves depends on a number of factors that we have discussed in previous chapters.

The formation of terrestrial-type planets is probably a common process. The rock-forming elements (silicon, oxygen, iron, and magnesium) that make up the bulk of Earth have been identified in the spectra of other stars and are thought to be abundant throughout the universe. The volatile elements on which life depends—carbon, nitrogen, hydrogen (as water), phosphorus, and sulfur—are seen in interstellar clouds and are likewise thought to be abundant elsewhere. Disks of dust and gas are known to exist around many young stars, so the general conditions that are believed to lead to planet formation are commonplace. If the formation of other planetary systems has followed the same general pattern as that of our solar system, it is likely that planets formed in their inner parts would have been chemically much like Earth. In particular, they are likely to have had enough water to form an ocean and enough carbon to have a carbon cycle. A planet that is similar in size to Earth might also be expected to have enough internal heat to power Earthlike plate tectonics.

The Habitable Zone around the Sun

Whether another planet could have an Earthlike climate depends on how far from its star the planet forms and on how fast the parent star evolves in luminosity. As mentioned earlier, a fundamental requirement for life as we know it is that the planet's surface temperature remain in the range at which liquid water can exist. The region in space around a star where this condition is satisfied is called the **habitable zone (HZ)**, or **ecosphere**. Because stars increase in luminosity as they age, their habitable zone moves outward with time. The region where a planet can remain habitable for some finite time interval is called the **continuously habitable zone (CHZ)**. The CHZ represents the overlap between the HZ at some initial time, t_0, and at some later time, t_1 (Figure 5). It is defined for some specific interval, $\Delta t = t_1 - t_0$. For our Sun, we usually take t_0 to be the time the Sun formed (4.6 b.y. ago) and t_1 to be the present, so $\Delta t = 4.6$ b.y.

A point of clarification should be added here. Liquid water may actually exist on a planet at almost any distance from its parent star. Jupiter's moon Europa is a prime example. Europa is thought to have a subsurface ocean that is kept warm by tidal heating. Jupiter and Europa are well

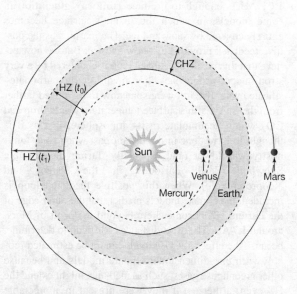

FIGURE 5 The relationship between the habitable zone (HZ) and the continuously habitable zone (CHZ). The CHZ is defined for some particular time interval $\Delta t = t_1 - t_0$, taken here to be 4.6 b.y.

outside the conventional habitable zone in our own solar system, and yet liquid water and life may exist there. However, if life does exist on Europa, it is buried beneath the icy surface and is not detectable remotely. If we are interested in finding life on planets around other stars, we must concentrate on those on which organisms can modify the planet's atmosphere. So, the habitable zone of interest is that for which liquid water exists *at a planet's surface.*

How wide is the current habitable zone around our own Sun? Climate models can be used to help answer this question. So far, only one-dimensional, radiative-convective models have been used, but ultimately this question could be investigated with three-dimensional general circulation models. The one-dimensional models predict that the inner edge of the HZ around our own Sun is at about 0.95 AU. Inside this distance, a planet's stratosphere is predicted to become wet, and water is lost rapidly by photodissociation followed by the escape of hydrogen to space, as is thought to have occurred on Venus. Note that this result is consistent with the predictions for Earth's future climate discussed earlier in this chapter. Figure 1 indicates that Earth's surface temperature should start to increase rapidly beginning about 1 billion years in the future, when solar luminosity has increased by about 10%. If Earth were located at 0.95 AU rather than at 1 AU, the inverse-square law predicts that the solar flux would be higher by a factor of $1/(0.95)^2$, or 1.11. In either case, an increase of approximately 10% in the solar flux would be enough to drive off Earth's water.

Identifying the outer edge of the habitable zone is a little trickier. Early calculations by some climate modelers suggested that the outer edge is very close to Earth's current orbital distance of 1 AU. Moving Earth out to even 1.01 AU is enough to produce **runaway glaciation** in some models, in which the planet's surface becomes entirely covered by snow and ice. The reason was the positive feedback provided by snow and ice. But we now believe that this positive feedback loop is countered by a very strong negative feedback loop involving the carbonate–silicate cycle. If Earth were somehow to be moved farther from the Sun, Earth's surface temperature would drop and CO_2 would accumulate in its atmosphere, just as it is thought to have done in the distant past when solar luminosity was lower (and especially during the possible Snowball Earth episodes in the Paleo- and Neoproterozoic). When this positive feedback loop is included, the climate models predict that the outer edge of the current HZ is somewhere beyond the orbit of Mars, around 1.7 AU. The exact distance is difficult to determine, because the effect of CO_2 clouds cannot be estimated reliably with one-dimensional climate models and because other greenhouse gases, such as methane, might extend the HZ even farther out if they were present in appreciable concentrations in a planet's atmosphere. As we mentioned earlier, Mars had liquid water on its surface early in its history even though it appears to have been outside the HZ at that time, according to Figure 5. Perhaps the HZ is wider than we think.

Because the CHZ represents the overlap between two HZs at different times in the Sun's history, it is narrower than the HZ. A planet near the outer edge of the current HZ would have been outside the HZ 4.6 b.y. ago when the Sun was only 70% as bright as it is today. When we take into account the change in solar luminosity, the outer edge of the 4.6-b.y. CHZ is estimated to lie in the vicinity of 1.4 AU. (Note again that the CHZ is defined only for some specific time interval.) This estimate is conservative because it does not take into account the possible warming caused by CO_2 clouds on planets near the outer edge of the HZ. So, the actual width of the CHZ may be even greater. Evidently, the habitable region around our own Sun is much wider than early predictions had suggested.

Habitable Zones around Other Stars

The same type of climate stability calculations described above can be performed for stars other than our Sun. The results are summarized in Figure 6, which shows the instantaneous HZ midway through a star's main-sequence lifetime. (It is difficult to show CHZs on such a plot, because stars of different masses evolve at different rates.) The vertical scale shows stellar mass relative to the Sun's mass; the horizontal scale shows distance in astronomical units. The basic result is very simple: To have a surface temperature similar to Earth's, a planet orbiting a dim, red star would have to be closer than 1 AU to that star, whereas a planet orbiting a bright, blue star would have to be farther than 1 AU from that star.

Problems occur, however, for stars much earlier or later in the main sequence than our own Sun. For dim, red stars, the habitable zone falls within the **tidal locking radius** of the star, that is, the distance from a star within which a planet is likely to rotate such that it always faces the star. The Moon shows only one side to Earth; the reason is that it is close enough to Earth for its rotation to have been damped by tides. An astronomer would say that the Moon exhibits **captured rotation**. Close to the star, the tidal forces increase faster than the amount of available starlight. Thus, a planet that is close enough to a dim, red star to be within its habitable zone is likely to develop a captured rotation. (Note from Figure 6 that Mercury is within our Sun's tidal locking radius. However, it avoids this fate because it is caught in a resonance that causes it to spin 3 times for every 2 orbits around the Sun.) The planet would then have one hot, permanently sunlit side and one cold, perpetually dark side. Its atmosphere might freeze out on the dark side, making the entire planet uninhabitable.

Bright, bluish stars pose other problems for planetary habitability. The most serious is that they have relatively short main-sequence lifetimes. The rate of energy generation

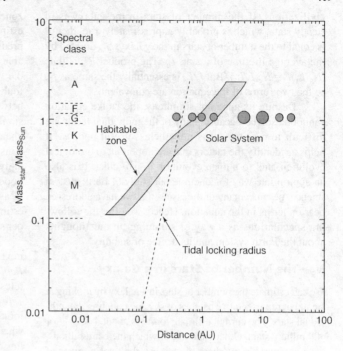

FIGURE 6 Habitable zones for other main-sequence stars. The HZ is plotted midway through the star's main-sequence lifetime. (*Source:* J. F. Kasting et al., *Icarus* 101, 1993, pp. 108–128.)

in a star increases with a star's mass much faster than the mass itself does. The result is that hot, massive stars exhaust the hydrogen in their cores much faster than does a star like the Sun. The hottest, most massive type of star stays on the main sequence for only a few tens of millions of years, compared with 10 billion years for our Sun. Thus, if life were to originate on a planet circling a bright star, it would have much less time to evolve than it did here on Earth.

Hot, blue stars pose another potential problem for life in that they emit a significant fraction of their radiation at ultraviolet wavelengths. According to Wien's law, as the temperature of the star's surface increases, the peak wavelength of its emitted radiation decreases. The Sun's effective surface temperature is 5780 K; hence, its radiation peaks at about 0.5 µm, near the middle of the visible part of the electromagnetic spectrum. Hot, blue stars can have surface temperatures of up to 25,000 K, so their radiation peaks well into the ultraviolet. The relative amount of UVB and UVC radiation emitted by such a star is orders of magnitude greater than that emitted by our own Sun. Hence, a planet orbiting a hot, blue star would need to have an extremely well-developed ozone screen in order for its surface to be habitable by advanced life. The good news is that the shorter UV wavelengths that split O_2 and make ozone are even more strongly enhanced in these stars, so such "super" ozone screens might actually exist.

We conclude that stars not too different from our Sun are the ones most likely to harbor habitable planets. Among such stars, the chances of there being an Earthlike planet appear to be pretty good.

THE DRAKE EQUATION

The last chapter of many introductory astronomy textbooks is devoted to speculation about the possibility of life elsewhere in the universe. The discussion is generally framed in terms of the **Drake equation**, a relatively innocuous-looking formula used to estimate the number of other intelligent civilizations in our galaxy with which we might one day establish radio communication. The equation was proposed by Frank Drake, an astronomer now at the University of California at Santa Cruz. The late astronomer Carl Sagan of Cornell University also had a hand in crafting the equation and wrote about it extensively in his books *Cosmos* and *Intelligent Life in the Universe* (with I. S. Shklovskii).

The equation can be written as follows: *N,* the number of advanced, communicating civilizations in the galaxy, is expressed as the product of seven terms:

$$N = N_g f_p n_e f_l f_i f_c f_L$$

where N_g = number of stars in our galaxy; f_p = the fraction of stars that have planets; n_e = the number of Earthlike planets per planetary system; f_l = the fraction of habitable planets on which life evolves; f_i = the probability that life will evolve to an intelligent state; f_c = the probability that intelligent life will develop the capacity to communicate over long distances (e.g., by radio telescope); and f_L = the fraction of a planet's lifetime during which it supports a technological civilization.

An alternative form of the Drake equation replaces the factors N_g and f_L with R (the average rate of star formation in the galaxy) and L (the lifetime of a technological civilization). If the number of stars in the galaxy is in steady state, which is probably approximately true, then R is equal to the number of stars in the galaxy, N_g, divided by the average lifetime of a star, L_s. The product RL is thus $(N_g/L_s)L = N_g(L/L_s)$. But L/L_s is essentially the same as f_L, so the two forms of the equation are equivalent.

Despite its apparent simplicity, the Drake equation cannot be solved because many of the individual terms are difficult to estimate. It is nonetheless useful because it helps us identify the factors that are important to biological evolution, and to human evolution in particular. It is also an appropriate way to conclude our study of Earth system science, because many of the issues that we have addressed bear on terms in the equation. Hence, we offer the following speculations as a way of summing up our thoughts about the Earth system and its degree of stability.

N_g—The Number of Stars in a Galaxy

We can estimate the number of stars in a galaxy by looking at small but representative patches of sky and counting the individual stars. The current estimate for N_g is about 4×10^{11}, or 400 billion, stars. Other galaxies, of which there are billions, have comparable numbers of stars, so the total number of stars in the universe is very much larger than this. But the distances separating galaxies are so large (2 million light years or greater) that the possibility of radio communication with another civilization is too remote to consider.

f_p—The Fraction of Stars That Have Planets

In the previous section, we discussed briefly the fraction of stars that have planets. Astronomers believe that planetary formation is a natural accompaniment to the formation of stars. One problem that we did not mention is that well over 50% of the stars in our galaxy are members of binary (two-star) systems or other multiple-star systems. Such stars may not form planets, but theoreticians are not certain. Even if they do, it seems unlikely that many of these planets would be located within the habitable zone of one of the stars. So, let us assume that only single stars have planets; hence we can conservatively assign f_p a value of about 0.1.

For now, this value for f_p is only a guess. Within the next few years, however, it should be possible to measure this number directly. As mentioned earlier, planets have now been discovered around roughly 300 main-sequence stars. So far, only the largest and closest-in planets have been discovered, because these are the easiest to detect. As observational technology improves, however, and as astronomers accumulate data on stellar motions over longer periods, it should be possible to determine whether planetary systems like our own are commonplace.

n_e—The Number of Earthlike Planets per Planetary System

We have already addressed the number of Earthlike planets per planetary system in our earlier discussion of habitable zones around stars. On the basis of our relatively optimistic estimate of the width of the CHZ around our own Sun, we predict that solar-type stars are very likely to harbor habitable planets. Our estimate of the 4.6-b.y. CHZ width, about 0.4 AU, is roughly equal to the mean spacing between the four innermost planets in our own solar system, which lie between 0.4 AU and 1.5 AU. Thus, if planets are spaced similarly around other solar-type stars, there is a very good chance that one of them will be within the CHZ. To be conservative, we will estimate this probability at 50%. Only stars of spectral type close to our own sun look to be good candidates, however. This cuts down the number of available stars by a factor of about 5. So, a preliminary estimate of n_e would be 0.5×0.2, or 0.1 Earthlike planets per star.

A better estimate for n_e may be available within the next few years. In March of 2009, NASA launched its *Kepler* mission. *Kepler* is a 0.95-m diameter optical space telescope—about half the size of the *Hubble Space Telescope*—that is staring at a patch of the Milky Way, looking for transits of Earth-sized planets. A **transit** is when a planet passes in front of a star, temporarily blocking out some of its light. *Kepler* is able to monitor the brightness of approximately 150,000 stars to an accuracy of 1 part in 10^5. Because Earth is about $1/100^{\text{th}}$ the diameter of the Sun, it would block out about 1 part in 10^4 of the Sun's light if seen in transit from a great distance. Hence, *Kepler* should be able to detect Earth-sized planets, if they exist. We need to wait several years, though, because one would want to see more than one transit in order to be sure that the signal was being produced by a planet.

f_l—The Fraction of Habitable Planets on Which Life Evolves

The fraction of habitable planets on which life evolves is one of the most poorly understood terms in the Drake equation. Chemists and biologists are uncertain as to how it occurred, so it is impossible to say whether it was a likely or an unlikely event here on Earth.

Two experimental approaches could eventually shed light on the origin-of-life question. One would be to create life in a test tube. The other would be to detect life elsewhere in the universe. Of these, the approach that appears most feasible at present is the detection of life elsewhere. We have already sent two *Viking* spacecraft out from Earth in the late 1970s with the express intent of searching for life on Mars. Neither spacecraft found life on the martian surface; indeed, they all but proved that it could not exist. (The martian soil is so highly oxidized that organic material cannot survive very long.) It now seems unlikely, though not impossible, that life will be found on Mars or anywhere else in our own solar system.

Other planetary systems are a different matter, however. Life around other stars may be detectable by at least

FIGURE 7 The Arecibo radio telescope. (*Source:* David Parker/SPL/Photo Researchers.)

two methods. One method is radio communication. The giant radio telescope at Arecibo, Puerto Rico, is capable of communicating with another, similarly equipped civilization anywhere in our galaxy (Figure 7). A new array of smaller telescopes, the Allen Telescope Array, now being constructed at Hat Creek Observatory in northern California will have capabilities similar to or exceeding that of the Arecibo telescope. If we manage to communicate, however, we will no longer need the Drake equation, as we will have found the answer to our question.

The second method of detecting life is to build large telescopes in space and use them to view planets around other stars directly. Two different types of telescopes are being considered. The first is a large (4- to 8-m diameter) visible telescope that is equipped with a **coronagraph** (a device that would block out the light from the star and allow us to observe the much dimmer planets orbiting around it). NASA's proposed mission for this option is called *TPF-C*, for *Terrestrial Planet Finder—Coronagraph*. A second idea is to fly an array of telescopes that would operate at longer, thermal\ infrared wavelengths. Planets appear somewhat brighter relative to their parent star at these wavelengths because the thermal infrared is where their own emitted energy is concentrated. It takes a bigger telescope to see planets at these wavelengths, however, and so the plan would be to fly several of them together and have them act as an **interferometer**, an instrument in which their images would be electronically combined. In principle, such an instrument could be used to cancel out the light from the star and to let through only the light from the planets

around it. NASA has long-range plans for a four-telescope array called *TPF-I*, for *Terrestrial Planet Finder—Interferometer*, that could image Earth-sized planets out to a distance of about 50 light years. This instrument would allow us to look for planets around more than 100 single, solar-type stars.

Both *TPF-C* and *TPF-I* should be able to perform **spectroscopy** on a planet's atmosphere—a technique in which the composition of a material, such as a gas, is analyzed according to the details of its electromagnetic spectrum. By doing this at visible/near-infrared wavelengths, the *TPF-C* mission should be able to look for the presence of O_2, O_3, and H_2O in a planet's atmosphere. Absorption bands caused by these gases can be detected in **Earthshine** data, that is, light reflected from the dark side of the Moon (Figure 8). This light came originally from the Sun, then was reflected by Earth before being reflected a second time by the Moon; hence, it contains a spectrum of Earth's atmosphere. O_2 has a strong absorption band at 760 nm (7600 Angstroms) that is particularly prominent. Nearly all of Earth's O_2 has been produced by photosynthesis. Hence, the observation of O_2 in the atmosphere of an extrasolar planet would be reasonably strong evidence for life. (That said, one can think of several ways in which significant quantities of O_2 could be produced abiotically. Hence, one would want to do a more detailed analysis before jumping to any conclusions.)

FIGURE 8 Visible/near-IR spectrum of Earth, taken from "Earthshine" data. The wiggly curve at the top shows the actual data. The smooth curve running through it shows the model fit (from below). (*Source:* N. J. Woolf, P. S. Smith, W. A. Traub, and K. W. Jucks, "The Spectrum of Earthshine: A Pale Blue Dot Observed from the Ground," *Astrophysical Journal* 574, 2002, pp. 430–433.)

Detecting O_3 would tell us essentially the same thing, because O_3 is produced photochemically from O_2. And, of course, liquid water is essential for Earth-type life, so detecting water vapor in a planet's atmosphere would be an indirect indication that life might be possible on the planet's surface.

An infrared interferometer should also be able to look for H_2O and O_3, and it should be able to detect CO_2 as well (Figure 9). CO_2 can also be seen in the atmospheres of Venus and Mars; however, these atmospheres contain only small amounts of O_2 and, hence, do not show evidence of O_3. So, we should be able to distinguish a habitable planet like Earth from uninhabitable neighbors like Venus and Mars. Note that, regardless of whether one is operating in the visible or in the infrared, this method of detecting extraterrestrial life is much more general than radio communication, because it requires evolution only to the bacterial level of complexity.

In the meantime, as we do not know how to estimate f_l, we shall for the moment leave its value unassigned.

FIGURE 9 Infrared spectra of the atmosphere of Earth, Venus, and Mars. Only Earth shows the presence of H_2O and O_3. (*Source:* R. Hanel, Goddard Space Flight Center.)

f_i—The Probability That Life Will Evolve to an Intelligent State

The probability that life will evolve to an intelligent state is another poorly understood term in the Drake equation, in part because it is not entirely obvious what intelligence actually is. Are humans the only intelligent species on this planet? Or should we include dolphins and perhaps a few other species that are not that far behind in terms of mental capabilities?

If we confine our discussion of intelligence to the Drake equation, the appropriate definition becomes clear: To be detectable by radio communication, a species must have the type of intelligence to develop electronic equipment and other aspects of a technological civilization. For this ability, they probably have to have fingers instead of fins. So, in terms of the Drake equation, an intelligent species needs to be fairly similar to our own.

We will not attempt to elucidate here the many factors involved in the evolution of human intelligence. We can, however, point out two topics that we have discussed in previous chapters that bear on this question. The first is the rise of atmospheric oxygen about 2.4 billion years ago. The rise of oxygen was an absolute necessity not only for human evolution, but also for the evolution of all multicellular life. Indeed, its importance is even more fundamental: Even single-celled eukaryotes (cells with nuclei) require oxygen for their metabolism. Although we cannot be certain that biological evolution would have proceeded elsewhere as it did on Earth, chances are that oxygen is a metabolic requirement for all advanced organisms.

Was the rise of oxygen a likely event? Now that the cyanobacteria-like microfossils found in the Apex Chert Formation of Australia have been called into question, we are no longer certain that oxygenic photosynthesis was an early biological invention. Evolving this capability could have taken as long as 2 billion years. Thus, it is difficult to say how long it might take elsewhere. Once photosynthesis had been invented on Earth, the atmosphere was almost bound to become oxidizing, sooner or later. We still do not understand exactly why the rise in atmospheric O_2 was delayed for several hundred million years following the initial appearance of cyanobacteria. The Earth itself may have had to evolve to a slightly less reduced state before atmospheric O_2 could accumulate. But if Earth could do this, then another Earthlike planet should be able to do the same thing. Thus, the rise of oxygen in a planet's atmosphere may be a relatively commonplace event *if* photosynthesis itself has been invented elsewhere.

A second important factor that must influence biological evolution is the frequency of large impacts. Energetic collisions with asteroids or comets have evidently caused mass extinctions of organisms on our planet and have paved the way for the evolution of new life-forms. Humans might not have evolved if the

Cretaceous–Tertiary impact event had not eliminated the dinosaurs. Impacts that were either too large or too frequent would have a detrimental effect on biological evolution, however. The lunar cratering record indicates that large (100-km diameter) impactors probably hit Earth until as late as 3.8 b.y. ago. These events would have sterilized most of Earth's surface. In our own solar system, the flux of these large impactors decreased to close to zero after the first few hundred million years. The same, however, would not necessarily be true of other planetary systems.

The key factor in our solar system that controls the impact flux that hits Earth is the planet Jupiter. Jupiter is directly responsible for at least some of the impactors that have hit Earth over the past few billion years, because that giant planet perturbs asteroids from certain regions in the asteroid belt into Earth-crossing orbits. But Jupiter may also protect us from cometary impacts by deflecting incoming comets before they can enter Earth-crossing orbits. If other planetary systems have similar cometary fluxes, the presence of a giant planet like Jupiter may be essential to ensuring environmental stability on the inner planets.

Like f_l, we do not know what f_i should be, so we will leave it undefined as well.

f_c—The Probability That Intelligent Life Will Develop the Capacity to Communicate over Long Distances

We cannot assess with confidence the numerical probability that an extraterrestrial civilization will develop radio communication. But we may be able to say something about how the planetary environment influenced the emergence of a technologically advanced civilization on Earth. Yale anthropologist Elizabeth Vrba has suggested that our prehuman ancestors were forced out of their forested environments in Africa around 2.5 m.y. ago by ecological changes associated with the Pleistocene glacial cooling. According to Vrba, these changes led to the replacement of forests by vast areas of savannah (grassland). Our ancestors adapted to their changed environment by developing a more upright manner of walking and by developing weapons with which to hunt the large herbivores that grazed on the savannah.

These changes in lifestyle may also have accelerated intellectual development in humans. Whether the same evolutionary changes would have taken place in the absence of climate change is not clear. But we can see how mildly destabilizing events such as climate change may have helped guide, and perhaps accelerate, both the evolution of humans and the gradual emergence of civilization.

A second, somewhat better documented correlation between climate change and the development of civilization is seen at the end of the last ice age, about 10,000 years ago. At about this time, agricultural societies emerged spontaneously in several different regions of the world, including Mesopotamia, China, and the Indus River valley in India. Very likely, the switch from hunter-gatherer societies to agricultural-based societies was facilitated by the improved climatic conditions. Again, this switch could have occurred without any forcing from climate. But, Milankovitch cycles do seem to have played some role in the development of our current civilization.

Imagine what might happen, though, on an Earthlike planet without a large moon. The Milankovitch climate cycles might then be driven by a chaotically varying planetary obliquity. They would probably appear to be regular and to have relatively small amplitudes on a time scale of tens to hundreds of thousands of years, but on longer time scales the planetary obliquity might reach extreme values. What this would do to the emergence of agriculture (and to the soil itself) is unclear. We suspect, however, that it would make the emergence of civilization much more difficult.

Collecting Terms to This Point

Let us stop for a moment to take stock of what we have learned so far. If we combine what we know with what we do not know about the terms in the Drake equation, we are left with

$$N = N_g f_p n_e f_l f_i f_c f_L,$$
$$\approx (4 \times 10^{11}) \times (0.1) \times (0.1) f_e f_i f_c f_L$$
$$= 4 \times 10^9 f_l f_i f_c f_L,$$

where we have inserted approximate values for the three leading terms, N_g, f_p, and n_e, and where the symbol $\approx$ means "approximately equals." Our point in writing the equation in this manner is the following: Only the physical science terms in the Drake equation can be assigned numerical values with any degree of certainty. (Even these terms might be subject to considerable debate.) The last four terms deal with biological and sociological evolution and are much more speculative.

Suppose, however, that we are optimistic about the chances of life originating elsewhere and of the evolution of intelligence and civilization. Carl Sagan, for example, was always an optimist, and he estimated (in *Cosmos*) that the product $f_l f_i f_c$ is equal to about 1/300. If we accept his estimate and round off our numbers, the Drake equation boils down to

$$N = 10^7 f_L.$$

Under these assumptions, whether N is large or small depends exclusively on f_L, the fraction of a planet's lifetime during which it supports a technological civilization. So, let us speculate for a moment about the magnitude of that factor.

f_L—The Fraction of a Planet's Lifetime during Which It Supports a Technological Civilization

The remaining uncertainty in the Drake equation is the fraction of a planet's lifetime during which it supports a technological civilization. Let us assume that the average lifetime of planets themselves is about 10 b.y., the approximate main-sequence lifetime of the Sun. The question then becomes: How long does an average technological civilization last? How long will ours last? The answer clearly depends on what eventually causes our demise. If we do ourselves in by a nuclear war, the answer could be as short as 100 years. If other civilizations annihilated themselves in the same way, the factor f_L would be equal to 10^2 years/10^{10} years = 1×10^{-8}, and N would be a paltry 0.1. A value of N below one implies that we might well be the only technological civilization in the entire galaxy.

If left to natural causes, however, the lifetime of our civilization could be much longer. The average longevity of a species in the geologic record is about 1 million years. If we use this value for civilized species, we get $f_L = 10^6/10^{10} = 1 \times 10^{-4}$ and $N = 1000$. But civilized species are much smarter than average and, thus, might survive much longer. If we are able to deal successfully with all our other problems, humans should be able to survive for at least another 500 m.y., the time scale for the loss of C_3 photosynthesis. But we can overcome this problem as well if we build the solar shield discussed earlier in this chapter. In that case, humans could conceivably survive until the Sun leaves the main sequence, roughly 5 billion years from now. If technical civilizations in general were this long-lived, f_L could be as high as $5 \times 10^9/10^{10} = 0.5$ and N would be 5,000,000.

Future technological innovations, such as interstellar space flight or planet-sized solar shields, could allow us to outlive even this disaster. But the basic point has already been made: If technological civilizations can survive for an appreciable fraction of a planetary lifetime, then the number of such civilizations in the galaxy could be quite large. For $N = 5,000,000$, the average distance between civilizations should be about 250 light years. We can imagine that a slow dialogue might take place by radio communication were two such civilizations to discover each other's existence.

ENSURING OUR LONG-TERM SURVIVAL

What are the chances that we can overcome all our potential problems and survive for hundreds of millions years? We have discussed a number of current environmental problems in previous chapters. Could any of them trigger our downfall?

CO_2-induced global warming might lead to drastic environmental changes and even to the relocation of large numbers of people, but it is not likely to result in the demise of all of civilization. Ozone depletion is potentially more dangerous, because UV radiation is directly harmful to almost all forms of life. However, we are already dealing with it in what looks to be an effective manner. Loss of biodiversity might pose a significant threat to global food production, but it does not seem likely by itself to wipe out the human population. Human population growth itself might be the most significant problem, but even this will ultimately be self-limiting. Either the availability of food or competition for other resources will eventually cause the population to stabilize, hopefully at a comfortable and sustainable level.

If we avoid nuclear self-destruction, the most significant threat to our continued existence over very long time scales might come from large impacts. The expected frequency of impact events the size of that at the Cretaceous–Tertiary is about one per 10^8 years. Would a 10-km-diameter impactor destroy civilization? It is difficult to say. On the basis of the amount of energy released, the effects would be far more devastating than those of an all-out nuclear war. The initial firestorm ignited by the reentry of impact ejecta into the atmosphere could destroy agricultural crops around the world within hours. The dust generated by the impact would reach the stratosphere and would linger there for 6 months to a year. Photosynthesis might be shut off during much of this time, and continenal interiors could become quite cold. (Coastal areas would remain relatively warm because of the large heat capacity of the oceans.) Some of us might be able to survive such a catastrophe by taking advantage of our already fairly advanced technology, but the number of people killed would still likely be in the billions.

Fortunately, there is no reason why such a catastrophe need ever happen. We are already aware of the existence and approximate orbital parameters of many of the Earth-crossing asteroids, and we have the technology to improve considerably on this database. Within a few years, a space-based telescope dedicated to searching for asteroids and comets could map out all of the potentially dangerous objects in the solar system. Indeed, the construction of such a telescope has already been suggested and seems likely to happen in the wake of the Comet Shoemaker–Levy impact with Jupiter, which helped alert lawmakers to the potential danger of such impacts. With sufficient advance warning of an impact, we may already be capable of avoiding it. A spacecraft, for example, could be sent to rendezvous with the object and then to detonate a small nuclear device on one side of the object to deflect its orbit. (Blowing it to pieces as done in the movie *Deep Impact* would be energetically difficult or impossible for large bodies and would create showers of smaller objects that might still cause significant damage.) As time passes and our space technology improves, there is little doubt that we will be able to construct an asteroid defense system, if we decide to do so. So, there is no reason why we need go the way of the dinosaurs. We know enough about the dangers of the Earth system to survive for longer than they did, if we can survive the danger that we pose to ourselves.

Chapter Summary

1. The Sun continues to brighten at a rate of about 1% per hundred million years.
   a. The resulting increase in Earth's surface temperature could lead to rapid loss of water in about a billion and a half years.
   b. Long before this occurs, first C_3 and then C_4 plants might die off as atmospheric CO_2 concentrations fall below the level required to sustain photosynthesis. The CO_2 decrease is predicted to result from the same feedback of surface temperature–silicate weathering rate that is thought to have stabilized Earth's climate throughout the planet's history.
   c. All of these changes could potentially be averted by constructing a solar shield at the L_1 Lagrange point between Earth and the Sun.
2. Venus and Mars may have been more Earthlike in the distant past, but they evolved along very different climatic paths.
   a. Venus lost its water because it was too close to the Sun. After that, CO_2 and sulfur gases accumulated, forming the hot, dense atmosphere that exists today.
   b. Mars had liquid water flowing on its surface early in its history, despite the lower solar luminosity at that time. A dense CO_2 atmosphere filled with clouds of CO_2 ice may have provided the necessary greenhouse warming. Mars may have cooled down because it was too small to maintain plate tectonics and to keep recycling CO_2 back into its atmosphere.
3. At least 300 Jupiter-sized planets have been detected around nearby main-sequence stars. Earth-sized planets have not yet been observed, but it should eventually be possible to look for them. Climate calculations predict that at least some of these planets should lie within the habitable zone around their parent star. Stars not too different from our Sun appear to be the best candidates for harboring habitable planets.
4. The information gleaned about climatic stability on Earth may be fed into the Drake equation to estimate the probability that advanced, technological civilizations exist elsewhere in the galaxy.
   a. Some of the factors in this equation are already known, and other factors may be determined observationally in the foreseeable future. In particular, we may be able to look for the presence of photosynthetic life on planets in other solar systems by analyzing their atmospheres spectroscopically and by looking for the presence of ozone.
   b. The largest single uncertainty in the Drake equation is the lifetime of a technological civilization, a factor that is largely under that civilization's control. If technological civilizations are able to persist for an appreciable fraction of their planet's lifetime, then the chances that other civilizations exist in our galaxy appear to be very good.

Key Terms

captured rotation
CO_2 compensation point
continuously habitable zone (CHZ)
coronagraph
Drake equation
Earthshine
ecosphere
extrasolar planets

habitable zone (HZ)
interferometer
Lagrange points
main-sequence star
photorespiration
radial velocity method
red giant
runaway glaciation

runaway greenhouse
spectroscopy
super-Earth
tidal locking radius
transit
white dwarf

Review Questions

1. How should future solar evolution affect climate and life here on Earth?
2. What is the evidence that Venus once possessed more water than it does today? How did it lose its water, and how did its atmosphere evolve afterward?
3. What is the evidence that Mars was warmer and wetter in the past? Why did Mars cool off over time, even though the Sun has become brighter?
4. How is the habitable zone around a star defined?
5. What is the relationship between the instantaneous habitable zone and the continuously habitable zone around the Sun? How wide are these zones thought to be?
6. Why are bright, blue stars and dim, red stars not good candidates for supporting habitable planets?
7. What factors in the Drake equation are we capable of estimating today?
8. How do we know that planets exist around other stars? How many such planets have been detected to date?
9. How might the presence of life on another planet be inferred from the composition of that planet's atmosphere?
10. What factors might limit the lifetime of a technological civilization? Could any of today's global environmental problems (global warming, ozone depletion, and loss of biodiversity) destroy our technological society?

Critical-Thinking Problems

1. The inner edge of the HZ is currently estimated to be at a distance of 0.95 AU from the Sun. Where would it have been 4.6 b.y. ago when solar luminosity was about 70% of its present value? Would Venus, which orbits the Sun at a distance of 0.72 AU, have been inside or outside this critical distance? (*Hint:* Remember the inverse-square law.)

2. How long do you think our present, technological civilization will last, and what factor (or combination of factors) do you think will bring it to an end? Write a one- to two-page typewritten essay defending your opinion.

Further Reading

General

Bennett, Jeffrey. 2008. *Beyond UFOs: The search for extraterrestrial life and its astonishing implications for our future.* Princeton, NJ: Princeton University Press.

Dorminey, B. 2002. *Distant wanderers: The search for planets beyond the solar system.* New York: Copernicus Books.

Kasting, J. F. In press. *How to find a habitable planet.* Princeton, NJ: Princeton University Press.

Sagan, C. 1980. *Cosmos.* New York: Random House.

Ward, P., and D. Brownlee. 2000. *Rare Earth: Why complex life is uncommon in the universe.* New York: Copernicus Books.

Ward, P., and D. Brownlee. 2003. *The life and death of planet Earth.* New York: Times Books.

Advanced

Angel, R. 2006. Feasibility of cooling the Earth with a cloud of small spacecraft near the inner Lagrange point (L1). *Proceedings of the National Academy of Sciences of the United States of America* 103 (46): 17184–89.

Caldeira, K., and J. F. Kasting. 1992. The life span of the biosphere revisited. *Nature* 360:721–23.

FIGURE 3 The surface of Venus, as observed by radar from the Magellan spacecraft. (*Source:* Jet Propulsion Laboratory, NASA Headquarters.)

Human Threats to Biodiversity

Key Questions

- Where is species loss occurring, and why?
- Why should we care about species loss?

- Could the loss of biodiversity have important consequences for humans and for the health of the Earth system?

Chapter Overview

Humans are responsible for a rate of species extinction that rivals any of the mass extinctions Earth has experienced in the past. Most of this species loss is occurring as a result of human land-use practices that destroy natural habitats, and we may soon reach the point at which not only are species becoming extinct, but we are destroying whole ecosystems. This species loss is particularly severe in tropical rainforests. Focusing on ecosystems rather than simply considering individual species is important. The loss of biodiversity could affect the health or stability of the planet and may well threaten world food supplies.

INTRODUCTION

In this chapter we address the issue of biodiversity and the loss of species. The rate of species loss due to human activity in the present is equal to, or greater than, the rate of species loss that marked past mass extinctions, and that most of this loss is caused by changes in land use.

It is generally thought that one-third to one-half of all land surfaces have been transformed by human activity and even areas that have been set aside from development (forest preserves, national parks, etc.) are usually not entirely "natural" systems—most are managed or manipulated in some way. Is this human imprint a bad thing? In the context of this text, we could say—not at all. Ecosystems are subsets of the (global) biosphere—assemblages of animal, plant, fungal, and microbial species that interact with each other and their surrounding environment. Ecosystems are not static and that they are not divorced from their environment: Environmental change can lead to ecosystem changes, and ecosystems can change their environment.

Humans can simply be regarded as one of the species in the global ecosystem. We interact with other species and with our environment and, in doing so, we modify that environment, just like any other component of the system. The only difference—and it is a big one—is that we now have the capability to produce major changes on a global scale. In that sense, we are certainly quantitatively different from other components of the system. Again, we can ask if this is a problem, but the answer this time is "it depends." From a global systems perspective, this is probably not an issue. We already know that no matter how much greenhouse gas we add to the atmosphere, the climate change will be less than the kinds of climate change Earth has experienced in the past. (We are thinking here specifically of the Snowball Earth episodes.) If our actions result in wholesale mass extinction, the topic of this chapter, we also know from that over millions of years the system will recover.

So what's the problem? We can answer this two different ways. On the one hand, we can say that this is a valid but maybe somewhat bleak worldview, albeit a rather convenient one that tends to absolve us of responsibility. On the other, we could argue that we are not qualitatively the same as other species. Our intelligence and our ability to conceive of abstract notions of right and wrong, and the fact that we can think in terms of ethical rights and responsibilities, all suggest that we play a qualitatively different role in the ecosystem. We would certainly make that argument—but not necessarily in the context of this text. Although we will return to the moral issue later, for most of this chapter we will take a more pragmatic approach and ask whether the actions we are taking are likely to have serious detrimental effects to ourselves.

It turns out that even this is not an easy question to address. The implications of species loss can be harder to grasp than are those of other environmental threats we have discussed previously. It is relatively easy to see the impact of the loss of stratospheric ozone or of a change in climate. Most of us have experienced extreme summers or winters in the past and can imagine what it might be like if those extremes were to become the norm in the future. Few of us, however, have any direct experience of species loss or of the consequences that it might entail.

Recall that a definition of a species is that it consists of closely related organisms that can potentially interbreed. On evolutionary time scales, new species continuously develop and others go extinct; in fact, the average lifetime of most species is between 1 and 10 million years. When we consider that life has been present on Earth for the past 3.5 billion years, it is apparent that many species have evolved and disappeared over that time period. Indeed, most of the species that have ever lived are now extinct. However, the fossil record shows that the rate of **speciation** (the origination of new species) is slightly greater on average than the rate of extinction. Consequently, there are more species today than there have ever been at any single time in the past.

- How many species are living today? We do not know for certain. Approximately 1.4 million species have been described, and new species are being found faster than they can be catalogued.

- How many more species have yet to be discovered? Estimates range from 10 million to 100 million. Beetles make up a large proportion of the known species, prompting J. B. S. Haldane's famous quote (referring to the work of Darwin), "From the fact that there are 400,000 species of beetles on this planet, but only 8,000 species of mammals, he [Haldane] concluded that the Creator, if He exists, has a special preference for beetles" (report of a lecture given by Haldane in 1951). However, despite the preponderance of beetles, there are certainly still many plant and invertebrate species yet to be discovered.

- How many species go extinct each year? Again, we do not know. The estimates are based on the proportion of species that are lost; hence they also depend on the estimates used for the existing number of species.

It is difficult to obtain reliable numbers on extinction rates. We do not know how many species there are and it is likely that many species go extinct without us ever knowing they existed. Based on what little we do know, some estimates suggest that at the present rate of extinction, one-quarter of all species on Earth may be lost within the next 50 years. If we accept 100 million as the number of existing species, then the extinction rate is half a million species per year. If 10 million is closer to reality, then the extinction rate is approximately 50,000 species each year. This is a somewhat circular argument! In addition, we are multiplying the number of species (which we don't know) by an extinction rate (that we also don't know) to arrive at a number of extinctions per year that obviously has little real quantifiable meaning. However, it is probably safe to say that a substantial number of species disappear every day as a direct consequence of human activity.

Why is this massive species loss occurring, and does it make a difference to us? These are the questions that we address in this chapter. Before we do, it is important to note that there is likely to be some uncertainty in many of the numbers presented here. While some information is factual—we have evidence of certain species going extinct in a particular location at a particular time—much of what we report here concerns estimates of species loss and habitat destruction. How these estimates are made varies by country and region and over time. Estimates of habitat destruction may be made by field surveys, satellite analyses, or interviews with landowners. Estimates of species loss depend on how well we know the existing species, which again varies by region, and what we know about the relationship between extinction and habitat loss for a particular ecosystem in any given region. Frequently, these estimates are made on detailed studies of small regions, which are then extrapolated to the larger scale. Furthermore, any large-scale analysis is expensive and time consuming, so they tend to be infrequent. The result of all this is that there is large uncertainty in these numbers, and the numbers you see quoted may be fairly old, which means that you often find little agreement in the published estimates from different sources. This is not a major problem for our purposes here—the estimates of species loss and habitat destruction are sufficiently large that it is obvious that a problem exists, even though precise numbers may not be available.

Much of our discussion in this chapter revolves around ecosystems. Note, however, that we know very little about ecosystems from an Earth systems perspective. Although some studies describe the cycling of a particular nutrient through a given ecosystem or the transfer of energy or water through that ecosystem, there are very few studies of how any particular ecosystem functions in its totality. Furthermore, we have little idea of how a particular assemblage or distribution of ecosystems interacts at the global scale. Ecologists have been studying ecosystems for some time and have made extensive use of systems theory. We could fill this chapter with diagrams illustrating the different functions of numerous ecosystems, but none of them would answer the questions posed earlier: Why is the species loss occurring? Should we care about it?

There is a possible relationship among diversity, community stability, and environmental stability; however, very little work has actually been done along these lines. In the remainder of this chapter, we describe some of the ecosystems in which species are being lost and some of the reasons why this loss is occurring. We then talk about the value of species, revisiting the idea that biodiversity is vital for the long-term health of our planet.

The Importance of Ecosystems

Why is the concept of an ecosystem important in our discussion of biodiversity and species loss? When we deal with systems, a perturbation to one part of the system can have impacts throughout the system. Because there is an interdependency among species in an ecosystem, if one species is removed, the loss of other species may follow. How significant a loss will depend on the role that the removed species plays in the ecosystem. Biodiversity should not be measured simply in terms of the number of species but should also describe the interactions among those species. We can suggest further that to know the number of interactions might not be sufficient; it is quite likely that interactions among some species will be more important than others. Ecologists use the term **keystone species** to describe a species that plays a vital role in the operation of an ecosystem.

The El Niño–Southern Oscillation (ENSO) events provide a graphic illustration of the importance of ecosystems. When the westward-flowing ocean current in the tropical Pacific Ocean slows, warm water flows back toward the South American coast, preventing the upwelling of cold, nutrient-rich water off the coasts of Peru and Ecuador. The loss of these nutrients prevents the growth of the phytoplankton that form the basic food source for the local fish population. The reduction of the fish population in turn results in the loss of the birds that feed on those fish. The end result is a massive drop-off in the marine and bird populations and a drastic change in the local ecosystem.

These losses are not permanent: After several years the populations gradually grow back to their previous levels. If there were a drop-off of species found only in this locality, however, such a disturbance could easily lead to their extinction. In fact, the warmer waters that appeared off the western coast of South America during the 1982 ENSO event also killed large areas of coral, and three coral species that lived only in this area went extinct.

THE MODERN EXTINCTION

The Beginnings

The modern mass extinction episode began when the first humans evolved and spread to colonize larger and larger areas (Figure 1). Estimates suggest that approximately 70% of the large mammal genera of the late Pleistocene epoch are extinct. A similar percentage of the large bird genera has also been lost. The archeological evidence shows that the losses coincide with the spread of human populations:

- When the first humans arrived in Madagascar in about A.D. 500 there were 6 to 12 species of large flightless birds, 17 genera of lemurs, and numerous species of other large birds and mammals. Within a very short time the flightless birds were gone, as were seven of the lemur genera, plus one species of aardvark, a pygmy hippopotamus, and two species of large land tortoises.
- Humans arrived in New Zealand around A.D. 1000. Since then, 20 species of large land birds and 22 other species of flightless birds have been hunted to extinction.
- As they spread through the western Pacific, the Polynesians killed off more than half of the native species they found. Species that are indigenous, or native, to a particular location are called **endemic species**. The distribution of these species is limited to relatively small geographic spaces and are, therefore, most at risk of extinction if their habitat is lost or degraded.
- The native Hawaiians extinguished 35 to 55 species of land birds. Fifty species remained when Captain Cook arrived in 1778, and one-third of those are now extinct.

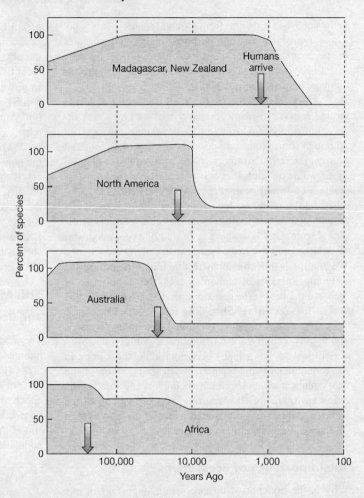

FIGURE 1 The extinction of large mammals and birds corresponds to the spread of human populations. Humans evolved first in Africa; in fact, they coevolved with other animals there over millions of years. As a result, the curve for Africa stands out from the others.   (*Source:* E. O. Wilson, *The Diversity of Life*, New York: Norton, 1992.)

There is evidence of a similar loss of species in North America. The first humans who crossed from Siberia into North America found vast grasslands with herds of large mammals, including bison, antelope, and mammoth, together with numerous large birds and other mammals that are now extinct. However, there is an additional explanation for the North American extinction besides hunting. The Pleistocene was a period of large glacial advances and retreats, which accompanied significant swings in mid- and high-latitude climate. Fossil evidence suggests that anomalously high extinction rates coincided with large climate changes. Humans arrived in Australia 30,000 years ago, and there is fossil evidence of the existence of a large number of species that are now extinct. However, the extinction was more gradual than elsewhere, and Australia suffered a long period of drought between 26,000 and 15,000 years ago, when the most rapid species loss also occurred.

When attributing blame for the extinctions in North America and Australia, a good case can be made for both climate change and overhunting. However, in other parts of the world, such as New Zealand, the Pacific islands, and Madagascar, there is no indication of a significant climate change. In those areas, the evidence supporting overhunting appears overwhelming.

The Present Day

As we move forward in time, the predominant agent of destruction has changed from overhunting to habitat destruction, and the pace of species loss has increased dramatically. Across Europe, from the hedgerows of southern Britain to the vine-covered hills of Cyprus, are widely diverse landscapes and ecosystems; all of them, except for the high peaks of the Alps and the Pyrenees, have been created by human activity. It is becoming increasingly difficult, if not impossible, to find landscapes anywhere in the world that have not been modified in some way by human actions. Today this activity almost always involves changes in land use, resulting in habitat destruction and species loss. With few exceptions, human land use leads to a reduction in biological complexity and reduced biodiversity. One interesting exception is the hedgerows of southern England. The original forest was cleared and the land used for cultivation. Later, the large medieval fields were subdivided, and hedgerows were planted to separate the individual fields. These hedgerows actually support a more diverse ecosystem than did the original forest. However, changes in farming practices are leading to the removal of many of these hedgerows in the latest chapter of human modifications to the British landscape.

FIGURE 2 Distribution of tropical rainforest. (*Source:* Adapted from the United Nations Food and Agricultural Organization, Global Forest Resources Assessment, 2000.)

TROPICAL DEFORESTATION The greatest rate of species loss today is found in the tropical forests (Figure 2). The climates of these forest regions are characterized by high rainfall (in excess of 2 m/yr), high mean annual temperatures, and low seasonal contrasts. For the most part, the forests are located in the areas of trade-wind convergence associated with the Hadley circulation.

These forests cover approximately 7% of the land surface, yet they are thought to contain over half of the planet's plant and animal species. The importance of the tropical forests is illustrated in Figure 3, which shows the number of species (amphibians, birds, mammals, and reptiles) in various terrestrial biomes, together with the number of species that are endemic to that biome.

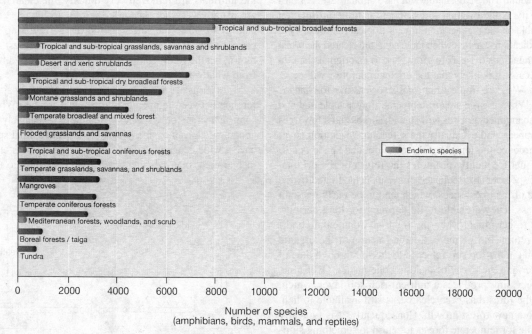

FIGURE 3 The number of species in different terrestrial biomes (*Source:* R. Lindsey, "Tropical Deforestation," NASA Earth Observatory Reference, 2007, (http://earthobservatory.nasa.gov/Library/Deforestation/.)

The dominance of the tropical forest is very clear. Great Britain has 1,430 species of flowering plants and 35 native tree species, whereas the Malay Peninsula, with only half the area of Great Britain, has 7,900 flowering plants and 2,500 native tree species. Of the slightly more than 9,000 known bird species in the world, almost half live in the Amazon Basin or in Indonesia. Studies in Peru found 300 tree species in a 2.5-acre plot (approximately 10,000 m^2), and 1,000 tree species were found in a combined census of ten 2.5-acre plots in Borneo. In contrast, there are only 700 native tree species in the whole of the United States and Canada. Quite obviously, the greatest potential for species loss is in the tropical forests. However, although this chapter focuses on loss of biodiversity, it is important to recognize that tropical deforestation has other regional and global consequences (see the Box "A Closer Look: Other Consequences of Tropical Deforestation").

Impact of Forest Clearance   There are no hard and fast rules, but in general the number of species living in a tropical rainforest is related to the area of forest coverage: A 10-fold increase in area results in double the number of species. Applying these numbers to the Atlantic coast of Brazil, where the forest has been reduced to less than 1% of its original cover, suggests that the forest biota may have already decreased by 75%. Similar losses are occurring throughout the tropics. Harvard University biologist Edward O. Wilson concludes that, even using the most optimistic and conservative estimates, 27,000 species are lost each year—that is, 74 species per day or 3 species every hour—simply as a consequence of tropical deforestation.

If an area of temperate forest is cleared and then abandoned, something very similar to the original forest will grow back within 100 years, and it will have similar levels of biodiversity as the original forest. There is little information available on the regeneration time of tropical rainforests, but the indications are that when large areas are cleared the forest takes hundreds of years to grow back to its original state. In some cases it is likely that the original rainforest will never return. Why are tropical rainforests so sensitive to change?

When a large area of temperate forest is cleared and then abandoned, grasses will spread, shrubs and a few trees will appear, and eventually the spreading vegetation cover will produce the temperature, moisture, and shade conditions that frequently promotes the return of the original forest species. This sequence of events is facilitated by the nature of the trees' seeds, which tend to be fairly resistant to stress. They are able to lie dormant for long periods, ready to germinate when the right environmental conditions return. Furthermore, a large fraction of the organic material in the forest is returned to the soil through the fall of litter and the decay of dead organic matter. Over time, this recycling produces a nutrient-rich soil layer, which, after the forest has been cleared, is still available to help promote new forest growth. Consequently, it is typically possible for temperate forests to return to something similar to the original forest cover.

The situation in tropical forests is very different. Figure 4 illustrates the nutrient flow through a forest–soil system. In simple terms, there are three primary nutrient reservoirs: the trees, the litter, and the soil. The transfer of nutrients to the litter is controlled by the death rate, the transfer to the soil is determined by the rate of decomposition, and the transfer back to the trees depends on the photosynthetic uptake. Tropical forests return little organic matter and few nutrients to the soil. When trees die and decompose, the nutrients in them are returned to the living biomass very quickly. This scenario implies a very efficient nutrient recycling system: higher temperatures and moisture conditions favor rapid decomposition, whereas extensive root systems (roots constitute 60% of the biomass) extract the nutrients from the soil very quickly. In tropical forests, therefore, high rates of decomposition and photosynthetic uptake cycle the nutrients rapidly through the soil and back to the trees, making the living biomass the major nutrient reservoir. In temperate forests the rate of decomposition is lower, as is the rate of photosynthetic uptake, and nutrients tend to accumulate in the organic litter and in the soil.

There is a further important difference between tropical and temperate forests. After rainforests have been cleared, heavy rains, characteristic of the tropics, wash away much of the organic material that does enter the soil, leaving behind soils that are very acidic and nutrient deficient. In contrast to the seeds of temperate forest plants, the seeds of the tropical forest plants tend to be less resistant to stress and typically germinate within a few weeks. For small clearings this is not a problem: Dead organic matter is rapidly broken down, releasing nutrients that are used for new growth. Where the clearing is extensive, however, the nutrients are removed very quickly, the cleared areas are usually very hot (because there is no longer a forest canopy to shade the surface), and the germinating seeds cannot survive. Eventually vegetation and a forest cover return, but the forest composition is normally very different from what was there before the land was cleared.

In terms of species loss, there is yet another major difference between temperate and tropical forests. Whereas some temperate forest species are confined to relatively small geographic locations, many of the plant and animal species have a wide geographic distribution. If the forest is cleared in one area, many of the species will continue to thrive

FIGURE 4   Nutrient flow through a forest–soil system.

A CLOSER LOOK
Other Consequences of Tropical Deforestation

Clearing tropical forests and converting the land to other purposes, such as agriculture and grazing, has other consequences besides contributing to an overall loss of biodiversity. At the local scale, deforestation tends to result in soil degradation and increased erosion. Without the continuous addition of fertilizer, the nutrient-poor soils rapidly lose their usefulness for agriculture. Where before much of the rainfall was intercepted by the tree canopy, now more of it reaches the surface directly, leading to erosion, which increases as agricultural productivity and surface cover decrease. The result is very rapid soil loss. Deforestation also has an effect on local rainfall. Estimates from the Amazon Basin indicate that approximately half its precipitation is derived from recycled water. In other words, rainfall occurs and the water is intercepted by the canopy; some is used by the trees and some is returned to the atmosphere through evapotranspiration, the combined effect of water loss by evaporation and by transpiration (the transfer of water, in vapor form, from plants to the atmosphere through pores in the leaves). The water that is returned to the atmosphere falls again as rain elsewhere in the basin. When large areas of forest are cleared, a large proportion of the rainfall is lost as runoff, evapotranspiration decreases, and rainfall over the basin as a whole decreases. Several groups of researchers have used atmospheric general circulation models to examine these processes. The models suggest that deforestation has its greatest impact on the local climate by changing the albedo, the surface hydrology, and the surface roughness. (Surface roughness is important because it affects the windflow, which, in turn, affects evaporation and the transfer of latent and sensible heat.)

One such study was carried out in 1989 by J. Lean and D. Warrilow at the British Meteorological Office. They simulated the replacement of all the tropical forests and savannahs in South America (north of 30° S) by tropical pastures and examined the effect that this simulation had on the climate model. Box Table1 presents some of the results, comparing observational data with the model simulation before (the control run) and after the deforestation. We can see from the table that the control run produces a little too much rainfall and runoff and slightly underestimates evaporation, but it generally produces a climate very similar to the observed climate.

More interestingly, when we compare the deforestation experiment with the control run, we see some major differences and some interesting contradictions. Overall, the hydrologic cycle is weakened, which is what we would expect, except that runoff decreases instead of increases. Also, the net radiation (the total amount of available energy) decreases, but temperature goes up. The reasons for this lie in the multiple interactions that occur in the climate system. The pasture has a higher albedo than that of the forest or the savannah, so deforestation increases the albedo and reduces the incoming solar energy. These effects contributed to the decrease in net radiation. Temperatures go up instead of down, however, because, prior to deforestation, evaporation had a cooling effect on the forest; when the forest is removed and evaporation decreases, the cooling effect is reduced and temperatures increase despite the reduction in net radiation.

The surface runoff is determined by several factors, including the rate at which water infiltrates the soil (which is the only soil parameter changed in this model for the deforested case). The infiltration rate is reduced for the deforested soil, so runoff should increase. However, runoff is also affected by the intensity and frequency of the precipitation events. Infrequent, high-intensity events deliver rain to the surface faster than the soil can remove it, and there is high runoff. If the same amount of rain falls in more-frequent, less-intense events, water is delivered to the surface at a slower rate, more infiltrates, and runoff is reduced. In the deforestation case, runoff is reduced because, although less water infiltrates the soil and is held by the vegetation, there is also a decrease in frequency and intensity of rainfall events. The soil moisture shown in Box Table 1 is not the total amount stored in the soil but actually the amount that is available to the vegetation. The decrease that the model shows in available soil moisture is due to the rooting depth of the vegetation: The shallower roots of the pasture cannot reach down far enough to tap the water that exists at greater depth. These and additional interactions are illustrated in a systems diagram (Box Figure 1). Here we see that runoff and temperature have both positive and negative couplings from other system components, thus allowing for their apparent contradictory response to what we might, at first, have expected. Numerous other model experiments have been carried out since the late 1980s. Some show similar temperature changes while others show a smaller change, but all show a large impact on precipitation and evaporation—indicating that the presence or absence of the forest has a significant impact on the regional climate.

BOX TABLE 1	Impacts of Deforestation on Local Climate		
Surface Variable	Observed	Control*	Deforested*
Evaporation (mm/d)	3.34	3.12	2.27 (−27.2%)
Precipitation (mm/d)	5.26	6.60	5.26 (−20.3%)
Soil moisture (cm)		16.13	6.66 (−58.7%)
Runoff (mm/d)	2.76	3.40	3.00 (−11.9%)
Net radiation (W/m²)		147.3	126.0 (−14.5%)
Temperature (°C)	24.0	23.6	26.0 (+2.4°C)

*Model simulations are averaged over 3 years.

Source: Adapted from J. Lean and D. Warrilow, "Simulation of the Regional Climatic Impact of Amazon Deforestation," Nature 342, 1989, pp. 411–413.

(continued)

A CLOSER LOOK (CONTINUED)

BOX FIGURE 1 Systems diagram linking tropical forest cover with global climate as well as local climate and hydrologic parameters.

In addition to these local effects, deforestation has an impact on the global climate. Some recent studies suggest that tropical deforestation can also affect rainfall over larger areas. Some model results, for example, show that Amazon deforestation could affect rainfall distributions in Mexico and Texas. The tropical forests also represent a large store of organic carbon. When the forests are cut and burned to clear the land for agricultural use, this carbon is returned to the atmosphere as carbon dioxide, which contributes to the buildup of atmospheric greenhouse gases. Approximately half of the postindustrial increase in atmospheric CO_2 has come from tropical deforestation.

elsewhere and can eventually return to recolonize the cleared regions. Some tropical forest species also have extensive distributions, but a significant proportion of the plant and animal species live only in very small geographic areas. Over time, the overall forest structure might not change and the same families of plant and animal life will be present, but the actual species composition can change very rapidly. Thus, when a large area of tropical forest is cleared, all the species that were found only in that area go extinct.

There were about 8 million km^2 of tropical rainforest in 1989—half of what existed in prehistoric times. In the late 1980s, this forest was being removed at a rate of 1.8% (140,000 km^2) per year. The total global cover of tropical rainforest in 1989 was approximately equal to the area of the contiguous 48 states of the United States; at a clearance rate of 1.8%, an area of tropical forest the size of Florida was being removed each year. The Food and Agriculture Organization (FAO) of the United Nations estimates that the rate of forest clearance in the tropics was slightly lower in the 1990s, but that the difference is not statistically significant. The FAO does not provide numbers for tropical forests as a single category, but it does present data by country, and the reports and data for the 2005 assessment of global forest resources are downloadable from the FAO website (http://www.fao.org/foresry/fra2005/en/). A NASA

study took the top 20 countries that cleared the most forest between 1990 and 2005, and all of them contain tropical forest, with the largest losses being in Brazil and Indonesia (Figure 5). What effect does this have on biodiversity and species loss? If a million years is the typical lifetime of a species, then the normal extinction rate is one in 1 million species per year. If we use 10 million as a conservative estimate of the number of species that live in the rainforests, then the background extinction rate should be 10 species per year. What is the actual extinction rate? No one knows for certain, but we presented Wilson's estimates earlier: 27,000 species per year due to forest clearance alone. Even with these conservative estimates, the extinction rate due to human activity is 3,000 times greater than the background rate of extinction.

Reasons for Forest Clearance   Why is so much forest being destroyed? The superficial response is to say that the forests are cleared for logging; to open new areas for agriculture and cattle ranching; and for large-scale development, which includes hydroelectric projects, exploitation of mineral resources, resettlement projects, and so on. Approximately 8 million hectares (80,000 km^2) of forest are cleared for agriculture each year. These numbers (and the ones that follow for logging and ranching) are from the

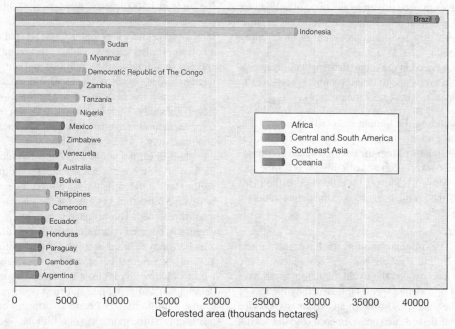

FIGURE 5 Area of forest lost from the 20 countries that cleared the most forest between 1990 and 2005. (*Source:* R. Lindsey, "Tropical Deforestation," NASA Earth Observatory Reference, 2007, http://earthobservatory.nasa.gov/ Library/Deforestation/.) The NASA figure is based on data from the 2005 UN Food and Agriculture Organization Global Forest Resource Assessment.

1980s. The proportions may have changed slightly in the 1990s, but they still give a good estimate of how the bulk of the forest clearing is occurring. For agricultural production, the traditional procedure is to cut and burn the forest and then use the cleared area to grow crops, a practice known as *slash-and-burn* agriculture. The burning releases nutrients to the soil and provides fertilizer for the crops. After several seasons the nutrients are depleted, and the farmer moves on to slash and burn a new area. This is not necessarily as wasteful as it sounds: If the areas are small and the old fields are left fallow for a sufficient time (up to 30 years), enough vegetation grows back that nutrient levels are replenished and the area can be burned and cultivated again. Problems occur when large areas are cleared or when the vegetation is not given enough time to regenerate. In these cases the soil loses its fertility, crop yields decrease, and permanent soil degradation is commonly the end result. This type of damage is normally caused by population increase; however, in some areas extensive deforestation is caused by the production of commercial crops (cash crops), which are typically used for export, by large agricultural plantations.

Apart from agriculture, approximately 50,000 km^2 of forest is cleared for timber, pulp, and other wood products each year. The most extensive logging is taking place in Asia and West Africa. Approximately half of what is cut is exported, with Japan taking the largest amount and the United States being the next largest importer. Wood is also cut for fuel use: For almost half the world's population,

wood is the principal energy source for cooking and heating. Large areas are also being cleared for cattle ranching— approximately 20,000 km^2 per year in Latin America. Much of the beef once went to the United States, but most Latin American beef is now consumed in Latin America or in Europe. Cattle ranching is particularly destructive, because once large areas are cleared for pasture, soil degradation, erosion, and compaction from hooves and vehicles soon makes the land unusable, requiring more forest to be cleared.

The previous description reflects the obvious transition from one land cover, the forest, to something else, as the human use of the land changes. What it hides is a multitude of social, economic, and political forces that are causing the land use to change. The particular combination of factors varies from place to place and through time, but examples might include the following:

- Growing population pressures that force an increasing number of people into the forested areas, requiring an expansion of food crops.
- Unequal division of land that results in a very small proportion of the population owning a very large fraction of the existing developed land. This arrangement forces people who do not own land to develop new areas, encroaching farther and farther into the forest.
- Deliberate resettlement programs in which governments encourage migration into the forests to reduce population pressures elsewhere. Such programs

themselves may be driven by the hope of solving (or hiding) political and economic problems in other areas—poverty and unemployment in large cities, for example.

- A growing need in the industrializing nations to produce cash crops and to develop mineral resources to pay ever-increasing international debts.

Understanding the human factors that are causing forest clearance in a particular location is essential if efforts are to be made to stem the tide of tropical deforestation. Preaching conservation and offering plans for the sustainable use of forest resources do little good if the plans do not address the problems that led to the deforestation in the first place.

HOTSPOTS The tropical rainforests have the largest extinction rates, but they are not the only places where species are at risk. Around the world, numerous areas have large numbers of endemic species threatened by the loss of habitat. In the late 1980s, Norman Myers of Oxford University identified 18 such areas. In each case the habitat had been reduced to less than 10% of its original cover or was expected to be reduced to that amount within the next few decades. This work was expanded and updated in the late 1990s. Myers and colleagues defined regions containing a distinct and identifiable assemblage of plant and animal species as "biogeographic units." **Hotspots** in this study were then defined as biogeographic units containing at least 0.5% of the world's 300,000 known vascular plants

(i.e., at least 1,500 different plant species). In addition, to be considered a hotspot, the region must have also lost 70% or more of its primary vegetation. Once an area was defined as a hotspot, further data were also collected on the vertebrate species (mammals, birds, reptiles, and amphibians—fish were excluded because of generally poor data availability).

Twenty-five hotspots were identified—up from 18 in the earlier study. Their locations are shown in Figure 6 and some of their characteristics in Table 1. These 25 hotspots comprise only 1.4% of Earth's land surface, yet contain almost half of all the world's species of vascular plants and 35% of all vertebrate species (again excluding fish). These regions are, at the same time, amongst the most biologically diverse terrestrial systems on the planet—and also the most threatened. The primary vegetation in these regions originally covered approximately 17.5 million km^2. This area has been reduced to a little over 2 million km^2—just 12% of the original cover. A considerable amount of the world's biodiversity (at least as counted by numbers of endemic plant and vertebrate spiecies) is, therefore, confined to just 2 million km^2 of earth's surface. For comparison, this is only a little more than one-fifth the size of the United States.

Myers and colleagues analyzed the biodiversity data in a number of ways and identify the regions most threatened if we continue present rates of habitat destruction. Madagascar, the Philippines, and Sunderland rise to the top of the list. Also in the most threatened category are Brazil's Atlantic forest, the Caribbean, the tropical Andes, and the Mediterranean basin. Organizations such as

FIGURE 6 Hotspots of habitat loss—areas with many species that live nowhere else and that are in greatest danger of extinction as a result of human activities. (*Source:* N. Myers et al., "Biodiversity Hotspots for Conservation Priorities," *Nature* 403, 2000, pp. 853–858.)

TABLE 1 The 25 Hotspots Identified by Norman Myers and Colleagues

Hotspot	Remaining Primary Vegetation (km²) (% of original extent)		Plant Species	Endemic Plants (% of the 300,000 global plants)		Endemic Vertebrates (% of 27,298 global vertebrates)[1]	
Tropical Andes	314,500	(25.0)	45,000	20,000	(6.7)	1,567	(5.7)
Mesoamerica	231,000	(20.0)	24,000	5,000	(1.7)	1,159	(4.2)
Caribbean	29,840	(11.3)	12,000	7,000	(2.3)	779	(2.9)
Brazil's Atlantic Forest	91,930	(7.5)	20,000	8,000	(2.7)	567	(2.1)
Choc/Darien/Western Ecuador	63,000	(24.2)	9,000	2,250	(0.8)	418	(1.5)
Brazil's Cerrado	356,630	(20.0)	10,000	4,400	(1.5)	117	(0.4)
Central Chile	90,000	(30.0)	3,429	1,605	(0.5)	61	(0.2)
California Floristic Province	80,000	(24.7)	4,426	2,125	(0.7)	71	(0.3)
Madagascar[2]	59,038	(9.9)	12,000	9,704	(3.2)	771	(2.8)
Eastern Arc & Coastal Forests of Tanzania/Kenya	2,000	(6.7)	4,000	1,500	(0.5)	121	(0.4)
Western African Forests	126,500	(10.0)	9,000	2,250	(0.8)	270	(1.0)
Cape Floristic Province	18,000	(24.3)	8,200	5,682	(1.9)	53	(0.2)
Succulent Karoo	30,000	(26.8)	4,849	1,940	(0.6)	45	(0.2)
Mediterranean Basin	110,000	(4.7)	25,000	13,000	(4.3)	235	(0.9)
Caucasus	50,000	(10.0)	6,300	1,600	(0.5)	59	(0.2)
Sundaland	125,000	(7.8)	25,000	15,000	(5.0)	701	(2.6)
Wallacea	52,020	(15)	10,000	1,500	(0.5)	529	(1.9)
Philippines	9,023	(3.0)	7,620	5,832	(1.9)	518	(1.9)
Indo-Burma	100,000	(4.9)	13,500	7,000	(2.3)	528	(1.9)
South-Central China	64,000	(8.0)	12,000	3,500	(1.2)	178	(0.7)
Western Ghats/Sri Lanka	12,450	(6.8)	4,780	2,180	(0.7)	355	(1.3)
SW Australia	33,336	(10.8)	5,469	4,331	(1.4)	100	(0.4)
New Caledonia	5,200	(28.0)	3,332	2,551	(0.9)	84	(0.3)
New Zealand	59,400	(22.0)	2,300	1,865	(0.6)	136	(0.5)
Polynesia/Micronesia	10,024	(21.8)	6,557	3,334	(1.1)	223	(0.8)
Totals	2,122,891	(12.2)	*	133,149	(44)	9,645	(35.0)

[1]Excludes fish.

[2]Madagascar includes nearby islands of Mauritius, Reunion, Seychelles, and Comores.

*Totals cannot be calculated because of overlap between hotspots.

Conservation International (http://www.conservation.org/xp/CIWEB/home) are using this information to try and target conservation funding. Conservation International has since updated its "Hotspot" analysis and has added several more regions to those shown in Figure 6 and Table 1. It now identifies 34 hotspots (http://www.biodiversityhotspots.org/Pages/default.aspx) with an interactive map that describes each location.

Myers's assessment is based on biodiversity, size of area, and degree of degradation. The analysis could be expanded in other socioeconomic dimensions to assess existing and potential socioeconomic pressures that result in habitat destruction in these regions. In the context of this book, we can also look at this with respect to other global pressures, such as global warming. Sixteen hotspots are in the tropics, while none are in the polar regions. This is the reverse of the potential global warming changes where the magnitude of the temperature change is greatest at high latitudes and least in the tropics. The remaining hotspots are predominantly mediterranean or sa-

vanna regions that are still very diverse, but also have the potential to see some significant climate change during this century. The *IPCC Climate Change 2001: Impacts, Adaptation and Vulnerability* report specifically focuses on the Cape Floristic Province and the Succulent Karoo in South Africa as examples of mediterranean and savanna hotspots that, beyond all of the existing threats to biodiversity, are further threatened as these geographic settings limit the ability of species to migrate as climate changes. These findings are also confirmed in the Fourth IPCC assessment report.

While these hotspots represent one attempt to identify biologically diverse regions that are under pressure from human activities, the list does not end here; many more places could be included. This discussion of hotspots neglects a huge area of the planet: the oceans. However, we know much less about life in the oceans than we do about the terrestrial biota. One ocean ecosystem that is receiving considerable attention at present is the coral reef. Despite its appearance, coral is actually an animal. Found in shallow tropical seas, coral reefs are the most productive and diverse of ocean ecosystems. The reef is dynamic, continuously changing, and very fragile. It is easily damaged by shifting sand and storms; left alone, it normally recovers quickly. However, most coral reefs are located close to shore, so any natural damage is now augmented by human activities, notably pollution, mining for coral rock, collection of coral specimens, overfishing, and damage from accidental grounding by ships.

Coral reefs tolerate only a narrow range of ocean temperatures between 21 and 29°C—growth rates are very slow at temperatures higher and lower than this. They also require sunlight for their symbiotic algae (*zooxanphellae*), so while they have been found at depths of 90 m (300 ft), they grow better at depths shallower than 18–27 m (60–90 ft). Consequently, coral reefs tend to occupy a very narrow range of coastal locations in the tropics (Figure 7). It is estimated that coral reefs cover a little over 280,000 km^2. However, they are found off the coasts of over 100 different countries and they are thought to contain at least 25% of all marine species, including 700 species of coral and over 4,000 different fish species.

While coral reefs all around the world are directly affected by human activities such as those listed above, possibly the greatest impact is likely to be an indirect ef-

fect of climate change. Increased ocean temperatures result in episodes of coral bleaching on many reefs. Bleaching is caused by the loss of the symbiotic zooxanthellae (single-celled algae that live in the tissue of the coral animals). This loss is considered to be a general response of the coral to stress. Stress can result from numerous causes, including excessive hot or cold temperatures, chemical pollution, or dilution by freshwater. Even a 1°C temperature rise, if it persists for a few days, can cause the coral to begin to expel its zooxanthellae. In recent years there have been documented occurrences of coral bleaching associated with ENSO events, and it is thought that an increased incidence of ENSO events may be one outcome of global warming. At the same time, one of the more certain impacts of global warming will also be a general increase in surface ocean temperatures. There is a further direct effect of increasing concentrations of atmospheric carbon dioxide. Additions of CO_2 to the atmosphere causes a reduction in the carbonate ion concentration of seawater. Carbonate and calcium ions are combined by corals as they build their skeletons. The reduction in carbonate ion concentration is another stress that is applied globally to all coral reefs. Taken together (increasing ocean temperatures, possible increases in ENSO events, and reduced carbonate ion concentrations),

FIGURE 7 Distribution of tropical coral reefs.

there is growing concern that damage to coral reefs may be a significant and early impact of global warming on the world's ecosystems.

Studies in the late 1990s suggested that almost 60% of the world's coral reefs may be threatened by human activity. A recent study led by Callum Roberts of Harvard University identified 10 marine biodiversity hotspots analogous to those described earlier for terrestrial systems. These are all coral reef systems covering almost a quarter of the world's coral reefs, and 8 out of 10 of these reefs are adjacent to terrestrial biodiversity hotspots. Many areas have attempted to reverse the damage by establishing marine parks and by controlling the human activities that take place on or near the reefs. These measures help prevent accidental damage to the reef but offer little protection from the more pervasive damage of environmental pollution and global warming.

WHY WE SHOULD CARE ABOUT BIODIVERSITY

You probably live in or close to a city; approximately half the world's population lives in urban areas. Although you may have seen one city building knocked down to be replaced by another or an open field turned into a shopping mall, you probably do not have much firsthand experience in large-scale habitat destruction. Unless you are a tropical ecologist or a scuba diver, the closest you may ever get to the backwaters of the Amazon or to a coral reef is a nature program on television. In the 1600s and 1700s, forests were cut down in Europe and in what would become the United States to power steam engines and to expand agriculture to support growing populations. You could say that, in doing so, we were able to support a workforce and develop the technology that eventually enabled us to see the remaining forests or the reefs on those television sets. You might also argue that if the industrializing nations need or want to do the same now, or if Californians prefer suburbs to chaparral, that is their decision and why should we get excited about it? These are valid questions. We are going to try to answer them in several ways—first by looking at why individual species may be important, and then by stepping back and looking at the importance of biodiversity to the Earth system as a whole.

Instrumental and Intrinsic Values of Species

Ecologists tend to discuss the value of a species in terms of its *instrumental* or *intrinsic value*. A species' **instrumental value** is the degree to which the existence of the species benefits another species in some way. We are normally the other species, and the value or benefit is typically economic. A species' **intrinsic value**, conversely, is its value for its own sake, regardless of whether we benefit by it or not. Some argue, for example, that all species and all individual organisms have the same rights to exist that humans

do—that humans have no greater value than any other species. Others argue that humans are unique: We dominate over nature, nature is ours to exploit, and other species have no individual rights per se. Still others argue that this very uniqueness in fact imposes a special responsibility: We are capable of moral and ethical judgments, and these should include concern for other species. Assigning an economic value is relatively easy; assigning intrinsic value, however, is a moral and ethical issue that is more subjective. The assignment of intrinsic value varies from society to society and from individual to individual, according to their outlook on nature.

INSTRUMENTAL VALUE   We can look at instrumental value from several perspectives. We can view species as being resources:

- *Medicine.*   Of all pharmaceuticals produced in the United States, 25% contain ingredients originally derived from native plants. The often-quoted example is a plant called the rosy periwinkle, which grows only on Madagascar and fortunately was not a victim of the large species loss that has occurred on the island. In the 1960s scientists extracted two substances from the plant: vincristine and vinblastine, which became our primary defense against childhood leukemia and Hodgkin's disease. Before the discovery of these drugs, childhood leukemia was almost always fatal; since the 1960s, with the use of vincristine, there is now a 95% chance of remission. These two drugs, developed from a single plant species, now represent a $100 million-a-year industry—just a small part of the $8 billion a year derived from pharmaceuticals based on "natural" products. How many other rosy periwinkles are waiting to be discovered, and how many disappear every year without us even knowing they existed?
- *Scientific value.*   Although a considerable amount of discovery takes place in scientific laboratories, much of what we know about evolution and ecology, and our understanding of how natural systems work, has been derived from the study of species and ecosystems in their natural state. However, our understanding of these systems and how they interact, particularly at the global scale, is far from complete. At the present rate of habitat destruction, we are in danger of wiping out whole ecosystems without ever understanding how they operate or what role they may have played in regional or larger-scale ecology.
- *Recreational and aesthetic value.*   It is difficult to assign a monetary amount to the scientific value of species and ecosystems. However, it is much easier to assign such a number to their recreational value. Each year, more than 50 million people in the United States spend a total of $38 billion on recreational hunting or fishing. There are also the millions of

people who escape the cities to spend their weekends or vacations walking, climbing, and photographing the mountains, forests, and beaches of the more "natural" parts of the world. They may sail on rivers, lakes, or the ocean, sit on shore and admire the view, or simply drive by and look. The continuing popularity of television nature shows also attests to the aesthetic value we place on the natural world, whether we ever get to see it in person or not.

- *Commerce.* There are both direct and indirect commercial benefits to be gained from the natural environment. Direct commercial interests revolve around activities such as logging, commercial fishing, and the collection and sale of exotic plant and animal species. Indirect benefits arise from recreational activities that support commercial interests, for example, in travel, accommodations, restaurants, sporting goods stores, and so on. The business of arranging tours to remote locations, such as trekking in the Himalayas and hunting and photographic safaris in East Africa, is thriving. There is also now a growing business in ecotourism, where tourists visit places specifically to observe rare or endangered species or ecosystems.
- *Agriculture, forestry, aquaculture, and animal husbandry.* Those of us who live in the developed world, in particular, tend to regard food production as simply one component of our industrialized society; we see little connection between miles of uniform crops and mechanized production, and the grasslands or forests that would otherwise be there. In reality, there is a very close connection, and the existence and maintenance of our agricultural food supply is much more dependent on natural species than many people realize. We will return to this connection when we look at the value of species from the perspective of a global system.

The Loss of Biodiversity

Now we will step back from individual species and consider the whole diversity of life. What are the consequences involved in the loss of that biodiversity?

BIODIVERSITY AND FOOD SUPPLY Biodiversity is of critical importance to the modern agricultural techniques we employ to feed our ever-growing global population. Most people are well aware of many of the local environmental problems that can arise from our attempts to increase productivity: soil degradation and erosion, salinization, groundwater pollution from fertilizer and pesticides, and so on. From our larger-scale or global perspective, however, a more serious problem is developing with respect to the basic ingredients we need for modern agriculture—the seeds themselves.

Early farmers and agronomists noted that some varieties of a crop are more productive, more disease-resistant,

or more drought-tolerant than others. The selective use of different strains or varieties resulted in increased productivity. Today biotechnology and gene splicing can produce new crop varieties to order. At first glance it is hard to see the problem: With modern techniques we can produce seeds with high yields and *uniform* characteristics. Crops can be planted, harvested, processed, packaged, and transported all with minimum human intervention—just what we need to keep the world fed. Unfortunately, we never quite manage to feed the world. However, the lack of adequate food supplies is a result of social, political, and economic factors that determine the global distribution of resources, not an inability to produce enough food for all. The potential problem with modern agriculture is not that it is not productive enough but that it is *uniform.*

We have already seen that the ability of an ecosystem to resist change is partly determined by its biodiversity. The same goes for individual species. A food crop such as corn or rice in its *natural* state is likely to consist of many different strains growing together. Some are more productive than others, some more drought-resistant; some would be resistant to one pest, others more resistant to a different pest. In any year, whatever the conditions, whatever pests flourish, there is a good chance that some corn or rice will grow, whichever strain is best adapted to that particular set of conditions.

Over time the environmental conditions change, and the pests and diseases that attack a particular plant evolve. At the same time the crop plant also changes, and new strains evolve that are resistant to the new conditions. Every strain carries its own particular genes. *Genes* are units of heredity; they control the life processes of all cells and contain the information that controls how the genes work—in other words, the information that produces exactly that strain of corn or rice. With thousands of subtly different strains, there is a vast natural reservoir of genetic material available that ensures the long-term health and survival of the species. Vitality depends on diversity.

However, the whole approach to modern agriculture is uniformity. The object is to reduce diversity as much as possible, to make a high-yield variety of a crop that is resistant to drought and a particular assemblage of pests and diseases. This variety flourishes for a few years until a new strain of pest or disease evolves, against which it has no defense. At that point it is back to the drawing board, or the biotechnology lab, where the scientists mix-and-match until they produce a corn variety that is resistant to the new conditions. Everything is fine for a few more years. So, where does the genetic mix-and-match material come from? It comes from very specialized seed banks that have been established around the world. We have not actually destroyed the diversity of our food crops, we have simply concentrated it in a few locations. The International Storage Center for Rice Genes in the Philippines, for example, keeps more than 86,000 varieties of rice. The geneticist needing some new rice strains to work with simply goes to the seed bank and makes a withdrawal.

But the genes in the seed bank are, in a sense, frozen in time. They represent the state of genetic diversity that the rice had achieved when the bank was established. The diseases and pests, conversely, do not live in seed banks—they exist in the wild and mutate and evolve, continuously producing new strains. In some cases they produce something that the seed bank cannot deal with. Then our only recourse is to return to the wild. The geneticist goes back to the "genetic home" of the species and searches for a wild variety that has the traits needed to solve this particular problem. However, if the natural habitat is destroyed, the only repository of genetic diversity is in seed banks, which are more vulnerable to accidents (such as fire), war, or sabotage.

Despite our modern techniques, despite seed banks and biotechnology, ultimately the health of our food crops depends on the continued survival of a diverse population of wild strains. This is where our real problem emerges.

Humans make use of a huge number of different food crops. Yet, the bulk of the world's food supply and animal feed comes from just 130 species of plants. The ultimate storehouses of the genetic material we need to ensure long-term health and high productivity are restricted to only 12 locations around the world. These 12 centers of genetic diversity, called *Vavilovian centers* in honor of Russian geneticist N. I. Vavilov, who first described them, are shown in Figure 8. Each of these centers is located in an area where population pressures or development are placing an increasing stress on the existing natural habitat.

Just how vulnerable we might be is illustrated by an episode in the late 1970s that threatened the rice crop of Southeast Asia. The rice, a basic food source for hundreds of millions of people in the region, was threatened by a disease called grassy stunt virus. Scientists searched through the gene banks—through 47,000 varieties of rice—and eventually found the genetic material that would allow the crop to resist the disease, in a single wild species from a valley in India. Soon after the retrieval of the material, the valley was flooded in the construction of a new hydroelectric project. Less fortunate were the Irish in the mid-1800s. It is thought that potatoes were cultivated by the Incas as early as 400 B.C. They were brought to Europe by the Spanish in the mid-16th century. Potatoes eventually became a staple crop for the Irish. The potato blight (a fungus, *Phytophthora infestans*) arrived at the end of the growing season in 1845. It had little effect that year, but the next year it completely devastated the potato crop. Together with other political, economic, and social factors that all played a role in the ensuing famine, the collapse of the farm economy killed over 1 million people and eventually forced the emigration of a further 1.5 million. Ireland lost over a quarter of its 8 million population. The blight is still present in various parts of the world, including the United States, where, in fact, there have been recent concerns that strains of the fungus have been developing that show increased resistance to the fungicides currently used to protect the crops.

FIGURE 8 The 12 centers of genetic diversity. All of the genetic diversity essential for maintaining the world's food supply is limited to just these 12 areas. (*Source:* S. C. Witt, *BriefBook: Biotechnology and Genetic Diversity*, San Francisco: CSI, 1985.)

BIODIVERSITY AND STABILITY As an extreme case of loss of biodiversity, imagine what would happen if we were suddenly to cut down all the world's forests. Would we suffocate? No, we would not quickly run out of oxygen, even though green plants are responsible for the buildup of oxygen that gave us the atmosphere we breathe today. Even if we removed all the photosynthesizing organisms on the land and the phytoplankton in the sea, it would still take us millions of years to suffocate. (You can calculate just how long in "Critical-Thinking" Problem 3 at the end of this chapter.)

We would not suffocate if we lost all the photosynthesizing organisms, but would we starve? Yes. Without these primary producers at the base of the food chain, all higher-order consumers, including humans, would quickly run out of food. We are not separate from the rest of Earth's biota; we are an integral part of the Earth system. Without the rest of the system in place, we could not survive. Our existence depends on the continued presence of a flourishing biota, and, as we have seen, diversity enhances the health and vitality of the biota. The greater the number of species in an ecosystem, the healthier the ecosystem will be. The more diverse the ecosystem, the greater chance it can survive disruption: If one species is lost from a diverse ecosystem, some other species is likely to continue in a similar role, performing a similar function in the ecosystem. For the ecosystem to be healthy or productive, how diverse does it have to be?

Studies of productivity in different ecosystems have shown that productivity increases as biodiversity increases. Other studies have shown that the resilience of an ecosystem—how well it is able to withstand different types of stress—also increases as biodiversity increases. Both the productivity and the stability of an ecosystem are strongly affected by biodiversity. However, these studies also suggest that beyond a certain level of biodiversity, there is little further increase in either productivity or stability. Although we can document this threshold for individual ecosystems in particular locations, however, we still do not fully understand what this means at the global scale.

Beyond the moral or ethical issue and beyond the potential medical or economic value of individual species, we can still ask the following question: If we kill off a large number of the species existing on Earth, will it matter?

At present there are two very different views on the importance of biodiversity. One, put forward by Stanford University ecologists Anne and Paul Ehrlich, likens biodiversity to the rivets on an airplane. Each species has a small but important role to play in the overall functioning of the ecosystem, just like the rivets on the airplane. If you remove the rivets (or species) one by one, sooner or later the stress on the system becomes so great that it fails: The airplane falls out of the sky, or the ecosystem collapses. The second hypothesis was proposed by Brian Walker, an ecologist for the Australian Commonwealth Scientific and Industrial Research Organization. He suggested that, in fact, most species are superfluous and that the system is maintained by a few keystone species. In this case, loss of species is not a problem as long as you do not lose the keystone species.

Where does this leave us? If we wiped out all tropical rainforests but replanted an equal area of temperate forest, while the new forest continues to expand it would release oxygen and take up CO_2. If we were to plant a large enough area, we could replace the biomass of the tropical forests and even begin to take up some of the CO_2 released by the burning of fossil fuels. (To take up all of the CO_2 that could be released by the burning of fossil fuels, we would need to more than double the organic carbon content of living biomass and soils.) However, we would have exterminated more than half the species on Earth. We cannot tell what repercussions this might have throughout the Earth system. If we accept the rivet hypothesis, then we might imagine a loss of half the species on Earth as catastrophic. If we assume that only the keystone species are really important or that, for any ecosystem, there will be redundancy in the roles played by different species, then we can accept the loss of some species. Multiple species of insects, for example, might fill similar niches and interact with the rest of the ecosystem in similar ways. Wipe out one, and the rest of the ecosystem might never notice. If we could pick and choose which species should live and which should die, then maybe we could reduce the number of species in the world by half, and the rest of the Earth system would continue along quite happily.

But extinction does not happen that way. As the human population grows, so do our demands on natural resources. The loss of habitat caused by our building of cities, extraction of minerals, logging of forests, and conversion of forests and grasslands to agriculture and grazing lands kills many species and can destroy whole ecosystems. The destruction is not selective; neither are the effects. From a long-term perspective, we can judge that the Earth system is very resilient. It can recover from very large perturbations, and no doubt Earth will recover from this one, although it may take tens of millions of years. In terms of individual species, it is a very different matter. Although past extinction events were different in cause and structure to the present one, it might be worth considering that whenever such a large extinction event occurred in the past, the species at the top of the food chain before the event were no longer there once it was all over. Dinosaurs ruled the Mesozoic Earth and are now extinct. Humans could be next.

We do not know enough about how most ecosystems operate or about how important different ecosystems are for the overall global system. For purely pragmatic reasons, it makes sense to slow the rate of habitat destruction and the extinction of species. Pragmatism aside, we pose the following ethical question: Does any species have the right to exterminate another?

Chapter Summary

1. A mass extinction episode as large as those that have occurred periodically throughout Earth's history is taking place today. It is a result of the spread of human populations and the destruction of much of the world's most productive natural habitats.

2. Much of this species loss is taking place in the tropical rainforests of the world, which are also the most diverse of the terrestrial ecosystems.
   a. The tropical rainforests are thought to contain three-quarters of all the living things on Earth and two-thirds of all plant and animal species.
   b. Deforestation in the tropics is wiping out species faster than they can be catalogued and much faster than they can be studied. Every day, species are going extinct that we do not even know exist.

3. The instrumental value of a species can be viewed in different ways—for example, their potential value as pharmaceuticals, their recreational value, their scientific value, or their commercial value.
   a. The diversity of species has value in terms of the productivity and stability of ecosystems and plays an important role in the stability, or health, of the Earth system as a whole.
   b. The destruction of tropical forests has other impacts besides the reduction of global biodiversity. It also results in large changes in local climate and the hydrologic cycle, and, through the release of CO_2, it has an impact on the global-scale climate.

4. Biodiversity, or the loss of biodiversity, is of critical importance to modern agricultural production. Current practices, particularly in industrialized nations, are to increase productivity through increased specialization and the use of a limited number of selectively developed varieties of crops.
   a. When only a few varieties of a particular species exist in a location, they become particularly vulnerable to new strains of diseases or pests that may evolve.
   b. Diversity is essential for maintaining the long-term health and survival of a species, but modern agriculture is dependent on reducing that diversity.
   c. In the case of particular food crops, we compromise by building large reservoirs of genetic diversity in specialized seed banks.
   d. As new diseases arise or as new pests evolve, the genetic material contained in these seed banks might not be sufficient to develop a resistant variety of the crop. We then have to turn to the region in the world where the plant first evolved (the genetic home of the plant) to look for a wild strain that might be resistant to that particular threat.
   e. The vast majority of the world's food and animal feed crops come from just 12 regions, each located in an area where population pressures or development are placing an increasing stress on the existing natural habitat.

Key Terms

endemic species	instrumental value	keystone species
hotspots	intrinsic value	speciation

Review Questions

1. Explain why it is difficult to give an accurate count of the number of species that go extinct each year.
2. Use a diagram to help explain the relationships among ecosystems, communities, and species.
3. What is meant by the term *habitat*? Explain its importance to issues of biodiversity and extinction.
4. What is meant by the term *keystone species*? Explain why it is important to issues of biodiversity and extinction.
5. Where does the greatest rate of species loss occur today?
6. If a large area of temperate forest is cleared, it can commonly grow back fairly rapidly to something that closely resembles the original forest. If a large area of tropical forest is cleared, regrowth is slow and the original forest cover may never return. Explain why these forests respond differently to clearing.
7. Describe three consequences of tropical deforestation other than loss of biodiversity.
8. List four social and economic factors that contribute to tropical deforestation.
9. What characterizes the 24 hotspots identified by Norman Myers?
10. What is meant by the instrumental and intrinsic values of species?
11. Explain why lack of diversity in food crops might present problems for the world food supply.
12. Why is there a relationship between biodiversity and the long-term health of an ecosystem?
13. Explain the difference between the Ehrlichs' rivet theory and Walker's theory of the importance of biodiversity.

Critical-Thinking Problems

1. It is possible for the northern boreal forest to have a significant impact on the larger-scale climate. Using the information you now have about the possible impacts of anthropogenically induced greenhouse climate change, expand on this diagram and discuss the implications in terms of climate and forest cover.

2. Consider the following set of statements for a situation in the tropical forest where forest is cleared for crops:

   - Forest clearance requires access to the forest (roads).
   - An increasing population requires access to services and commodities (a town or city).
   - Settlements require roads.
   - Construction and forest clearance are easier (may increase) if roads are present.
   - The presence of roads and settlements attracts more people into the region.
   - Forest clearings rapidly lose productivity, requiring more clearing.
   - Clearing results in loss of biodiversity.

   Take these statements as a minimum; you might think of some other conditions or relationships that could also be included. Construct a systems diagram showing how the statements all interact. Describe what the diagram shows. Are any feedback loops present? If so, are they positive or nega-

tive? Is this a useful way of looking at some of the forces that promote deforestation? Is anything missing that you think should also be taken into account?

3. What would happen to atmospheric oxygen if photosynthesis were to shut off suddenly? Photosynthesis is the source of most of the O_2 in the atmosphere, so it is reasonable to guess that O_2 would decline. Analyze how it would do so by performing the following calculations:

   a. Forests and soils together contain about 2200 Gton of carbon. The amount of carbon stored in the living marine biomass is negligible in comparison. The atmosphere contains 3.8×10^{19} mol of O_2. By what percentage would atmospheric O_2 decrease if Earth's biota were to die suddenly and if the forest and soil organic carbon were to be oxidized? (*Hint:* Remember that in the decay of organic matter, 1 mol of carbon reacts with 1 mol of O_2.)

   b. Approximately how long would this process take? Assume the decay proceeded at the modern rate of 30 Gton(C)/yr.

   c. The remaining atmospheric O_2 would have to be removed by the weathering of kerogen and other reduced minerals (iron and sulfides) in rocks. Kerogen is weathered at a rate of 0.05 Gton(C)/yr. Express this rate in terms of moles of carbon per year. If the oxidation of iron and sulfides were to use up oxygen at this same rate, how long would it take for atmospheric O_2 to disappear?

Further Reading

General

Baskin, Y. 1997. *The work of nature: How the diversity of life sustains us.* Washington, DC: Island Press.

Eldredge, N. 1998. *Life in the balance: Humanity and the biodiversity crisis.* Princeton, NJ: Princeton University Press.

Wilson, E. O. 1992. *The diversity of life.* New York: Norton.

Advanced

Balich, M. J., E. Elizabetsky, and S. A. Laird, eds. 1996. *Medical resources of the tropical forest.* New York: Columbia University Press.

APPENDIX

Units and Unit Conversions

Common Unit Equivalences

1 kilometer (km)	= 1000 meters (m)
1 meter (m)	= 100 centimeters (cm)
1 centimeter (cm)	= 0.39 inches (in)
1 mile (mi)	= 5280 feet (ft)
1 foot (ft)	= 12 inches (in)
1 inch (in)	= 2.54 centimeters (cm)
1 square mile (mi^2)	= 640 acres (a)
1 kilogram (kg)	= 1000 grams (g)
1 pound (lb)	= 16 ounces (oz)
1 fathom	= 6 feet (ft)

Unit Conversions

To convert:	Multiply by:	To find:
Length		
inches	2.54	centimeters
centimeters	0.39	inches
feet	0.30	meters
meters	3.28	feet
yards	0.91	meters
meters	1.09	yards
miles	1.61	kilometers
kilometers	0.62	miles
Area		
square inches	6.45	square centimeters
square centimeters	0.15	square inches
square feet	0.09	square meters
square meters	10.76	square feet
square miles	2.59	square kilometers
square kilometers	0.39	square miles
hectares	10,000	square kilometers
Volume		
cubic inches	16.38	cubic centimeters
cubic centimeters	0.06	cubic inches
cubic feet	0.028	cubic meters
cubic meters	35.3	cubic feet
cubic miles	4.17	cubic kilometers
cubic kilometers	0.24	cubic miles
liters	1.06	quarts
liters	0.26	gallons
gallons	3.78	liters
Masses and Weights		
ounces	20.33	grams
grams	0.035	ounces
pounds	0.45	kilograms
kilograms	2.205	pounds

The International System of Units (SI)

Basic Units

Quantity	Unit	SI Symbol
Length	meter	m
Mass	kilogram	kg
Time	second	s
Thermodynamic temperature	Kelvin	K
Amount of substance	mole	mol

Prefixes

Prefix	Multiply Unit by:	Symbol
tera	10^{12}	T
giga	10^{9}	G
mega	10^{6}	M
kilo	10^{3}	k
hector	10^{2}	h
deka	10	da
deci	10^{-1}	d
centi	10^{-2}	c
milli	10^{-5}	m
micro	10^{-6}	μ
nano	10^{-9}	n
pico	10^{-12}	P
femto	10^{-15}	τ
atto	10^{-18}	a

Derived Units

Quantity	Unit	Expression
Area	square meter	m^2
Volume	cubic meter	m^3
Frequency	hertz (Hz)	s^{-1}
Density	kilogram per cubic meter	kg/m^3
Velocity	meter per second	m/s
Acceleration	meter per second squared	m/s^2
Force	newton (N)	kg $\cdot$ m/s^2
Pressure	newton per square meter	N/m^2
Work, energy, quantity of heat	Joule (J)	N $\cdot$ m
Power	watt (W)	J/s

APPENDIX

Temperature Conversions

$$T(°F) = T(°C) \times 1.8 + 32$$

$$T(°C) = \frac{T(°F) - 32}{1.8}$$

$$T(°C) = T(K) - 273.15$$

APPENDIX

Periodic Table

Key:

H	SYMBOL
1	ATOMIC NUMBER
1.008	ATOMIC WEIGHT
Hydrogen	NAME

( ) = ESTIMATES

1 IA	2 IIA	3 IIIB	4 IVB	5 VB	6 VIB	7 VIIB	8 VIIIB	9 VIIIB	10 VIIIB	11 IB	12 IIB	13 IIIA	14 IVA	15 VA	16 VIA	17 VIIA	18 VIIIA
H 1 1.008 Hydrogen																	**He** 2 4.00 Helium
Li 3 6.94 Lithium	**Be** 4 9.01 Beryllium											**B** 5 10.81 Boron	**C** 6 12.01 Carbon	**N** 7 14.01 Nitrogen	**O** 8 16.00 Oxygen	**F** 9 19.00 Fluorine	**Ne** 10 20.18 Neon
Na 11 22.99 Sodium	**Mg** 12 24.31 Magnesium											**Al** 13 26.98 Aluminum	**Si** 14 28.09 Silicon	**P** 15 30.97 Phosphorus	**S** 16 32.07 Sulfur	**Cl** 17 35.45 Chlorine	**Ar** 18 39.95 Argon
K 19 39.10 Potassium	**Ca** 20 40.08 Calcium	**Sc** 21 44.96 Scandium	**Ti** 22 47.88 Titanium	**V** 23 50.94 Vanadium	**Cr** 24 52.00 Chromium	**Mn** 25 54.94 Manganese	**Fe** 26 55.85 Iron	**Co** 27 58.93 Cobalt	**Ni** 28 58.69 Nickel	**Cu** 29 63.55 Copper	**Zn** 30 65.39 Zinc	**Ga** 31 69.72 Gallium	**Ge** 32 72.61 Germanium	**As** 33 74.92 Arsenic	**Se** 34 78.96 Selenium	**Br** 35 79.90 Bromine	**Kr** 36 83.80 Krypton
Rb 37 85.47 Rubidium	**Sr** 38 87.62 Strontium	**Y** 39 88.91 Yttrium	**Zr** 40 91.22 Zirconium	**Nb** 41 92.91 Niobium	**Mo** 42 95.94 Molybdenum	**Tc** 43 (97.9) Technetium	**Ru** 44 101.07 Ruthenium	**Rh** 45 102.91 Rhodium	**Pd** 46 106.42 Palladium	**Ag** 47 107.87 Silver	**Cd** 48 112.41 Cadmium	**In** 49 114.82 Indium	**Sn** 50 118.71 Tin	**Sb** 51 121.76 Antimony	**Te** 52 127.60 Tellurium	**I** 53 126.90 Iodine	**Xe** 54 131.29 Xenon
Cs 55 132.91 Cesium	**Ba** 56 137.33 Barium	**La** 57 138.91 Lanthanum	**Hf** 72 178.49 Hafnium	**Ta** 73 180.95 Tantalum	**W** 74 183.85 Tungsten	**Re** 75 186.21 Rhenium	**Os** 76 190.2 Osmium	**Ir** 77 192.22 Iridium	**Pt** 78 195.08 Platinum	**Au** 79 196.97 Gold	**Hg** 80 200.59 Mercury	**Tl** 81 204.38 Thallium	**Pb** 82 207.2 Lead	**Bi** 83 208.98 Bismuth	**Po** 84 (209) Polonium	**At** 85 (210) Astatine	**Rn** 86 (222) Radon
Fr 87 223.02 Francium	**Ra** 88 226.03 Radium	**Ac** 89 227.03 Actinium	**Rf** 104 (261) Rutherfordium	**Db** 105 (262) Dubnium	**Sg** 106 (263) Seaborgium	**Bh** 107 (262) Bohrium	**Hs** 108 (265) Hassium	**Mt** 109 (266) Meitnerium	Unnamed Discovery 110 Nov. 1994	Unnamed Discovery 111 Nov. 1994	Unnamed Discovery 112 1996		Unnamed Discovery 114 1999		Unnamed Discovery 116 1999		Unnamed Discovery 118 1999

ALKALI METALS · **ALKALI EARTH METALS** · **HALOGENS** · **NOBLE GASES**

LANTHANIDES:

Ce 58 140.12 Cerium	**Pr** 59 140.91 Praseodymium	**Nd** 60 144.24 Neodymium	**Pm** 61 (145) Promethium	**Sm** 62 150.36 Samarium	**Eu** 63 152.97 Europium	**Gd** 64 157.25 Gadolinium	**Tb** 65 158.93 Terbium	**Dy** 66 162.50 Dysprosium	**Ho** 67 164.93 Holmium	**Er** 68 167.26 Erbium	**Tm** 69 168.93 Thulium	**Yb** 70 173.04 Ytterbium	**Lu** 71 174.97 Lutetium

ACTINIDES:

Th 90 232.04 Thorium	**Pa** 91 231.04 Protactinium	**U** 92 238.03 Uranium	**Np** 93 237.05 Neptunium	**Pu** 94 (240) Plutonium	**Am** 95 243.06 Americium	**Cm** 96 (247) Curium	**Bk** 97 (248) Berkelium	**Cf** 98 (251) Californium	**Es** 99 252.08 Einsteinium	**Fm** 100 257.10 Fermium	**Md** 101 (257) Mendelevium	**No** 102 259.10 Nobelium	**Lr** 103 262.11 Lawrencium

Index

455

456

460